SACRED TRAINING

A HALAKHIC GUIDEBOOK
FOR MEDICAL STUDENTS AND RESIDENTS

SACRED TRAINING

A HALAKHIC GUIDEBOOK
FOR MEDICAL STUDENTS AND RESIDENTS

EDITORS
JERRY KARP, MD, PhD
MATTHEW SCHAIKEWITZ, MD

THE *VERAPO YERAPE* SERIES

AMMUD PRESS

Sacred Training
A Halakhic Guidebook for Medical Students and Residents

Part of the *Verapo Yerape* series

Cover design by Sari Kopitnikoff (sarinks.com)

ISBN 978-0-578-44116-0, *paperback*

Published by Ammud Press, New York

The editors welcome feedback at sacredtraining@gmail.com.

Rabbi Mordechai Willig
4499 Henry Hudson Parkway
Riverdale, New York 10471
718.796.8208

מרדכי ווילִיג
ריווערדיל, נוא יארק

כ׳ טבת תשע״ח

יום הזכרון של הרמב״ם זצ״ל

אבא אומנא (מקיז דם. רש״י) הוה אתי לי׳ שלמא ממתיבתא דרקיעא כל יומא. ולאביי כל מעלי יומא דשבתא. לרבא כל מעלי יומא דכפורי. הוה קא חלשא דעתי׳ דאביי משום דאבא אומנא. אמרו לי׳, לא מצית למיעבד כעובדי׳ (תענית כא:). ופירשו שהקפיד על צניעות לנשים, ריפא בחנם לעניים, באופן שלא התביישו, ולרבנים נתן כסף לבריאותם. בקיצור, יש לרופא יכולת לקדש שם שמים שאין לרבנים אף כאביי ורבא.

תלמידים המתמחים בבית ספר לרפואה איינשטיין הוציאו ספר ״אימון קדוש״, וכמו אבא אומנא הם מקדשים שם שמים כרופאים מומחים המדקדקים בהלכה ובמוסר רפואי ויהודי כאחד. רבים מהמאמרים נכתבו כמילוי חובה לסיום הלימודים, וכולם עוסקים בהלכה למעשה. אזכיר במיוחד את ״עשרה מאמרות״ של תלמידי היקר ר׳ יעקב מרדכי קארפ נ״י, שצולל במים אדירים של התלמוד והראשונים וממשיך עד שיטות פוסקי זמננו בהיקף ובבהירות. לדעתי, ספר זה עצמו מהוה קידוש שם שמים, שתלמידים, שראשם ורובם שקועים בלימוד רפואי להצלת נפשות, מצליחים להתרכז גם בלימוד תורה ע״מ ללמד.

יהי רצון שהמחברים שיחיו, ביחד עם קודמיהם והבאים אחריהם שם, ועם אלפי הרופאים הדתיים שדורנו זכה להם, ימשיכו לקדש שם שמים, עד שנזכה לכל המחלה וכו׳ לא אשים עליך כי אני ה׳ רופאך, בב״א.

כברכה ועתירה

מרדכי ווילִיג

Rabbi Hershel Schachter
24 Bennett Avenue
New York, New York 10033
(212) 795-0630

הרב צבי שכטר
ראש ישיבה וראש כולל
ישיבת רבינו יצחק אלחנן

מכתב ברכה

דפדפתי קלת בספר וראיתי כמה וכמה מהמאמרים נכתבו מתוך רגינות ויראת
שמים ויראת חטא, ויישר כחכם על המפעל הקדום הזה, ויה"ר שיתקבלו הדברים
בספני"י אצל שאר התלמידים, ותרבה הדעת.

צבי שכטר

ז' טבת, תשע"ה

ישיבת רבני יצחק אלחנן
Rabbi Isaac Elchanan Theological Seminary
An Affiliate of Yeshiva University

Erev Rosh Chodesh Shevat 5779

I have read many selections of *Sacred Training* edited by Matthew Schaikewitz and
Jerry Karp, both young ambitious talmidei chachomim and young aspiring doctors
who will serve Hashem and His creations with dedication, empathy and creativity.
Those sections organize careful and comprehensive research with clarity and with a
deep appreciation of the way in which halachic decisions and directions are formed.
This will serve all medical students, researchers and doctors as a guide for the
observance of halocho and give them the pathway to further study the halochos that
apply to many situations in which they will find themselves.

However, this volume is far more than another contribution to the library of volumes
giving access to the profundity of Torah thought and practice. It is the record, a deeply
inspiring record, of the yearning of young scholars to serve Hashem with humility,
integrity, commitment and dedication, without compromising the responsibilities of
endless study, early professional achievements and family obligations. It is a tribute to
the breathtaking appreciation that the practice of medicine, easing the suffering of
another, is in our view both a calling and a gift from on High, and has a lofty place in
the elegant and elevating tapestry of the fullness of His Torah.

Rabbi Yaakov Neuberger

בס"ד

Tevet 5779

This *sefer* is so much more than a masterful presentation of the timely halakhot relevant for medical students and residents. It goes beyond teaching Torah in a written format and educating the next generation of aspiring Jewish medical professionals. What strikes me as one of its most salient features is that from within the depths of its pages, I can almost hear a chorus of voices singing מה אהבתי תורתך, כל היום היא שיחתי.

The authors of the various pieces, many of whom I am honored to call my friends and colleagues, are medical professionals in every sense of the word. They are dedicated to their patients, to honing their craft, and to healing a broken world. But that doesn't define them. What defines them is that all of that (and more) stems from a deep-seated dedication, devotion, and commitment to the דבר ה'. It's evident from reading the individual chapters. It's evident from the multiple levels of edits and back and forth that the authors worked so diligently on to insure the most accurate and effective means of transmitting Hashem's Torah. It's evident from the lives that these amazing professionals live, as sincere עובדי ה' who are combining the talents He granted them with their hard earned skills and experience to improve and save other people's lives.

Whether each and every topic speaks to you or is relevant in your schooling, practice, or everyday life, every reader will gain not only a deeper appreciation and understanding of the topic at hand, but also a sense of how living a life dedicated to עבודת ה' can be interwoven with a professional medical career. We live in a world where we are often presented with conflicts between religion and science, between faith and empirical realities, and between living spiritually inspired lives and those dedicated to facts and evidence. This *sefer* sheds a beautiful light, the light of Torah, on these false dichotomies, by explicitly and implicitly presenting a worldview that sees all aspects of human life and endeavors as a seamless tapestry, woven by the original Artist Himself.

This *sefer* is a project that has been a dream of so many for so long. It's my sincere hope and prayer that it is only the first step in their efforts to better the world through both their dedication to Hashem and to their professions, and perhaps most importantly, by their dedication to the interconnectedness of the two.

יהי רצון שיזכו ללכת מחיל אל חיל, להגדיל תורה ולהאדירה.

With tremendous pride in their accomplishments and ברכת התורה,

Rabbi David Shabtai, MD

ADULT EDUCATION ■ CHESED ■ CHEVRA KADISHA ■ HOSPITALITY ■ MIKVAH
K.A.D.I.S.H. ■ MEN'S CLUB ■ SINGLES ■ SISTERHOOD ■ TEEN & YOUTH PROGRAMS

Rabbi:
Haim Jachter

Chairman:
Yaakov Varon

Treasurer:
Yosef Negari

President:
Yehoshua Murad

Shaarei Orah

The Sephardic Congregation Of Teaneck

1425 Essex Road - Teaneck, NJ 07666
(201)833-0800 - http://www.sephardicteaneck.org

ב״ה

5 Kislev 5778
November 23, 2017

Michtav Bracha

I am thoroughly impressed with the outstanding compendium of articles on Halacha and the Study of Medicine, which I have read in its entirety, edited by my dear Talmid Dr. Jerry Karp. The articles examine a wide variety of topics with clarity and significant depth and offer practical insight and guidance while avoiding definitive Psak Halacha. I wish to add two important points: 1) Rav Yosef Dov Soloveitchik in a personal conversation in 1981 expressed strong opposition to Kohanim attending medical school. 2) Sephardic Jews should consult with an expert in Sephardic Halacha in matters of Jewish Law.

With Berachot,

Rabbi Haim (Howard) Jachter
Rabbi, Congregation Shaarei Orah, the Sephardic Congregation of Teaneck
Dayan, Beth Din of Elizabeth
Rebbe, Torah Academy of Bergen County

Contents

Preface

We started working on this book not long after we began our medical studies. We noticed that many of the halakhic issues which we were encountering in our medical training were not directly addressed by any book we could find. Most books on medical *halakhah* were geared toward full-fledged physicians, rather than those in training. Furthermore, many medical *halakhah* books are geared toward those in Israel, where the hospital systems are different from those that American medical students encounter, and are written in modern or rabbinic Hebrew, leaving many American medical students unable to access the topics which they need to learn to observe *halakhah* in their complex situations. We were especially motivated by an observation made by Rabbi Tzvi Sinensky, rabbi of the Albert Einstein Synagogue at the time when we began this project. In one of his last *derashot* to the community, he pointed out that the dearth of accessible resources for observant Jewish medical students has significant consequences. Particularly in the realm of *Shabbat* observance, medical students must make a difficult choice when planning their residency options, one that has monumental ramifications for their future careers, with few resources to guide them. They may have heard that there are halakhic concerns with working in a hospital on *Shabbat*, but many do not fully understand what these are, and cannot be expected to make a well-informed decision; if they choose a residency that does not accommodate *Shabbat*, they do not know how to act in accordance with *halakhah* while there. Even those who have the requisite background in reading halakhic works face a new obstacle to learning these important topics during their medical training, namely the significant time constraints they experience during this exceedingly busy phase in their careers. Compounding the problem, many communal rabbis to whom these students might turn are not intimately familiar with the hospital setting and the responsibilities of a medical student and resident, and they may be unable to render rulings which are grounded in the unique reality of the medical training world.

For these reasons, we recruited other students to work together with us in writing this book. We have tried to present discussions of halakhic topics, providing extensive background information necessary to appreciate the relevant halakhic issues, followed by detailed exposition of the modern-day views on the subject. We included topics which we know Jewish medical students ask about, questions which many of us brought to *poskim* ourselves. Throughout, we have avoided presenting definitive halakhic rulings; rather, we aim to provide balanced discussion of the varying approaches and encourage the reader to choose his or her own halakhic advisor with whom to discuss questions that arise. Discussions of *Shabbat* and residency comprise a large section of the book, as we know that this is among the weightiest issues which an observant Jewish medical student will face. We know that this topic is contentious among observant Jewish doctors as well as *poskim*. Those who advocate for avoiding the hospital on *Shabbat* at all costs, and those who advocate for the best training possible even if this means working on *Shabbat*, both make strong arguments. We have tried our best to give a balanced presentation of the many issues, giving voice to both sides. In contrast to the extensive coverage of *Shabbat*-related topics, we have included relatively little discussion of many classic Jewish medical ethics topics, especially those that relate to the value of life (contraception and abortion, reproductive technologies, triage, palliative care, the definition of death, and other related topics). This omission is due in part to the complexity of these issues and the difficulty inherent in providing guidance that would apply to every specific situation. Moreover, we believe that it is more helpful to discuss these situations through the lens of *lifnei ivver*. With regard to procedures, medical students are, at most, providing assistance during a procedure whose halakhic permissibility is questionable; most residents, with the exception of urology and gynecology residents, do not perform such procedures. Complex ethical situations are also largely handled based on the attending physician's directives, rather than decisions made by medical students or even residents. Given this reality, we did not discuss any of these topics directly in this book, but we instead include a chapter by Rabbi Yair Hindin, former rabbi of the Albert Einstein Synagogue, on the prohibition of *lifnei ivver*, which we believe will be more helpful in providing guidance to the Jewish medical student and resident for these situations.

We hope this book is useful to Jewish medical students, residents and even physicians who have finished their training. We also believe that many of these topics are relevant to other healthcare professionals, including dentists, nurses, therapists, and others. We hope this work may also be helpful for community *poskim* who may be discussing these issues with medical students and practitioners.

We knew when we started this project that we could not write the entire work by ourselves. This book is possible because of those authors who agreed to participate in this project, who spent time researching, writing, discussing the issues with us, editing, and proofreading. Almost all the authors are members of the Albert Einstein Synagogue community, including medical students and their spouses. Despite their busy lives, they dedicated themselves to writing clear, comprehensive, helpful guides for other observant Jewish medical students struggling with halakhic issues that arise during the course of medical training. We are indebted to them and hope their work serves the larger community of observant Jewish medical professionals.

In preparing the chapters that comprise this book, the authors made extensive use of the classic medical halakhic literature. We are grateful for the use of the Morris Broder Library at the Albert Einstein Synagogue, which contains a vast collection of medical *halakhah* works that have been indispensable in preparing this book. Among the most valuable have been two works which we also advise the reader to consult: Dr. Abraham S. Abraham's four-volume *Nishmat Avraham* commentary on *Shulchan Arukh* (published by the Schlessinger Institute, now in its third edition, 2015, also translated by the author into a three-volume English series by the same name, ArtScroll, 2000), and Rabbi Dr. Avraham Steinberg's *Encyclopedia Hilkhatit Refu'it* (also published by the Schlessinger Institute, second edition, 2006; also translated into English by Dr. Fred Rosner as *Encyclopedia of Jewish Medical Ethics*, Feldheim, 2003). In both cases, we recommend consulting the Hebrew volumes if possible, as the English translations are abridged; regardless, these two works provide an essential resource for those interested in medical *halakhah*, and we are immensely grateful for these valuable works.

We were inspired by the substantial support we received from the Albert Einstein Synagogue community and beyond in working on this volume. First and foremost, we are grateful for the support and encouragement we received from the Einstein community rabbis during our time working on the book. Rabbi Tzvi Sinensky, Rabbi Yair Hindin, and Rabbi Elliot Schrier all encouraged us and also provided practical guidance about how to bring this work to completion. Additionally, we received much helpful guidance from Rabbi Dani Zuckerman, who also helped to shape the direction of the work and provided editorial support. His suggestions about how to bring this project to completion have made a marked impact on the final product. We also appreciate the editorial contributions of Aviva Bresler, Tzipa Chaim, Mordy Fenster, Ari Friedman, Marc Herman, Yosef Krausz, Rabbi Daniel Kronengold, Eli Miller, Sarah Mizrachi, and Mordechai Siev. Many members of the community, too numerous to list here, provided a sounding board for the ideas expressed in the book, made useful suggestions about the practical aspects of publishing, and encouraged us to see the project to its completion; we are sincerely grateful.

From the inception of this project, we received support from Rabbi Menachem Penner and Rabbi Daniel Feldman at YU/RIETS to continue working on it and bring it to completion. We are grateful for Rabbi Feldman's assistance in bringing the work to publication, and for continually making time for us even with his myriad other responsibilities. Shaul Seidler-Feller made crucial contributions to the project, and we are lucky to have been recipients of his generosity and thoughtfulness. We also thank Rabbi Yaakov Neuberger, Rabbi Hershel Schachter and Rabbi Mordechai Willig at RIETS for their encouragement, their generosity in giving their time to read this book and provide helpful comments, and also more generally for their support of the Albert Einstein Synagogue community. In the same vein, we have been fortunate to have contact with Rabbi Dr. Howard Apfel and Rabbi Dr. Edward Reichman. Both have been invaluable resources for our community, giving of their time to share their knowledge of medical *halakhah* and their relevant experience with our community. We also thank Rabbi Dr. Reichman for contributing the foreword to the book, and for serving as a faculty sponsor for the reading electives at Albert Einstein College of Medicine which yielded many chapters in the book; he has been a constant source of encouragement. We are grateful to Rabbi Chaim Jachter, who read the book and provided valuable comments, often pointing out when we had missed an important detail. Our discussions with him about residency and *Shabbat*, both from halakhic and communal perspectives, have also had a significant impact on that section of the book. Finally, we are indebted to Rabbi Dr. David Shabtai, who read the work in its entirety, provided detailed feedback to us, and made invaluable suggestions on navigating the complex world of publishing. We are very fortunate to have benefited personally from his expertise.

We are unendingly grateful to our wives for providing crucial feedback, support and encouragement throughout this project, even as it has continued for years. This work also reflects the constant inspiration we have received from our parents and families. Finally, we pray that Hashem, who has undoubtedly helped us to bring this work to fruition, will continue to guide us and our community of Jewish medical professionals to thrive and continue performing sacred work in this complex but rewarding world of medicine.

Jerry Karp
Matthew Schaikewitz

Foreword

The History of the Jewish Medical Student Dissertation: An Evolving Jewish Tradition

Rabbi Edward Reichman, MD

Professor, Emergency Medicine
Professor, Education and Bioethics
Albert Einstein College of Medicine

As you leaf through this volume, I suspect you are thinking that this is just another book covering topics related to medicine, Judaism, and ethics. You would be sorely mistaken. It is technically true that the topics relate to Judaism and medicine, and that our generation has seen a fair share of such contributions, but this work is a historically significant and unique volume that represents the pinnacle of a revolution – a revolution in the learning of Torah and its application to the modern world. I beseech you to see beyond the one tree used to create the paper for this book, and behold the vast forest and acreage of rabbinic and medical literature wherein this towering tree is perched.

This volume was written by Jewish medical students, physicians-in-training, on Jewish law and the practice of medicine. The students who have contributed to this book may not realize that this work is at once both completely ordinary, and perhaps even expected, yet simultaneously extraordinarily novel. The innate and intense desire of Jewish physicians to relate their medical practice, training, and knowledge to their Jewish tradition has been reflected in every generation through the literary contributions of Jewish doctors. Today's students are part of a centuries-old tradition of Jewish medical students who have written about aspects of Judaism and medicine. But this present offering is the apex of this unique, and I dare say elite, genre. In this brief essay, I will focus on the contribution of Jewish medical students to the literature of Judaism and medicine over the centuries.

We focus here on the works of medical students in particular as a means of highlighting the evolution of the literature of Judaism and medicine.[1] All of the works discussed below were written by students during their medical training, and in most cases, in fulfillment of requirements for graduation. While these contributions span across time, location, languages and topics, they are all conceptually united in the desire to synthesize medical training with Judaism. In essence this is a manifestation of the ideal form of *Torah u-Madda*.[2]

Jewish Medical Student Dissertations of the Past

The requirement to complete a dissertation in order to graduate medical school dates back many centuries. When Jews attended medical schools they of course were required to write such dissertations. However, Jews were only allowed entry to conventional medical schools in the late 16th – early 17th century.[3] While the overwhelming majority of Jewish

1   The literature of Judaism and medicine is rich and includes contributions by both physicians and laymen. Here we focus exclusively on medical student contributions. References to the dissertations presented here were gleaned from the following sources: M. Steinschneider, *"Schriften uber Medicin in Bibel und Talmud und uber Judische Aerzte,"* *Wiener Klinische Rundschau* Nr. 25, u. 26 (1896), 1–12; H. Friedenwald, "The Bibliography of Ancient Hebrew Medicine," in his *The Jews and Medicine* (Johns Hopkins Press, 1944), 99–145; *idem., Jewish Luminaries in Medical History* (Johns Hopkins Press, 1946); N. Koren, *Jewish Physicians: A Bibliographical Index* (Israel Universities Press: Jerusalem, 1973), H. S. Hes, *Jewish Physicians in the Netherlands 1600–1940* (Van Gorcum: Assen, 1980); W. Kaiser and A Volker, *Judaica Medica des 18 und des Fruhen 19 Jahrhuderts in den Bestanden des Halleschen Universitatsarchives* (Halle, 1979); ProQuest Dissertations database; website catalogues of the National Library of Medicine (especially indexcat.nlm.nih.gov; I thank librarian Steven Greenberg for his assistance in navigating this database); online catalogues of multiple European universities; articles on specific personalities and dissertations as referenced below. See also the important work, M. Komorowski, *Bio-bibliographisches Vereichnis Judischer Doktoren im 17. Und 18. Jahrhundert* (K. G. Saur: Munich, 1991).

2   This is intended to be a representative, not exhaustive study. To my knowledge no one has yet studied or catalogued all the medical dissertations of Jewish students that relate to Jewish topics. This remains a desideratum, perhaps for a future dissertation. Regretfully, my limited facility in foreign languages, assistance from Google Translate notwithstanding, has restricted this analysis to some cursory observations and comments.

3   See Abdelkader Modena and Edgardo Morpugo, *Medici e chirurghi ebrei dottorati e licenziati nell'Università di Padova dal 1617 al 1816* (Bologna, 1967); E. V. Ceseracciu, "Ebrei laureate a Padova nel Cinquecento,"

students would choose a conventional medical topic for their dissertation, some had both the desire and capability to address a topic related to Judaism and medicine. It is to a number of these extant works and authors, few in number though precious in quality, that I draw your attention in this essay. I have chosen a representative number of works to give the reader an appreciation that as long as there have been Jewish physicians, there have been physicians who view their medicine through the prism of the Torah. This approach surely begins at the early stages of medical training and tangible expression of this fact is reflected in the choice of topic for the required university dissertation.

Salomon Bernard Wolffsheimer
Topic: Gynecology and Fertility in Rabbinic literature[4]
Language: Latin
Date: 1742
University: Fridericiana/Halle, Germany (established 1694)

Salomon Bernard Wolffsheimer[5] wrote his medical dissertation on a Jewish topic, gynecological and fertility issues in rabbinic literature, in 1742. It is peppered with Talmudic references in addition to references to Maimonides.[6] He discusses fertilization, menstruation and fertility in both contemporary medical and rabbinic literature. Indeed, as is the case with most all the subsequent dissertations we will discuss, the objective is to compare and contrast the rabbinic approach to that of contemporary medicine. Wolffsheimer attended the University of Halle, one of the most liberal German universities in terms of granting medical degrees to Jews. Of all the Jewish student dissertations found in the archives of the University of Halle from the 18th and 19th centuries, Wolffscheimer's is one of two that were on Jewish topics.[7] The work of Wolffsheimer

---

Quaderni per la storia dell'Università di Padova 13 (1980), 151–168; D. Carpi, "Jews who received medical degrees from the University of Padua in the 16th and early 17th centuries," (Hebrew) in *Scritti in memoria di Nathan Cassuto* (Ben Tzvi Publishers: Jerusalem, 1986), 62–91.

4   *De causis foecunditatis Ebraeorum nonnulis sacri codicis praeceptis innitentibus* (Frediriciana, 1742).

5   Koren, op. cit., 140.

6   The final pages of Wolffsheimer's dissertation mentions other graduates, one of which is (Johan) Gottlob Kruger, also a graduate of the class of 1742. It appears that Kruger wrote his dissertation on Maimonides, though I could not find any such reference. Though not Jewish, Kruger is mentioned by the 19th-century author Pinchas Horowitz in his *Sefer Ha-Berit*. See D. Ruderman, *A Best-Selling Hebrew Book of the Modern Era: The Book of the Covenant of Pinhas Hurwitz and Its Remarkable Legacy* (University of Washington Press, 2015), 147.

7   See W. Kaiser and A. Völker, *Judaica medica des 18. und des frühen 19. Jahrhuderts in den Beständen des halleschen Universitätsarchives* (Halle,

was referenced in another Jewish medical student dissertation almost a century later regarding the impact of *milah* on fertility.[8]

Benjamin Wolf Gintzburger
Topic: Medicine in the Talmud
Language: Latin
Date: 1743
University: Gottingen, Germany

While Wolffsheimer narrows his analysis to one topic, Gintzburger provided a survey or overview of Talmudic medicine. In 1743, Benjamin Wolff Gintzburger completed his dissertation on Talmudic medicine in fulfillment of his requirement for graduation from the medical school of the University of Gottingen, Germany.[9] According to some accounts, he was the first Jewish medical graduate from this university.[10] Given the history of the admission of Jewish medical students to universities in Europe, writing a dissertation on Talmudic medicine as a Jewish student in 18th century Germany is nothing short of remarkable.

Gintzburger's work is frequently cited as one of the earliest works on Talmudic medicine by a Jewish physician, and it represents an ideal

---

1979). The other is by Meyer Levin, *Analecta historica ad medicinam Ebraeorum* (1798). See below, n. 19.

8   See Salomo Ludovici (Ludovicus, Ludwig) Manson, *Dissertatio medica inauguralis de legislatura Mosaica* (Hague, 1835), 20. Manson was a graduate of the University of Leiden in the Netherlands. He is not listed in Koren, but is listed in Hes, 198, though there is no accompanying biographical information. I found reference to Manson as a student at Leiden University in *Annales Academiae Lugduno-Batavae* 1831–1832 (Luchtmans Publisher, Lugduni Batavorum Academic Publication, 1833), 19 and 30. He received commendation for his academic accomplishments. See https://books.google.com/books?id=Jn1FG9In7FgC&pg=RA8-PA24-IA21. Manson's dissertation is a classic example reflecting the notion that principles of hygiene ultimately derive from the Torah and this is a reason why Jews have been relatively spared in epidemics. He invokes not only the works of the Talmud, but also those of Rambam, Ramban, Ibn Ezra, Kimchi, and Abarbanel.

9   *Disputation inauguralis medica qua medicinam ex Talmudicis* (Gottingen, 1743); F. Schiller, "Benjamin Wolff Gintzburger's Dissertation on Talmudic Medicine," *Koroth* 9:7–8 (Fall 1988), 579–600. For additional biographical notes on Gintzburger, see N. M. Gelber, "History of Jewish Physicians in Poland in the Eighteenth Century," (Hebrew) in Y. Tirosh, ed., *Shai le-Yeshayahu: Sefer yovel le-Rav Yehoshua Wolfsberg*," (Ha-Merkaz le-Tarbut shel ha-Po'el ha-Mizrachi*; Tel Aviv, 5716), 347–371, esp. 356; *Koroth* 9 (Special Issue, 1988) [Proceedings of the Third Symposium on Medicine in the Bible and Talmud], 255–261; J. Efron, *Medicine and the German Jews: A History* (Yale University Press: New Haven, 2001), 190–197.

10   J. Efron, *Medicine and the German Jews* (Yale University Press, 2001), 191.

way for a student to marry his medical training with his Torah observance.[11] While one cannot verify the primacy of this work, Ginstzburger mainly cites references from the Talmud and no reference appears to any previous work on Talmudic medicine. He does reference the classic work of Thomas Bartholin, a Danish physician and theologian, on Biblical medicine, *De morbis biblicis miscellanea medica* (1672). The earliest work on Biblical medicine known to have been written by a Jewish physician is that of Benjamin Mussaphia.[12] His 173-page work, published in 1640, lists all the verses from the Bible that relate, in the broadest sense, to medicine. Each of the roughly 650 verses cited is followed by a brief explanation. It is possible that Gintzburger was not familiar with Mussaphia's work. Gintzburger attempted to place the medicine of the Talmud into an historical context, stating that a small portion of the Talmud precedes the time of Galen, while the remainder is either coeval or of a later date. That is why, he claims, much of the Talmud agrees with the Galenic tradition. Of note the dissertation is 23 pages in length, relatively short as compared to comparable dissertations. In addition, while there are numerous rabbinic references there are no Hebrew characters in the printed work, something found in later Jewish dissertations.

The topic of Biblical medicine was by no means the exclusive provenance of the Jews. In fact in the same year as Gintzburger's thesis was published, the Christian Hebraist Johannes Jacob Schmidt published an expansive work on Biblical medicine spanning some 800 pages. However, while many Christians (often Hebraists), including medical students, wrote on Biblical medicine, Talmudic medicine was another matter, and was generally the domain of the Jewish students. In any case, the exploration of the relationship of medicine to the Bible and Talmud would become a theme for Jewish medical students from then onwards.

We know from another source that Gintzburger was a religious student who encountered conflict between his religious obligations and his medical training, as evidenced by a question he posed to one of the

11 For references on the history of the study of Biblical and Talmudic Medicine, see E. Reichman, "Biblical and Talmudic Medicine: A Bibliographical Essay," in F. Rosner, *Encyclopedia of Biblical and Talmudic Medicine* (Jason Aronson, 2000), 1–9. To this I would add the journal, *Revue d'histoire de la médecine hébraïque*; H. Friedenwald, "The Bibliography of Ancient Hebrew Medicine," *Bulletin of the Medical Library Association* 23:3 (January, 1935), 124–157; the bibliography for C. D. Spivak's entry on Biblical and Talmudic medicine in the *Jewish Encyclopedia* (Funk and Wagnalls, 1906), s. v. "Medicine."

12 See H. Friedenwald, "Bibliography of Ancient Hebrew Medicine," in his *The Jews and Medicine* (Johns Hopkins Press: Baltimore, 1944), 112; D. Margalit, "Rav Binyamin Mussaphia," *Koroth* 2:7–8(1960), 307–318.

leading rabbinic figures in Germany of his time, Rabbi Yaakov Emden. The query, published in Rabbi Emden's collected responsa, regards the permissibility of performing dog dissection on the Sabbath. The literary quality of the question, written in Hebrew, attests to the education of Gintzburger. Rabbi Emden's response, addressing both human and animal dissection, serves as a basis for modern discussions on autopsy and anatomical dissection in Jewish law.[13] In the course of his response, Rabbi Emden asked of Gintzburger to share with him any information he possessed about the practice of alchemy, especially amongst Jewish practitioners, including a request to search the medical library at his university.[14]

The importance of Gintzburger's work is evidenced by its citation in other medical works. In addition, in 1779, it was translated into German, with additions, by the Jewish physician Solomon Schlesinger.[15] Both Jew and non-Jew alike referenced his work in subsequent medical dissertations at other universities.[16] One of his mentors at Gottingen University, the famed Albrecht von Haller, a Swiss anatomist often referred to as the "father of modern physiology," included a brief section on Talmudic medicine in his *Bibliotheca Anatomica*.[17] There he relies heavily on his student Gintzburger's work, including reference to the Talmudic origin

---

13 *She'eilat Yaavetz*, n. 41. On the history of anatomy in rabbinic literature, see E. Reichman, "The Anatomy of Halakhah," in Y. Steinberg, ed., *Berakhah Le-Avraham* (Jerusalem, 2008), 69–97. On the issues faced by Jewish students training in medicine over the centuries, see, E. Reichman, "From Maimonides the Physician to the Physician at Maimonides Medical Center: The Training of the Jewish Medical Student Throughout the Ages," *Verapo Yerape: The Journal of Torah and Medicine of the Albert Einstein College of Medicine* 3 (2011), 1–25.

14 M. Kahana, "The Scientific Revolution and the Encoding of Sources of Knowledge: Medicine, Halakhah, and Alchemy in Hamburg-Altona, 1736," (Hebrew) *Tarbitz* 82:1 (*Tishrei-Kislev* 5774), 165–212, esp. 190–192. *Idem.*, "An Esoteric Path to Modernity: Rabbi Jacob Emden's Alchemical Quest," *Journal of Modern Jewish Studies* 12:2 (July, 2013), 253–275, esp. 254–255.

15 See Steinschneider, op. cit., p. 5. Schlesinger was a graduate of the University of Frankfurt on the Oder in 1770. See Koren, 120.

16 Gintzburger's name appears with slightly variant spellings by subsequent authors – Ginzburger, Gunzburger, Gintsburger. Pannajota Houth references Gintzburger in his dissertation for the University of Leiden some thirty years later (Pannajota Fridericus Houth, *Dissertation medica inauguralis exhibens tentamen de succis corporis humani accuratius definiendis et ordinandis* (Leiden University, 1778), 67).

17 (Zurich, 1774), 126.

of the cauda equina syndrome.[18] Gintzburger is also cited by a number of later Jewish medical students in their respective dissertations.[19]

Markus Moses
Care of Newborn Children Based on the Verse in Ezekiel 16:4
Language: Latin
Date: 1766
University of Butzow

Markus Moses was the son of the Chief Rabbi of Pressburg, Moses Lemberger.[20] Tragically, his wife and two children died and he ended up wandering to Butzow in 1763. He was taken in by Aron Isak, the leader of the small Jewish community. At that time a recent law was enacted requiring any new Jewish visitors to be reported to the authorities so they could be taxed sixteen schilling a day for their stay. The objective was to prevent Jews from becoming beggars. Moses and the community could not afford the tax. Isak found Moses to be a brilliant young man and suggested he attend the local medical school, thereby absolving him from taxes.

Moses was the first Jew to receive a medical degree from Butzow University, an institution that existed a total of a mere twenty-nine years. While at Butzow, Moses did much of his research with Olaf Tychsen, a Christian Professor of Oriental Languages. Tychsen had studied Hebrew with famed Rabbi Yonatan Eibeschutz in Altona and apparently received some form of *semikhah*, quite a rarity for non-Jew.[21] He became a missionary and it has been suggested that Tychsen may have tried to convert Moses, though unsuccessfully.

Moses completed three theses on Jewish related topics under the tutelage of Tychsen prior to his final dissertation: one on kosher and

18 Francis Schiller relates in his excellent essay on Gintzburger cited above that this fact was the stimulus for his researching and writing on Gintzburger.
19 Meyer Levin, *Analecta historica ad medicinam Ebraeorum* (Halle, 1798), 50 and 52. He traces the history of medicine in Jewish literature from the Biblical to the Arabic period; S. Cohen, *De medicina Talmudica* (University of Viadrina, 1846) cites Gintzburger extensively (see below); David Carcassone, *Essai historique sur la médecine des Hébreux, anciens et modernes* (Montepellier, 1815), 54. Carcassone was a surgeon in Napoleon's army. Another Jewish physician, the German field surgeon Dr. Georg Hartog Gerson, served the allied armies at that time.
20 The biographical information of Moses is largely derived from D. Wilk, "Markus Moses' Doctoral Dissertation or Who Remembers Butzow," *Koroth* 9:3–4 (1986), 408–426.
21 See S. Z. Leiman, "Two Cases of Non-Jews with Rabbinic Ordination: One Real and One Imaginary," *Seforim Blog* (November 16, 2006), http://seforim.blogspot.com/2006/11/dr-leimans-post-two-cases-of-non-jews.html (accessed July 30, 2015).

non-kosher animals, one on diseases in old age as reflected in *Kohelet*, chapter 12, and one on the Samaritan Torah.

Moses' dissertation was based on a verse in Ezekiel (16:4), "On the day you were born your cord was not cut, nor were you washed with water to make you clean, nor were you rubbed with salt or wrapped in cloths." The verse alludes to the use of salt in bathing the newborn, a treatment suggested in his day to combat smallpox. Moses attempted to show that the Jews had used this method for centuries and it may have been responsible historically for the lower incidence of smallpox in the Jewish population. He ends his dissertation with a suggestion that salting the newborn be re-introduced as a prophylactic against smallpox. Upon graduation, Tychsen interceded on Moses' behalf securing permission for him to take an oath that would not conflict with the Jewish religion.[22]

Simon Wolf Worms
Topic: The Impurity of Human Sperm
Language: Latin 28 pages
Date: 1768
University of Giessen

One of the more unique topics chosen for a Jewish student dissertation that I have encountered is that of Simon Wolf Worms. He writes on the reasons why male reproductive seed conveys ritual impurity (*tumah*) according to Jewish law. He marshals a wealth of contemporary medical experts as well as references from the Talmud and the likes of Abarbanel. He includes analysis of a number of Biblical verses regarding the emission and impurity of male seed. The Biblical verses are printed in Hebrew characters.

Simon's father, Asher Anshel Worms, was also a physician and author who graduated in 1723.[23] Simon published posthumously his father's work *Seyag Le-Torah*, a masoretic commentary on the Torah. The work, which was circulated in manuscript prior to publication, was apparently

---

22 See Wilks, *op. cit.*, 417–418. In the epilogue Wilks notes how both Isak and Tychsen became famous in their own right. He neglects to note the role played by Tychsen in one of the most famous chapters in medical halakhic history – the early burial controversy. Tychsen is known for influencing the Duke of Mecklenburg Schwerin in 1772 to require a three-day waiting period between determination of death and interment so as to prevent the possibility of premature burial. This specifically targeted the Jews, who were known for their practice of quick burial, and sparked a decades-long debate amongst rabbinic authorities of that time.

23 According to Koren (p. 140), Asher Anshel Worms graduated from the University of Gottingen, thus preceding Gintzburger. However, as the university opened in 1734, this appears to be a mistake.

plagiarized by Joseph Heilbronn,[24] a fact alluded to in the book's introduction. Simon's father also wrote a commentary on the song from the Hagaddah, *Chad Gadya*,[25] as well as books on algebra and chess.

Benzion Raphael Kohen (Benedetto) Frizzi
Topic: Medicine in the Bible as it Relates to Public Health[26]
Language: Italian
Date: 1787–1790
University of Pavia, Italy
688pp.

Benzion Raphael Kohen (Benedetto) Frizzi was a true Renaissance man – physician, mathematician, philosopher, public intellectual and theater critic.[27] He began his multivolume *Dissertazione di polizia medica sul Pentateuco* (Pavia, 1787–1790), a thematic analysis of medicine and public health in the Torah and Jewish tradition, while still a medical

24 *Meivin Chiddot* (Amsterdam, 1765). Heilbronn attempted to defend himself in a pamphlet, *Merivat Kodesh* (Amsterdam, 1766), to which, according to C. B. Friedberg, in his classic bibliographical index *Beit Eked Sefarim*, letter *"peh"* n. 643, Simon Wolf Worms replied, defending his father, in a pamphlet called *Prodogma Chadashah* (Amsterdam, 1767). I was unable to find this pamphlet, though I did discover that the last page of Heilbronn's *Meivin Chidot* contains a letter written by Heilbronn in his own defense with the identical title, *Prodogma Chadashah*. I do not know if there is another letter of Simon Wolf Worms of the same title, or if Friedberg erred and misattributed the letter to Worms instead of Heilbronn.
25 *Biur Maspik Chad Gadya* (London, 1785).
26 *Dissertazione di polizia medica sul Pentateuco sopra le leggi, e formalità Ebraiche in istato di malattia, e ceremonie funebri, e sepolcrali* (Pavia, 1787–1790).
27 On Frizzi, see S. Simonsohn, *History of the Jews in the Duchy of Mantua* (*Kiryat Sefer*: Jerusalem, 1977), 649, n. 226; Friedenwald, op. cit., 115. On his work, see B. Dinaburg, "Ben Tzion Hakohen Frizzi and His Work *Petach Einayim*," (Hebrew) *Tarbitz*, 20 (1948/49), 241–64; L. Dubin, "Medicine as Enlightenment Cure: Benedetto Frizzi, physician to eighteenth-century Italian Jewish Society," *Jewish History* 26 (2012), 201-221. Dubin states that Frizzi was the first Jew to graduate the University of Pavia. Frizzi was preceded by Abraham Portaleone, who graduated the University of Pavia medical school more than two centuries earlier in 1563. For the text of Portaleone's diploma, see V. Colorni, *Judaica Minora* (Milan, 1983), 487–489. While Portaleone did not write on Judaism and medicine, he authored a magisterial, vintage Renaissance work, *Shiltei Gibborim*, on all aspects of the ancient Temple, including the sacrifices, the identity of the animals, musical instruments and incense used in the temple service. This work has recently been republished with accompanying essays and copious footnotes. See Y. Katan and D. Gerber, eds., *Shiltei Ha-Gibborim* (*Machon Yerushalayim*, 5770).

student in Pavia. It is an elaborate study of the diseases of the Bible and their treatment, from a public health perspective. The six volumes were organized according to the main themes of food, marriage, pregnancy, childrearing and education, hygiene of homes and streets, and funeral customs. Though not arranged in Biblical order, this work in fact provided a scientific, naturalist, and rationalist commentary on the Torah, as well as mini-treatises on Biblical medicine, subsequent Jewish medical history and public health. Frizzi later wrote a magnum opus of over 1000 pages on the medical and scientific aspects of the Talmud.[28]

Abraham Hartog Israels
Topic: Gynecology in the Talmud[29]
Date: 1845
Language: Latin
University: Groningen, Netherlands

Abraham Hartog Israels wrote his dissertation on Talmudic gynecology in 1845 for the University of Groningen in the Netherlands. The final chapter of his dissertation addressed the issue of cesarean sections[30] and Israels suggested, based on his interpretation of the Talmudic passages,

28 John Efron's wonderful work chronicles the preoccupation of Jewish physicians with the epidemiology and etymology of Jewish diseases in 18th and 19th century Germany. A number of medical dissertations of Jewish students addressed this topic. See his *Medicine and the German Jews* (Yale University Press, 2001). Other Biblical themes that are found in 18th–19th century medical dissertations include an analysis of the disease *tzara'at* (identified as leprosy), as well as a description of the Torah as the source of principles of hygiene and sanitation. An example of a Jewish medical student dissertation on leprosy is that of Jonas Lehmaier. He started his medical studies in 1834 at the University of Erlangen and transferred to the University of Munich in 1835. He graduated in 1838 offering a dissertation on Biblical leprosy, *Ueber den in der Bibel erwähnten Aussatz* (Nurnberg, 1838). Ignaz Kahn wrote his dissertation on the hygiene in the Bible, *Ueber den medicinisch-polizeylichen Sinn der Mosaischen Gesetze* (Bavaria, 1825). He cites Frizzi (p. 16) who also dealt with public health and hygiene in his works. The dissertations on these topics number in the dozens with many if not most written by Christians.

29 *Dissertatio historico-medica inauguralis exhibens collectanea gynæcologica ex Talmude Babylonico* (Groningen, 1845).

30 In Friedenwald's catalogue of his library, *Jewish Luminaries in Medical History*, there is a note accompanying the listing of Israels' dissertation that an English translation of the final chapter (dealing with cesarean section) is inserted into the book. I was able to acquire a copy of this translation, which was done by the Baptist E. Ernest Reid in 1896. Israels relates that the main thesis that Jews were performing cesarean sections in Talmudic times was advanced earlier by Dr. David Mansfield (*On the Antiquity of Gastrotomy and Hysterotomy on the Living*, Brunswick, 1824 [German])

that living cesarean section (i.e., a living mother being delivered of a living baby) was performed in Talmudic times.[31] This sparked an intense debate in the medical literature over the next few decades.

Israels would ultimately become the Netherlands' first professor of the history of medicine and also made important contributions to medical education and public health.[32]

Sigismund Cohen
Topic: Talmudic Medicine[33]
Date: 1846
Language: Latin
University: Viadrina

Sigismund Cohen, following in the footsteps of Gintzburger just over a century earlier, wrote a survey of Talmudic medicine. In addition to the copious primary citations from the Talmud, he makes frequent reference to his predecessor. The fact that Gintzburger's small volume was so heavily relied upon over one hundred years after its publication is evidence that few significant strides had been made in the field of Talmudic medicine in the intervening period.

Cohen completed medical school just one year after A. H. Israels, and already cites the latter's dissertation. In particular he mentions the debated assertion of Israels that the Jews in the times of the Talmud were performing cesarean section on living women, something not known to have been done by anyone else.[34]

Based on the biographical information provided at the end of the dissertation, Cohen appears to have had a more academic, secular education as opposed to the classic Biblical and Talmudic study. In addition, Cohen may have been the first Jewish student to reference the recently published book of the French Jewish scholar, Eliakim Carmoly, *Histoire des médecins juifs, anciens et modernes* (1844).[35] While the reliability of Carmoly's work was called into question later by critics, it nonetheless

---

but had been rejected by his contemporaries. Israels resuscitates the theory and vigorously defends it.

31 On the history of living and post mortem cesarean section in rabbinic literature, see E. Reichman, "A Matter of Life 'in' Death," *In the Pathways of Maimonides: Studies in Maimonides, Medical Ethics and Jewish Law: A Tribute to Dr. Fred Rosner*, eds. K. Collins, E. Reichman, A. Steinberg (Maimonides Research Institute, 2015).

32 See H. S. Hes-Swartenberg, "Abraham Israels, M.D. 1822–1883," *New York State Journal of Medicine* (August, 1979), 1445–1447.

33 *De medicina Talmudica* (Bratislav, 1846).

34 See Cohen, 27–28.

35 While Israels had cited earlier articles of Carmoly, he did not cite the book.

contains a wealth of valuable information. Selections were translated into English just one year after publication.[36]

Gideon Brecher (Gedaliah ben Eliezer)
Topic: Magic and Magical Healing in the Talmud
Year: 1850
Language: German
University: Vienna Erlangen

Gideon Brecher (1797–1873), also known as Gedaliah ben Eliezer, was an Austrian physician and writer. Brecher was the uncle, by marriage, to perhaps one the greatest bibliographers in Jewish history, Moritz Steinschneider. Amongst the latter's voluminous works are essential bibliographies of books and manuscripts on the topics of science and medicine in rabbinic literature. Brecher was born in Prossnitz, Moravia. He was the first Jew of Prossnitz to study medicine or any other professional field. Brecher received his Master of Surgery and Obstetrics in Budapest in 1824. He received his medical degree from the University of Erlangen in 1849. His thesis was *Das Transcendentale, Magie und magische Heilarten im Talmud* (Vienna, 1850).

Brecher's fame in Jewish literature rests principally on this work and upon his lucid commentary on the *Kuzari* of Judah ha-Levi, which appeared with the text in four parts.[37] Brecher's correspondence with Samuel David Luzzato about this commentary was also published. His 267-page dissertation is well-researched with copious notes and incorporates much Hebrew text.

Joachim Halpern
Topic: Surgery in the Talmud (*Beitrage zur Geschichte der talmudischen Chirurgie*)
Date: 1869
German 25 pages
University: Hiesiger

Joachim Halpern is possibly the first author to systematically discuss surgery in the Talmud.[38] He discusses topics such as trauma, amputations, fractures, and trephining. He was born in Vilna, and his biography appended to the dissertation is brief without much detail. His work is used as a source for the entry of Charles Spivak in the Jewish Encyclopedia on the topic of surgery in the Talmud. Halpern's initial

---

36 *History of the Jewish Physicians*, from the French of E. Carmoly, by John R. W. Dunbar (J. Murphy: Baltimore, 1845).
37 Prague, 1838–1840.
38 Others had discussed circumcision and bloodletting.

thesis on surgery in the Talmud was supplanted by Preuss' more expansive work on the same topic thirty years later.[39]

Judah Loeb Katznelson
Topic: **Anatomical Pathology in the Talmud in Relation to Greco-Roman Medicine**[40]
Year: 1889
Language: Russian
University: St. Petersburg, Russia

Dr. Judah Loeb Katznelson, a Russian-Jewish physician, poet and novelist wrote extensively on Biblical and Talmudic medicine.[41] After completing his initial medical training, Katznelson opted to write a dissertation and take special exams in order to practice academic hospital-based medicine. The topic of his dissertation in Russian was normal and abnormal anatomy in ancient Hebrew literature in relation to ancient Greco-Roman medicine. It was later translated into German and published in an academic journal.[42]

Despite the comprehensiveness of Julius Preuss' work, there have been a number of noteworthy contributions thereafter. Dr. Judah Loeb Katznelson wrote extensively on Biblical and Talmudic medicine after his medical thesis. He wrote a small volume in Hebrew on Talmudic anatomy in 1886 entitled *Remach Eivarim*, wherein Katznelson posits a creative physiological explanation to account for the rabbinic description and enumeration of 248 limbs in the body. This anatomical essay, in a revised form, was later incorporated into his magnum opus, *Ha-Talmud Ve-Chokhmat Ha-Refuah,* which was written in Hebrew and published

---

39   See J. Preuss, "Chirurgisches in Bibel und Talmud," *Deutche Zeitschrift fur Chirurgie* 59 (1901), 507–534. Halpern's work is cited in a historical treatise on trephining. See K. Seydel, *Antiseptik und Trepanation* (Munich, 1886), 2, where Halpern is cited as evidence that trephining is mentioned in rabbinic literature.

40   Katsenelson, Lyov [Izrailevich], *Anatomiya (normalnaya i patologicheskaya) v drevneyevreĭskoĭ pismennosti i otnosheniye yeya k drevnegrecheskoĭ meditsinĭe. Istoriko-meditsinskiy edyud* (Y. I. Liberman: St.-Peterburg, 1889), 162 p.

41   For a brief biography, see H. A. Savitz, "Judah Loeb Katznelson (1847–1916): Physician to the Soul of His People," in his *Profiles of Erudite Jewish Physicians and Scholars* (Spertus College Press: Chicago, 1973), 56–61. On the literary contribution of Katznelson, see M. Waxman, *A History of Jewish Literature* 4 (Bloch Publishing: New York, 1947), 154–156. For his contribution, as well the contribution of others, to Biblical and Talmudic Medicine, see *ibid.*, 702ff.

42   Judah Leib Benjamin Katzenelson, "De Normale und Pathologische Anatomie des Talmud," *Historische Studien aus dem Pharmakologischen Institute der Kaiserlichen Universität Dorpat* (1896).

posthumously in 1928 by his family. This work contains essays on hemophilia as described in the Talmud, the dermatological conditions of the Bible, including *tzara'at*, from a medical perspective, a dictionary of medical terminology translated into Greek, Russian and Hebrew, and a commentary on the section of the Talmud that deals with the laws of *kashrut*. In addition to all his other accomplishments, Katznelsen was a gifted Hebrew writer, and I have thoroughly enjoyed some of his short stories.[43]

Charles David Spivak (Chaim Dovid Spivakofsky)
Topic: Menstruation in the Talmud
Year: 1890
Language: English
University: Jefferson Medical College

Chaim Dovid Spivakofsky was born in Russia and received a traditional Jewish education. He moved to America at age twenty-one, adopting the name Charles Spivak, and attended medical school in Philadelphia. Spivak wrote his thesis in 1890 as a student at Jefferson Medical College on menstruation from a historical perspective, with special reference to the Talmud. It won a prize for best essay by a student and was subsequently published in a reputable medical journal.[44] Spivak's linguistic ability and expression, coupled with his literary references and allusions, are quite impressive, all the more so given the fact that he was not a native English speaker.

After artfully dismissing both ancient and most contemporary theories of menstruation, Spivak writes, "I shall approach the main subject of this essay, which aims to present, for the first time, I think, both the theory of menstruation, as it was understood by the Rabbis of the Talmud, as well as a brief summary of their observations of this

---

43 One of my favorites is entitled *Kevurat Neshamot* (The Burial of Souls). This is a story written with literary allusions to Purim, about an unlearned king who seeks to obtain a copy of all the Hebrew books ever written, using the bibliography of Rabbi Chaim Yosef David Azulai (known as *Chida*) (1724–1806) as a guide, only to bury them in an inaccessible non-Jewish cemetery. The *Chida* visits the king in a dream and informs him that these are not mere books, but that the authors' souls, additional souls associated with the books, are inextricably bound with the works. By burying the books, he would in essence be burying their souls. He beseeches the king to repent. While I have not seen anyone analyze this work, it is clearly a metaphor for the recent sale of the extraordinary library of Joseph Almanzi, comprised largely of the library of the *Chida* (purchased years earlier by Almanzi's father), to the British Library, akin to an inaccessible cemetery where the books would be "buried" and not available for the Jewish community. See, W. Wright, "The Almanzi Collection of Hebrew Manuscripts in the British Museum," *Journal of Sacred Literature and Biblical Record* 18 (July, 1866), 354–365.

44 *The Times and Register* 22:7 (February 14, 1891), 128–131.

phenomenon." Wolffsheimer (see above) devoted some discussion to the rabbinic theories of menstruation, but this was not his focus. He notes that the Talmudic scholars presaged the notion that menstruation is associated with ovulation. About a decade after Spivak's paper was published, a French medical student wrote his dissertation on a similar topic, focusing on the laws of *niddah* and the different types and colors of menstrual blood, asserting that the rabbis of the Talmud had perfect knowledge of the physiology of menstruation.[45]

Spivak went on to become a prominent physician in Denver and founded the National Jewish Hospital for the Treatment of Consumptives (patients with tuberculosis). He would continue to write about the Jews and medicine, including the entry on Biblical and Talmudic Medicine in the Jewish Encyclopedia.[46] In a series of letters about this project to Judge Mayer Sulzberger, a noted Philadelphia jurist, Spivak wrote, ''I work slowly but steady. It takes a great deal of time to go over carefully and conscientiously all the tracts of the Talmud. I intend to take in all the writings of the ancients... I intend to devote many months and if necessary years, to the labor of digesting and arranging the material which I now have at hand.''[47]

Spivak's article in JAMA on a specific anatomical prayer[48] was the impetus for a recent essay on anatomical references to prayer in general.[49] Spivak's National Jewish Sanatorium was formally nonsectarian, though most of the patients and many of the consulting physicians through the 1930's were Jewish. Spivak and his colleagues also fostered

45 Emanuel Rosenbaum, *Une conférence contradictoire religieuse et scientifique sur l'anatomie et physiologie des organes génitaux de la femme, à l'École de Rami fils de Samuel et Rabbi Yitshac fils de Rabbi Yehoudou, à la fin du 2e siècle. Extrait du Talmud, traité de la "menstruation," traduite et expliquée* (Paris, 1901) 87 p. I was unable to procure the original dissertation, but found a review of it in *Archives D'Anthropologie Criminelle* 17 (1902), 173–174. The journal reviewed the dissertations of the last year, which included that of Rosenbaum. I suspect Rosenbaum would not have seen the essay of Spivak, which was published in a lesser known English academic medical journal.

46 I. Singer and C. Adler, eds., *Jewish Encyclopedia* 8 (Funk and Wagnalls, 1912), 409–414.

47 *Catalogue of Historical Collectible Auctions* (2005), lot 357 [American Judaica].

48 C. D. Spivak, "An Anatomic Prayer: A Hymn Based on an Ancient Fragment of Osteology," *Journal of the American Medical Association* 67:14 (September 30, 1916), 1037–1038.

49 See E. Reichman, "The Anatomy of Prayer," in D. Z. Feldman and S. W. Halpern, eds., *Mitokh Ha-Ohel: Tefillah* (Yeshiva University Press, 2014), 37–52. For a recent biography of Spivak, see J. E. Abrams, *Dr. Charles David Spivak: A Jewish Immigrant and the American Tuberculosis Movement* (University Press of Colorado: Denver, 2009).

a visible Jewish atmosphere at the institution, which offered kosher food and Yiddish discourse and exhibited respect for Jewish traditions.[50]

David Macht
Topic: Maimonides' Contribution to Jewish and Medical Literature
Year: 1905
Language: English
University: Johns Hopkins

Born in Moscow in 1882, David Macht immigrated to the United States where he completed his medical training at Johns Hopkins University in 1906. While I could not ascertain the topic of his medical dissertation, in his last year of medical school Macht read a paper before the Johns Hopkins Hospital Historical Club (December 11, 1905) on Moses Maimonides, analyzing his halakhic, philosophical and medical works. This paper was subsequently published in the Johns Hopkins Hospital Bulletin[51] and concludes with the Hebrew date Kislev 8, 5666, followed by words, which I suspect never appeared in the pages of this journal, neither before nor since, in Hebrew, "*tam ve-nishlam shevach le-Kel borei olam.*"

Macht was a prolific writer, publishing three books and over 900 original articles in the fields of science and medical/scientific history. Of the roughly one hundred works he wrote on medical history, many are devoted to Biblical and Talmudic medicine, with special emphasis on the pharmacological and physiological interpretations of Biblical and rabbinic passages.[52] One of his books is devoted to the *ketoret*, the incense that was burned in the *Beit ha-Mikdash*, the Holy Temple. The identity of the ingredients of the *ketoret* had occupied a significant chapter of the magnum opus of the Renaissance physician Dr. Abraham Portaleone (1542–1612), *Shiltei Ha-Gibborim.*[53] Based on the Biblical episode of

50 Abrams, *op. cit.*, 10.
51 187 (October, 1906), 332–337. See http://babel.hathitrust.org/cgi/pt?id=uva.3470085740;seq=376 for the text of this article.
52 David Wilk composed a brief bio-bibliography of Macht's medical historical contributions which was published in *Koroth* 8:7–8 (August 1983), 305–317.
53 See the recent annotated edition with accompanying essays, Y. Katan and D. Gerber, eds., *Shiltei Ha-Gibborim* (*Machon Yerushalayim*, 5770). See also A. Berns, "'I Seek the Truth from Whomever Pronounces It': Abraham Portaleone and the Ancient Israelite Incense," in his *The Bible and Natural Philosophy in Renaissance Italy* (Cambridge University Press, 2014); *idem.*, "Judah Moscato, Abraham Portaleone, and Biblical Incense in Late Renaissance Italy," in *Studies in Jewish History and Culture, Volume 35: Rabbi Judah Moscato and the Jewish Intellectual World of Mantua in the 16th–17th Centuries* (Brill, 2012).

Korach, where Moshe asked Aharon to carry the *ketoret* into the midst of the camp to stop the plague,[54] rabbinic sources and Jewish physicians have recommended the use of *ketoret* in times of plague throughout the centuries.[55]

In 1928, Macht received the first degree of advanced research awarded at Yeshiva College, New York, being made Doctor of Hebrew Literature. From 1933 to 1941 he served as visiting professor of general physiology at Yeshiva College.

Aron Sachs
Topic: Obstetrics and Gynecology in the Talmud[56]
Year: 1909
Language: German
University: Leipzig

In his brief biography, which was customarily published at the end of many dissertations, Sachs describes his early childhood and mentions that he received private lessons in Talmud. In addition to the classic work of Israels, he was the beneficiary of the recently published works of Dr. Julius Preuss and Wilhelm Ebstein.[57] While Preuss had written a number of articles on Biblical and Talmudic medicine by 1909, the year of Sachs' dissertation, his magnum opus, *Biblisch-Talmudische Medizin*, would only appear two years later. While it is virtually impossible to discuss Biblical and Talmudic medicine today without mentioning Preuss, he does not receive more attention in this essay as his contributions began after his student years. Preuss' medical school dissertation was on syphilis and tabes dorsalis.[58] Of note, Sachs neglects to cite D. Schapiro's work, published just a few years earlier, devoted exclusively to obstetrics and gynecology in rabbinic literature.[59] He may not have had access to this book, as it was published in France and in French.[60]

54 Numbers 17:11.
55 See, for example, Avraham Yagel, *Moshia Chosim* (Zuan di Gara: Venice, 1587), 17r–18r. On Yagel, see D. Ruderman, *Kabbalah, Magic, and Science: The Cultural Universe of a Sixteenth Century Jewish Physician* (Harvard University Press: Cambridge, 1988).
56 *Die Gynäkologie in der Bibel und im Talmud* (Leipzig, 1909).
57 *Die Medizin im Alten Testament* (Stuttgart, 1901).
58 See. F. Rosner, trans. and ed., *Julius Preuss' Biblical and Talmudic Medicine* (Hebrew Publishing Company: New York, 1978), xv.
59 D. Schapiro, *Obstetrique des Ancien Hebreaux* (Paris, 1904).
60 Another Frenchman, Isadore Simon, wrote on obstetrics in the Talmud and quotes Schapiro. See I. Simon, "La gynécologie, l'obstétrique, l'embryologie et la puériculture dans la Bible et le Talmud," *Revue d'Histoire de la médecine hébraïque* 4 (September–December 1949), 35–64. Simon's medical dissertation was on Asaph ha-Yehudi's astrological writings (*Asaph Ha-Iehoudi médecin et astrologue du Moyen Age. Avec une étude sur*

Harry Austryn Savitz
Jews and Medicine
Date: 1924
Language: English
Harvard University

Harry Austryn Savitz left his native Russia at age 5 and eventually came to the United States in 1911.[61] The son of Rabbi Isaac Savitsky, he attended yeshivah as a young man. He graduated from Harvard College in 1921 and from Harvard Medical School in 1925. While a medical student at Harvard, he read a paper before the Phi Delta Epsilon Fraternity, which he later published.[62] It discusses the elements of hygiene and preventive medicine found in the Torah, highlighting the recent realization that many of the foods proscribed by the Torah, such as pork, oysters and rabbit, carry infectious diseases. He quotes Fielding Garrison that the ancient Hebrews were the founders of prophylaxis and the high priests were true medical police (p. 394). Savitz enumerates a number of Jewish physicians and scientists, both of the past and present, who contributed to the advances in many different medical specialties.

Savitz's cousin, with whom he shared a name, was the famous Harvard professor Harry Austryn Wolfson, the first chairman of a Judaic Studies Department in the United States. His professional specialties were internal medicine and geriatrics. He was for many years on the staff of Beth Israel Hospital and taught physical diagnosis at Tufts Medical School. Dr. Savitz combined his medical career with community service. For 25 years he was medical director of Associated Jewish Philanthropies of Greater Boston, now called Combined Jewish Philanthropies, the major fundraising and service agency for the Jewish community.

His later writings include *Profiles of Erudite Jewish* Physicians, profiling the likes of Yaakov Zahalon, Yitzchak Lampronti and Judah Loeb Katzenelson (see above), and *A Physician's Harvest*.

For a number of these authors discussed above, such as Frizzi, Katznelsen, Spivak, Macht and Savitz, their medical student dissertation was but one of many subsequent contributions in the field of Judaism and medicine. For the others, it was most likely their one and

---

la médecine dans la Bible et le Talmud. Ouvrage accompagné de textes hébraïqueset d'une bibliographie, 1933). Another more recent dissertation by a French medical student focused on this very topic. See Gérard Rosenbaum, *Université Paris VII Faculté de Médecine Xavier-Bichat Année 1976 Thèse pour le Doctorat en Médecine – Contribution à l'étude de l'obstetrique dans la Bible et le Talmud* (Paris, 1976) 36 p.

61 Biographical information from J. L. Franklin, "Obituary for Harry Austryn Savitz," *Boston Globe* (September 24, 1994).

62 H. A. Savitz, "*The Jew in Medicine*," *Jewish Forum* 7:4 (June, 1924), 393–399.

only venture into this literary world. There are of course many physicians who contributed to the interface of Judaism and medicine later in their medical careers, and chose not to devote their theses to this topic, but they all share the same attraction to the relationship of Judaism and medicine, as observed by Karl Sudhoff in recounting his meeting with Julius Preuss in the early 20th century:

> In the one hour we were together Preuss permitted me ... to see so deeply into his soul, that I knew his hope was to be a classical philologist – this man, whose practical course of life made his dream impossible because he was a Jew. He had become a physician and his remarkable talent for historical and philological investigation directed him to the study of the history of his specialty as an avocation and *in particular to that branch which inevitably attracts every Jewish physician of the old stamp, namely, Biblical and Talmudic medicine.*[63]

Jewish Medical Student Dissertations of the Present

This attraction is no less true today for physicians of the "new stamp," than it was two hundred and fifty years ago, though the manifestation of this attraction has evolved. While the dissertations of Jewish medical students today represent a continuation of those of the past, there is a clear paradigm shift in the topics addressed. For our discussion, I focus specifically on the dissertations written by students at the Albert Einstein College of Medicine, where I am affiliated.[64] Similar to other institutions of higher learning in both the past and the present, Albert Einstein College of Medicine requires of its students to complete a scholarly dissertation as a requirement for graduation. A number of chapters published in the present volume are in fulfillment of this requirement.[65] What sets them apart from their predecessors is the unique focus on the halakhic aspects of medicine.

The first English work to address issues of medical *halakhah* in a comprehensive fashion was that of Rabbi Lord Jakobovits. While he was

---

63 Fred Rosner, *Medicine in the Bible and the Talmud: Selections from Classical Jewish Sources* (Ktav, 1995), 24. Karl Sudhoff (1853–1938) was a pioneer in the history of medicine and established the premier journal in the field, later named *Sudhoff's Archives.*

64 For the purposes of our discussion, I include research papers written as part of research electives as well as scholarly papers written in fulfillment of the graduation requirement. The length of these papers range from 10 pages to around 100 pages, with the average range being around 20–30 pages.

65 Over the last fifteen years I have had the great pleasure of mentoring electives, research papers, and dissertations (known at Einstein as Scholarly Papers) by Jewish medical students at Einstein.

not a physician, I mention his work as representing both a new chapter and a transition to the literature of today. *Jewish Medical Ethics*, an expansion of Rabbi Jakobovits' Ph.D. dissertation, not only addresses medical halakhic sources from the beginning of life to the end of life, it is also a rich repository of historical literature and the interrelationship of medical history and halakhic literature. This book initiated the modern field of Jewish medical ethics, which has evolved into a purely halakhic endeavor. The historical dimension has been unceremoniously dropped. In fact, when I did an elective in my fourth year at Einstein in medical history, and spent time at the Wellcome Institute for the History of Medicine Library in London, the librarian approached me and said, "I believe the last religious Jew we saw here was Rabbi Jakobovits." This generation of Jewish physicians in general, and religious Jewish physicians in particular, is far less interested in the historical aspects of Judaism and medicine. We can speculate as to the reasons, but it is certainly true. The contribution of Jewish physicians today has taken a new direction. Most are now researching and writing in medical *halakhah*, and with good reason.

There may be a number of reasons for this – the medicine is more halakhically complicated; the Jewish education of the average Orthodox Jewish student is far more advanced than in the past; we are standing on the shoulders of those who have written on medical *halakhah* (Dr. Rosner, Rabbi Tendler, Rabbi Bleich, Dr. Steinberg, Dr. Abraham), and have a treasure trove of existing medical halakhic literature to guide our research. Digital libraries, as well as translations allow us access to an immense amount of relevant material.

It is not only the preoccupation with medical *halakhah* that has evolved, it is also the place of publication. Students and young physicians have chosen to publish their articles in Jewish periodicals rather than in conventional academic medical journals. Dr. Fred Rosner published countless papers in premier medical journals. Perhaps the sophisticated level of halakhic discourse and jargon would preclude publication in a general medical journal, and furthermore, the desired feedback for the authors would only be possible with a similarly educated audience. Einstein students have published their research in contemporary Jewish journals including *Tradition*, *Journal of Halacha and Contemporary Society*, *B'or HaTorah*, and *Assia – Jewish Medical Ethics*. In fact, Einstein has started its own medical *halakhah* journal, *Verapo Yerape*, where many of the students' essays are published.

As evidence of the evolution of the medical student dissertation in the 20th and 21st centuries, I list below a selection of dissertation topics of Einstein students I have mentored since 1999. These are in addition to the topics covered in this book. The focus in almost every case is on the halakhic ramifications of the topic. While these papers are on file with the medical school, and some have been published in peer-reviewed journals, there is no official policy to formally publish and record the medical school dissertations. Perhaps we should return to this practice to preserve these wonderful contributions for the future and to facilitate access to these works for academic study.

Partial List of Research and Dissertation Topics of Einstein Medical Students Relating to Judaism and Medicine, 1999–2015

Stem Cell Research*, Gastric Bypass, The Cholera Epidemic and Rabbi Yisrael Salanter, Definition of Death*, Eight Month Baby in Rabbinic and Medical Literature*, Abortion*, Contraception*, Autopsy*, Coercion and Autonomy, Confidentiality, End of Life Issues*, Nutrition and Hydration, Fetal Surgery, Genetic Engineering, Cloning, Assisted Reproduction*, Pre-Implantation Genetic Diagnosis, Malpractice*, Living Organ Donation*, Neonatology*, Shabbat and the Practice of Medicine*, *Metzitzah be-Peh*, Cosmetic Surgery*, Triage*, Physicians Fees, Placebo*, Trans Fats and Preventive Medicine, Gynecological Procedures and Their Impact on the Laws of *Niddah**, Organ Donation after Cardiac Death, Surrogate Motherhood*, Ambiguous Genitalia and Sex Change Operations, Psychiatric Practice and *Shabbat*, Use of Computers on *Shabbat**, Informed Consent in the Pediatric Population*, Cornea Transplants, Suicide in Jewish Law, Intravenous Feeding and Fasting, Jaundice and Circumcision, The Treatment of Obesity, Sex Selection, Alternative Medicine, The Kohen and the Practice of Medicine, Anatomical Dissection*, Labor and Delivery on the Sabbath, Use of a Breast Pump on the Sabbath.

*Multiple students chose this topic for their research.

Conclusion

The nature of the contribution of Jewish physicians to Jewish medical literature has evolved considerably over time. Beginning in the 1700's, physicians began focusing on Biblical and Talmudic medicine. This was expanded to include the history of the Jews and medicine in the post-Talmudic period up to the pre-modern era. The present iteration of Jewish physicians contributing to Jewish medical literature has charted a different course, focusing primarily on medical *halakhah*.

There are a number of factors that set the present work apart from its predecessors. The authors are students at a medical school under the aegis of Yeshiva University, a religious Jewish institution. The sheer number of students contributing is remarkable. While I have no statistics to back this claim, Einstein has likely produced more dissertations by Jewish students on Jewish topics than any other medical school in history. (This would need to be compared to dissertations from Israeli schools.) The high level of Torah learning reflected in this volume is also unique, as is the participation of women in this project. Furthermore, as opposed to the purely academic writings of their predecessors, these student essays have a practical religious focus, intended to provide general halakhic guidance to those who follow in their footsteps. This is indeed a revolutionary shift in content. While these factors represent a significant increase in both the quantity and halakhic quality of such contributions, they are clearly continuing in the tradition of, and standing on the proverbial shoulders of, their predecessors.

We have seen that across the continents, across the centuries, and across the languages Jewish medical students have expressed their religious beliefs through writing dissertations on Jewish topics. While for some of these students this was their one and only venture into this area, for many this was just the beginning of a lifelong journey exploring the world of *Torah u-Madda*. Knowing the students who have contributed to this volume, I suspect many of them have embarked on just such a journey.

Section I
Pre-Clinical Training

Chapter 1

The Hippocratic Oath in *Halakhah**

Menachem Lazar

Hippocrates, often considered the father of Western medicine, lived in ancient Greece shortly after the building of the Second Temple. Despite his numerous contributions to academic and clinical medicine, Hippocrates is likely best known to modern students of medicine through the Hippocratic Oath, a text attributed to Hippocrates and traditionally administered to students shortly before their graduation from medical school.

Before addressing halakhic considerations related to this practice, we note that taking this oath, a tradition followed in the vast majority of medical schools in the United States,[1] is in no way required to be either licensed as a physician nor to be board-certified.[2] Thus, the practical interest in taking this oath is less a question of professional

---

*   This chapter is dedicated to the memory of R. Aharon Lichtenstein *zt"l*, with whom I first learned *Massechet Shevuot*.

1   This is a somewhat new phenomenon. In 1928, less than half of all medical schools in the United States administered any type of oath (E.J. Carey, *Acad. Med.* 3:2, 1928). By the late 1950's almost three-quarters of schools did so (D.P. Irish and D.W. McMurry, *J. Chronic Dis.* 18:3, 1965), and at the turn of the century all schools administered some kind of oath (A.C. Kao and K.P. Parsi, *Acad. Med.* 79:9, 2004).

2   This might be contrasted with other professional oaths, including those taken by lawyers, members of the military, senators, cabinet members, and the President of the United States. In the majority of those cases, one may not assume the given position without either swearing or affirming that one will carry out the duties of the position. On occasion, other professions have also required some oath or affirmation to be licensed. In Texas, for example, public accountants must swear in order to be certified as such.

3

necessity and more a question of tradition, one in which many would like to participate.

The Oath

The substance of the Hippocratic Oath is largely innocuous. The starting physician pledges to respect his or her teachers and to teach the art of medicine to other worthy students. He or she commits to heal patients, respect their privacy, neither harm nor take advantage of them or their families, nor to assist them in suicides or abortions. Finally, the physician agrees to abstain from performing surgeries, which should be left to trained surgeons. Although wording of the oath varies today from school to school, these themes, derived from the oldest extant copies of the text, are largely shared by most modern versions.[3]

No individual part of this oath appears particularly problematic from a halakhic point of view. Indeed, many of its themes seem entirely consistent with, if not identical to, traditional Jewish values. However, recitation of the Hippocratic Oath still raises several halakhic issues related to *shevuah*, an oath in Jewish law.

Obligations of *Shevuah*

The Torah gives us the ability to obligate ourselves in or prohibit ourselves from otherwise permissible behavior: "If a man makes a vow to God or makes an oath to prohibit himself, he shall not violate his word; according to whatever came out of his mouth he shall do."[4] Such a vow is known in rabbinic literature as a *shevuat bitui*, literally a vow of expression. Willing violation of a *shevuah* can be punished with lashes; inadvertent violation results in the obligation to bring a sacrifice. Rambam[5] counts both a positive commandment to fulfill one's commitments and also a prohibition of swearing falsely.

False Gods

The original text of the Hippocratic Oath invokes the names of several Greek gods including Apollo, Hygieia, and Panacea. Swearing in the name of pagan gods almost certainly violates the Biblical prohibition of *ve-shem elohim acheirim lo tazkiru*, swearing in the name of false gods.[6] The original text of the oath is thus clearly problematic and may not

3   W.J. Friedlander, *Soc. Sci. & Med.* 16:1, 1982.
4   Numbers 30:3.
5   *Sefer Ha-Mitzvot*, Pos. 94, Neg. 61; *Hilkhot Nedarim* 1:4.
6   Exodus 23:13; Rambam, *Hilkhot Avodah Zarah* 5:10; *Shulchan Arukh*, *Yoreh De'ah* 147:1. *Sefer Ha-Chinukh* 86 suggests that others interpret this verse differently; see *Minchat Chinukh* ad loc.

be recited under any circumstances. In contemporary times, however, various modified versions of the text are used and hardly any graduating medical student is asked to invoke the names of ancient pagan gods. We are then left to contend with several more broadly-applicable questions surrounding oaths: are oaths in general permissible and advisable? Is the Hippocratic Oath recognized by *halakhah* as a *shevuah*? What should happen if the *shevuah* leaves one conflicted between his or her commitment to fulfill the *shevuah* and other responsibilities, halakhic or otherwise?

Inadvisability of *Shevuot*

In concluding his discussion of the laws of *shevuot*, Rambam[7] summarizes the accepted rabbinic attitude towards taking unnecessary oaths: "It is a great good for a person to not swear at all." Although in limited circumstances taking an oath is permitted[8] or even obligatory,[9] those cases are generally viewed as exceptions.

Many understand this discouraging attitude as stemming from a blanket fear that the oath may be violated, even if inadvertently. The Gemara[10] thus relates a story in which inadvertent violation of a *shevuah* appears to be punished by Heaven with the death of a child. Further highlighting the severity with which the *halakhah* treats this topic, Rambam[11] counts the violation of a *shevuah* among the most severe of sins, the only non-capital crime described in such terms. Given the ease with which commitments are often made and broken, it seems only wise to distance one's self from *shevuot* – and their punishments – as much as possible.[12]

Other sources suggest a secondary concern, independent of any fear that a *shevuah* might eventually be violated. In a chapter detailing

7   *Hilkhot Shevuot* 12:12.
8   Based on *Nedarim* 8a, Rambam (*Hilkhot Shevuot* 11:3) permits taking a *shevuah* to encourage oneself to fulfill a *mitzvah*; see also *Shulchan Arukh*, *Yoreh De'ah* 203:6.
9   See Rambam in *Sefer Ha-Mitzvot* Pos. 7 and *Hilkhot Shevuot* 11:1, who counts as a *mitzvah* swearing truthfully in the name of God when necessary. However, see also Ra'avad (comments to *Minyan Ha-Mitzvot Ha-Katzar*) and Ramban (*Sefer Ha-Mitzvot* Pos. 7, and in commentary on Deuteronomy 6:13) who disagree.
10 *Gittin* 35a. See *Kesef Mishneh* on *Hilkhot Shevuot* 12:12, who cites this episode as the source for Rambam; see also *Mishneh Le-Melekh* who disagrees.
11 *Hilkhot Shevuot* 12:1–2.
12 Authorities debate the propriety of taking a *shevuah* in cases of impending financial loss and similar situations; this, however, is not our concern. See extensive discussion in Ch. 1 of R. Yitzchak Eliyahu Shatzman's *Kol Nidrei*.

some *halakhot* of pursuing a profession, *Tur*[13] writes that one should be very careful of swearing even truthfully, and cites a story from the Midrash[14] in which thousands of cities were destroyed as punishment for an unnecessary truthful *shevuah*. Even if prudence would dictate distancing ourselves from the mere possibility of swearing falsely, disregard for that caution is unlikely to itself be grounds for such severe punishment. Instead, it seems, swearing in God's name, when doing so is not absolutely necessary, is itself dishonorable and offensive. In a sense, it is a particularly egregious example of taking God's name in vain.[15]

Status as *Shevuah*

Of course, the general inadvisability of taking a *shevuah* is not particularly relevant if the case before us is not first established as a bona fide *shevuah*. Indeed, a reader may wonder whether the Hippocratic Oath is recognized by *halakhah* as a *shevuah*, given that this pronouncement is often made in English, without the wording of an oath, and even without the name of God. Moreover, in some cases the oath is not made directly, and instead graduating students respond "Amen" after the oath is recited by a person leading the commencement ceremony.

In accordance with an opinion of Rashba,[16] Rama[17] states that there is no difference between a *shevuah* stated in Hebrew and one stated in any another language. Even use of the word *shevuah* is unnecessary, and a synonym is sufficient.[18] Moreover, while early commentators debate whether a *shevuah* made without explicit reference to God is punishable when violated, all agree that such a *shevuah* still entails all prohibitions associated with *shevuah*.[19] Finally, the Gemara[20] makes clear that a *shevuah* need not be recited directly, but can also be made by responding affirmatively to the administering of a *shevuah* by another person. Early authorities elaborate that this is true even if the person

---

13 *Orach Chayyim* 156:1.
14 *Midrash Rabbah, Mattot* 22:1. See also *Vayikra Rabbah* 6:3 that tells a variation on the story told in *Gittin*, in which children die as a result of a truthful *shevuah*.
15 See *Mishneh Le-Melekh* on *Hilkhot Shevuot* 12:12, mentioned above, who disagrees with the *Kesef Mishneh*'s explanation of Rambam.
16 *Teshuvot Ha-Rashba* 1:842.
17 *Yoreh De'ah* 237:1.
18 Rambam, *Hilkhot Shevuot* 2:5–6; *Shulchan Arukh, Yoreh De'ah* 237:4. From these sources it appears that use of the phrase "I promise" would also constitute a *shevuah* and should, consequently, also be avoided.
19 Rambam, *Hilkhot Shevuot* 2:2–4 and Ra'avad ad loc; *Shulchan Arukh, Yoreh De'ah* 237:1.
20 *Shevuot* 29b.

administering the oath is not Jewish.[21] Moreover, this is true even if the person responding did not use the exact word "Amen," but instead used any synonymous phrase.[21]

The above *halakhot* – largely uncontested by earlier or later authorities – indicate that, under normal circumstances, recitation of the Hippocratic Oath would entail the full halakhic obligations of a *shevuah*. Indeed, in discussions related to the Hippocratic Oath, several contemporary authorities have taken for granted its status as a proper *shevuah*.[22]

Although we have previously noted the inadvisability of taking oaths generally, the *halakhot* of *shevuah* are worth considering, as they may relate to cases in which a *shevuah* has already been made, perhaps inadvertently, or without full understanding of its halakhic implications.

Intention

For a *shevuah* to be binding, it must involve both purposeful intent and an explicit expression of that intent.[23] The typical graduating student, between listening to speeches and other parts of the commencement program, might by rote read the Hippocratic Oath with his or her classmates, without sufficient intention to make this a binding oath. This may leave room for leniency in some cases in which the oath was already taken.

Moreover, even when there is no question that a *shevuah* was in fact made, the particular intention of the person making it must still be considered.[24] When physicians commit to not harm patients, for example, they do not mean that they will not prescribe bitter-tasting medicines. Although in some sense this can be construed as "harming a patient," this was clearly not the intention of one who took this oath. Early authorities, based on statements in the Gemara, have codified a general principle that we follow the vernacular and intention of a speaker when interpreting *shevuot*.[25] This principle must be taken into consideration when establishing what behaviors were and were not included in a particular *shevuah*.

21 Rambam, *Hilkhot Shevuot* 2:1, *Shulchan Arukh, Yoreh De'ah* 237:2.
22 *Torat Ha-Refuah* of R. Shlomo Goren, *Tzitz Eliezer* of R. Eliezer Waldenberg; both sources are discussed later in this chapter.
23 *Shevuot* 26b; Rambam, *Hilkhot Shevuot* 2:10–15; *Shulchan Arukh, Yoreh De'ah* 210:1, 239:1. Later authorities debate whether a written commitment can also effect a *shevuah*.
24 Rambam, *Hilkhot Nedarim* 8:8; *Shulchan Arukh, Yoreh De'ah* 218:1, 239:1.
25 Rambam, *Hilkhot Nedarim* 9:1, 9:13; *Shulchan Arukh, Yoreh De'ah* 217, 239:1.

Shevuot Concerning *Mitzvot*

The Gemara[26] teaches that an oath made to fulfill or violate a *mitzvah* is not binding. If one swore, for example, to not eat *matzah* on the first night of Pesach,[27] or else to withhold testimony in court,[28] such a *shevuah* would not be binding. However, the Gemara[29] also cites an important exception to this principle: if one swore in a general manner, grouping together the performance of a *mitzvah* with other, elective behavior, then such a *shevuah* would be binding even on the *mitzvah*. For example, if one swore to not eat *matzah* all year long, then one would be prohibited from eating *matzah* all year long, even on Pesach itself; eating *matzah* at the *seder* would then be punishable as would violation of any other *shevuah*.

This *halakhah* is relevant in our case, as certain obligations imposed by the Hippocratic Oath may eventually come into conflict with other obligations. For example, a physician may be asked to testify in court regarding the condition of a patient to help ensure the safety of that patient or others. While providing such testimony may fulfill a Biblical obligation of providing testimony,[30] it does so at the expense of violating patient confidentiality. For a physician who has taken the Hippocratic Oath, disclosing confidential information would constitute a violation of a *shevuah*. The reader can certainly imagine other situations of potential conflict.

Several contemporary authorities have considered practical questions that have arisen in this context. R. Shlomo Goren[31] addressed a question from a neurologist who had diagnosed a patient with epilepsy and was concerned that the patient may continue to drive, despite considerable dangers. The neurologist asked R. Goren whether he was permitted, or perhaps even obligated, to divulge the information he knew to appropriate authorities. R. Goren advised the questioner to counsel his patient directly about the legal and halakhic prohibitions involved in driving, and, barring any evidence indicating the contrary, the physician

26 *Shevuot* 27a. See also Rambam, *Hilkhot Shevuot* 1:6, 5:14–16 and *Shulchan Arukh, Yoreh De'ah* 236:2,5 and 239:4–8.
27 Yerushalmi *Shevuot* 3:4, Rambam, *Hilkhot Shevuot* 1:6, 5:18, *Shulchan Arukh, Orach Chayyim* 485:1, *Yoreh De'ah* 236:5.
28 *Shevuot* 29a, Rambam, *Hilkhot Shevuot* 5:15. Under certain conditions, providing testimony in court is a Biblical obligation. See Leviticus 5:1; *Bava Kamma* 55b; Rambam, *Minyan Ha-Mitzvot Ha-Katzar* Pos. 178 and *Hilkhot Edut* 1:1; and *Shulchan Arukh, Choshen Mishpat* 28:1.
29 *Shevuot* 21b, 22b, 23b, 24a, 24b; see also Rambam, *Hilkhot Shevuot* 5:18 and Rama, *Yoreh De'ah* 239:4, 236:5.
30 See note 28.
31 *Torat Ha-Refuah*, in a chapter entitled "Preserving patient confidentiality of a patient diagnosed with epilepsy."

could presume that the patient will follow his advice. In such a situation, the physician would be forbidden from violating both the civil law regulating confidential medical information as well as the Hippocratic Oath he had taken. Only in cases in which the patient adamantly refuses to cease driving, and in which the physician believes that continued driving poses risk to the patient or others, did R. Goren recommend approaching a *beit din* to help annul his vow.

R. Eliezer Waldenberg[32] discussed a similar case in which a physician had taken the Hippocratic Oath and was subsequently asked to testify in court regarding a patient. Because the *shevuah* was taken in a general manner, we would expect that the oath also prohibits the physician from providing testimony in court, despite it being a *mitzvah*. However, R. Waldenberg suggested that a physician, and certainly a religious one, does not have in mind when taking this oath to withhold testimony where doing so would violate a *mitzvah*. For this reason he ruled that the physician may testify in court.[33]

This conclusion, a tremendous leniency, appears at odds with another accepted *halakhah*. In particular, the Gemara itself provides an example, discussed above, of a person who swears not to eat *matzah* throughout the year, and concludes that he is forbidden from eating on *Pesach* as well. Neither the Gemara nor later authorities suggest that the *shevuah* be binding only during the year, but that an exception be made for *Pesach*, as a religious person would not have had in mind to prohibit himself from fulfilling a *mitzvah*. Instead, it appears that the simple understanding is that people do not always think carefully about potential repercussions of their verbal commitments. Given that many beginning physicians are likely not thinking about complex eventualities and halakhic repercussions of taking the Hippocratic Oath, it seems difficult to justify R. Waldenberg's retroactive understanding of intention, at least in our case.

Two points might be noted in analyzing the discussions of R. Goren and R. Waldenberg. First, both tacitly assumed that the Hippocratic Oath is recognized by *halakhah* as a bona fide *shevuah*. Second, neither offered a general advisory against recitation of the Hippocratic Oath, and instead considered how to deal with its potential halakhic ramifications. It is possible that both overestimated the importance of taking this oath, and had either known that there is in fact no legal nor professional responsibility to do so, they would have advised against its recitation, at least in its classical form as a *shevuah*.

---

32 *Tzitz Eliezer* 13:81.
33 See also *Tzitz Eliezer* 13:104, 15:13, 16:4, in which R. Waldenberg repeats this suggestion.

Annulment

The Torah provides a number of mechanisms through which a *shevuah* can be invalidated or annulled. A person who regrets having made a *shevuah* and for whom the *shevuah* creates suffering can approach a group of three people, at least one of whom is familiar with the *halakhot* of *shevuot*. The petitioner explains the *shevuah* that has been made and explains that had he or she fully understood the consequences of the *shevuah*, he or she would never have taken the *shevuah* in the first place. The three people then confirm with the person that this is indeed the case, after which they can verbally annul the oath.[34]

Like the taking of *shevuot*, their annulment has also been traditionally approached with trepidation. Rambam writes: "We do not annul oaths except for a matter of *mitzvah* or for extenuating circumstances."[35] For this reason, and given the intricacy of the laws of the annulment of *shevuot*, even a brief summary of all pertinent laws is not possible in this space. A person finding oneself in such a situation is encouraged to speak with a competent halakhic advisor familiar with these *halakhot*. The importance of fulfilling one's duties as a physician in the most desirable fashion appears to constitute "extenuating circumstances," if not an outright *mitzvah*, which may be sufficient grounds for annulment.[36]

Conclusions

Given the general *halakhic* reluctance to engage in *shevuot*, and given the lack of professional need to take the Hippocratic Oath, it appears that the responsible choice for an observant student would be to abstain from taking this *shevuah*. Those desiring to participate in this part of the commencement ceremony might consider altering the text they recite in such a way that makes clear that they are not making a *shevuah*.

Nonetheless, it appears that recitation of the Hippocratic Oath, certainly when done so with full awareness of what is being said, creates a binding *shevuah* in the full halakhic sense. Despite tension created with other *mitzvot*, each part of the *shevuah* is binding because the statements are made in a general manner, and are not made to specifically prevent one from performing a *mitzvah*. Therefore, one who has taken the Hippocratic Oath must exercise extreme caution in situations in

---

34   *Bekhorot* 36b; *Hilkhot Shevuot* 6:1–5; *Shulchan Arukh, Yoreh De'ah* 228.
35   *Hilkhot Shevuot* 12:12; also Rama, *Yoreh De'ah* 203:3.
36   A reader may wonder whether the yearly recitation of the *Kol Nidrei* prayer on *Yom Kippur* might provide a source for leniency regarding the *shevuah* in question. Rama (*Yoreh De'ah* 211:1) notes that we do not rely on *Kol Nidrei* to permit vows without subsequent consultation with a halakhic advisor, except for in dire need.

which the plain meaning of what one stated entails particular behavior. This is true even when halakhic obligations resulting from the *shevuah* come into dissonance with particular *mitzvot*. Great care should be taken in particular in the area of patient privacy.

Regardless of whether or not one makes a verbal declaration such as the Hippocratic Oath, many of the obligations described therein should be intimately felt by the religious physician as he or she begins the sacred mission of healing others. In such work, one plays a small role alongside the Almighty, as it were, in fulfilling *ani Hashem rofe'ekha*, "I am God your healer." This is a mission to which, in some sense, the graduating student has since long ago been "perpetually sworn from Mount Sinai."[37]

---

37 *Shevuot* 27a and *Nedarim* 8a.

11

Chapter 2

Practical Halakhic Questions for Anatomy Students*

Matthew Schaikewitz, MD

Anatomical dissection has long been celebrated as a rite of passage for students on their journey to becoming a physician. While engaging in this time-honored practice is certainly rewarding, the coursework is both physically and mentally demanding. The all-encompassing nature of medical school in general and anatomy in particular often leaves students with little time to research the halakhic issues which arise or even to ask questions that arise to a qualified halakhic authority. In the hope of raising awareness of the issues at hand, this chapter will address the following practical issues encountered by students of anatomy: 1) bone boxes and *tumat kohanim*, 2) bringing a visitor to the lab, 3) proper conduct in the presence of cadavers, 4) wearing *tzitzit* in the lab and 5) washing hands after lab. The fundamental question of dissection has been discussed elsewhere.[1]

1) Bone Boxes and *Tumat Kohanim*

As part of the anatomy course, many students are offered the option of keeping a box of bones to aid in the study of osteology. In the ensuing discussion, we will address the question of whether the bone box is capable of transmitting *tumah* (ritual impurity) to *kohanim* just as corpses transmit *tumah* to *kohanim*.

---

*   This chapter is adapted from an article by the author, "Practical Halachic Questions for Anatomy Students," *The Journal of Halacha and Contemporary Society*, Vol. LXVIII (Fall 2014), pp. 81–101.

1   See *Nishmat Avraham, Yoreh De'ah* 349:2; *Encyclopedia Hilkhatit Refuit* vol. 4, s.v. *nituach ha-met*, especially pp. 593–632. See also several related issues that are discussed in Chapter 19.

Although *kohanim* today are already in a state of *tumah* and currently have no method of purification, almost all *rishonim* maintain that there is still a Biblical commandment prohibiting a *kohen* from coming into contact with a human corpse.[2] While Ra'avad[3] implies that there is no prohibition today because *kohanim* are already in a state of *tumah*, many claim that Ra'avad only refers to the absence of punishment but that he maintains a prohibition still exists.[4] In the forthcoming paragraphs, then, we will assume that this prohibition is still in effect.

Tumat Ohel and Non-Jewish Corpses

One of the ways in which a *kohen* can contract *tumah* is by being under the same roof as a human corpse. This is referred to as *tumat ohel*, and it is this law which poses the greatest concern for the *kohen* and the bone box. While this law certainly applies to Jewish corpses, there is a debate among *rishonim* whether the same is true for the corpses of non-Jews. This debate is particularly relevant for our discussion of medical schools in North America because it seems reasonable to assume[5] that the bones found in the boxes are of non-Jewish origin. Rambam[6] and others maintain that the law of *tumat ohel* is limited to Jewish corpses, whereas *Tosafot*[7] write that the law applies to non-Jewish corpses as well. Although most *rishonim* rule that there is no *tumat ohel* for non-Jewish corpses, *Shulchan Arukh*[8] writes that it is proper to be careful to avoid walking over the graves of non-Jews, and Rama[9] adds that even though there are lenient opinions it is proper to be stringent.[10] *Shulchan Arukh*

2   See *Nishmat Avraham, Yoreh De'ah* 369:1.

3   *Hasagot Ha-Ra'avad* on Rambam *Hilkhot Nezirut* 5:15.

4   See *Pitchei Teshuvah, Yoreh De'ah* 372:9 and Responsa *Chatam Sofer, Yoreh De'ah* 339. According to *Dagul Me-Revavah, Yoreh De'ah* 372, Ra'avad may even hold there is a Biblical prohibition.

5   We can invoke the principle of following the majority. If the bones come from cadavers from across the globe, we can assume that each set of bones originates from a non-Jewish person because most people in the world are not Jewish. Similarly, if the bones are collected exclusively from cadavers within the United States, we can follow the majority and assume that the bones originate from a non-Jewish cadaver. For medical schools in Israel, however, if the bones used to study osteology are gathered from Israeli citizens, then this majority would likely not be in effect.

6   *Hilkhot Tumat Meit* 1:13 and *Hilkhot Avel* 3:3.

7   *Bava Metzia* 114a s.v. *mahu.*

8   *Yoreh De'ah* 372:2.

9   Ibid.

10   It should be emphasized that *Shulchan Arukh* and Rama are not referring to the prohibition of touching non-Jewish corpses. Avoiding physical contact with non-Jewish cadavers is not an added stringency because it is prohibited by Rambam in addition to *Tosafot*. See *Shakh, Yoreh De'ah* 372:4.

and Rama are discussing a case in which the *kohen* walks directly above the source of *tumah*, in which case the *kohen* himself creates an *ohel* over the corpse. Although this is a different scenario than the case of the *kohen* and corpse being under one roof, almost all authorities assume that *Shulchan Arukh* and Rama also invoke stringency when the corpse and *kohen* are both under one roof.[11]

Combinations of Bones Capable of Imparting *Tumat Ohel*

Until now our discussion has focused on the ability of an entire corpse to transmit *tumah*. Our next task is to determine if isolated human bones are capable of imparting *tumah*, and, if so, which combinations of bones are required. Stemming primarily from a Mishnah,[12] Rambam[13] codifies the laws governing *tumat ohel* as they relate to isolated bones which are not attached to flesh. According to Rambam, any one of the following collections of bones is capable of imparting *tumat ohel*: 1) the spine, 2) the skull, 3) the majority of the stature of a person (*rov binyano*), 4) the majority of the total number of bones in the body (*rov minyano*), or 5) one quarter of a *kav* of bones (*rova ha-kav*), which is a volume of bones equaling roughly one pint.[14] After analyzing this list, one might conclude that nearly all bone boxes are capable of imparting *tumat ohel* because they satisfy the requirement of *rova ha-kav*. After all, virtually all bone boxes will have a volume of bones greater than the measurement of one pint. While this may indeed be true for Rambam, it is important to mention that other *rishonim* disagree about the nature of *rova ha-kav*. *Tosafot*[15] and others propose an alternative understanding of *rova ha-kav*, and the bones found in current bone boxes would not satisfy this requirement.[16] Although Rambam's requirement of *rova*

---

11 The term used in halakhic literature to describe a scenario where the *kohen* and source of *tumah* are both under one roof is *ohel hamshakhah* (literally, a contiguous covering). The simple understanding of *Shulchan Arukh* and Rama is that they also invoke stringency in the case of *ohel hamshakhah*. See, however, *Be-Ikvei Ha-Tzon* by R. Herschel Schachter (*siman* 35 footnote 16) for two opinions which claim that *Shulchan Arukh* and Rama do not invoke stringency in the case of *ohel hamshakhah*.

12 *Ohalot* 2:1.

13 *Hilkhot Tumat Meit* 2:8–10. The opinions of Rambam from the upcoming discussion which lack citations refer to this source.

14 According to *Midot Ve-Shiurei Torah* by R. Chayyim Benish, a *kav* in contemporary measurements is between 1.38 liters (1.5 quarts) and 2.4 liters (2.5 quarts), according to the various opinions. Taking an intermediate value of two quarts per *kav*, one quarter of a *kav* is approximately one pint.

15 *Nazir* 49b s.v. *ve-al chatzi kav atzamot*.

16 According to *Tosafot*, not all bones are capable of transmitting *tumat ohel* even though they comprise a volume of *rova ha-kav*. Instead, only bones

ha-kav is under debate, most of the other criteria listed by Rambam are agreed upon by *Tosafot* and other authorities. Therefore, we will briefly analyze the remaining items listed by Rambam in order to determine whether all authorities would assume the boxes convey *tumat ohel*.

Spine

With regard to the spine, Rambam writes that if even one vertebra is missing from the eighteen total vertebrae, there will be no *tumat ohel*.[17] Rambam also implies that the vertebrae alone – without the ribs – are capable of transmitting *tumat ohel*. However, *Tosafot*[18] and Rosh[19] suggest that some of the ribs need to be attached to the spine to impart *tumat ohel*.

Skull

Rambam writes that a complete skull will impart *tumat ohel*, but if it is missing a *sela* (volume of an ancient coin) it is considered like any other bone. *Shulchan Arukh*[20] writes that a *sela* is one-third of a *tefach*, whereas *Shakh*[21] maintains that the size is slightly smaller.

Rov Binyano

Rambam writes that the entire *binyan* (structural frame) of a person consists of two bones in the calf, the bones in the thighs, the ribs, and the spine. He writes that an example of *rov binyano* is two bones in the calf and one bone in the thigh. He is presumably referring to the tibia, fibula, and femur, ruling that these three bones can collectively impart *tumat ohel*.

Rov Minyano

The Mishnah[22] states that there are 248 *eivarim* in the human body, and Rambam[23] and others write that each *eiver* must contain a bone.

---

which derive from *rov minyan* or *rov binyan* can combine to the necessary volume capable of transmitting *tumat ohel*. According to this interpretation, bones comprising the numeric or structural majority of the skeleton will transmit *tumat ohel* only when they are whole. If only fragments of these bones remain, however, there will still be *tumat ohel* if the pieces combine to the volume of *rova ha-kav*.

17 As evidenced by Mishnah *Ohalot* 1:8, these eighteen vertebrae do not include the cervical vertebrae.

18 *Nazir* 52a s.v. *tehorah*.

19 *Nazir* 52a s.v. *ta shma shedrah she-geirad* through s.v. *tehorah*.

20 *Yoreh De'ah* 30:2.

21 *Yoreh De'ah* 30:5.

22 *Ohalot* 1:8.

23 *Hilkhot Tumat Meit* 2:3 in reference to an *eiver* capable of transmitting *tumah* on its own. R. Ovadiah mi-Bartenura (*Ohalot* 1:7) writes explicitly that an *eiver* must consist of bone.

Rambam, in accordance with the Beraita,[24] writes that *rov minyano* is no fewer than 125 bones, even if a particular individual has more or fewer than the normal 248 bones.

As mentioned previously, Rambam's definition of *rova ha-kav* will almost certainly be satisfied by all bone boxes. To determine if one's particular bone box will impart *tumah* according to other *rishonim* as well, one would need to examine the bones and see if they meet the other criteria as enumerated by Rambam and the other *rishonim*. In practice, however, it would be difficult to posit that the opinion of Rambam should be ignored. Additionally, the boxes will likely contain the requisite amount of bones according to the other opinions as well. Therefore, it is suggested that medical students assume that their bone boxes contain the requisite amount of bones capable of transmitting *tumat ohel*.

Bones Originating from Multiple Corpses

Even if a bone box contains a combination of bones which usually transmits *tumat ohel*, another consideration may challenge the ability of the bone box to impart *tumah*. The Mishnah[25] says that, according to the accepted opinion, a spine, skull, or quarter-*kav* of bones which originates from two corpses does not impart *tumat ohel*. Rambam[26] codifies this law as well. Although not explicit in the Mishnah or Rambam, it would appear that *rov binyan* and *rov minyan* would also only impart *tumat ohel* if the bones originated from the same corpse.[27] At the present time, this author could not determine whether these boxes typically contain bones from a single cadaver or from multiple cadavers. If the bones in the boxes originate from different cadavers, it is possible that the collection of bones is incapable of imparting *tumat ohel*.

Can the Box Itself Block the Spread of *Tumah*?

A further factor which must be elucidated is whether the closed box itself can serve as an *ohel* to prevent the potential *tumah* from spreading. The Mishnah[28] says that to serve as an *ohel*, the dimensions of the covering must be at least one square *tefach* and the covering must be at least one *tefach* above the object transmitting *tumah*. Even if these

24 Gemara *Bekhorot* 45a.
25 *Ohalot* 2:6.
26 *Hilkhot Tumat Meit* 4:1.
27 In *Sefer Taharat Ha-Kohanim* p. 84, Rabbis Munk and Lombard write that all of the five collections of bones listed above (spine, skull, *rov binyan*, *rov minyan*, and *rova ha-kav*) must originate from the same corpse to impart *tumat ohel*. See *Chazon Ish, Taharot* 21:7 s.v. *ve-hena* where it is explained why two corpses cannot combine to transmit *tumat ohel* in these cases.
28 *Ohalot* 3:7

requirements are met, however, not all materials can serve as an *ohel* to effectively block the spread of *tumah*. Rama[29] writes that any material which itself can become *tamei* cannot prevent the spread of *tumah*. Therefore, if the bone box itself is capable of contracting *tumah* it will not provide an adequate barrier against the spread of *tumah*. If the box is fashioned from wood or metal, for example, the box will not block the spread of *tumah* because metal and wooden utensils are themselves capable of becoming *tamei*.[30] On the other hand, if the box is made from plastic, a material not capable of becoming *tamei*,[31] then it may be able to block the spread of *tumah*.

How Does *Tumah* Spread Throughout a Building?

In order to ease the studying process, some students may decide to bring their bone boxes into their homes, which might entail bringing the boxes within close proximity to *kohanim* in a residential setting. The medical student may reside in an apartment building where a *kohen* lives in the same building or even on the same floor. Because the bone boxes may be capable of transmitting *tumat ohel*, our next task, then, is to determine how *tumah* spreads throughout a building. Most authorities maintain that when an apartment door is closed, the *ohel* is restricted to the apartment and, as a consequence, *tumat ohel* is confined to that apartment.[32] However, when the door to the apartment is opened, the *ohel* is extended to include the hallway and therefore *tumah* spreads throughout the hallway. A *kohen* who happens to be in the hallway when the door is opened would be under the same *ohel* as the bone box and he would contract *tumah*. Similarly, if the doors to two apartments on the same floor were opened simultaneously, the apartments would be considered two parts of the same *ohel* and *tumah* could spread throughout both apartments even if a bone box was only in one of them.

While closed rooms are generally capable of blocking the spread of *tumah*, an additional law regarding *tumat ohel* indicates that *tumah* can spread even past a closed room. This unique law is referred to as *sof tumah latzeit*. This law states that any room or corridor through which

---

29 *Yoreh De'ah* 371:1.
30 Rambam, *Hilkhot Keilim* 1:1.
31 *Baddei Ha-Shulchan, Hilkhot Niddah* 190:107. He derives this law from *Chazon Ish* (*Hilkhot Mikva'ot* 126:7) who writes that a vessel made from rubber does not contract *tumah*.
32 *Taz* (*Yoreh De'ah* 371:3) maintains that a closed door which is attached to the wall by metal hinges does not effectively block *tumah* from spreading past the door. However, *Nekudot Ha-Kesef* (ad loc.) rejects *Taz*. See *Nishmat Avraham* (*Yoreh De'ah* 372:1, p. 559) that in practice we are not concerned for the opinion of *Taz*.

a corpse will eventually exit is considered as if the corpse is there now.[33] While most authorities discuss the principle of *sof tumah latzeit* in the context of whole cadavers, logically this rule should apply to any part of a cadaver which is able to convey *tumat ohel*.[34] If the law of *sof tumah latzeit* applies to the bone boxes, this rule would dictate that there is *tumah* in any location through which it is likely that the student would leave the building carrying the box. In an apartment complex, this could include the stairwells, the elevators, the lobby, and any main floor on which the anatomy student resides. In practice, however, contemporary authorities seem to agree that *sof tumah latzeit* does not apply to the corpses of non-Jews.[35] Therefore, assuming that the bone boxes originate from non-Jewish cadavers, one need not be concerned for *sof tumah latzeit* with regard to the bone boxes.

Summary

There are certainly concerning issues regarding the ability of the bone boxes to convey *tumat ohel* and transmit *tumah* to *kohanim*. Based on our discussion, one should assume that the bone boxes are capable of transmitting *tumat ohel*. However, the law of *sof tumat latzeit* likely does not apply. The halakhic status of the bone boxes has ramifications for both the student in possession of the box as well as for the *kohen* in question. If the student wishes to bring the box to a location where *kohanim* may be present, the student should be aware that the box can transmit *tumah* within the same *ohel*. This may pose a problem for a student who wishes to carry the box into an apartment building, as it is prohibited for a non-*kohen* to cause a *kohen* to contract *tumah*. When bringing the box into the building, a *kohen* in the parking garage or lobby at the same time as the box would contract *tumah*. The student and the *kohen* should also be aware that even if the bone box is inside

33 See Rama, *Yoreh De'ah* 371:4.
34 See *Taharat Ha-Kohanim* by Rabbis Munk and Lombard, p. 116, for two reasons offered to explain the concept of *sof tumah latzeit*: 1) there is a concern that the corpse will suddenly be taken out through an exit without ample warning or 2) since the cadaver will eventually leave through an exit it is considered as if it is already there. According to both lines of reasoning, it would appear that the law of *sof tumah latzeit* should apply to any part of a corpse capable of transmitting *tumat ohel*.
35 *Gesher Ha-Chayyim* (1:6:3) writes that since *tumat ohel* for non-Jewish corpses is only rabbinic, we are not stringent regarding *sof tumah latzeit* for non-Jewish cadavers. See *Be-Ikvei Ha-Tzon* 35:9 by R. Herschel Schachter where other opinions are cited that *sof tumah latzeit* does not apply to non-Jewish cadavers. See also *Divrei Soferim* by R. Nachum Yavrov, *Hilkhot Aveilut* 371:28 for multiple authorities who maintain that *sof tumah latzeit* does not apply to non-Jewish corpses.

of an apartment, the bones can transmit *tumah* to the hallway if the door is open. Additionally, the bones can transmit *tumah* into another apartment on the same floor if the doors to both of the apartments are open simultaneously. Because of the concerns we have mentioned, the medical student is encouraged to speak with a halakhic authority about bringing a bone box to a location where *kohanim* are likely to be present. Similarly, a *kohen* is advised to speak with a halakhic authority about dwelling in an apartment building where medical students may have bone boxes or about visiting such a building.

2) Bringing a Visitor to the Lab

Some medical schools have the practice of allowing students the opportunity to bring a guest to anatomy lab. This allows a friend or relative of the student the opportunity to explore the lab and to examine the dissected cadavers. Assuming it is permissible for the student to engage in the dissection, one would initially think that it should certainly be permissible for a guest to visit the lab and examine the cadavers. After all, students are engaged in full dissection of the cadavers while a visitor will likely only observe the scene. It will be explained shortly, however, that an argument could be made to permit the student to dissect while forbidding the guest from visually examining. In analyzing this question, it will prove necessary to address two main issues: 1) whether it is forbidden to derive benefit, or *hana'ah*, from non-Jewish cadavers[36] and 2) whether visiting the lab constitutes *hana'ah*.[37]

The Prohibition of Deriving Benefit from Cadavers

Virtually all authorities maintain that the prohibition of deriving benefit from Jewish corpses is Biblical in nature.[38] Most *rishonim* rule,

36 The topic of deriving benefit from non-Jewish corpses is discussed at length in *Nishmat Avraham, Yoreh De'ah* 349:1 (pp. 510–515). Many of the sources presented here were drawn from that discussion. We focus on non-Jewish cadavers based on the assumption that the cadavers in North American medical schools are not Jewish. As explained earlier in our discussion of the bone boxes, we can use the principle of following the majority. If, however, one has reason to believe that his or her cadaver is Jewish, then one could not rely on the majority.

37 The question of visual examination constituting *hana'ah* is described at length by R. J. David Bleich in *Cadavers on Display*, Tradition 40:1 (Spring 2007), pp. 87–97. Many of the sources presented here were drawn from this article.

38 The Gemara (*Avodah Zarah* 29b) implies that the prohibition is Biblical. See *Nishmat Avraham, Yoreh De'ah* 349:2(2) (p. 517) who notes that although most authorities maintain the prohibition is Biblical, *She'eilat Yaavetz* writes that the prohibition is rabbinic.

however, that there is no *issur hana'ah* (prohibition of deriving benefit) from non-Jewish corpses, and the Yerushalmi[39] seems to say so explicitly. Nevertheless, *Shulchan Arukh*[40] rules in accordance with the minority view among *rishonim*[41] that one may not derive benefit from non-Jewish cadavers.[42] Rama does not argue with *Shulchan Arukh*, and other authorities, including *Levush*,[43] rule explicitly that one may not derive benefit from non-Jewish corpses. Despite the ruling of *Shulchan Arukh*, however, many later authorities, including *Gra*,[44] *Shakh*,[45] and *Chatam Sofer*[46] rule in accordance with the majority of *rishonim* that one may derive benefit from non-Jewish cadavers.

Although most *rishonim* and many *acharonim* rule that one is permitted to derive benefit from non-Jewish cadavers, leading rabbis such as R. Shlomo Zalman Auerbach and R. Moshe Feinstein are not willing to diverge from the ruling of *Shulchan Arukh* except under special circumstances. For example, *Nishmat Avraham*[47] writes in the name of R. Shlomo Zalman Auerbach that it is only permissible to derive benefit from non-Jewish corpses when doing so fulfills a useful purpose like learning medicine. In a different context, R. Moshe Feinstein[48] writes concerning cadaveric transplants that since the overwhelming majority of specimens originate from non-Jewish cadavers and since this is a case of great need, one may rely on the opinions who maintain that it is permissible to derive benefit from non-Jewish cadavers.

The aforementioned opinion of R. Shlomo Zalman Auerbach and the longstanding practice of Jewish medical students to participate in anatomy lab indicate that we are lenient with this potential *issur hana'ah* for the purpose of learning medicine. Still, it is not clear

39 *Shabbat* 10:5. See *Korban Ha-Edah* (ad loc s.v. *be-meit akum*) who writes explicitly that non-Jewish corpses are *mutarim be-hana'ah*.
40 *Yoreh De'ah* 349:1.
41 *Rashba*, responsa 365.
42 Although *Shulchan Arukh* only states that it is forbidden to derive benefit from the burial shrouds of Jewish and non-Jewish cadavers, it is clear from context that *Shulchan Arukh* agrees that it is also forbidden to derive benefit from the cadavers themselves. As to whether the prohibition regarding non-Jewish corpses is Biblical or rabbinic, one might reason that if the law parallels the prohibition regarding Jewish corpses it should be Biblically mandated with regard to non-Jewish corpses as well. However, *Pitchei Teshuvah*, *Yoreh De'ah* 349:1 quotes an opinion that the prohibition is rabbinic.
43 *Yoreh De'ah* 349:1.
44 *Yoreh De'ah* 349:1.
45 *Nekudot Ha-Kesef*, *Yoreh De'ah* 349:1.
46 Responsa *Yoreh De'ah* 336.
47 *Yoreh De'ah* 349:1(1.i).
48 *Iggerot Moshe*, *Yoreh De'ah* 1:229:6. See also the opinion of R. Moshe Feinstein regarding requesting autopsies in *Moriah*, Elul 5744, pp. 59–60.

whether this dispensation should be granted to visitors of the lab. While this allowance may be appropriate for those engaged in the lofty practice of studying medicine, perhaps the potentially valuable experience of visiting the lab is not crucial enough to justify halakhic dispensation permitting benefit from cadavers. What is left to be determined, then, is whether visiting the lab would constitute proscribed *hana'ah*.

Does Learning Constitute Benefit?

The first consideration we will address is whether one derives benefit according to Jewish law by examining a cadaver and subsequently gaining a greater understanding about the workings of the human body. In other words, does the intellectual experience of learning constitute *hana'ah*? This question has been addressed by numerous authorities in the context of performing an autopsy in order to gain medical information which could help treat future patients. In addressing the autopsy question, *Noda Be-Yehudah*[49] does not explicitly mention the concern of *hana'ah*, and his omission seems to indicate that acquiring medical information does not constitute *hana'ah*. Indeed, *Har Tzvi*[50] writes explicitly that gaining information by watching a dissection does not constitute *hana'ah* and he believes this is the opinion of *Noda Be-Yehudah* as well. *Chatam Sofer*[51] cites the responsum of *Noda Be-Yehudah* but writes explicitly that an autopsy would constitute *hana'ah* from the deceased and that *Noda Be-Yehudah* would agree to this position.[52] Ostensibly, the problematic *hana'ah* mentioned by *Chatam Sofer* is the medical information gained from the autopsy. However, it is unclear according to *Chatam Sofer* whether the *hana'ah* stems from the acquisition of medical information per se or whether it is considered *hana'ah* because that information will be used to treat patients in the future. If learning itself constitutes *hana'ah*, then the lab visitor may be deriving benefit from the cadavers. However, if implementation of the knowledge in the future is necessary to constitute *hana'ah*, then the lab visitor will likely not be deriving benefit from the cadavers.

---

49 Responsa *Yoreh De'ah* 210.
50 Responsa *Yoreh De'ah* 278.
51 Responsa *Yoreh De'ah* 336.
52 *Chatam Sofer* explains that *Noda Be-Yehudah* did not mention the prohibition of *hana'ah* because he was only addressing the concerns of the questioner. The one asking the question was concerned about the prohibition of desecration of the dead but did not ask whether the autopsy would be in violation of the prohibition of deriving benefit from the dead.

Does Gazing Constitute Benefit?

The second major consideration is whether gazing at a cadaver constitutes forbidden benefit. One of the primary sources which addresses this question is the Gemara[53] which states that "sound, sight, and smell are not subject to *me'ilah*." *Me'ilah* is the prohibition of deriving *hana'ah* from consecrated property of the Temple. While gaining benefit from Temple property is normally subject to the prohibition of *me'ilah*, this Gemara seems to suggest that gaining benefit by gazing at the Temple property is not considered a forbidden act. This would imply that the act of gazing is not formally included in the term *hana'ah* under Jewish law. However, the Gemara explains further that that although there is no concern of *me'ilah* in these cases, a prohibition still exists. The simple reading of the Gemara is that gazing at the Temple property does not constitute *me'ilah* on a Biblical level but is nevertheless forbidden due to rabbinic prohibition.

What emerges from the Gemara is that although the prohibition may only be rabbinic, gazing at the Temple property still constitutes a forbidden form of benefit. It remains to be determined, however, whether the act of gazing constitutes forbidden benefit only with regard to *me'ilah* or whether it also constitutes benefit regarding other objects for which *hana'ah* is prohibited. R. Ovadia Yosef[54] proves from many authorities that the prohibition associated with "sound, sight, and smell" is not limited to *me'ilah* but rather applies to all *issurei hana'ah*. One of his many proofs is from the opinion cited in *Beit Yosef*[55] and the ruling of *Shulchan Arukh*[56] that it is forbidden to gaze at the beauty of *avodah zarah* (an object of idol worship) as this constitutes forbidden benefit. It would appear therefore, according to R. Ovadia Yosef, that even if the lab visitor merely benefits from the sight of the cadavers, this could constitute forbidden *hana'ah*.

One may argue that there is room for leniency with regard to gaining benefit from the sight of a cadaver because this action is considered an unusual form of benefit. Indeed, some authorities[57] maintain that deriving benefit from a corpse in an unusual manner is not Biblically prohibited. However, R. Akiva Eiger[58] writes explicitly that receiving benefit in an unusual manner from a cadaver is forbidden even for the

53 *Pesachim* 26a.
54 *Yabbia Omer* 6, *Orach Chayyim* 34:3–5.
55 *Beit Yosef, Yoreh De'ah* end of 142.
56 *Yoreh De'ah* 142:15.
57 Radvaz (responsa 3:548) writes explicitly that receiving benefit from a corpse in an unusual manner is only rabbinically prohibited. Some also infer from *Mishneh Le-Melekh, Hilkhot Avel* 14:21 that receiving unusual benefit from a corpse is not Biblically prohibited.
58 *Chidushei R. Akiva Eiger, Yoreh De'ah* 349:1.

sake of a sick person, and R. Moshe Feinstein[59] and R. Shlomo Zalman Auerbach[60] favor the position of R. Akiva Eiger.[61]

Even if there is a prohibition of gazing at a corpse, this prohibition would likely not be transgressed by merely looking. Regarding the Gemara's statement that sight does not constitute *me'ilah*, Rashi[62] describes "sight" as "benefitting from the beautiful appearance of the *heikhal* [a section of the Temple]". According to this definition, the type of visual examination which constitutes *hana'ah* is more than just looking but actually taking pleasure in the appearance of the forbidden object. For our purposes, merely observing or identifying a bone or blood vessel would likely not constitute forbidden benefit, whereas staring awestruck at the beauty of the human body would perhaps be included in the prohibition of forbidden benefit.

Summary

After outlining the various opinions among the later authorities regarding deriving benefit from non-Jewish cadavers, we set out to determine whether a lab visitor would be in violation of this potential prohibition. We noted that the two main concerns are that the visitor will gain a new understanding of the workings of the human body or that the visitor will gaze at the beauty of the human body. Ultimately, whether or not it is problematic for a guest to visit the anatomy lab may depend on the experience of each individual visitor. A person who increases his knowledge of human anatomy or gazes wondrously at the beauty of the human body may in fact be gaining prohibited benefit.

3) Proper Conduct in the Presence of Cadavers

Medical schools currently have policies mandating proper respect of the cadavers in anatomy lab. Although exceptions exist, students by and large abide by expected codes of conduct and treat the cadavers with dignity. Respect for the cadavers, as expected by school policy and anatomy professors, does not necessarily mean that idle conversation, laughing, and making occasional jokes is forbidden in the anatomy lab. On the contrary, many claim that, within reason, making occasional jokes is a normal way of acting and even a necessary adaptation to the somewhat uncomfortable experience of cadaveric dissection. The

---

59 *Iggerot Moshe, Yoreh De'ah* 1:229 end of section 5.
60 *Minchat Shlomo tinyana* 97.
61 Some maintain that unusual benefit from non-Jewish cadavers would be permitted even according to R. Akiva Eiger. See R. J. David Bleich's *Contemporary Halakhic Problems*, vol. II, p. 64 where the opinion of R. Shlomo Zalman Auerbach is quoted.
62 *Keritot* 6a s.v. *u-mareh*.

following few sources may indicate, however, that Jewish law demands a higher level of respect for the dead than is expected by others.

Shulchan Arukh, based on the Gemara,[63] rules that one should not engage in levity (*kallut rosh*) in a cemetery.[64] *Shakh*[65] writes that levity is forbidden because it demonstrates a lack of respect for the dead, or a lack of *kavod ha-meit*. While *Shulchan Arukh* only mentions the prohibition of levity within the confines of a cemetery, R. Yechiel Michel Tukachinsky[66] writes that it is forbidden to engage in levity in front of a corpse even outside of a cemetery. He explains that if one should refrain from levity in a cemetery where the corpses are hidden from view, one should certainly refrain from levity when a corpse is lying in plain sight.

From these authorities it is clear that levity is not an ideal mode of conduct in the anatomy lab.[67] Of course, one can only be expected to try one's best in this area, and it is recognized that maintaining seriousness throughout the many hours of anatomy lab can be a real challenge. I would like to bring this discussion to the fore, however, to serve as a reminder to students to try their best to engage in the dissections with utmost respect for the cadavers and with the conscious awareness that they are handling human beings created in the Divine image.

4) Wearing *Tzitzit* in the Lab

In general, the obligation to wear a *tallit katan* is not taken lightly. Although technically one is not required to wear a four-cornered garment in order to become obligated in *tzitzit*, it has become a universal custom for males to wear a *tallit katan* in order to have a constant reminder of the *mitzvot*.[68] R. Moshe Feinstein[69] writes that it is forbidden to deviate from this practice. Given the importance of wearing *tzitzit*, we will assume that one should wear them in the lab until proven otherwise.

---

63 *Megillah* 29a.
64 *Yoreh De'ah* 368:1. Elsewhere, in a discussion of inappropriate behavior in the synagogue, *Shulchan Arukh, Orach Chayyim* 151:1 lists *sechok* (laughter), *bittul* (mocking), *and sichah beteilah* (idle conversation) as examples of *kallut rosh*.
65 *Yoreh De'ah* 368:1.
66 *Gesher Ha-Chayyim*, vol. 1, ch. 5 section 1:3–4.
67 The technical application of this requirement to non-Jews has been discussed elsewhere. See this author's article in *Journal of Halacha and Contemporary Society*, Fall 2014 (LXVIII).
68 *Shulchan Arukh, Orach Chayyim* 24:1. *Shulchan Arukh* 24:6, quoting *Menachot* 43b, explains the great reward for those who are scrupulous in this *mitzvah*. See *Menachot* ibid. for additional benefits.
69 *Iggerot Moshe, Orach Chayyim* 4:4.

It becomes apparent from *Shulchan Arukh* that the presence of cadavers themselves is not sufficient reason to refrain from wearing *tzitzit*. This can be derived from the statement of *Shulchan Arukh* that one is permitted to enter into a cemetery wearing *tzitzit* as long as they are covered.[70] The same law applies to one who is within four *ammot*[71] of a corpse.[72] The reason why the *tzitzit* should not be exposed is because doing so is considered mocking the deceased as they can no longer perform this mitzvah. This prohibition is termed *lo'eg la-rash*.[73] Because the only stated reason for covering the *tzitzit* in a cemetery is *lo'eg la-rash*, it appears that the authorities do not consider wearing the *tallit katan* in front of a cadaver to be a disgrace to the *tzitzit*. Furthermore, assuming that the cadavers in anatomy lab are non-Jewish, the *tzitzit* could even be exposed in the lab. Because non-Jews are not obligated in the mitzvah of *tzitzit*, there is no concern of *lo'eg la-rash*.

Despite the fact that cadavers themselves do not constitute a disgrace to the *tzitzit*, one might reason that the anatomy lab is still a dirty place and wearing the *tallit katan* in the lab would be disgraceful to the *tzitzit*. At first glance, however, this argument could easily be rejected, based on the following reasoning. *Shulchan Arukh* writes that one is permitted to wear the *tallit katan* in the bathroom.[74] It is important to keep in mind that that the bathrooms of previous generations were not as clean as modern-day bathrooms, and yet we find that it was permitted to wear the *tallit katan* into those bathrooms. Although many would not consider the anatomy lab to be a particularly clean place, it is likely cleaner than the outhouses of previous generations. Because one wears the *tzitzit* in the bathroom, it would seem that the *tzitzit* should be worn in anatomy lab as well.

However, anatomy lab may in fact be more problematic than the bathrooms of yesteryear. Currently, cadavers in the lab are preserved in chemicals which give off a foul odor. Students report that the smell of the chemicals permeates one's clothes and even remains on the clothes for days or weeks after leaving the lab. Because of this odor, one could argue that although no visible dirt stains the *tzitzit* in lab, they do become dirty and disgraced through the smell. This is in contrast to wearing the *tallit katan* in an outhouse or bathroom where the *tzitzit* are not physically dirtied. If the smell in the lab is pungent enough to cause a disgrace to the *tzitzit*, it may be forbidden to wear the *tallit katan* in the lab.

70   *Shulchan Arukh, Orach Chayyim* 23:1.
71   Four *ammot* is roughly six to eight feet.
72   Ibid. 23:3.
73   See Proverbs 17:5.
74   *Orach Chayyim* 21:3, as explained by *Taz*.

Regardless of whether one does or does not wear the *tallit katan* in the lab, the following three points will be useful for anatomy students to clarify the procedure of making new blessings on the *tzitzit*:

1. When taking off one pair of *tzitzit* and changing into a new pair of *tzitzit*, a blessing should be recited on the new pair.[75]
2. When taking off one *tallit katan* for an extended time and replacing the same *tallit katan*, a new blessing may be required. The underlying question is whether the original blessing can still be linked to the second donning of the *tallit katan*. All authorities agree that a significant break in time (*hefsek*) would mandate a new blessing, but there is a dispute with regard to the amount of time that constitutes a *hefsek*.[76] Because there is a large range of opinions about how much time constitutes a *hefsek*, a halakhic authority should be consulted.
3. It is common that students change clothes in a bathroom before and after anatomy lab. However, it is forbidden to recite a blessing in the bathroom. If one needs to recite a blessing over the *tallit katan*, one may still don the *tzitzit* while in the bathroom. After leaving the bathroom one should shake the *tallit katan* and then recite the blessing.[77]

5) Washing Hands after Lab

Shulchan Arukh[78] writes that the hands must be washed after walking in a cemetery[79] or after touching a cadaver. Even outside of a cemetery, it is customary to wash hands while in the presence of even one cadaver.[80] The reason that one should wash hands in these cases is because of *ruach ra'ah*, an impure spirit. It is not explicit from *Shulchan Arukh*, however, whether the requirement of washing hands is limited to Jewish corpses or if it also extends to non-Jewish corpses. Later authorities who discuss this question seem to concur that there is no distinction

---

75 The blessing on the new *tallit katan* according to Rama, *Orach Chayyim* 8:6, is "*al mitzvat tzitzit.*"

76 See R. Simcha Bunim Cohen's *Laws of Daily Living* pp. 236–238, citing *Halikhot Shlomo* 3:7, that even an activity lasting three hours may not constitute a *hefsek*. In many institutions, anatomy lab sessions last less than three hours.

77 Precedent for this procedure is based on *Shulchan Arukh, Orach Chayyim* 8:10 who writes a similar law regarding one who dons the *tallit katan* when his hands are unclean.

78 *Shulchan Arukh, Orach Chayyim* 4:18.

79 *Shulchan Arukh* actually writes "one who walks between cadavers," but this is understood by later authorities to mean walking in a cemetery.

80 *Magen Avraham, Orach Chayyim* 4:21, *Mishnah Berurah* 4:43, and *Arukh Ha-Shulchan* 4:21. While *Arukh Ha-Shulchan* limits the requirement to a case where one is within four *ammot* of the deceased, *Mishnah Berurah* does not explicitly limit the case to within four *ammot* of the dead.

between the cadavers of Jews and non-Jews with regard to hand-washing. *Kaf Ha-Chayyim*[81] writes that the hands should be washed after touching a non-Jewish corpse, and R. Yitzchak Yosef[82] writes that one must wash hands after taking leave of a non-Jewish cemetery.

Even if we assume that the cadavers in anatomy lab are of non-Jewish origin, it appears from the aforementioned opinions that the hands should be washed after lab to remove the *ruach ra'ah*. In all instances in which one washes the hands to remove *ruach ra'ah*, the authorities advise that one should try to wash the hands immediately.[83]

Our next task is to determine the proper method in which the hands should be washed. In order to remove the *ruach ra'ah* which descends on a person who is sleeping overnight, the hands are washed three times[84] from a vessel.[85] Are these two requirements – washing three times and washing from a vessel – necessary to remove the *ruach ra'ah* from cadavers? While many[86] assume that washing one time suffices, some[87] are stringent and require three times. With regard to washing from a vessel, many leading authorities do not mention this requirement and imply that a vessel is not required. Nevertheless, some[88] do require a vessel.

After having discussed the requirement and proper method of washing the hands after lab, we must re-examine whether an additional hand-washing is truly necessary after lab. After all, virtually all students wash their hands with soap and water after each lab session for hygienic reasons. Once the students have already washed their hands in this method, are they obligated to wash again to remove *ruach ra'ah*? In other words, will washing and scrubbing the hands under running tap water effectively remove *ruach ra'ah*? The argument could be made that once the hands have already been washed and scrubbed in this manner, another washing is not necessary.[89] As noted earlier, many authorities

---

81   *Orach Chayyim, chelek* 1, 4:81.

82   *Yalkut Yosef, Orach Chayyim* 4:57.

83   *Mishnah Berurah* 4:38 citing *Peri Megadim*. See also *Mishnah Berurah* 4:43 citing Rama that one should not enter into another house or building before washing the hands.

84   *Shulchan Arukh, Orach Chayyim* 4:2.

85   *Shulchan Arukh, Orach Chayyim* 4:7.

86   *Magen Avraham* 4:17 is lenient, and his opinion is quoted by *Arukh Ha-Shulchan* 4:21. *Mishnah Berurah* 4:39 initially writes that washing three times is not necessary, and afterwards he cites authorities (using the term *yesh omrim*) who require washing three times. By citing the second set of authorities as a *yesh omrim*, *Mishnah Berurah* implies that there is room to be lenient.

87   See *Mishnah Berurah* ibid.

88   See *Piskei Teshuvot chelek* 1 *siman* 4 footnote 164 for a synopsis of opinions.

89   In other words, this method of washing might work in a *be-di'eved* (*ex post facto*) situation, as will now be explained.

assume that washing three times is not necessary after handling cadavers. In addition, Rama[90] writes in the case of removing *ruach ra'ah* upon awakening in the morning that although one should ideally use a vessel and *ko'ach gavra* (direct human force), if neither are used the washing still works *ex post facto*.[91] If we combine these opinions together, it would seem that an additional hand-washing to remove *ruach ra'ah* would not be necessary after the lab. Ultimately, this likely depends on the location of the sink used to wash the hands with soap and water. If the sink is located outside of the lab, then one would likely not be required to wash again. If the sink is located inside of the anatomy lab, however, then washing hands there may not remove the *ruach ra'ah* because immediately after washing the hands one is still in close proximity to the cadavers and one is again susceptible to *ruach ra'ah*. It would appear that in this case one should wash again, but it may not be necessary to wash from a vessel three times.

90 *Orach Chayyim* 4:7.
91 This is how *Mishnah Berurah* 4:16–17 explains Rama.

Chapter 3

Studying Medicine on *Shabbat*

Yair Saperstein, MD

The question of whether one may study medicine on *Shabbat*[1] is one that is relevant for every medical student and doctor. Students begin medical school mostly in the classroom and take tests on a regular basis. After the student finishes pre-clinical studies, studying medicine becomes even more important: continued reading is a necessity to learn the intricacies of medicine and to keep up to date with the progression of medicine, both of which are important for patient care. But is this reading allowed on *Shabbat*? To explore this question, we will start with the rabbinic decree against certain reading material on *Shabbat* and then elucidate which categories of reading material are included in this prohibition. The categories we will address specifically are: Torah, business material, *sifrei chokhmah* (general knowledge literature), and medicine.

The Rabbinic Prohibition of *Shtarei Hedyotot* on *Shabbat*

The discussion of permissible *Shabbat* reading material – and forbidden reading material – stems from a rabbinic decree instituted against reading "*shtarei hedyotot*"[2] on *Shabbat* and *yom tov*.[3] While the original

---

1   *Shulchan Arukh (Orach Chayyim* 307:17) groups *Shabbat* and *yom tov* together. In this chapter, I refer to both *Shabbat* and *yom tov*, even where only *Shabbat* is written. Further discussion is warranted to highlight any fine differences between the two with regards to the permissibility of studying certain subjects, including medicine, on their respective days.
2   The scope of this term is a matter of debate and is addressed below.
3   Codified in *Shulchan Arukh, Orach Chayyim* 307:12–13. See below.

enactment of this decree is nowhere explicitly stated, its existence is apparent by two other rabbinic decrees that were introduced to support it:[4]

1. The Mishnah[5] states that one preparing a meal with a specific number of guests who wishes to check that there are enough desserts may count the number of guests and the number of desserts on *Shabbat* orally, but may not read these numbers off of a written note.[6] Abaye explains that we are concerned one will come to read *shtarei hedyotot* on *Shabbat*.[7] This demonstrates that the prohibition of reading *shtarei hedyotot* on *Shabbat* is so strong that another prohibition – that of reading off a guest/dessert list – was instituted to support it.

2. The Mishnah[8] records the prohibition of reading some portions of *Tanakh* on *Shabbat*.[9] In the Gemara,[10] R. Nechemiah suggests that the reason for the prohibition was to strengthen the prohibition against reading *shtarei hedyotot*.

Defining *Shtarei Hedyotot*

Thus, there is a rabbinic prohibition against reading *shtarei hedyotot* on *Shabbat*. But how does one define the term *shtarei hedyotot*? Which categories of reading material are prohibited?

---

4   For further discussion, see R. Howard Apfel, "Reading Options on Shabbat," *The Journal of Halacha and Contemporary Society*, Volume LIV: Fall 2007.

5   *Shabbat* 148b.

6   Rashba to *Shabbat* 148b s.v. *moneh*, citing Rabbeinu Yonah, writes that one may not even read these numbers silently. In contrast, Rabbeinu Baruch of Magentza, cited in *Hagahot Maimoniyot* (*Shabbat* 23:9), allows one to silently read letters delivered on *Shabbat* from outside the *techum Shabbat*. See also *Yalkut Yosef* (*Shabbat* vol. 2, 307:12–17). See also footnote 23.

7   An alternate explanation is offered by R. Bibi in the Gemara, who explains that we are concerned one may come to erase from the list.

8   *Shabbat* 115a.

9   At that time, a regular lecture on *halakhah* was delivered in the *beit midrash* on *Shabbat* afternoon. For this reason, it was prohibited to read the riveting *Ketuvim* since it was feared that one would become distracted, lose track of time, and not attend this lecture. This decree of refraining from reading *Ketuvim* on *Shabbat* does not apply nowadays because we no longer have a set time for such a lecture in the *beit midrash*. See *Ba'al Ha-Ma'or*, *Shabbat* 43a in *dappei ha-Rif* s.v. *ve-ha*.

10 *Shabbat* 116b.

One group of thought defines *shtarei hedyotot* as business-related documents. Rashi,[11] *Tosafot*,[12] Ramban,[13] Rashba,[14] and Rosh[15] thus prohibit reading business material on *Shabbat*. However, all non-business material such as *sifrei chokhmah* is permitted as *Shabbat* reading material. One is then permitted to read medical literature on *Shabbat*.[16]

A second group of thought defines *shtarei hedyotot* as any non-Torah document. Rambam[17] and others thus prohibit *sifrei chokhmah* as *Shabbat* reading material. However, we will discuss below whether medicine is, according to some, nevertheless an exception to this prohibition.

Understanding the Prohibition of *Shtarei Hedyotot*

Before we proceed with our discussion, it is important to first understand the basis of this decree of *shtarei hedyotot*.[18] The first group of thought considers the decree a part of the overarching rabbinic enactment to actively make *Shabbat* different from a weekday. This, in turn, is based on a verse in Isaiah, the source of *kavod Shabbat*: "If you restrain, because of *Shabbat*, your feet, from performing your affairs on My holy day... and you honor it (*ve-kibadto*) by not doing your ways (*me-asot derakhekha*), seeking your wants (*mimtzo cheftzekha*), and speaking words (*ve-dabber davar*)..."[19] The Gemara[20] explains that each phrase in this verse teaches us how we are to make *Shabbat* different from a weekday:[21] (1) one must honor *Shabbat* with special garments ("and you honor it"), (2) one must walk differently ("by not doing your ways"), (3) one must refrain from activities that further one's own wants ("seeking

---

11 *Shabbat* 149a, s.v. *kol hani*. Note that Rashi in *Shabbat* 116b s.v. *shtarei hedyotot* actually defines the term broadly as social letters.

12 *Shabbat* 116b, s.v. *ve-kol she-ken*.

13 Cited in responsa of Rashba, 7:346.

14 Responsa, 7:288, 7:346; Rashba's commentary to *Shabbat* 149a s.v. *u-le'inyan*. Note that Rashba, in contrast to Ramban, nevertheless outlaws reading social letters.

15 *Shabbat* 23:1.

16 Explicitly stated in responsa of Rashba 7:288.

17 Rambam, *Peirush Ha-Mishnayot*, *Shabbat* 23:2 s.v. *ha-ta'am*. Rambam thus prohibits reading social correspondence. Note that Rambam equates *Shabbat* and *yom tov*. See also Rambam in *Mishneh Torah*, *Shabbat* 23:19 (as explained by *Maggid Mishneh*). See also footnote 21.

18 Cf. R. Howard Apfel, "Reading Options on Shabbat," *The Journal of Halacha and Contemporary Society*, Volume LIV: Fall 2007.

19 Isaiah 58:13. The next verse continues, "...Then you shall delight with Hashem..."

20 *Shabbat* 113a.

21 Rambam (*Shabbat* 24:12–13), explains that making *Shabbat* different requires a *shevitah ha-nikkeret*, a "recognizable rest."

your wants" – *mimtzo cheftzekha*)[22] and (4) one's speech must not be like that of weekdays ("and speaking words").[23] Thus, the first group of thought considers reading *shtarei hedyotot* – business documents – a violation of the third clause from the verse in Isaiah, *mimtzo cheftzekha*. Reading business documents is an intrinsically weekday-related activity, and is therefore prohibited, whereas reading *sifrei chokhmah* is not intrinsic to weekdays, and is thus permitted.

The second group of thought, one might suggest, understands the rabbinic decree of *shtarei hedyotot* as based on the rabbinic dictum in Yerushalmi[24] that *Shabbat* and *yom tov* were given to Israel for Torah study alone. Thus, this second group of thought considers *shtarei hedyotot,* meaning any non-Torah documents, including *sifrei chokhmah,* as prohibited. Again, we will discuss below if medicine is perhaps an exception to this rule.

Finally, to further elucidate the two schools of thought, we will describe how they differ in their explanation of a related Gemara that forbids reading the descriptive captions under *deyukna'ot,* artistic images on *Shabbat.*[25] According to the first school of thought, which considers *shtarei hedyotot* to be business documents only, the prohibition of reading these captions is intended to prevent one from also reading *shtarei hedyotot* on *Shabbat.* This is because the captions themselves are *not* considered *shtarei hedyotot,* as they are not themselves business documents. According to the second opinion, the descriptive captions under the images are themselves within the scope of *shtarei hedyotot* prohibited on *Shabbat.*[26]

22 *Shulchan Arukh (Orach Chayyim* 306:1) codifies this third clause as prohibiting one from pursuing one's usual activities even if they do not involve performance of a *melakhah*. (As an example, on *Shabbat* it is prohibited to check the train schedule.)

23 The Gemara clarifies that *hirhurim,* thoughts related to weekday matters, are permissible. However, *Shulchan Arukh (Orach Chayyim* 306:8) writes that because of *oneg Shabbat,* the *mitzvah* to enjoy *Shabbat,* it is a *mitzvah* for one to avoid thinking of one's daily activities, and to consider as if all of one's work is done.

24 *Shabbat* 15:3.

25 *Biur Halakhah* 307:16 s.v. *ve-over* quotes those that limit this prohibition to captions under images for idolatry, including *Tosafot,* Rosh, and later, *Eliyah Rabbah,* though he notes that some are stringent for the captions under an artistic scene made for beauty as well.

26 See, for example, Me'iri *Shabbat* 149a s.v. *katav.*

Rulings

Shulchan Arukh[27] first cites the second school of thought, forbidding all non-Torah literature including *sifrei chokhmah* on *Shabbat* and *yom tov,* though he then cites the first school of thought permitting it. *Mishnah Berurah*[28] rules that we may be lenient, though he cites *Eliyah Rabbah* who notes that one who fears Heaven should be stringent, in deference to the opinions of those who forbid it.[29] Similarly, *Arukh Ha-Shulchan*[30] writes that it is permissible to study subjects other than Torah on *Shabbat,* but it is laudable to speak only words of Torah to respect the holy day of *Shabbat.* [31] It appears that *Mishnah Berurah* and *Arukh Ha-Shulchan* rule in accordance with the first explanation of *shtarei hedyotot,* thereby permitting *sifrei chokhmah,* but say it is preferable to be stringent in accordance with the second view, in deference to that opinion.[32] *Magen Avraham*[33] seems to take a different angle within the first opinion, permitting *sifrei chokhmah,* as he writes that

---

27 *Orach Chayyim* 307:17. Interestingly, *Shulchan Arukh* (*Orach Chayyim* 307:16) forbids reading Sefer Immanuel, and *sifrei milchamot* on both *Shabbat* and weekdays, as he considers it a violation of the verse "*al tifnu el ha-elilim,*" "Do not turn unto the idols," by virtue of being *moshav leitzim,* the pastime of fools.

28 307:65.

29 He specifically cites Rambam and Ran.

30 *Orach Chayyim* 307:11.

31 Similarly, Rama in *Darkei Moshe* (*Orach Chayyim* 307:7) allows reading social correspondences that contain *divrei Torah* based on an exception to the third clause in Isaiah that allows one to pursue *cheftzei shamayim,* Heavenly wants. Rama (*Orach Chayyim* 307:16) additionally writes that discussions on secular topics and reading war stories are permissible if conducted in Hebrew, the holy language. See also *Mishnah Berurah* (307:58) who writes that certain Jewish history books are permitted to read, as from them one can gain fear of Heaven. Similarly, *Kitzur Shulchan Arukh* (90:11) writes that one may read certain Jewish history books that inspire fear of Heaven on *Shabbat.* See below in the "Studying Medicine" section that when the studying constitutes a *mitzvah,* it is permissible to study material that may otherwise have not have been allowed on *Shabbat.*

32 In a similar vein, R. Yehoshua Neuwirth (*Shemirat Shabbat Ke-Hilkhatah* 29:46–47) writes that according to the letter of the law, one may read the news in a newspaper. However, one may not read or even look at the business matters in the newspaper, e.g., advertisements.

33 *Orach Chayyim* 301:4. Similarly, although *Shulchan Arukh* (*Orach Chayyim* 307:1) codifies the fourth clause of Isaiah, that which forbids speaking of weekday matters, prohibiting speaking excessively of "*devarim beteilim,*" idle topics, Rama explains that if one enjoys telling stories or similar activities, then it is permissible. See R. Dovid Ribiat's *The 39 Melochos,* vol. 4, *Koteiv,* footnote 156 for further discussion.

if one enjoys the reading, he may read non-prohibited secular literature for pleasure on *Shabbat*.

Studying Medicine

As discussed above, there are two groups of thought as to the scope of the rabbinic prohibition against reading *shtarei hedyotot* on *Shabbat*. The first school of thought considers business-related documents as prohibited, but permits *sifrei chokhmah*. Thus, medicine as a literature category is obviously permitted reading. The second school of thought, however, considers all non-Torah reading to be prohibited on *Shabbat*. Even so, medical reading may be a possible permitted exception if it is considered a *mitzvah*.

Some explain this exception as follows: The Gemara[34] cited the verse in Isaiah (quoted above) as the source for *kavod Shabbat*. The third clause, *mimtzo cheftzekha,* obligates one to not pursue his own activities on *Shabbat*. However, the Gemara explains, *cheftzei shamayim mutarin,* pursuing God's wants is permitted – in other words, doing a *mitzvah* is allowed.[35] Thus, if medicine is considered a *mitzvah*, it may be a possible permitted exception.

Indeed, R. Dr. Avraham Steinberg writes that it seems all of the *poskim* – that is, even those who rule in accordance with the second school of thought prohibiting other *sifrei chokhmah* on *Shabbat* – would be lenient with respect to learning medicine on *Shabbat*, because it is "*be-geder mitzvah*," within the purview of [being considered a] *mitzvah*. Thus, he rules, it is permissible for one to study medicine on *Shabbat*.[36] However, R. Shlomo Zalman Auerbach[37] is of the opinion that only a doctor, not a student, may study medicine on *Shabbat*, because only for a doctor does this reading constitute both gaining general knowledge

---

34 *Shabbat* 113a.

35 Note that this assumes the second school of thought bases the rabbinic decree of *shtarei hedyotot* on the verse in Isaiah, in contrast to what we wrote above. See *Yalkut Yosef* (*Shabbat* 2:307, *mah mutar likro be-Shabbat*, 29, footnote 24).

36 *Assia* vol. 2, page 16. Among his supporting sources, he cites Ramban that Chazal believed it was important for one to study medicine in general in order to gain knowledge of healing illness (*Iggeret Ha-Ramban Le-Chakhmei Tzarfat*, at the end of *Kovetz Teshuvot Ha-Rambam*, section 3, Lipsia). See also *Beit Yosef* 307 s.v. *katav*, where he quotes *Agur* who rules in accordance with Rashba and Ramban to allow reading medical textbooks.

37 *Nishmat Avraham* 307:6, page 311.

and a *mitzvah*. On the other hand, R. Moshe Feinstein[38] applies the leniency to both doctors and students.

Studying for a Test

Studying specifically for the purposes of preparing for an upcoming exam raises the further issue of *hakhanah*, preparing for a non-*Shabbat* activity.[39] For example, R. Shlomo Zalman Auerbach was in doubt regarding whether one may study secular subjects on *Shabbat* not for the knowledge but only to excel on a test during the week.[40] R. Shlomo Aviner[41] writes that *if* one follows the lenient view to permit studying *sifrei chokhmah* on Shabbat, "it includes school reading or studying for a test on the condition that one enjoys it. If such activities cause stress and fear over a test, one should refrain from studying."

Most interestingly, while R. Ovadia Yosef rules stringently in accordance with the second field of thought, that one may learn only Torah on *Shabbat*, he provides a single exception to the prohibition of *sifrei chokhmah*: a medical student who has a test after *Shabbat* and is pressured for time to study medicine (except for the study of surgery).[42]

---

38   Fred Rosner, "Rabbi Moshe Feinstein's Influence on Medical Halacha," The Journal of Halacha and Contemporary Society, vol 20 (1990). He writes that it is necessary to sacrifice some of the spirit of *Shabbat* in order to obtain the maximum training. This includes even attending lectures and conferences that "will add significantly to his mastery of the art and science of medicine…"

39   A violation of the third clause of Isaiah. See footnote 23.

40   *Shemirat Shabbat Ke-Hilkhatah* 28:84, footnote 206 ("*u-mistapek…*"). R. Dovid Ribiat (*The 39 Melochos, Koteiv,* footnote 158) posits the reason to be the issue of *hakhanah,* preparing for a non-*Shabbat* activity while it is *Shabbat.*

41   Online at http://www.ravaviner.com/2010/01/studying-secular-subjects-on-shabbat.html, Yeshivat Ateret Yerushalayim.

42   *Yalkut Yosef, Shabbat* vol. 2, *siman* 307, *mah mutar likro be-Shabbat,* 29; *dinei hakhanah mi-Shabbat le-chol,* 4. He also notes an exception to the exception, that one may not study surgery on Shabbat. Presumably he is discussing one learning by action in the operating or anatomy room. If one is studying by a non-Jewish teacher, he writes, it is permissible so long as he is sure he does not touch a dead body, or violate other prohibitions of *Shabbat.* He recommends consulting a competent halakhic authority. See footnote 24 in the chapter "*mah mutar likro be-Shabbat*" for a lengthy discussion.

Chapter 4

Copyright Law and Study Materials

Chaim Apfel, JD

T he days before a medical school exam present a formidable halakhic challenge for the medical student. Nervous about the upcoming exam or standardized test, and furiously attempting to devise a study strategy, the student will often consider using some form of professional study aid or review course. The problem is that many of these materials are prohibitively expensive. However, the medical student likely has friends who already took the exam who will offer to share a review book that was part of the course he or she took already. Alternatively, that friend may offer to provide a set of recordings made of the lectures that accompany the course.

The problem with accepting the friend's offer is that it most likely involves a violation of copyright law.[1] There is strong reason to believe that it is also prohibited by *halakhah* as well. This conclusion could theoretically be different both with regard to civil law and with regard to *halakhah* depending on a wide variety of variables; for example, how were the materials in question produced, who is the author of the alleged works, is one distributing the material or receiving it, and many more.

The focus of the chapter will be on the individual ramifications for violating a copyright rather than on the extent to which a *beit din* would impose a penalty. As will be made clear, there is a wide range of opinions regarding the applicability of intellectual property violations to *halakhah*. **While a rudimentary explanation of copyright law will be provided, the author makes no guarantees as to the accuracy and**

---

1   There is the additional issue regarding academic dishonesty. That issue is beyond the scope of this paper. However, the author has yet to see any halakhic authority that would not regard cheating to be *geneivat da'at*. See, e.g., *Iggerot Moshe, Choshen Mishpat* 2:30.

relevance of the information with regard to civil law. For any questions regarding state, federal, or international copyright law the reader is strongly urged to contact an attorney.

Civil Law

Before the halakhic material is presented, it is useful to present some background about civil law. As will be discussed below, Jewish law does compel following civil law.

Copyrights are governmentally imposed restrictions on the use of "original works of authorship," regardless of whether or not they have been published. The law grants owners of copyrights the exclusive right to, amongst other things, reproduce and record the work, create derivative works that are based upon the work, or distribute copies of the work. The copyright owner may also authorize others to do any of the preceding activities.[2]

Copyright law is subject to many limitations and a complete list would be beyond the scope of this chapter. Arguably, the one of the most important limitations is infringing activities that are regarded as "fair use." The characteristics that are scrutinized to determine whether a particular use is considered to be fair or infringing have not been clearly defined. However, the law does mention certain purposes that will generally be considered "fair use," including, but not limited to, research, scholarship, teaching, criticism and reporting. The law also mentions four factors that judges will consider when deciding whether to rule that a particular activity was fair use.[3] These include:

1. The purpose and character of the use, including whether such use is of commercial nature or for a nonprofit educational purpose
2. The nature of the copyrighted work
3. The amount and substantiality of the portion used in relation to the copyrighted work as a whole
4. The effect of the use upon the potential market for, or value of, the copyrighted work

Another exception to copyright rules that could be relevant to any analysis of infringement discussed is the first sale doctrine. Congress has allowed the purchaser of copyrighted work from a copyright owner the right to display, sell, or dispose of that particular copy in any way. This right is limited to that particular copy. This rule does not allow for reproduction of the material. It also does not apply to people who have rented, borrowed, or acquired the item without being granted full

---

2 *Copyright Basics.* The United States Copyright Office. Available at http://www.copyright.gov/circs/circ01.pdf. Last accessed June 6, 2014.
3 *Fair Use.* The United States Copyright Office. Available at http://www.copyright.gov/fls/fl102.html. Last accessed June 6, 2014.

ownership. For example, licensed material, including most computer software, is excluded from being protected under the first sale doctrine because the copyright holder retains ownership.[4]

Ideas, systems or factual information that are conveyed in a work cannot be considered copyrighted material. Similarly, works that are considered to be standard information, such as calendars or rulers, are not considered to be copyrightable. There are many caveats to these rules. A licensed attorney should always be consulted before copying or making any use of material for which the copyright holder's permission has not been obtained.[5]

Dina De-Malkhuta Dina

One broad stroke for prohibiting copying material that may be under a copyright protection would be to prohibit it because the activity is illegal. The concept of *dina de-malkhuta dina*, literally that the law of the land is the law, is cited many times throughout the Gemara. The principle makes an activity a sin because the government has prohibited that activity. For the purposes of this chapter, it may render violation of a copyright protection prohibited according to *halakhah* because it is forbidden to violate civil laws. As we shall see, the applicability of the principle is based on assessments of the appropriateness of the law that are subjective. For practical purposes, an intellectually honest decision should be reached by determining how and why the law is applied by civil authorities and judging the findings according to standards that have been set down by halakhic authorities. While this is not the forum for a comprehensive study of *dina de-malkhuta dina*, there are some principles related to our topic that are important in considering whether a copyright violation will violate this principle.

The scope of civil legislation that has the potential to lead to a violation of *dina de-malkhuta dina* is a matter of some debate. Rosh,[6] for example, derives *dina de-malkhuta dina* from the government's position as the primary property owner. Under this view, the principle should be limited to laws that are associated with property ownership, such as taxes.[7] Other commentaries regard *dina de-malkhuta dina* to be a broader license to maintain order and social justice.[8] Some limit the scope of *dina de-malkhuta* to instances when the government stands to benefit directly from the law in question. Those who maintain this

---

4   *Copyright Infringement – First Sale Doctrine.* Department of Justice. Available at http://www.justice.gov/usao/eousa/foia_reading_room/usam/title9/crm01854.htm. Last accessed March 29, 2015.
5   *Copyright Basics.* n2.
6   *Nedarim* 3:11.
7   See *Yam Shel Shlomo, Bava Kamma* 6:14.
8   *Yam Shel Shlomo*, ibid.

opinion disagree as to whether the government is considered to have benefited from laws that do not affect government activity.[9]

Copyright law arguably does not have any relevance to land ownership. The goal of copyright legislation, as stipulated by Article I, Section 8 of the United States Constitution, is "[t]o promote the Progress of Science and the Useful Arts." Lawmakers have decided that the purpose of the promotion is to benefit the citizens rather than the author. Copyright is viewed primarily for the purpose of encouraging the commodity of human creativity. It is not a tool for social justice but of economic development. By these standards copyright law should not be applicable to *dina de-malkhuta dina*. However, exceptions can be made. It is not difficult to imagine that there could be individual instances when copyright law would benefit a government, for example, if the government owned the copyrights that are in question or if the copyright owner were receiving government funding. Ultimately, however, many instances of copyright violation occur when the only direct beneficiaries of a copyright protection would be private individuals and companies. Lawmakers have acknowledged the purpose of rewarding authors for their social contribution as a secondary concern, when it does not come into conflict with the primary purpose.[10] Under these circumstances copyright protection could be seen as encouraging social justice and then *dina de-malkhuta dina* would be applicable.

It is worth noting that according to the opinion that *dina de-malkhuta dina* is strictly applied to legislation related to land, perhaps the principle should not apply in Israel. There are those who argue that since Israel is considered to be the property of the Jewish people, and not the property of a centralized government, *dina de-malkhuta dina* should not apply in Israel.[11] However, many of those who maintain this position concede that laws that do not contradict Torah law and serve an important social function, as copyright law arguably does, can rise to be included under principles similar to *dina de-malkhuta dina*.[12] Reasons cited include, but are not limited to, adherence to the passage of *"ve-asita ha-yashar ve-hatov,"* "and you will do what is straight and

---

9 See Ramban, *Bava Batra* 55a s.v. *im ken*. See also *Encyclopedia Talmudit*, s.v. *dina de-malkhuta dina*, 299–301.

10 Report of the Register of Copyrights on the General Revision of Copyright Law. Printed for House Committee on the Judiciary (1961), 5–6.

11 See Ran, *Nedarim* 28a s.v. *be-mokhes ha-omed me-elav*, citing *Tosafot*.

12 See R. Nachum M. Weifish, "Specific Halachic Rulings of Leading Torah Scholars," *Copyright in Jewish Law* (2010) citing, inter alia, R. Yosef Shalom Elyashiv (17:1) and R. Moshe Halberstam (17:30).

good,"[13] as well as the value of conforming to the *minhag benei ha-ir*, the common city custom.[14]

One commonly cited position states that the laws would not apply to instances when the government applies a law that contradicts Torah law.[15] However, in civil cases, instances when one of the litigants is a Gentile allow for *dina de-malkhuta dina* to be applied regardless of Torah law.[16] Another commonly cited position adds that that if a law is unjust, it would not be subject to *dina de-malkhuta dina*.[17] The author is not aware of any commentaries that regard copyright law to contradict Torah law, even though many hold that it has no roots in classical Biblical law. It simply is not mentioned. However, because it could exist without nullifying any part of Torah law, it still could be regarded as subject to *dina de-malkhuta dina*. It would seem logical that if a person regarded any part of copyright law to be unconstitutional, then that may be considered an unjust rule, since the law should not have been included under the laws of the state.[18] However, one should discuss the matter with an attorney, who could reasonably be expected to be knowledgeable about this area, before making this determination. Even if the particular protection that is being violated is unconstitutional, that would only impact whether the prohibition of violating *dina de-malkhuta dina* would arise. There may be several other prohibitions involved, including many that will be discussed below, in addition to *chillul Hashem*.[19] Therefore, it is strongly advised that a competent halakhic authority should also be consulted.[20]

In conclusion, *dina de-malkhuta dina* provides an easily cognizable reason to assume that violating copyright law might be prohibited under certain circumstances. However, uncertainty as to the scope of *dina de-malkhuta dina* leaves open many possibilities for violating the law with an arguable assumption that no prohibition has been violated. Even according to the broadest understanding of *dina de-malkhuta dina*, that it is applicable when a law is set up to provide social justice, copyright protection only meets that test under American law when it serves to reward the author and does not conflict with the promotion of art amongst the population. There are also times when an action that might be considered a copyright violation would be unenforceable. For

13 Deuteronomy 6:18.
14 See R. Weifish, ibid., citing R. Moshe Halberstam as ruling that one should follow *minhag benei ha-ir* that is for public benefit even if most people do not do so.
15 *Shakh, Choshen Mishpat* 73:39.
16 Rambam, *Hilkhot Zekhiyah U-Matanah* 1:14–15.
17 See Ramban, *Bava Batra* 55a s.v. *im kein*.
18 See Ramban, ibid.
19 See R. Weifish, ibid., 17:31, citing R. Moshe Halberstam.
20 See R. Weifish, ibid., 17:3, citing R. Yosef Shalom Elyashiv.

example, direct copyright violation committed over the Internet is often not prosecuted for efficiency reasons even when evidence is available. It is unclear whether Jews are required to adhere to laws more strictly than the government does in circumstances when those laws are not often enforced against the broader public.

Furthermore, there are values and concerns that *halakhah* imposes upon us that the civil laws do not. There are instances when one can copy copyrighted works under protection of civil law due to myriad policy considerations. However, the damage caused by making the copy would still occur. As we shall see below, committing an act of copyright violation can give rise to other prohibitions that would still be in force independent of whether *dina de-malkhuta dina* can be applied.

The Prohibtion of Damaging

Before analyzing specific halakhic issues that can give rise to halakhic liability, it is important to appreciate how a monetary liability can give rise to a prohibition. Much of Jewish property law addresses issues of financial liability. It does not necessarily follow that being found liable in a court proceeding necessarily indicates the violation of a prohibition. However, there appears to be an assumption that some prohibition has been violated when a person causes damage to property. For example, the rule that is applied to cases of indirect damage is that the defendant cannot be penalized with a court-imposed punishment but is considered to have committed a sin.[21]

It is useful to understand what the prohibition could be in order to determine if it would be applicable to copyright law. Ramah[22] suggests two possible sources for the prohibition of causing damage: (i) *lifnei ivver*, placing a stumbling block before the blind;[23] and (ii) "*ve-ahavta le-rei'akha kamokha,*" loving one's neighbor as oneself.[24] Both of these Torah verses are applied broadly. Rambam,[25] for example, applies the prohibition of *lifnei ivver* both to facilitating a person to sin who is prone to sinning, as well as to knowingly giving bad advice to a person. The principle that unifies these seemingly disparate rules is that it is forbidden to facilitate negative consequences for a person who is susceptible to them occurring. While *ve-ahavta le-rei'akha kamokha* appears only to be compelling positive behavior, Hillel applied this verse to teach, "That which you do not like, do not do to your friend."[26]

---

21 See also Rambam, *Hilkhot Nizkei Mamon* 5:1; *Tur, Choshen Mishpat* 378; cf. *Mishneh Le-Melekh, Rotze'ach* 2:2.
22 *Yad Ramah, Bava Batra* 26a, *siman* 107.
23 Leviticus 19:14.
24 Leviticus 19:18.
25 *Hilkhot Rotze'ach U-Shemirat Nefesh*, 12:14.
26 *Shabbat* 31a.

This lesson appears, at least superficially, to be very similar to the general principle of *lifnei ivver*. Ramah appears to regard the prohibition against causing damage to be rooted in broad commandments against causing negative consequences to come to others. The details of whether the consequences contemplated are those suffered by a copyright owner will depend on more detailed analysis of these commandments further below.

R. Aharon Lichtenstein[27] suggests two additional possible prohibitions that may be violated when a person causes property damage. The first is *"ve-chei achikha imakh,"* "and your brother shall live with you," which is stated in the Torah within the context of *tzedakah* and usury.[28] However, Sma also applies it to price gouging.[29] R. Lichtenstein views Sma as broadening the scope of *"ve-chei achikha imakh"* to encompass all monetary prohibitions, which would also include the prohibition of causing property damage.[30] The other commandment R. Lichtenstein posits may be violated is *"ve-asita ha-yashar ve-hatov,"* "and you shall do what is straight and good."[31] Ramban, in his commentary on the Torah, frequently cites this commandment as compelling rational and moral behavior that goes above and beyond the strict letter of the law.[32] Ramban's interpretation would imply that causing property damage to others would be prohibited if the damaging activity is amoral. The standard is obviously amorphous and requires a certain degree of intellectual honesty.

The particulars of each prohibition will impact the analysis of a particular copyright situation, though this is not the forum for a lengthy analysis of each prohibition. For the sake of illustrating this point, it would be helpful to see the ramifications if the copyright owner were not Jewish. The verse *"ve-ahavta le-rei'akha kamokha"* only governs behavior relating to Jews. Similarly, *"ve-chei achikha imakh,"* since it enjoins taking interest, also only relates to Jews. It would seem reasonable that inferences related to the prohibition against causing damage would also only apply to Jewish-owned property under this analysis. On the other hand, the prohibition of *lifnei ivver* has been applied to behavior relating to non-Jews as well. It is noteworthy that *"ve-asita ha-yashar ve-hatov"* is so general a commandment that any analysis of its application to a particular situation would necessarily require a

---

27 *"Ha-issur lehazik," Shiurei Ha-Rav Aharon Lichtenstein: Dina De-Garmi* (2000), pp. 172–175.

28 Leviticus 25:36.

29 *Sma, Choshen Mishpat* 231:43.

30 R. Lichtenstein lists several other possible prohibitions that would be violated by causing property damage. However, the particulars of these prohibitions render them irrelevant to copyright issues.

31 Deuteronomy 6:18.

32 Ramban, Deuteronomy 6:18 s.v. *ve-asita*.

certain degree of intellectual honesty given the specifics of a situation. When confronted with a copyright issue, it would be reasonable to assume that any of these prohibitions could potentially be violated and to proceed with an analysis from there.

Copyright as a Tortious Act

While it seems clear from the above discussion that the Torah intended for it to be forbidden to cause damage to others. It remains to be seen whether copyright violation is an activity that is prohibited because of the damage it causes. These activities are called "*nezikin*" in halakhic literature, or torts in English. The next issue that we must discuss is whether copyright violation constitutes a form of damage. It is understandable that, in addition to broad social harm, copyright violations can cause great financial hardship for intellectual property owners. This can be due either to degradation in value of items that have already been developed or loss in potential future profits. At the very least, two theories of halakhic torts could be applicable under these circumstances.

The first of these tort theories is *hezek she-eino nikar*, literally, unrecognizable damage. This form of damage occurs when one causes property to lose value but there is no recognizable change in the property itself.[33] Examples of this form of damage may include causing *terumah* to become *tamei* (and thus prohibited for consumption), or rendering water with ashes from the red heifer unfit for use by using it as a counterbalance on a scale.[34] This category of damage could theoretically apply to any loss of value caused to any templates, digital products, books, videos or other materials that are already produced. However, it would be difficult to apply it to information providers, such as lecturers, who do not produce material, since there must be an object that is "damaged" for the act to be considered *hezek she-eino nikar*.

The second theory is the tort of *garmi* or *gerama be-nezikin*.[35] These torts apply whenever damage is caused through no direct result of any action on the part of the defendant.[36] This action does not need to result in any damage to any particular piece of property for damage to have arisen. For example, *gerama* or *garmi* applies if a person withholds

---

33 *Hilkhot Chovel U-Mazzik* 7:1. See also *Encyclopedia Talmudit*, s.v. *hezek she-eino nikkar*. While there is some debate as to whether this law is applied at all in the present day, the argument only appears to revolve around whether courts can administer compensation and not whether the act should be prohibited.

34 See Rambam, *Chovel U-Mazzik* 7:2,4.

35 See *Encyclopedia Talmudit*, s.v. *garmi*, s.v. *gerama be-nezikin*; while there are factors differentiating the two, as discussed there, they are beyond the scope of this discussion.

36 Ibid.

testimony that may affect the outcome of a civil case[37] or, according to many *poskim*, if a person burns a document evidencing debt.[38] In both of these instances there is no particular piece of property that has been damaged. However, the victim undoubtedly suffered financial loss.

The Right to Copyright Protection

Until this point, the discussion has analyzed whether actions committed in violation of another's copyright protection constitute a sin. The previous section discussed to what extent the harms caused by copyright violations fall into the categories of harms that *halakhah* recognizes. However, while these potential harms may be recognized with regard to actual properties, it does not necessarily follow that harm coming to an intellectual property can be considered actual damage. After all, if *terumah* is *tamei*, it has undergone a change in status. Likewise, if a debt document has been burned, a finite sum of money has definitely been withheld from a person who had a valid claim over it. When intellectual property is violated, the owner cannot point to a particular loss of assets. It does not automatically follow from these arguments that *halakhah* is at all concerned about recognizing intellectual property as an asset that can be damaged. This section will analyze whether a copyright is an actual right that Chazal have seen fit to protect. This analysis is relevant in instances when there are no concerns about *dina de-malkhuta dina*, for example if the violating activity could be considered fair use. It needs to be determined, when civil law is no longer a factor, whether there is halakhic precedent for protecting copyright ownership.

Zeh Neheneh Ve-Zeh Lo Chaser

All assumptions that copyright violation should be treated differently than other forms of damage arise because no measurable degradation has occurred to an asset, nor has the claimant been observably injured. The Gemara[39] limits the rights of private property owners to restrict access to others in instances when there is no measurable damage arising from that access. While many examples are discussed, one notable case is that of a squatter. Like a copyright violator, a squatter receives benefits from an asset, when the owner is legally empowered to exclude others from benefitting from the asset. In both instances, the use does not cause any degradation to the asset. The Gemara rules that a property owner cannot expel a squatter from private property when that

---

37 *Shulchan Arukh, Choshen Mishpat* 28:1.
38 Rambam, *Hilkhot Chovel U-Mazzik* 7:9. See also Rosh, *Bava Kamma* 9:13.
39 *Bava Kamma* 20b.

property has not been previously designated for renting.[40] The general rule that the Gemara cites is that in instances of *zeh neheneh ve-zeh lo chaser* (literally, this one benefits and this one does not lose) we are *kofin al middat Sedom*, we discourage values that were associated with the people who lived in Sedom.

To understand the background of the policy it is important to keep in mind that in Talmudic literature, the people of Sedom are portrayed as being particularly unsympathetic to the plight of their fellow man.[41] This ruling is designed to suppress the Sedomites' cultural apathy from becoming prevalent within a halakhic society. In modern times, a comparison could be made to the legal taboo known as "rent-seeking." The rent-seeker gratuitously imposes costs on the broader public without providing a social benefit.[42] By insisting on charging for something that does not demand any personal sacrifice, the only net outcome from the transaction is that a charge has been added to the expenses of the squatter.[43]

A copyright holder can be seen in many ways as a rent-seeker. When an infringer commits a copyright violation, the copyright holder has not suffered any direct economic damage. The total present value of the holder's assets has not been degraded at all. If there is no actual damage caused, then the action is presumably not a sin. If the squatter had been a sinner, then it is doubtful that there would be a public policy enabling the sinful behavior to persist. Therefore, in order to classify copyright infringement as prohibited by virtue of it being a damaging activity, it is necessary to identify something that has been damaged.

The most obvious economic harm that the holder can be said to have experienced is in the potential future sales that could have been squandered. However, there is strong reason to doubt that items that are not yet extant can be said to possess economic value within the halakhic legal system. When degradation is caused to components that only have the potential to be separate from a composite entity, but are not yet separate, we consider the composite entity to be damaged and not the individual components. For example, if damage is caused to fruit while they

40 It is noteworthy that *Tosafot* (ad loc, s.v. *ha*) cite some who rule that the owner does have the right to take steps to prevent the person from seeking benefit via entering the land. However, this is irrelevant to the case at hand where the benefiting party is already able to get access to the copyrighted material.
41 See, for example, *Sanhedrin* 109a–109b.
42 See David N. Laband and John Sophocleus, "The Social Cost of Rent-Seeking: First Estimates," *Public Choice* 58:3 (1988), 269–275.
43 In secular law, the public policy against rent seeking is arguably economic in nature. Rent seeking is seen as wasteful and society does not benefit from economic waste. However, the policy of *kofin al middat Sedom* in the Gemara is clearly meant to guard against broad social ethical corruption. For example, see how the policy is applied in *Avot* 5:10.

are still on the trees, the damage that is assessed is based on the value of the grove rather than the unpicked fruit.[44] Also, *halakhah* regards assets that may potentially come into the owner's possession, known as *davar she-lo ba le-olam*, as something that cannot be contractually conveyed.[45] If something cannot be traded or degraded then, economically speaking, the thing is ethereal.[46] Therefore, it is doubtful that loss of potential benefits can really be regarded as an economic loss for the purpose of avoiding the policy of *kofin al middat Sedom*.[47]

It is noteworthy that the loss does not have to be material to remove the case from the rent-seeking policy concerns. The Gemara[48] allows for damage as insignificant as dirtying the paint of a homeowner's wall to exclude an activity from falling under the classification of *zeh neheneh ve-zeh lo chaser*. *Ketzot Ha-Choshen*[49] rules explicitly that whenever there is a resultant loss, even if it is minute, it is no longer regarded as *middat Sedom*.

Does Copyright Violation Create Loss?

The scope of what constitutes a "loss" for the purpose of avoiding concerns of *kofin al middat Sedom* is debated in the Gemara.[50] The context of the issue discussed there is a dispute about how property should be divided amongst beneficiaries. One beneficiary requests a particular plot of land because it adjoins his or her property and would like to avoid receiving property that is landlocked by another beneficiary. All things being equal, it would appear that the beneficiary could claim that he or she has a stronger claim to the plot in question because it is a case of *zeh neheneh ve-zeh lo chaser*.[51] However, the Gemara provides three possible situations where the other beneficiaries could advance claims to counteract this argument such that the rule of *kofin al middat Sedom* would not apply: 1) where there is a qualitative difference between this field and others,[52] 2) where this field contains a feature (such as a water

---

44   *Bava Kamma* 58b.

45   *Shulchan Arukh, Choshen Mishpat* 209:4.

46   See Me'iri and *Nimukei Yosef* on *Nedarim* 83b; *Encyclopedia Talmudit*, s.v. *tovat hana'ah*, footnote 284.

47   Cf. responsa of Rosh 97:2, arguing that every instance of *zeh neheneh ve-zeh lo chaser* involves the loss of potential income that could have been charged by an owner.

48   *Bava Kamma* 20b.

49   154:1.

50   *Bava Batra* 12b.

51   See Rambam, *Hilkhot Shekhenim* 12:1.

52   The fields do not necessarily have different monetary values. For example, one may be larger but the other could have a higher crop yield. See Rashi ad loc s.v. *amrei* and *Chidushei Ha-Ri Migash, Bava Batra* 13a s.v. *chad gisa*.

source) that may prevent future loss, 3) where the other beneficiaries anticipate that potential detriment to the claimant beneficiary will add to the value of their property (e.g., if the claimant beneficiary did not receive the adjoining property, he would be more likely to rent out the landlocked property to others, and the additional tenant would increase the security of the other beneficiary's property located between the two). The Gemara concludes that in the first two situations, the other beneficiaries' claims are valid. In the third situation, the other beneficiaries' claims would not be valid.

Several important characteristics of a "loss" emerge from this Gemara that should be emphasized. One characteristic is that a loss does not need to involve a financial diminishment of assets. The first situation above makes clear that we do not apply the rule of *kofin al middat Sedom* if even a quality of the item in question that the owner wants to retain is lost, e.g., one beneficiary wants a field because of its higher crop yield, even if the field has the same value as other fields. Therefore, copyright violation may not be excluded from the category of loss even if the owner suffers no degradation in net assets.

The Gemara's second situation illustrates that the detriment to the owner, at the very least, does not need to be observable at the time the loss occurs, e.g., one beneficiary wants a field because it contains a water source that will prevent future loss. The potential benefit that could be provided is sufficient to override *kofin al middat Sedom* concerns. Therefore, a copyright owner can rely on the possibility of future detriments in calculating a loss. For example, if releasing the copyrighted information will lower the value of future products that the copyright holder intends to market, this would be considered loss. (Although, as will be discussed later, this type of loss will not necessarily be ruled as damage.) However, presumably potential detriments must be regarding something other than a *davar she-lo ba le-olam*, an asset that has not yet come into existence.[53] The only asset that the owner could claim as damaged is an asset that the owner already has. An asset that is already in the copyright owner's possession at the time of the infringement, such as study materials distributed with a course, could qualify. Therefore, copying or distributing these materials in a manner that could potentially lead to the copyright holder losing value on the undistributed copies would constitute a loss.

Finally, the Gemara's rejection of the beneficiary's claim in the third situation above demonstrates that a loss to the value in the object must still be objectively demonstrable. No loss can be based on a situation where the claim of loss is based on a tangential effect of the activity in

---

53 *Bava Metzia* 66b states that a person cannot sell a *davar she-lo ba le-olam.* If one does not have the ability to liquidate the item, then it would be illogical to assume that damage can be done to it.

question, e.g., one person may suffer a circumstantial hardship or lose out on a benefit not related to the infringed material. The burden is on the damaged party to present an argument that this damage is concrete and not merely theoretically possible. If a personal decision is to be made as to whether or not a potentially infringing activity would be prohibited, a person should consider whether that argument could be made. The additional value that another set of circumstances may result in a benefit or loss unrelated, or tangentially related, to the value of the item is not considered to be a factor in determining whether there has been a loss of value. Likewise, for a copyright violation to be prohibited, the damage caused must be clear and direct.

One instance when this distinction is important is when copyrighted material is publicly presented in a slide show. If the lecturer does not prohibit photography or recording devices, there would be nothing wrong with obtaining a copy for later use. Storing copyrighted material for the purpose of accessing it at a more convenient date is known as time shifting. Courts generally regard this to be a fair use.[54] Halakhically, it would appear to be permitted under the principle of *kofin al middat Sedom*. The copyright owner could not rely on the expectation that the time shifter would lay out additional cash to receive the item from the owner at a more convenient time. For example, suppose the copyright holder intended to release the slides with the purchase of an ancillary program that facilitates viewing the slides, but the time shifter chooses to view the slides through some other manner, such as a photograph taken at the time of the lecture. The time shifter has not caused any degradation to the value of the material, since that was paid for originally. Only the ancillary program, which the viewer was under no obligation to buy, has gone unsold. Therefore, anyone who was legally able to view those slides should be allowed to obtain them later through some other means such as an Internet download. Similarly, students that are able to access copyrighted material before the lecture is presented may do so if they have already purchased the right to access that lecture. The lecturer does not receive any benefit from the people actually attending the lecture, particularly if it is delivered online.

People who did not legally obtain access to the slides originally should not be allowed to access copies of the slides because doing so would degrade the value of the slides as a part of the lecturer's product. Even if they are not part of the lecturer's product package they are often sold separately to people who may not have wanted to purchase full access to the lecture. Similarly, posting the slides online for public access would presumably be regarded as degrading the slides' value by making them easily accessible to others.

---

54 See Sony Corp. of America v. Universal City Studios, Inc., 464 US 417 (1984).

It is possible for a copyright infringement to cause a loss that is not directly related to an extant item. For example, creating bootleg videos or recordings may not detract from the value of a particular item but they are unquestionably financially harmful to intellectual property owners.[55] However, it is more difficult to find a measurable loss if the copyright owner discontinued the material. Once the items are discontinued, their net worth to the owner should not degrade directly if they are copied or distributed by others. Distributing these materials could impact on the value of products that are derivations of the copyrighted material and the original copyright owner wishes to sell or distribute. In these instances, this author can see no comparison that can be drawn to laws related to monetary loss. Nonetheless, from the perspective of the copyright owner, the item has lost value.

Compensating the Copyright Owner for Benefit

There are numerous tangible benefits that can be derived from a respected copyright other than pecuniary. For example, a copyright restriction allows the copyright holder to provide related services or additional products that justify prices that adequately compensate the effort to develop the product without being restricted by the laws of supply and demand. Suppose a person may not pay the same amount for a review book as one would for a related course or for future editions of the product. However, the predominant amount of effort is arguably made when the research is compiled for the review book. If the review book became widely available as the result of a copyright violation, the course or any future editions of the material would not have as strong a demand. If the item can be provided without taking into account this initial effort, the copyright holder will have essentially lost out on the compensation for the development labor. The loss of the spent labor has no future financial value. It has already been spent. However, the experience lasts with the author and its waste would be unjustifiable. It would seem hard to believe that denying a person these benefits is sanctioned because we are concerned that the victim would be comparable to the people of Sedom.

Arguably, allowing copyright violators to cause the nonmonetary detriments to the copyright holder yields relatable, if not identical, end results as the underlying sins of causing damage seem constructed to

---

55 A study found that as a result of global online copyright piracy the US economy annually loses $12.5 billion of output and also has lost 71,060 jobs as of the date it was published. See Stephen. E. Siwek, *The True Cost of Sound Recording*, Institute for Policy Innovation (2007). Available at http://www.ipi.org/docLib/20120515_SoundRecordingPiracy.pdf. Accessed March 29, 2015.

avoid. As discussed above, Ramah[56] argues that the underlying sins violated by damaging one's property do not necessarily relate to the monetary loss caused by the damage. For example, *lifnei ivver* concerns even spiritual harm caused by committing sins.[57] In this instance, the copyright violator is still bringing about some detriment to the copyright holder that he was prone to experiencing regardless of measurable financial loss. Similarly, the purpose of *ve-ahavta le-rei'akha kamokha* can be viewed as being for the sake of preserving internal sensitivity of the violator than protecting the rights of third parties.[58] The connection between the prohibition of causing damage and these prohibitions would seem to be applicable in instances other than findings of measurable financial loss. Being callous to the copyright holder's plight would fail the spirit if not the substance of the commandment. It would seem that there must be some mechanism in place to prohibit causing non-monetary damages in addition to a prohibition of causing monetary damages.

In this vein, R. Yechezkel Landau wrote a responsum[59] regarding an author who had hired a printer to prepare copies of *Seder Nezikin* and *Seder Kodashim* with Rashi and *Tosafot* along with the author's own commentary on the bottom of the page. The printer followed the instructions of the author. However, after he was done printing the page, the printer retained the stencil he had made of the page without the author's commentary and printed his own edition of the material without the author's commentary. The author claimed that the printer was infringing upon his rights to the formatting he commissioned. R. Landau sided with the author to the extent that he obligated the printer to pay for the benefit he received for the work that the author did. He explicitly did not obligate the printer to pay for any loss that the author experienced.

It would appear that R. Landau did not see the issue of the alleged copyright violation as an issue of monetary damage. Rather the issue

---

56 *Yad Ramah, Bava Batra* 26a, *siman* 107.
57 Rambam, *Hilkhot Rotzea'ch U-Shemirat Nefesh* 12:14.
58 See Ramban, Leviticus 19:17, arguing that *ve-ahavta le-rei'akha kamokha* is a commandment meant to preserve the spiritual well-being of the comanded by advising them in the proper way to feel love for others rather than a commandment for the benefit of the object of the love. The commandment is for the person to love another person for the characteristics that the commanded would want to be loved and in the manner that the person would want to be loved, i.e., for characteristics that the commanded respects and without jealousy or ulterior motives. Ramban expressly rejects the possibility that it is a commandment for a person to take concrete action to benefit others by citing R. Akiva's dictum that a person should save their own life before they save another's.
59 *Noda Be-Yehudah, mahadura tinyana, Choshen Mishpat* 24.

was deriving benefit without paying. It is noteworthy that in this instance the author did not originate the infringed material, namely the Gemara, Rashi and *Tosafot*. The author did not have a claim over the portion of his books that were degraded by the printing. Therefore, the printer caused no damage to the author by reprinting the sources in public domain. However, the issue according to R. Landau was whether the author had a right to the work in organizing them. In this case the author had exercised control over the details of the formatting. The printer may have done the physical labor, however, at the time he was only acting as the agent of the author. Therefore, the commissioned work was entirely the author's. R. Landau noted that if the author had trusted the printer to format the content in the manner that the printer wanted, then the author would have no claim. The formatting would then be partially the product of the printer's artistic input. Since this did not happen, the labor was entirely the author's; the printer was just his agent. For this reason, R. Landau obligated the printer to pay for the benefit he received from the work that belonged to the owner.

On the other hand, the printer is not obligated to pay for the loss of value to the author's books, suggesting that we are not concerned about the damage to the author. Instead, the printer was only required to pay for the benefit he received from the author's extra output. This meant paying his portion of the stenciling costs according to the percentage of pages which were printed. The loss that the owner sustains allows for the owner to demand that the benefiting party pay for what was received. However, since the payments are not made for the actual loss incurred, we can infer that they are not meant to be compensation. This would imply that no damage, and therefore no sin, was actually committed. Only a legal obligation may have been incurred for experiencing the benefit. [60] This would imply that if there is no financial loss occurs to a copyright holder, no sin is committed by a violation of copyright protection. Notwithstanding, a legal right to compensation is in effect and therefore, the act should arguably be avoided.

R. Landau notes two other guidelines that are not applicable in the situation presented to him but which could theoretically be relevant in a situation of copyright infringement. The first is that a person may preemptively refuse to provide benefit to another person. This would mean that a copyright holder may expressly forbid for his or her material to be copied or transferred, and the copyright holder's wishes would need to be respected. The next section will include an analysis about whether using another's property in a manner that he or she does not

---

60 See *Tosafot, Bava Kamma* 20b s.v. *ha*, who explains that an obligation to pay can arise from benefit one receives from a situation that is detrimental to another even though the item was ruined and worthless to the owner as a result of the same occurrence but through no fault of the benefiting party.

want can constitute a sin. The second is that if one party does provide a benefit to another party, regardless of whether or not there is a loss, the benefiting party is responsible to pay for the benefit once it acknowledges purposely wanting to take advantage of that benefit. For copyright purposes this may occur if the infringing party advertises an infringing product using the trademark or reputation of the product that was copied, e.g., by using the original company's name. This causes the benefiting party to incur a legal obligation for the benefit even when no loss has occurred to the other party. However, it does not appear that the sin of damaging has been committed.

Using Materials That Have Been Copied by Someone Else

The largest group of people concerned with questions related to copyright infringement is the recipients of copyrighted material. Recipients are entirely passive in the affair and cannot realistically be found to have committed the prohibitions related to causing damage. In situations where causing damage is not the prohibition in question, all of the above analysis is no longer applicable. R. Zalman Nechemiah Goldberg[61] argues that there is a separate prohibition for an individual to use another's property in a manner the owner opposes. Under R. Goldberg's theory, a person who benefits from another person's property incurs a legal obligation under one of two possible categories. The first possible category is "theft." By misappropriating another person's property, one has committed theft and is thus required to reimburse the property owner. The second possible category is "uncompensated benefit." The infringer incurs a positive obligation to pay the owner for any benefit that he or she receives from the property in question.

There are a number of practical differences between the two categories. For example, the obligation is incurred for an act of theft regardless of whether or not the injured party is Jewish. Jews are obligated to return any stolen item to a Gentile. According to some authorities, however, the obligation does not extend to payments for benefits.[62] This assertion has been disputed by many current authorities, such as R. Yosef Shalom Elyashiv.[63]

---

61 R. Zalman Nechemiah Goldberg, "*Ha'atakah mi-kaseta le-lo reshut ha-be'alim*," *Techumin* vol. 6, pp. 185–207, available at http://zomet.org.il/?CategoryID=265&ArticleID=263.

62 See ibid.

63 See R. Nachum M. Weifish, "Specific Halachic Rulings of Leading Torah Scholars," *Copyright in Jewish Law* (2010) citing, inter alia, R. Yosef Shalom Elyashiv (17:3).

A more germane issue arises from the issue of receiving benefit from an item that has been previously copied. Frequently, study materials are disseminated in such a manner. The issue is to what degree a person may benefit from the infraction of another. R. Goldberg notes that *Shulchan Arukh* has inconsistent rulings regarding two forms of theft, *gezeilah* and *geneivah*. Regarding *gezeilah*, a person is forbidden from deriving any form of benefit from the stolen item.[64] In contrast, it is only forbidden to purchase items stolen by *geneivah*, but not to derive benefit from such items.[65] *Shulchan Arukh* states that the two infractions share a policy concern, to discourage stealing. In addition to this policy concern, benefiting from stolen items that were taken by a *gazlan* is also considered to be a form of *lifnei ivver*.[66] R. Goldberg explains that the difference between *geneivah* and *gezeilah* with regard to benefiting from the stolen item is linked to the concern of *lifnei ivver*: it is forbidden to benefit from a stolen item or receive such an item as a gift when acquiring that item ordinarily would constitute an act of *lifnei ivver*; however, when there is no concern of *lifnei ivver*, benefiting from the infraction does not result in a separate infraction. In general, a person who has misused property that is left in his or her possession when he or she does not have ownership is considered to be a *gazlan*.[67] Under R. Goldberg's analysis, a copyright holder maintains a certain degree of ownership by reserving copyright protections. Therefore, copyright violations can be seen as a form of misuse giving rise to the crime of *gezeilah*. Therefore, it should be forbidden to derive benefit from an item that was copied or distributed by another person.

In order for the copyright holder to reserve the rights so that *gezeilah* can occur, according to R. Goldberg, the author must specifically state that (i) the right to the item is withheld with regard to copying and (ii) that such copying will result in the sale being void.[68] Absent such a declaration, such as a simple admonition against copying, the only violation would be benefiting. When the violation is *gezeilah*, a

64 *Choshen Mishpat* 369:1–2.
65 *Choshen Mishpat* 356:1.
66 The differences between *geneivah* and *gezeilah* are beyond the scope of this chapter. R. Goldberg writes that regarding *gezeilah*, a person can be obligated in *lifnei ivver* because we can assume that the owner still has an opportunity to recover the stolen item. Therefore, if the *gazlan* were to dispense with the item, the possibility of performing the *mitzvah* of returning a stolen object (Leviticus 5:23) is lost. However, R. Goldberg assumes that regarding *geneivah*, we cannot assume that the item will be returned to the owner. Therefore, acquiring the item would not result in a transgression of *lifnei ivver* since the item is already considered to be beyond returning.
67 Rambam, *Hilkhot Gezeilah Va-Aveidah* 3:11.
68 No mention is made as to whether *geneivah* could apply to copyright infringement.

person should avoid facilitating it and then afterward benefiting from the physical item itself. Therefore, in these circumstances one should avoid getting copies of the actual original materials. If the material had been copied from previously copied material, there is only a prohibition of benefiting from it. Therefore, one should avoid encouraging the sin by purchasing copied material. However, R. Goldberg says that there may be room to allow a person to accept the copied material as a gift.[69]

Conclusion

The purpose of this chapter has been to present halakhic concerns that arise when committing copyright violations. However, it should be noted that authorities are not in uniform agreement regarding these assertions. For example, *Divrei Malkiel*[70] very explicitly rejects many of the underlying assumptions of intellectual property. He rejects any concerns that an intellectual property infringement can be considered a prohibition when it does not result in physical damage or denial of access to physical property. With a broad range of opinions, it is difficult to apply a formulaic answer. Clearly, a competent halakhic authority should be consulted. The Rabbinical Council of America has issued a policy statement calling for comportment with copyright laws.[71] It has stated that comportment with these laws is necessary to comply with *halakhah*.

To review, determining whether it is appropriate to copy or receive a copy of study materials without being authorized by the copyright holder will depend upon an intellectually honest determination of a number of questions. First, one must determine if the activity is a copyright violation. If it is a violation, there is halakhic debate regarding whether copyright law is included among those civil laws that would give rise to a sin when violated. If one is in a position to copy and distribute the material, one must determine whether copying or distributing the material was

---

69 This dispensation is only regarding the possible sin committed against the copyright owner. Separate issues arise with regard to cheating if the material was not supposed to be presented to the student to begin with. See note 1.

70 3:157. The case he discusses is a merchant who mimics the medicine of another merchant. The latter merchant had received a special government certificate that gave credence to its efficacy. This case seems more closely related to trademark violation more than copyright infringement. However, the broad conceptualization of intellectual property should still be applicable.

71 "Illegal Internet Downloading: RCA calls upon community to desist from downloading copyrighted music and other materials from the Internet." May 17, 2005. Available at http://www.rabbis.org/news/article. cfm?id=100596.

explicitly prohibited by the seller. One must also determine if either the copying or distribution of the material will cause the copyright owner a loss, regardless of how small. There is also halakhic debate regarding whether such activity would be considered a damaging activity under *halakhah* itself. If one is in a position to receive the material, one must inquire as to how the person who is providing it obtained the material. If one appears to be only financially liable, one should try to minimize the potential for loss to the copyright holder or provide compensation for the benefit received.

Section II
Clinical Training

Chapter 5

Morning Rituals After Staying Awake All Night

Rabbi Michael Kurin, MD

Over the course of medical school, the medical student is likely to stay awake all night several times, perhaps during the pre-clinical training years while studying for tests, or during the clinical training years when on overnight call. Whatever the impetus for staying awake all night, when it does happen, there are several halakhic issues that surface in the morning. These issues mostly revolve around the traditional blessings and prayers that are recited every morning when a person wakes up. This chapter will separately cover each blessing or prayer that is potentially problematic, explain the issues in depth, and attempt to reach conclusions.

Defining *Keva* versus *Arai*

Before delving into the particulars, we must first clarify what we mean when we discuss staying awake all night. Because many people who stay awake all night doze off at some point, whether intentionally or not, we would like to understand whether those who merely take a light nap are considered as if they stayed awake all night. What constitutes a halakhically significant sleep is itself a matter of debate. The source of this debate is a cryptic Talmudic passage[1] regarding the questions of if, when, and how one may sleep while holding or wearing *tefillin*.[2] The

---

1   *Sukkah* 26a–b.
2   In the Talmudic era men wore *tefillin* all day long and only removed them at night, as it is forbidden to wear, or perhaps even hold, *tefillin* while one is sleeping.

Gemara states that in certain situations[3] a person may sleep while wearing his *tefillin* if the sleep is *sheinat arai* ("temporary" sleep), but not if the sleep is *sheinat keva* ("sustained" sleep). However, what constitutes *sheinat arai* is unclear. From this same discussion in the Gemara, three possible definitions might emerge:

1. Within the discussion of sleeping while wearing one's *tefillin*, the Gemara mentions that *sheinat arai* is defined as sleeping for a shorter time than the time it takes to walk 100 *ammot*.

2. The Gemara also notes that one should not sleep more than the sleep of a horse during the daytime, which is defined there as the time it takes to inhale 60 breaths. From the text itself it is not clear whether this statement is related to the previous one about defining *keva* and *arai* in sleep. But as we will see, many authorities believe that this measure of 60 breaths is the definition of *sheinat keva*. It is likely they viewed this ruling as a dissenting opinion to the previous definitions of *sheinat arai*.[4]

3. The Gemara also cites R. Yochanan who states that to be sure one will sleep a *sheinat arai* and not a *sheinat keva* while wearing *tefillin*, one should go to sleep with one's head between one's legs. As Rashi[5] points out, this is a method to ensure that one does not come to *sheinat keva*, but is not necessarily a *definition* of what constitutes *sheinat arai*. However, R. Yochanan must have had some definition of *sheinat arai* in mind when he declared that sleeping with one's head between his legs would remain within its bounds.

Upon analysis of this Talmudic passage, two models for *sheinat arai* emerge. According to the first two definitions of *sheinat arai*, it is defined by the duration of sleep, either the time it takes to walk 100 *ammot*, or, alternatively, the time it takes to inhale 60 breaths.[6] However, according

---

3 The details of the circumstance when this is the case are debated by Rashi (*Sukkah* 26a s.v. *de-nakit lehu be-yedeh* and s.v. *de-manchei be-reisheh*) and Rambam (*Hilkhot Tefillin* 4:15–16), but that discussion is beyond the scope of this work.

4 *Sha'arei Teshuvah* (*Orach Chayyim* 4:17) notes that there are several opinions on the length of "60 breaths." The three major opinions are three hours, thirty minutes and 1/18th of an hour (slightly over 3 minutes). However, they do not explicitly relate this law to the definition of *sheinat arai* or *sheinat keva*.

5 *Sukkah* 26a s.v. *bein birkav*.

6 As we will see these time limits are difficult to determine, and it is possible that some authorities did not interpret them literally. However, while most assume that these two opinions are in conflict, it is worth noting that an extreme literalist approach could reconcile them. Since a normal respiratory rate typically ranges from 10–20 breaths per minute, a healthy person breathing quickly could take 60 breaths in about 3 minutes, which is in fact (as we will see) one of the opinions on the length of "60 breaths." The time to walk 100 *ammot* is generally assumed to be between 1 to 2 minutes

to the third definition, *sheinat arai* is not defined by the duration but rather by the quality of the sleep. Placing one's head between one's legs during sleep is a type of sleep that is *arai* by nature – it is of temporary quality. We will see that the *rishonim* and *acharonim* will either choose one of the two models in defining *sheinat arai*, or will accept both models as separate necessary components of *sheinat arai*.

Quality of Sleep

Most of the early *rishonim* chose quality of sleep as the accepted model for defining *sheinat arai*. Rambam,[7] citing the Gemara, writes that sleeping with one's head between one's legs is considered *sheinat arai*. He does not mention the other opinions of the Gemara that use time as the determining factor in *sheinat arai*. It is not clear whether Rambam feels that sleeping with one's head between one's legs is the only way to have *sheinat arai*, or whether this is merely an example that can be extended to other, perhaps more practical, ways of falling asleep in a manner that implies the intention of a *sheinat arai*. Rosh[8] and *Tur*[9] do, indeed, take this extra step. They explicitly write that *sheinat arai* is when one sleeps with one's head on one's hands while sitting in a chair. This is contrasted with *sheinat keva*, which is defined by a person sleeping in bed. To the author's knowledge, there is no Talmudic source for this particular formulation, so it is likely that Rosh and *Tur* are extrapolating from the Gemara's example of sleeping with one's head between one's legs. It is therefore also likely that they would extend this definition to any manner of falling asleep in which one clearly intends that one's sleep should be short-lived. Like Rambam, Rosh and *Tur* do not mention any time limit in this regard. For them, it is not the fact that one's sleep is likely to be short that makes it *sheinat arai*, but rather the fact that the way in which one is sleeping is not conducive to lengthy sleep, or is at least an abnormal way of going to sleep. *Shulchan Arukh* seems to accept both variations of this approach. He cites[10] Rambam, using sleep with one's head between one's legs as the exemplar of *sheinat arai*, and also likely implies[11] that the definition of *sheinat keva* is sleeping in bed,

---

by most authorities, but it is certainly possible that a person walking 100 *ammot* slowly and a person breathing 60 breaths quickly could actually be the same amount of time. Thankfully, this is not the approach of most authorities on this matter, as a time limit for *sheinat arai* in the 1–3 minute range would make matters quite difficult for practical situations which we will discuss later.

7   *Tefillin* 4:15.
8   *Teshuvot Ha-Rosh* 4:1.
9   *Orach Chayyim* 47:11.
10 *Orach Chayyim* 44:1.
11 *Orach Chayyim* 47:11.

which should imply further that conversely sleeping while sitting should be considered *arai*, in accordance with Rosh and *Tur*.[12]

Two other authorities who did not believe there is a time-based definition to *sheinat arai*, though for a different reason, are Ra'avad and *Magen Avraham*. Ra'avad[13] writes that there is no consensus measurement for *sheinat arai*. Therefore, when it comes to sleeping with *tefillin* he writes that one should not sleep with *tefillin* under any circumstance even when he feels his sleep is only *arai*. Unlike Rosh, *Tur*, and Rambam, Ra'avad is not necessarily accepting the non-time-based model for *sheinat arai*. He is simply arguing that even within the time-based model, since we do not have a consensus time limit we should act

12 For these *rishonim* it is necessary to reconcile their opinions with the fact that the Gemara, as mentioned above, does seem to explicitly define *sheinat arai* as the time it takes to walk 100 *ammot*. *Kesef Mishneh* (*Tefillin* 4:15) explains that Rambam did not believe there was a debate at all in the Gemara. The time it takes to walk 100 *ammot* was not a defining time limit for *sheinat arai*, but rather a description of the maximum amount of time one can possibly sleep with one's head between one's legs. The amount of time one sleeps was not intended to be part of the definition but was rather a description or explanation for how the method of sleeping with one's head between one's legs works. Alternatively, it is possible to interpret Rambam in a different light. It is possible he means that the time limit of 100 *ammot* is really the true definition of *sheinat arai*, and sleeping with one's head between one's legs is merely the practical application of how a person can fall asleep in a way in which one assures oneself that the sleep will not last longer than this time limit. However, while this is certainly possible, it is a less likely reading of Rambam, as if this were the case, Rambam should have at least mentioned this time limit of 100 *ammot* in his discussion. Indeed, for this reason, *Kesef Mishneh* explicitly writes that Rambam could not have accepted the view that 100 *ammot* is the defining factor for *sheinat arai*.

Regarding Rosh and *Tur*, *Beit Yosef* (*Orach Chayyim* 44:1) writes that it is possible they simply ruled against the opinion of 100 *ammot* in the Talmud. He supports this possibility by citing another Talmudic source which states that any sleep during the day is considered *arai* and any sleep at night is considered *keva*. Clearly, *Beit Yosef* explains, there are passages in the Talmud that do not accept the time limit of 100 *ammot*, and it is therefore possible that Rosh and *Tur* simply did not rule in accordance with that opinion. Of note, *Tur* and *Shulchan Arukh* (*Orach Chayyim* 4:16) do quote the aforementioned Gemara (*Sukkah* 26b) that one should not sleep longer than "60 breaths" during the day.

13 *Katuv Sham*, *Sukkah* 12a in *dappei ha-Rif*; cited in *Beit Yosef*, *Orach Chayyim* 44:1.

stringently. In a similar vein, *Magen Avraham*[14] writes that *sheinat arai* has no particular measure.[15]

Mishnah Berurah[16] writes that sleeping with one's head between one's legs is considered *sheinat arai* because it is not possible to sleep more than the time it takes to walk 100 *ammot*. However, it is likely that he does not mean that the time limit is the main criterion for *sheinat arai*, but rather that sleep in a manner that cannot lead to a lengthy sleep is the definition of *sheinat arai*. This is the likely explanation of *Mishnah Berurah* because elsewhere he explicitly rules in accordance with Rosh and *Tur* that *sheinat arai* is defined by sleeping on one's hands from a sitting position.[17]

Duration of Sleep

On the other hand, several later authorities do accept a time-based model for *sheinat arai*. *Magen Avraham*[18] cites the opinion that the limit of *sheinat arai* is the amount of time it takes to walk 100 *ammot*. He adds that this is approximately 1/67th of an hour, or slightly less than one minute.[19]

Taz[20] is the one authority to explicitly put both sources for the time-based model of *sheinat arai* together.[21] He argues that until proven otherwise, one should assume that the time period of 60 breaths is equal to

14 44:3.
15 Since *Magen Avraham* explicitly notes the opinion of 100 *ammot* (though he rules against it), it is not clear which model of *sheinat arai* he accepts. *Mishnah Berurah* seems to believe he accepts a non-time-based model, though it remains possible that he simply agrees with the position of Ra'avad that there is no consensus on the time limit for *arai*.
16 44:4–5.
17 47:23.
18 *Orach Chayyim* 44:3.
19 *Machatzit Ha-Shekel* (*Orach Chayyim* 44:3) comments that this calculation is dependent on a debate regarding the length of time it takes to walk one *mil*. According to the dissenting opinion on that matter, the amount of time to walk 100 *ammot* would actually be about 1/50th of an hour, or slightly more than one minute.
20 *Orach Chayyim* 44:1.
21 It should be noted that R. Ovadia Yosef understood that *Taz* held like Rosh and *Tur*; see *Yabbia Omer*, *Orach Chayyim* 8:5. Ironically, while R. Yosef wrote that *Taz* holds like Rosh and *Tur* as he himself does, he also suggested the possibility that even if we consider 60 breaths to define *sheinat keva*, it is not necessarily true that anything less than 60 breaths automatically becomes *arai*. It seems R. Yosef believed there could be some sort of "limbo" period where a person's sleep is neither considered *keva* nor *arai*. Unfortunately, he did not elaborate on what the status of such a sleep would actually be.

the time it takes to walk 100 *ammot*. Otherwise, he writes, there would be a discrepancy in the sources that would need to be reconciled.[22]

Both Quality and Duration of Sleep

All of this background is necessary to appreciate the rulings of modern authorities on this issue. Though there are several modern authorities who simply rule in accordance with Rosh and *Tur*, such as *Chayyei Adam*,[23] *Kaf Ha-Chayyim*,[24] and R. Ovadia Yosef,[25] many other modern authorities incorporated both models of *sheinat arai* into their definition. Many also assume that the time period of 60 breaths is relevant as a determining factor between *sheinat keva* and *sheinat arai*.

Or Le-Tziyyon[26] writes that one who sleeps in bed for 30 minutes or more has slept a *sheinat keva*. Conversely, one who sleeps in a sitting position with one's head resting on one's hands has slept a *sheinat arai*, even if one sleeps for longer than 30 minutes. According to *Or Le-Tziyyon*, 30 minutes is the equivalent of 60 breaths; indeed, to this author's knowledge, all authorities who use 60 breaths as part of their definition of *sheinat keva* will assume that 60 breaths is 30 minutes.[27] Secondly, we note that *Or Le-Tziyyon* uses two criteria, both of which must be fulfilled in order to achieve *sheinat keva*: sleep must last at least 30 minutes, and it must occur in bed. He has thus incorporated both time and quality of sleep into his definition. If even one of these two criteria is missing, the sleep would only be considered *sheinat arai*. It is important to note that according to this view, which we will see is shared by several other authorities, even one who sleeps for several hours in the sitting position is still considered to have slept only a *sheinat arai*.

22 *Taz* actually uses this line of thinking to argue against *Beit Yosef*. As we saw above, *Beit Yosef* explained that Rosh and *Tur* did not mention the time limit of 100 *ammot* for *sheinat arai* because they accepted a different textual source that said any daytime sleep is considered *arai*, regardless of the amount of time. *Taz* argues that there is actually no contradiction between the sources. Daytime sleep is considered *arai* specifically because there is a law that one cannot sleep more than 60 breaths during the day. Assuming that 60 breaths is the same as 100 *ammot*, then by definition any sleep that one has during the day will be within the time limit of 100 *ammot* and that is why it is considered *arai*.
23 9:7.
24 47:23 and 47:27.
25 *Yabbia Omer* 8:5.
26 Vol. 2, 1:7.
27 See *Orechot Halakhah*, Commentary to *Halikhot Shlomo, Hilkhot Tefillah*, chapter 6, *siman* 1.

Time of Sleep

Halikhot Shlomo[28] echoes *Or Le-Tziyyon*'s ruling, but with a caveat. At first he writes that one who sleeps in bed for more than 30 minutes has slept a *sheinat keva*. However, in the commentary *Devar Halakhah*[29] he limits this to one who sleeps before *chatzot* (midnight). However, if one sleeps after *chatzot*, even less than 30 minutes would still be considered *sheinat keva* since this is the part of the night when most of the population is sleeping.

Sleep Routine

An additional factor must also be introduced into the discussion. There is at least one authority who felt that within the "manner of sleep" model, the determining factor for *sheinat keva* should not be the location of the sleep alone but also incorporate one's entire bedtime routine. This view is attributed to R. Yair Bachrach who writes[30] that to accomplish *sheinat keva* one must sleep for several hours in bed and wearing pajamas. If one sleeps for an hour in bed wearing daytime clothes, this is still considered *arai*. Apparently, he has three necessary criteria for *sheinat arai*: length of time, location, and clothing. This opinion is quoted by *Minchat Yitzchak*[31] but he rejects it in favor of the simpler opinion of Rosh that any sleep in bed is *sheinat keva*. This opinion that one needs to wear pajamas to achieve a *sheinat keva* is rejected by most other authorities.[32]

Individual Intentions

One last criterion that is an important determining factor for several authorities is a person's individual intentions. Besides for the objective criteria of time and manner of sleep, for some authorities whether or not one considers a particular sleep episode to be one's main sleep for that night also weighs into the equation. *Keren Le-David*[33] writes that if one goes to sleep wearing one's daytime clothing, even for an hour or two, and then wakes up with the intention of going back to sleep for several hours in pajamas later on in the night, one's intentions dictate

28 *Hilkhot Tefillah* 6:1–3.
29 *Siman* 1.
30 *Mekor Chayyim*, 47:11.
31 10:7.
32 See *Halikhot Shlomo, Hilkhot Tefillah* 6:1–3, *Yabbia Omer* 8:5. See also Ariel Ozri's letter to the editor in the journal *Aliba De-Hilkheta, Chevrat Ohev Shalom. Piskei Teshuvot* (47:15), however, does at least partially accept this ruling.
33 *Siman* 11.

that the first episode is considered *sheinat arai*, and the second is considered *sheinat keva*. *Kaf Ha-Chayyim*[34] similarly writes that one who asks another to wake him or her up at a set time in the night so that he or she can get back to learning before going to sleep, even for more than 30 minutes and in bed, is considered to have slept only *sheinat arai* since one's clear intention is not to get his sleep for the night but merely to take a break from one's learning. Both of these rulings reflect the significance of a person's intentions, though both still require some sort of outward, objective expression of those intentions in order for the sleep to be considered *arai* only.

Devar Halakhah[35] takes this view one step further by giving significance to a person's intentions even without any outward expression of them. He writes that if one was only planning to sleep for a short while but ended up sleeping for more than 30 minutes, he is unsure whether this would be considered *sheinat keva* or *arai*. This bold statement demonstrates the importance of a person's intentions in determining whether his sleep is considered *keva* or *arai*: even when one sleeps for several hours, if one intended to sleep for less time, one's intention might potentially discount those hours of sleep and place one in the category of a person who has not yet halakhically slept.

Piskei Teshuvot[36] places an even greater significance upon the person's intentions. He first writes that the objective ruling is that one needs to sleep for at least 30 minutes in bed and have changed out of his or her daytime clothes in order to achieve *sheinat keva*. If any of these three criteria are missing, his or her sleep is only *arai*. *Piskei Teshuvot*'s ruling is the same as that of *Chavvot Ya'ir* above. However, he then qualifies: if a person intends to sleep in a different way than usual on a particular night and not follow one's typical bedtime routine, and one does not plan to sleep again in one's normal fashion later on in the night, one may achieve *sheinat keva* by sleeping in bed for 30 minutes even without changing one's clothes. Furthermore, he writes that while sleeping in the sitting position with one's head on one's hands is generally considered a *sheinat arai* regardless of all other factors, if a person is in a situation where that is the only way one can sleep on a particular night[37] and one has no intention to sleep in a bed at any point in the night, then even sleeping on a chair can count as *sheinat keva*, provided the sleep lasts at least 30 minutes and that the person intends for this to be his or her main sleep for the entire night. This opinion is particularly important for medical students who spend the night in a hospital on call and have the opportunity to nap but no access to a bed in the

34 47:27.
35 Commentary on *Halikhot Shlomo*, 6:2.
36 Volume 1, 47:15.
37 For example, if one does not have access to a bed.

call room. *Piskei Teshuvot* makes intention so significant that his initial objective ruling that all three criteria are necessary to achieve *sheinat keva* becomes almost irrelevant. Moreover, while other authorities had given credence to intent by allowing it to convert a lengthy sleep into *sheinat arai*, *Piskei Teshuvot* is more radical in that he also allows intent to convert a manner of sleep that would normally be considered *arai* into a *sheinat keva*.

Summary of *Sheinat Keva* and *Sheinat Arai*

In summary, it is clear that if one sleeps in a sitting position for less than 30 minutes, one's sleep is only *arai*, and thus not halakhically significant for the purposes of this essay. It is also clear that if one changes out of one's daytime clothes and sleeps in bed for more than 30 minutes, one has slept *sheinat keva*. If one does this without changing one's clothes, one has still slept *sheinat keva* according to most opinions, especially if one intends that this should be one's main sleep for the night. If a person sleeps in the sitting position for more than 30 minutes, there are some authorities who would consider this *sheinat keva*, although the majority opinion is that this would still be *sheinat arai*.[38] The two most debated scenarios are the person who sleeps in bed for less than 30 minutes and the person who sleeps in the sitting position for more than 30 minutes but with the intent that this should be his or her main sleep for the entire night. If a person expects to be in one of these two scenarios, he or she should consult a *posek* as to whether this sleep should be considered *sheinat keva* or *sheinat arai*.

In the remainder of this chapter, we will examine several issues that arise for a person with a sleep schedule that is abnormal for the general population but can be common for medical students. In discussing these issues, the halakhic ramifications of the definitions of *sheinat keva* and *sheinat arai* will become apparent. *Mishnah Berurah*[39] writes that one who has any *sheinat keva* is halakhically considered the same as one who slept the entire night. One who has only *sheinat arai* encounters the same halakhic issues as one who does not sleep at all.[40] With this in mind we can investigate the various components of the morning service whose

---

38 In this author's experience, there is a popular belief that any sleep longer than 30 minutes is considered *sheinat keva*. It appears this opinion is a clear minority and the need for sleep to take place in bed, with or without the 30-minute time limit, is the more accepted opinion. It should be noted, though, that R. Mordechai Willig uses 30 minutes as his definition of *sheinat keva* in his lecture titled "The Halachos of Staying Up All Night," available at http://www.yutorah.org/lectures/lecture.cfm/734390.

39 4:27.

40 In theory *Beit Yosef* (*Orach Chayyim* 4:13) does suggest that even if Rashba (see below for Rosh's and Rashba's opinions) only requires hand-washing

recitation may depend on whether or not a person has slept in a halakhically significant way during the night.

Blessing on Washing of the Hands

Regarding one who does sleep *sheinat keva* there is universal agreement that the blessing upon washing one's hands is the first blessing recited in the morning. However, there is debate as to why one is obligated to wash one's hands in the morning. There are three major opinions[41] on this matter:

1. Rosh[42] writes that one is required to wash one's hands in the morning since the hands became dirty overnight, and clean hands are a prerequisite to prayer.[43] It is inevitable that at some point during sleep a person will touch areas of his body that are normally covered, which creates a need to wash one's hands. According to Rosh, having clean hands is a requirement for all prayer, whether it be *shacharit, minchah* or *ma'ariv*. Fundamentally they are all the same, but Chazal only established the blessing on washing the hands before *shacharit*.[44]

in the morning when one has slept during the night, even a short nap would be enough to qualify one for the blessing on washing the hands. The reason for this is that *Beit Yosef* suggested the possibility that one only becomes a *biryah chadashah*, a renewed creation, after some amount of sleep. Any amount of sleep is enough for this, though, since one does not need to do anything in particular while one is sleeping to become a renewed creation. For Rosh, on the other hand, a short nap would certainly make no difference because there is no guarantee that a person dirtied one's hands in such a short amount of time. Although there is more room to say one should recite the blessing after a nap than after no sleep at all according to *Beit Yosef*, ultimately the obligation to wash one's hands after a nap is still questionable, so a person who napped would not receive a different ruling than one who did not sleep at all.

41 *Arukh Ha-Shulchan* (*Orach Chayyim* 4:1) notes that in truth there are really only two fundamentally different opinions regarding why we wash our hands. Rosh and Rashba both see the morning ritual wash as a preparation for *shacharit*, albeit for different reasons. The Zohar's requirement to wash is not connected to prayer at all, but a spiritual necessity without which one cannot touch certain parts of one's face. In fact, it is likely that these two fundamentally different reasons for washing our hands are not mutually exclusive, but are two separate requirements. Indeed, *Shulchan Arukh* (*Orach Chayyim* 4:13) clearly accepts both as separate requirements.

42 Responsa 4:1; commentary on *Berakhot* 9:23.

43 To clarify, prayer refers specifically to the *Shema* and the *Shemoneh Esrei*. Other prayers or blessings do not require ritually cleansed hands.

44 However, if one knows that his hands are unclean before *minchah* or *ma'ariv* (if one went to the bathroom, for example), then Rosh would say

2. Rashba[45] writes that ritual hand-washing with the blessing is specific to the morning, and its reason is that in the morning one has become a new, refreshed creation. Washing the hands indicates recognition of this refreshed holiness within oneself in preparation to serve God for another day, just as the high priest used to wash himself in the Temple.

3. A final opinion, usually attributed to the Zohar,[46] is that washing one's hands removes the *ruach ra'ah*, the evil spirit, that inhabits the body overnight.

Many later authorities clarify further that according to the Zohar's reasoning, that washing of hands is intended to rid ourselves of the evil spirit, washing the hands is not a *mitzvah*, but avoidance of a *sakkanah*, a danger.[47] Since it is not a *mitzvah*, one does not recite the blessing when washing one's hands for this purpose alone.[48] Rosh and Rashba are discussing hand-washing as a *mitzvah*, and therefore they discuss the recitation of a blessing. It is likely that *Beit Yosef*[49] agreed with this dichotomy as well, as he first discusses the opinions of Rosh and Rashba when a question of saying the blessing is relevant, and only later brings the Zohar into the discussion as an additional reason to wash one's hands in the morning even when Rosh's reasoning does not apply.[50]

Must One Who Did Not Sleep Wash One's Hands?

There is much debate over how to apply these different opinions to the situation where a person did not sleep overnight. *Beit Yosef*[51] writes that according to Rosh it would seem that one who stays awake all night should not be obligated to wash his or her hands in the morning, since without sleep we cannot assume that one's hands are certainly dirty. He is less certain about Rashba's position. He entertains the possibility that even according to Rashba one only becomes a refreshed creation after sleep, and thus one who does not sleep overnight would

---

that one should make the blessing on washing the hands before that *minchah* or *ma'ariv* as well.

45 Responsa 1:191.

46 *Parshat Vayishlach*, 169b; cited in *Beit Yosef, Orach Chayyim* 4:13.

47 It was believed that touching certain parts of one's body while the evil spirit still presided over one's hands (i.e., before one washed one's hands in the morning) could cause physical damage to those parts of the body that were touched.

48 *Magen Avraham, Orach Chayyim* 4:13; *Peri Megadim, Eshel Avraham,* 4:1.

49 *Orach Chayyim* 4:13.

50 It appears that he adopts this reasoning in *Shulchan Arukh* as well (see *Orach Chayyim* 4:13–14).

51 *Orach Chayyim* 4:13.

not be obligated to wash one's hands with a blessing. In the end, however, he concludes that Rashba would obligate one to wash one's hands every morning with a blessing regardless of sleep. *Beit Yosef* believes that Rashba's notion of a person becoming a refreshed creation every day implies a *takkanah*, an established law, that one washes his hands every morning for this reason. Even if technically one only becomes a refreshed creation after sleep,[52] once the practice of washing every morning has been established, one does not become exempt from it even when the initial reason for the practice does not apply. On the other hand, *Beit Yosef* does not believe Rosh's reasoning implies an established law.[53]

Beit Yosef is also uncertain about whether the Zohar's reasoning of the evil spirit applies to one who stayed awake overnight. At first he writes that even according to Rosh, who requires hand-washing to avoid praying with dirty hands, one who did not sleep and whose hands are clean should still be obligated to wash his hands to rid himself of the evil spirit, implying that the Zohar's reasoning does apply in this scenario. He then questions this, wondering whether the evil spirit only reigns over a person while he is sleeping. *Peri Megadim*[54] points out that this is actually a debate between the Zohar and *Orechot Chayyim*. According to the Zohar, the evil spirit indeed only reigns over a person while one is sleeping, and thus one who stays awake all night should not need to rid oneself of the evil spirit. According to *Orechot Chayyim*, however, the evil spirit reigns over everyone during the nighttime, regardless of sleep.[55] Rama[56] accepts the opinion of *Orechot Chayyim*.

52 *Beit Yosef* makes this connection between Rashba's notion of a refreshed creation and sleep, but Rashba himself makes no mention of sleep being a prerequisite to becoming a refreshed creation. Many later authorities repeat this connection that *Beit Yosef* makes, but its source is unclear.
53 *Taz* (*Orach Chayyim* 4:9) offers an explanation as to why *Beit Yosef* applied the principle of *lo plug*, that a practice is established and its performance is not dependent on the applicability of the original reason for the practice, to Rashba and not to Rosh. He writes that according to Rashba's view, it is plausible that one can thank God for His kindness in returning mankind's souls to them and refreshing their creation even if one happened to not sleep on that given day. The *mitzvah* of washing hands represents God's benevolence to the entire Jewish people. For Rosh, however, the law of washing hands is simply a protection to ensure that we don't pray with dirty hands. In that case, it only applies if the individual has dirty hands from sleeping.
54 *Eshel Avraham*, *Orach Chayyim* 4:11.
55 *Beit Yosef* also noted this comment of *Orechot Chaim* towards the end of his discussion in 4:13.
56 *Darkei Moshe* on *Beit Yosef*, *Orach Chayyim* 4:13.

Rama[57] rules that one who stays awake all night should wash one's hands without reciting the blessing. It appears that he accepts *Beit Yosef*'s understanding that Rosh would not require one who stayed awake all night to wash one's hands. As he is uncertain whether one should rule according to Rosh or Rashba, he determined it is best to wash one's hands without the blessing. It is safe to assume that *Shulchan Arukh* agrees, though he does not discuss this question.[58]

Bach[59] argues vehemently with *Beit Yosef*, claiming that both Rosh and Rashba imply the establishment of a *takkanah*. This being the case, it should make no difference whether the reason for this *takkanah* is to clean dirty hands or to recognize mankind's status as a refreshed creation. Once the law is established one is obligated to wash his hands and recite the blessing every day without question.[60] This view is espoused by the *Arukh Ha-Shulchan*[61] as well.

A third approach, attributed by *Arukh Ha-Shulchan*[62] to *Magen Avraham*,[63] suggests that the principle of *lo plug* should be applied to Rosh rather than Rashba. Since Rosh believes one must wash one's hands and recite a blessing before *minchah* and *ma'ariv* as well, if one's hands are dirty, this implies a level of consistency and permanence

57 *Orach Chayyim* 4:13.
58 As noted above, it is important to keep in mind that the debate between the Zohar and *Orechot Chayim* is not relevant to this question of whether one should recite a blessing on washing his hands after staying awake all night. Since the need to wash away the evil spirit is separate from the *mitzvah* of washing the hands, it will never require a blessing and there is never harm done in washing one's hands in any case of uncertain obligation.
59 *Orach Chayyim* 4:2, s.v. *ha-Beit Yosef he'erikh*.
60 *Bach* attempts to prove that the law has been established and is a permanent part of the daily routine, even according to Rosh, by referencing another ruling of Rosh. In that same responsum, Rosh also rules that one who wakes up early, before *alot ha-shachar,* should wash his hands with a blessing before reciting *birkat ha-Torah* and learning. *Bach* argues that *birkat ha-Torah* does not require the ritual hand-washing and therefore Rosh's ruling can only be explained if the need to wash one's hands in the morning is an established *takkanah* that applies whether or not one needs to clean one's hands for prayer. However, this is a difficult argument to understand, since Rosh may simply feel that one can fulfill the obligation to wash one's hands before *shacharit* even at this early time. He requires washing hands if they are dirty before every prayer service, but that does not necessarily have to mean that the washing must immediately precede the beginning of the service. Since the person in this scenario did sleep, he or she fulfills Rosh's criteria for the obligation to wash one's hands and there is no need to invoke the principle of *lo plug*. See *Magen Avraham* (4:12) who rejects *Bach*'s proof in this way.
61 *Orach Chayyim* 4:6.
62 *Orach Chayyim* 4:12.
63 *Orach Chayyim* 4:12.

to the practice of washing hands. On the other hand, since Rashba only requires hand-washing in the morning, this suggests that he does not apply the principle of *lo plug*. *Arukh Ha-Shulchan*[64] notes this opinion but rejects it outright since it goes directly against *Beit Yosef* and he does not see the logical connection between applying *lo plug* and the fact that Rosh believes one is obligated to wash his hands before every prayer service.[65] *Arukh Ha-Shulchan* does note, though, that *Magen Avraham* accepts the opinion of Rashba, but argues that Rashba's idea of a refreshed creation only applies after sleep. Thus, unlike *Beit Yosef* who was unsure whether Rashba would require washing the hands after being awake all night, *Magen Avraham* is the only major authority to suggest that Rashba would definitely not require washing the hands.[66]

To summarize, we have seen three approaches to the debate between Rashba and Rosh:

1. *Beit Yosef*: Rosh only requires hand-washing when a person dirtied his hands, whereas Rashba considered hand-washing a *takkanah* that is observed daily in all situations.
2. Rama: Hand-washing is a *takkanah* for both Rosh and Rashba, who both require hand-washing daily.
3. *Arukh Ha-Shulchan*'s reading of *Magen Avraham*: Neither Rosh nor Rashba consider hand-washing a *takkanah*, and both will require hand-washing only when one has slept.

In terms of practical *halakhah*, *Shulchan Arukh* and Rama rule that one who stays awake all night should wash one's hands without reciting a blessing, as noted above. *Bach* and *Arukh Ha-Shulchan* rule that one should recite the blessing when washing one's hands even if one did not sleep. *Sha'arei Teshuvah*[67] writes that due to the differing opinions

---

64 *Orach Chayyim* 4:12.
65 This reading of *Magen Avraham* is very difficult to understand, assuming that *Arukh Ha-Shulkhan* had the same version of *Magen Avraham* that we do. What *Magen Avraham* wrote, according to our text, is that *Bach*'s proof that *lo plug* should even be applied to Rosh was not a good proof. See note 60 above. *Arukh Ha-Shulchan* apparently thought *Magen Avraham* was supporting *Bach* by saying that since Rosh required hand-washing before other prayer services as well, it must be a *lo plug*. *Arukh Ha-Shulchan* went further, in fact, to argue that since *Magen Avraham* argued against *Beit Yosef* that the *lo plug* should be applied to Rosh, and all agree that *lo plug* can be applied to Rashba (except for this *Magen Avraham*), we should accept the application of *lo plug* for both opinions and definitely require a blessing when washing hands in the morning after not sleeping. Of course, this argument is at least partially based on his difficult reading of *Magen Avraham*, so it is hard to say whether this ruling should be factored into the practical *halakhah*.
66 *Be'er Heitev* (4:13) also writes this but it is not clear that he applies it as *halakhah* like *Magen Avraham* appears to do.
67 Commentary to *Shulchan Arukh* 4:13.

among the authorities, it is best not to recite the blessing. *Mishnah Berurah*[68] agrees to this, but suggests that if one uses the bathroom in the morning, one would certainly be able to say the blessing on washing the hands. This is because Rashba obligates one to wash one's hands every morning, regardless of whether one slept, according to the opinion of *Beit Yosef* and *Bach,* and Rosh would require one to wash one's hands before prayer if one used the bathroom and thereby dirtied them. Therefore, if one goes to the bathroom after being awake all night, one must wash one's hands according to both opinions.[69] R. Akiva Eiger[70] adds to this that even should one not agree to apply *lo plug* to Rashba, he believes that even a nap during the night would be enough to invoke the notion of refreshed creation. While normally *sheinat keva* is required to create an obligation of hand-washing for Rosh, Rashba only requires a short nap. Therefore, the combination of a short nap during the night with going to the bathroom in the morning would certainly cover all of the bases. However, given that most authorities do apply *lo plug* to Rashba, this is merely an extra stringency but not a necessity.

Waking before Dawn

The other relevant scenario to medical students is the case of one who wakes up in the morning before *alot ha-shachar*, dawn. Since one slept, one is certainly obligated to wash one's hands and recite the blessing, but the question is whether one should wash when one wakes up or only after dawn.

Rosh[71] writes that in this scenario a person should wash his or her hands upon waking up and recite the blessing as well. He adds that nothing needs to be repeated after dawn. Even if one went back to sleep after washing and reciting the blessing during the night, and then woke up a second time once it was morning, there is still no need to repeat the hand washing, according to Rosh, since that second sleep is considered only a nap. When one only naps, it is not inevitable that one will dirty one's hands. However, we must assume that according to Rosh if one does have a *sheinat keva*, one would need to wash one's hands again with a blessing.

Beit Yosef[72] also assumes that when one makes the blessing and washes one's hands upon waking during the night, one fulfills the *mitzvah* of washing one's hands for the morning. Therefore, he only discusses

---

68 *Orach Chayyim* 4:30.
69 This explanation is spelled out by the *Biur Halakhah* there, s.v. *ve-yittelem be-lo berakhah* (first paragraph).
70 Commentary on *Shulchan Arukh, Orach Chayyim* 4:13.
71 *Teshuvot Ha-Rosh* 4:1.
72 *Orach Chayyim* 4:14.

whether there is a need to wash one's hands a second time after dawn without a blessing because of the evil spirit. As *Magen Avraham* explains, it is also clear that *Shulchan Arukh*[73] distinguished between the *mitzvah* of washing the hands before prayer and hand-washing to remove the evil spirit. *Magen Avraham*[74] points out that when *Shulchan Arukh* discusses the person who already washed his hands before dawn, he only mentions the concern of the evil spirit as a potential reason to obligate a second washing of the hands, and not preparation for prayer. He explains that even if one goes back to sleep after initially washing one's hands with the blessing during the night, one has already fulfilled the *mitzvah*. One can only become a refreshed creation once, and not twice, *Magen Avraham* writes.[75] Therefore, the only question left for *Shulchan Arukh* to ask is whether the evil spirit can return either if one goes back to sleep or simply by the passing of the end of the night.[76] If the latter is true one would be obligated to wash one's hands again after dawn even if one did not go back to sleep during the night. Either way, *Magen Avraham* concludes, there would certainly be no need for a repeat blessing for the sake of just the evil spirit.

Rama[77] rules that one should wash one's hands without reciting another blessing whether or not one takes a nap after waking in the night. *Arukh Ha-Shulchan*[78] and *Mishnah Berurah*[79] rule according to Rama.

Biur Halakhah[80] discusses a similar scenario in which one woke up during the night and washed one's hands, but did not recite the blessing at that time. He writes that one is still able to say the blessing after dawn if one uses the bathroom. The reason for this is that according to Rosh, the use of the bathroom dirties one's hands again and obligates one to wash again with a blessing. According to Rashba, since one did not

---

73   *Orach Chayyim* 4:14.
74   *Orach Chayyim* 4:13.
75   *Magen Avraham* rules according to Rashba and not Rosh regarding the reason for the *mitzvah* of washing hands in the morning.
76   Whether the evil spirit creates a new obligation to re-wash one's hands after sleeping a second time at night is a question *Beit Yosef* discusses. His initial thought is that once the evil spirit was washed away during the night, it does not return a second time, and there should be no obligation to wash again. However, based on a different passage in the Zohar he concludes that in certain cases it is possible for the evil spirit to return. If one takes a nap that qualifies as *sheinat keva*, one should wash one's hands again when one wakes up the second time because the evil spirit will return when a person sleeps that length of time during the night (though according to *Beit Yosef*, the evil spirit does not enter the body during the day even when napping for that length of time). However, no blessing should be recited.
77   *Orach Chayyim* 4:14.
78   *Orach Chayyim* 4:13.
79   *Orach Chayyim* 4:32.
80   *Orach Chayyim* 4:14, s.v. *ve-yittelem be-lo berakhah* (second paragraph).

recite the blessing during the night when one washed one's hands, the blessing one recites in the morning after using the bathroom can be said with the intention that the blessing refers to one's initial hand-washing when one woke up during the night.[81]

Finally, *Biur Halakhah*[82] differentiates between one who wakes up before but close to dawn and one who wakes up near the beginning of the night. Until now our discussion has been about the former case. *Biur Halakhah* contends that in the latter case, it is difficult to say according to Rashba that a person becomes a refreshed creation so close to the beginning of the night. Therefore, assuming one does not experience another *sheinat keva* during that night, one still may be obligated in the *mitzvah* once morning comes, according to Rashba. For Rosh, however, one has fulfilled one's obligation provided one's hands remained clean after one washed them at the beginning of the night when one woke up. Therefore, he concludes in this scenario that it would be best for the person to use the bathroom again after dawn and then wash one's hands again with the blessing. In this way one becomes fully obligated according to both Rosh and Rashba.[83]

Birkat Ha-Torah

As was the case with the *mitzvah* of washing one's hands, whether or not one who stayed awake all night can recite *birkat ha-Torah* is dependent on what creates the obligation to recite this blessing every day. The issue here depends on whether the start of a new day creates a new obligation to recite the blessing, or whether sleep creates the new obligation.

Waking before Dawn

Mordekhai[84] writes that his teacher, R. Meir, would not recite a new *birkat ha-Torah* if he woke up before dawn, because he believed the

---

81 The reason for this difference is that according to Rosh one already cleaned one's hands when one washed them during the night. If one does not dirty one's hands again, one does not accomplish anything by washing them a second time, and thus cannot recite the blessing. For Rashba, however, if one washed one's hands without saying the blessing during the night, one has yet to acknowledge the refreshed creation and can therefore still do so when washing a second time in the morning.

82 *Orach Chayyim* 4:13 s.v. *kol ha-laylah.*

83 *Biur Halakhah* is the only authority known to this author to distinguish between the beginning of the night and the end of the night. It is also not clear where he draws the line between what is considered beginning and what is considered end of the night. Therefore, it is unclear how to put this comment of *Biur Halakhah* into practice.

84 *Berakhot* 1:29.

previous day's *birkat ha-Torah* functioned for 24 hours, until the next morning. Rabbeinu Tam[85] also believed that if one wakes up before dawn and wants to study Torah, one is able to do so without reciting the blessing on the study of Torah because one is still covered from one's previous day's blessing until dawn. R. Shmuel Shmelke Taubes[86] explains that according to Rabbeinu Tam neither the passage of night nor sleep is considered an interruption that would require a subsequent new blessing. Instead, Rabbeinu Tam required a new blessing every day because of the concept of *biryah chadashah*, the refreshed creation that occurs to a person every day. For Rabbeinu Tam, reciting *birkat ha-Torah* every morning is part of the fulfillment of renewing ourselves as creations on a daily basis.[87] Therefore, the obligation comes with each new morning regardless of sleep.[88] *Magen Avraham*[89] suggests another possibility as to why one may not be obligated to recite a new blessing until the morning even if one woke up before dawn. He writes that when we recite *birkat ha-Torah* each morning our intention is that it should last until the next morning, not shorter or longer, and it is due to this intent that a new blessing is recited each morning but is not necessary before then.[90]

85 Quoted in *Tosafot Berakhot* 11b s.v. *she-kevar*.

86 Printed in the back of the Gemara on this *Tosafot*, or in the *Yalkut Mefarshim* in some editions.

87 Alternatively, one could argue that Rabbeinu Tam and R. Meir believed that *birkat ha-Torah* lasts for an entire day, and it is unique among blessings in that it has a tolerance for interruption built into it. It is possible that they believed interruption from Torah study is a natural part of daily life and the blessing on the study of Torah was therefore created to last despite interruptions.

88 It is noteworthy that if R. Taubes is correct, it is possible Rabbeinu Tam's understanding of the *biryah chadashah* principle differs from that of Rashba. Earlier we noted that Rashba agreed one can fulfill the *mitzvah* of washing one's hands even before dawn. It seems Rabbeinu Tam does not agree, at least concerning *birkat ha-Torah*. There are several ways to resolve this discrepancy. First, perhaps this is simply a debate between Rashba and Rabbeinu Tam. They use the same terminology but their understanding of *biryah chadashah* need not be the same. Perhaps for Rashba, *biryah chadashah* happens when one wakes up or when dawn comes (whichever comes first) but for Rabbeinu Tam it just happens every morning regardless of sleep. Second, one does not need to accept R. Taubes's understanding of Rabbeinu Tam. Finally, there may be a difference between the obligation to wash one's hands and *birkat ha-Torah*, as appears in *Magen Avraham* (see below).

89 *Orach Chayyim* 47:12

90 It should be noted that *Beit Yosef* (*Orach Chayyim* 47:13) claims that Rabbeinu Yonah (*Berakhot* 6a in *dappei ha-Rif*, s.v. *ve-amar*) agrees with R. Meir and Rabbeinu Tam. However, in the text that we have, what Rabbeinu Yonah actually says is that one's *birkat ha-Torah* covers the nighttime as well. Presumably he means that it covers only the part of

Tosafot[91] reject the opinion of Rabbeinu Tam, presumably because they believe that sleeping is an interruption that does create a requirement for a new *birkat ha-Torah* when one wakes up, even if the time one wakes up is before dawn. The view that sleep is considered an interruption to *birkat ha-Torah* is most famously attributed to Rosh. Rosh[92] writes that as long as one has not yet gone to sleep at night, one is still covered from the morning *birkat ha-Torah*.[93] However, once a person goes to sleep, one has created an interruption to one's *birkat ha-Torah*, and one therefore needs a new blessing whenever one wakes up.[94] Rosh believed this was true not only for nighttime sleep but for any established sleep, even during the day. *Taz*[95] even argues that within the approach of *biryah chadashah*, one is obligated to recite this blessing after any time one has a *sheinat keva* because one becomes a new creation any time one wakes from a *sheinat keva*, even during the day.

Terumat Ha-Deshen[96] states that his uncle, R. Aharon, ruled according to Rosh and recited a new *birkat ha-Torah* when waking up before dawn. *Terumat Ha-Deshen* himself also followed this practice. *Beit Yosef*[97] cites *Agur*, who argues that Rabbeinu Tam, and presumably R. Meir, are solitary opinions on this matter, and the majority opinion is to follow Rosh and recite a new blessing after an established sleep. However, *Agur* is also quoted[98] as saying that although we follow Rosh at night, our practice is not to recite a new *birkat ha-Torah* after sleeping during the day. Apparently Rabbeinu Tam is only considered a negligible minority opinion when it comes to sleep during the night, whereas regarding daytime sleep we are concerned for the opinion of Rabbeinu Tam so we do not recite the blessing. This is in line with the principle *safek berakhot lehakel*, that we are lenient when it comes to blessings

---

the night when one learns before going to sleep. Therefore, his opinion on whether the blessing still endures after one has slept during the night remains unknown.

91 *Berakhot* 11b s.v. *she-kevar*.
92 *Berakhot* 1:13.
93 *Ma'adanei Yom Tov* (commentary on Rosh, *siman 60*) explains that while normally in the Jewish calendar the day follows the night, in this case the nighttime is considered the time to make up for all of the learning one did not have time to do during the day. Therefore, regarding *birkat ha-Torah*, night follows day.
94 This, of course, is true only for an established sleep but does not apply to a person who only naps. However, Rosh here seems to define *sheinat keva* as that which one does in bed, rather than on a table or wherever one happens to be. Normally we define *sheinat keva* as a length of time greater than 60 breaths, as explained earlier in our discussion of washing hands.
95 *Orach Chayyim* 47:9.
96 2:123.
97 *Orach Chayyim* 47:13.
98 In *Divrei Chamudot* on Rosh, *siman 77*.

of questionable obligation. *Divrei Chamudot*[99] writes that he personally did recite a new blessing even after established sleep during the
day as did his teacher, R. Yaakov Ginzberg. *Peri Megadim*[100] explains
that although we are generally lenient when it comes to blessings, many
authorities ruled that the obligation to recite *birkat ha-Torah* is actually
of Biblical origin, unlike most other blessings. Therefore, when it comes
to *birkat ha-Torah*, one should recite the blessing after sleep during the
day rather than being lenient.

Staying Awake All Night

This debate is relevant to the person who stays awake all night. If we
rule according to Rosh and those who agree with him that new blessings
on Torah study are required after any sleep, it would seem that one who
stays awake all night should not require a new blessing in the morning,
since there was no interruption to one's *birkat ha-Torah* from the previous day. However, if we rule according to Rabbeinu Tam and R. Meir,
sleep does not have an effect on *birkat ha-Torah* and therefore whatever
creates the daily obligation to recite the blessing anew will still apply to
a person who stays awake all night.

 Shulchan Arukh, in discussing the recitation of *birkat ha-Torah*,
writes several ambiguous rulings on this subject, leading to some difficulty in understanding his position on the issue. Specifically, he records
three rulings:

1. **Sleeping during the day:** He first writes[101] that *sheinat keva* during
   the day is an interruption with regard to *birkat ha-Torah*, in accordance with the opinion of Rosh. However, he adds that there are
   those who say it is not an interruption (in accordance with the opinion of Rabbeinu Tam and R. Meir), and that this is the common
   practice (not to recite a blessing after daytime sleep). *Mishnah
   Berurah*[102] suggests that people should not follow this practice, but
   should recite a new blessing after daytime sleep. He cites many early
   and late authorities who ruled that one should recite a new blessing
   even after daytime sleep, and says that one who relies on them and
   recites a new blessing even during the day is praiseworthy.

2. **Learning at night:** He next writes[103] that when one learns at night
   before going to sleep one does not need to recite a new blessing,
   since in this regard the night follows the day. *Mishnah Berurah*[104]
   points out that this implies that once one does sleep at night, one is

99 Comments on Rosh, *siman* 77.
100 *Eshel Avraham, Orach Chayyim* 47, *se'if katan* 11.
101 *Orach Chayyim* 47:11.
102 *Orach Chayyim* 47:25.
103 *Orach Chayyim* 47:12.
104 *Orach Chayyim* 47:28.

obligated to recite a new blessing when one wakes up, even if it is still in the early part of the night.[105]

3. **Waking before dawn:** His final ruling[106] is that one who wakes up before dawn should recite *birkat ha-Torah* when one wakes up, even though the new day has not yet started. This is consistent with *Mishnah Berurah*'s understanding of *Shulchan Arukh*'s previous ruling.

According to *Mishnah Berurah*, it appears that *Shulchan Arukh*'s general view is that one should not recite a new blessing after sleep during the day, but rather one should recite a new blessing after sleeping at night, even if it is still far from the upcoming morning. Although *Shulchan Arukh*'s opinion about daytime sleep and nighttime sleep can be clarified in this way, its implications for one who stays awake all night are subject to much debate. *Magen Avraham*[107] noted that *Shulchan Arukh* specifically writes that one does not need a new blessing at night as long as one has not yet gone to sleep. Therefore, *Magen Avraham* argues, a new blessing is required only when a person goes to sleep. Thus, if one stays awake all night, one should not recite a new blessing in the morning. However, *Magen Avraham* finds this notion problematic, since *Shulchan Arukh* also rules that the practice is not to recite a new blessing after daytime sleep. *Magen Avraham* believes that this is a contradiction. If we rule according to Rabbeinu Tam and R. Meir that we do not recite a new blessing after daytime sleep, then we should also rule according to them that it is the new day, the idea of a refreshed creation, which creates the daily obligation for a new blessing every morning, rather than sleep. According to that view, one should still recite a new blessing every morning even if one stayed awake all night. However, *Shulchan Arukh*'s implication is that one who stays awake all night should not recite a new blessing in the morning. *Magen Avraham* therefore rules against what he believes to be the implication of *Shulchan Arukh* and says that one who stays awake all night should recite a blessing in the morning. *Magen Avraham* was attacked for this view in two ways:

1. Several authorities did not agree that *Shulchan Arukh* implies that one who stays awake all night should not recite a blessing in the

---

105 He even says that the opinion quoted in the previous line of *Shulchan Arukh* that did not require a new blessing after daytime sleep would agree that a new blessing is required once the sleep occurred at night. It is not clear that this is true, of course, since if that opinion represents the view of Rabbeinu Tam, the new blessing is only required once the morning comes. There is also disagreement about this circumstance among modern authorities as well. R. Mordechai Willig (in his shiur, "The Laws of Staying Up All Night," available at http://www.yutorah.org/lectures/lecture.cfm/734390) rules that if one takes a nap in the beginning of the night and then wakes up while it is still the early part of the night, one should not recite a new blessing, against the opinion of *Mishnah Berurah*.

106 *Orach Chayyim* 47:13.

107 *Orach Chayyim* 47:12.

morning.[108] *Arukh Ha-Shulchan*[109] argues that *Shulchan Arukh* only intended that one does not need a new *birkat ha-Torah* at night as

108 In addition to *Arukh Ha-Shulchan*, several other explanations are given to explain *Shulchan Arukh*'s ruling:
- *Machatzit Ha-Shekel* (*Orach Chayyim* 47:12) argues that *Shulchan Arukh* only intended to highlight the notion that when one does sleep at night, one's awakening can define a new calendar day, even before dawn. When *Shulchan Arukh* implies that one should recite a new blessing after sleeping at night even if the morning has not yet come, he is not ruling according to Rosh that it is the sleep which causes this obligation for a new blessing. Instead, he is arguing that the definition of a new day, when Chazal established that one should recite a new blessing, is when one wakes from one's nighttime sleep. If one stays awake all night, one should certainly still say recite a new blessing in the morning, because that is the law established by Chazal, and the morning marks a new day by default. However, when one does sleep at night, one's awakening marks the new day, rather than dawn. This is not because sleep directly obligates a person to recite a new blessing, as Rosh would have it, but rather because sleep defines the new day, and the new day is what drives the obligation for a new blessing. Of note, despite this reading, *Machatzit Ha-Shekel* states that it would be ideal for one who stays awake all night to hear the blessing from someone else who did sleep, rather than saying reciting it oneself.
- *Peri Megadim* (*Orach Chayyim* 47:12) makes a similar argument to resolve the contradiction noted by *Magen Avraham*. His original contribution to the discussion is his suggestion that our intent when reciting *birkat ha-Torah* is that the blessing should cover us either until the next morning, or until we wake from the night's sleep. Based on this intent alone it is clear that one who stays awake all night still needs to recite a new blessing in the morning. This also explains why one who wakes up before dawn can recite a new blessing immediately without needing to wait until the morning. *Arukh Ha-Shulchan* (*Orach Chayyim* 47:23) makes a similar argument that *birkat ha-Torah* is designed to last for 24 hours, or until a person wakes from nighttime sleep, since that brings an early end to his 24-hour window. However, rather than focusing on intent when reciting the blessing, *Arukh Ha-Shulchan* explains that the blessing is designed to cover 24 hours because a person is obligated to study Torah day and night, for the entire 24-hour day. Sleep does not interrupt that obligation, but when the sleep occurs at night it creates the beginning of a new 24-hour window upon awakening.
- *Peri Megadim* (ibid.) also gives an alternative explanation that when one wakes from nighttime sleep, one recites a new blessing even before dawn because nighttime sleep, unlike daytime sleep, is such a major interruption that even we, who normally rule according to Rabbeinu Tam, accept that it requires a new blessing. According to this approach too, one who stays awake all night should still recite a new blessing in the morning in accordance with Rabbeinu Tam.

109 *Orach Chayyim* 47:23.

long as one has not gone to sleep. That, however, is only before dawn. After dawn, *Shulchan Arukh* would agree that one must recite a new blessing, regardless of whether or not one slept.[110]

2. Most authorities do not agree with *Magen Avraham* that there is a contradiction in *Shulchan Arukh*. Gra[111] argues that *Shulchan Arukh* really ruled according to Rosh that sleep is an interruption, and was only conceding that the common practice is not to recite a new blessing during the day after sleep. Therefore, the fact that he rules according to Rosh that one only needs a new blessing after one sleeps at night is no surprise. Furthermore, he adds that the accepted opinion to not recite a blessing during after daytime sleep is that of *Agur*,[112] and not Rabbeinu Tam or R. Meir. *Agur*, according to Gra, only ruled that one should not recite a blessing after daytime sleep as a leniency because we are lenient regarding blessings of uncertain obligation. He did not intend, Gra argues, that his ruling should be applied to the situation of one who stays awake overnight, which would lead to a "stringency" of reciting a questionable blessing that Rosh would not have required. Thus, Gra believes that one who stays awake all night should not recite a new blessing in the morning. R. Akiva Eiger[113] uses this same argument as well.[114] However, he adds that if one sleeps during the daytime and then stays awake overnight, one should certainly be obligated to recite a new blessing in the morning according to all opinions: according to Rabbeinu Tam, because a new day started, and according to Rosh, because one has already been obligated since the previous day when one slept.

110 To explain why *Shulchan Arukh* would need to explicitly rule that one does not need a new blessing at night when that ruling does not apply to the next morning, *Arukh Ha-Shulchan* says that one may have thought that if one recited one's previous *birkat ha-Torah* before dawn and then stayed awake late into the following night, one should have to recite a new *birkat ha-Torah* at night once it has been 24 hours since one's last *birkat ha-Torah*. *Shulchan Arukh* intends to negate that idea, and says that one never needs a new blessing at night as long as one has not yet gone to sleep, even if it has been more than 24 hours since the last time one said the blessing. Whether or not this is what *Shulchan Arukh* intended, what is important is that *Shulchan Arukh* does not necessarily imply that one who stays awake all night should not recite a blessing in the morning.

111 *Orach Chayyim* 47:12 s.v. *af im*.

112 See *Be'er Ha-Golah, Orach Chayyim* 47:50 who also writes this.

113 *Orach Chayyim* 47:12.

114 He goes even further to question whether *Magen Avraham* is correct that *Shulchan Arukh* really implies that one who stays awake all night should not recite a blessing in the morning. Although he thinks this is not correct, he gives *Magen Avraham* more authority than himself, so he concludes that we should assume *Magen Avraham* is correct. It is therefore not clear how R. Akiva Eiger would rule in practice.

In summary, while *Shulchan Arukh*'s opinion is unclear, Gra believes that one who stays awake all night should not recite a new blessing in the morning. R. Akiva Eiger can likely be placed in this camp as well. On the other hand, *Magen Avraham, Machatzit Ha-Shekel, Peri Megadim* and *Arukh Ha-Shulchan* all maintain that one is obligated to recite a new blessing in the morning after staying awake all night. *Peri Chadash*[115] writes that we fundamentally rule according to Rosh that one who stays awake all night should not recite a new blessing in the morning, but to be safe it would be best to hear the blessing from somebody else. *Mishnah Berurah*[116] agrees that it is best to hear the blessing from somebody else, but if that is not possible one should not recite the blessing because we are lenient about blessings of questionable obligation (*safek berakhot lehakel*). Instead, he writes, one can have in mind that the *Ahavah Rabbah* blessing one recites before the *shema* during *shacharit* will function as one's *birkat ha-Torah* for that day. He adds that if one takes this approach, one should make sure to learn something or at least read a few verses of Torah immediately after *shacharit*. *Mishnah Berurah* does cite the suggestion of R. Akiva Eiger that if one took a nap during the day and then stayed awake all night, one should certainly recite one's own *birkat ha-Torah* in the morning. *Shulchan Arukh Ha-Rav*[117] also rules that it would be best to hear the blessing from somebody else, but unlike *Peri Chadash* and *Mishnah Berurah*, he writes that if nobody else is available, one should recite the blessing on one's own. This is also the view of the author of the *Piskei Teshuvot*.[118]

Reciting a Second *Birkat Ha-Torah*

We must also discuss the situation where someone sleeps or takes a nap at night but then wakes up before dawn. We have already seen that *Shulchan Arukh*[119] rules explicitly that such a person should recite *birkat ha-Torah* when he or she wakes up, even though it is still nighttime. This ruling is virtually unanimous.[120] The question that does arise, though, is whether this person should recite a second *birkat ha-Torah* once the morning comes.

115 *Orach Chayyim* 46:8.
116 *Orach Chayyim* 47:28.
117 *Orach Chayyim* 47:7.
118 *Orach Chayyim* 47:16.
119 *Orach Chayyim* 47:13.
120 However, there is some debate about what to do if one wakes up when it is very early in the night, as noted earlier. Also, R. Shlomo Zalman Auerbach (*Devar Halakhah* on *Halikhot Shlomo, Tefillah* 6:1) writes that one who naps, even for longer than 30 minutes, at the beginning of the night, and still intends to sleep again later in the night, has no obligation to recite a new *birkat ha-Torah* until after one wakes up the second time.

Hagahot Maimoniyot[121] cites a responsum written by Ri to R. Asher of Lonil. In the responsum, Ri states that it is believed that Rashi would repeat *birkat ha-Torah* in this situation, just as one recites a blessing on the Torah during communal Torah reading even though one has already recited one's daily *birkat ha-Torah*. In the responsum, Ri disagrees with Rashi, arguing that the blessing during communal Torah reading is an exception to the rule and one should not repeat one's *birkat ha-Torah* at dawn. *Beit Yosef*[122] points out that according to Rosh one certainly would not need to repeat one's blessing because one did not go back to sleep. The question only applies to those who follow the view of Rabbeinu Tam. Even so, *Beit Yosef* concludes, like Ri and *Hagahot Maimoniyot*, that one should not repeat *birkat ha-Torah*. It seems that Rashi is a lone opinion on this matter.

What is a much-debated question, however, is the scenario in which a person wakes up before dawn and recites *birkat ha-Torah*, but then goes back to sleep again before dawn and does not wake up again until after dawn. Regarding this situation, *Sha'arei Teshuvah*[123] acknowledges differing opinions on this matter, and concludes that it should depend on one's intent. If one had in mind that the *birkat ha-Torah* one recited in the middle of the night should only cover the learning one plans to do that night until one goes back to sleep, then one should recite a new blessing when one wakes for the second time in the morning. Otherwise, we assume that one's intent is that one's blessing should cover the entire upcoming day, and therefore one would not need to repeat one's blessing even though one went back to sleep. *Arukh Ha-Shulchan*[124] also writes that this should depend on one's intent, although he explains this in a different way by adding that it should also depend on the time of night. If one wakes up in the night and plans to go back to sleep for more than 30 minutes before dawn, and one woke up before *chatzot*, one should refrain from reciting *birkat ha-Torah* and should only recite it after waking up the second time. If, however, one woke up for the first time after *chatzot*, one should recite the blessing then and have in mind that it should cover the entire upcoming day. If one wakes up, even before *chatzot*, and does not plan to go back to sleep, one should recite *birkat ha-Torah* at that time with the intent that it should cover the entire upcoming day. Even if one ends up falling asleep again, one would not need to repeat *birkat ha-Torah*. *Mishnah Berurah*[125] concedes that according to *Shulchan Arukh* one should not repeat *birkat ha-Torah* even if one went back to sleep. However, he points out that this is all according to the ruling of *Shulchan Arukh* that our practice

121 *Hilkhot Tefillah* 7:20.
122 *Orach Chayyim* 47:13.
123 *Orach Chayyim* 47:12.
124 *Orach Chayyim* 47:23.
125 *Orach Chayyim* 47:29.

is not to require a new blessing after daytime sleep. *Mishnah Berurah* himself,[126] though, ruled that ideally one should recite a new blessing even after daytime sleep. He writes, therefore, that here certainly one has even more reason to recite a new blessing since one fell asleep during the night.

Birkhot Ha-Shachar[127] and *Elokai Neshamah*

The next part of the order of morning blessings for which there is questionable obligation after being awake overnight is *birkhot ha-shachar* and *Elokai neshamah*. In particular, there are two blessings that comprise *birkhot ha-shachar* which indirectly refer to waking from sleep, while an additional blessing makes direct reference to sleep. The blessings that are indirectly related to waking from sleep are the first of the *birkhot ha-shachar* in which we thank God for giving us the understanding to distinguish between day and night ("*asher natan la-sekhvi vinah lehavchin bein yom u-vein laylah*"),[128] as well as the blessing of *poke'ach ivrim* ("Who opens the eyes of the blind"). The blessing directly related to sleep is "*ha-ma'avir sheinah me-einai u-tenumah me-afappai*," "Who removes sleep from my eyes and slumber from my eyelids." Although *Elokai neshamah* is not technically one of the *birkhot ha-shachar*, the halakhic issues and arguments surrounding its recitation after staying awake overnight are the same, and thus it is grouped together with the *birkhot ha-shachar* by the *poskim*. As we will see, virtually all authorities agree that the blessings which only indirectly refer to sleep can be recited in full by one who did not sleep overnight. This section will therefore focus on "*ha-ma'avir sheinah…*" and *Elokai neshamah*, about which there is debate as to whether they can be recited when one did not sleep.

According to *Shulchan Arukh*,[129] one for whom the content of one of the *birkhot ha-shachar* is not relevant should still recite that blessing in the morning, only without uttering God's name. Rama[130] disagrees, arguing that these blessings do not refer to the one reciting as an individual. Rather, they are intended to be generalized statements of gratitude for that which God gives to mankind every day. Therefore, one can recite the full blessing even when the content does not apply to him or

---

126 *Orach Chayyim* 47:25.
127 In this essay, *birkhot ha-shachar* refer to the series of blessings that are typically recited by the *chazzan* at the beginning of the *shacharit* service, beginning with *asher natan la-sekhvi vinah*, and ending with *ha-gomel chasadim tovim le-ammo yisra'el*.
128 There is actually debate whether we are thanking God for giving *us* this ability or for giving roosters the ability to recognize morning.
129 *Orach Chayyim* 46:8.
130 *Orach Chayyim* 46:8.

her on that day. One would think this implies that even one who did not sleep overnight should still recite even those *birkhot ha-shachar* that are about sleep. However, despite this statement of Rama, which is accepted in Ashkenazi practice, later authorities debate whether Rama's ruling applies to all of the *birkhot ha-shachar* or only to some.

Peri Megadim[131] cites *Eliyah Rabbah* who states that one who did not sleep overnight should still recite *poke'ach ivrim*. However, he continues, one should not recite *Elokai neshamah* or *"ha-ma'avir sheinah…"* This, of course, raises the question of why one should differentiate between these two *birkhot ha-shachar* that both reference sleep. One possibility is that only *"ha-ma'avir sheinah…"* references sleep directly, while *poke'ach ivrim* contains only an indirect reference to sleep. Another possibility is that *poke'ach ivrim* is written in third-person plural form, whereas *ha-ma'avir sheinah **me-einai** u-tenumah **me-afappai*** is written in the first-person singular. It is possible that Rama's ruling to recite the blessing even when it does not apply to the individual only extends to those blessings written in third-person plural that describe what God gives to the world and not specifically to the person reciting the blessing. Other authorities refer to this type of blessing as referencing *minhago shel olam*, the ways of the world. On the other hand, the blessings written in first-person singular are from the perspective of the individual, and therefore should not be recited if they do not apply to that individual. This is in fact one suggestion quoted by *Sha'arei Teshuvah*.[132]

However, this approach has numerous difficulties. Most notably, several of the other *birkhot ha-shachar* are also written in first-person singular, such as *"she-asah li kol tzorki"* ("Who has provided me my every need"). Therefore, this theory does not explain the uniqueness of the *"ha-ma'avir sheinah…"* blessing.[133] This objection was noted by *Peri Megadim*.[134] Although *Peri Megadim* does accept the ruling that only *"ha-ma'avir sheinah…"* and *Elokai neshamah* should be omitted by one who stays awake overnight, he leaves the explanation for the

---

131 *Eshel Avraham* 46:12.

132 *Orach Chayyim* 46:8, *se'if katan* 12.

133 One could argue that in fact *"ha-ma'avir sheinah…"* is not unique, and the same principle would apply to *"she-asah li kol tzorki"* and other blessings worded similarly. One would not recite any of these blessings if the content did not apply to that individual. However, the difference is merely a practical one, that a person can create a situation in which *"ha-ma'avir sheinah…"* would not apply, namely by not sleeping. A situation in which *"she-asah li kol tzorki"* would not apply, however, is not possible so one will never be exempted from that blessing. The problem with this solution is, as *Peri Megadim* points out, that the *"she-asah li kol tzorki"* blessing has been traditionally linked to putting on one's shoes, and apparently is not intended to refer to God's fulfillment of all of a person's needs.

134 *Eshel Avraham* 46:2.

uniqueness of these blessings as an open question that requires further investigation.[135]

In terms of practical *halakhah*, whatever the reason, *Peri Megadim* believes that one who stayed awake all night should not recite "*ha-ma'avir sheinah…*" or *Elokai neshamah*. Others quoted by the *Sha'arei Teshuvah* believe that even these should be recited daily by everybody regardless. He adds that there may also be mystical meanings behind these blessings, which further argues for reciting them all daily. *Sha'arei Teshuvah*[136] himself concludes that due to the debate it is best to hear those two blessings from somebody else who did sleep, having in mind to fulfill one's obligation through his or her recitation. Even more ideal, adds *Sha'arei Teshuvah,* would be to ensure that one does sleep at

135 *Ateret Zekeinim* (*Orach Chayyim* 46:6, s.v. *ha-noten la-ya'ef ko'ach*) offered a different approach to differentiate between the various *birkhot ha-shachar*, and in doing so also expanded his list of blessings that would not be included in the Rama's ruling. He uses a similar terminology of contrasting blessings written from an objective standpoint about general phenomena to blessings about subjective personal experiences, though he defines the parameters differently. He states that the blessings that one recites even when they do not apply to that individual are those that pertain to phenomena without which the world could not survive. "*Ha-noten la-sekhvi vinah*" and "*roka ha-aretz al ha-mayim*" ("Who placed the land over water") fall into this category. The subjective individualistic blessings are those that pertain to items one can survive without, such as clothing. The latter are not recited when they do not apply to that individual on a given day. He does not explicitly note his implication that man can survive without sleep, but he certainly intends to include "*ha-ma'avir sheinah…*" in his list of subjective blessings that one does not recite when they do not apply. This implication that man can survive without sleep certainly makes his theory hard to accept. He does add an alternative explanation, more similar to that of *Peri Megadim* though still an expanded form, in which he argues that the objective *birkhot ha-shachar* hold true as statements even when a person does not perform the act associated with them on a given day. "*Roka ha-aretz al ha-mayim*," for example, is still a true phenomenon for which one can thank God even if he or she did not step on the ground. "*Ha-maavir sheinah…,*" presumably, is not a statement that has relevance in a general, objective way unless the one reciting the blessing has experienced awakening from sleep. The differentiation between the objective and subjective blessings according to this theory is not about the language of the blessing, as *Peri Megadim* believed, but is instead focused on the content of the blessing. Still, it is hard to fully understand *Ateret Zekeinim's* argument here. "*Ozer Yisra'el be-gevurah,*" ("Who girds Israel with strength") for example, is explicitly placed in the subjective, individualistic camp by *Ateret Zekeinim*, apparently because the content should not be meaningful as a general statement unless the one reciting it has put on a belt. It is hard to understand why this should be the case. His argument here seems somewhat arbitrary.

136 *Orach Chayyim* 46, *se'if katan* 12.

least the minimal amount to obligate oneself in these blessings according to all opinions.[137] *Mishnah Berurah*[138] rules in accordance with *Sha'arei Teshuvah*. They do not explicitly write what a person should do if one is unable to find somebody else to recite the blessings on his or her behalf. *Arukh Ha-Shulchan*,[139] on the other hand, rules according to the opinions in *Sha'arei Teshuvah* that one should recite even *Elokai neshamah* and *"ha-ma'avir sheinah..."* even after being awake overnight. He argues that the ruling of *Eliyah Rabbah* quoted by *Peri Megadim,* that one should not recite those two blessings, only applies to the opinion of *Shulchan Arukh* that one should never recite the *birkhot ha-shachar* when they do not apply to that individual. He believes it obvious that Rama would require recitation of all blessings regardless of sleep because all of the blessings are on *minhago shel olam,* the ways of the world. Given this debate,[140] the safe practice for one who stays awake all night would be to hear *Elokai neshamah* and *"ha-ma'avir sheinah..."* from somebody else who did sleep.[141] All of the remaining *birkhot ha-shachar* may be recited by one who did not sleep.

137 This minimal amount of time is whatever is necessary to achieve *sheinat keva*, discussed above.

138 46:24.

139 *Orach Chayyim* 46:12.

140 One possible way of avoiding this issue that has been suggested by R. Aryeh Lebowitz ("Ten Minute Halacha – Netilas Yadayim and Birchos Hashachar After Staying Up All Night," available on http://www.yutorah. org/lectures/lecture.cfm/793712) is by taking a nap in the afternoon prior to staying awake all night. This is based on *Agur* who cited from R. Yehuda of Speyer (quoted in *Beit Yosef, Orach Chayyim* 231:1) that one should recite *Elokai neshamah* even after waking from a daytime nap. *Beit Yosef* (*Orach Chayyim* 231:1) contends that this is not our practice. Based on this, some have argued that if one did take a nap in the afternoon prior to staying awake overnight, he should certainly recite *Elokai neshamah* and all of the *birkhot ha-shachar* the next morning according to all opinions. The argument is that if the *birkhot ha-shachar* are objective, based on *minhago shel olam*, then certainly one should recite them regardless of sleep. If the *birkhot ha-shachar* are about one's personal experience of waking from sleep, then one still became obligated from one's previous day's nap. However, this argument was not made in any of the sources and certainly has its flaws. It is quite possible, for example, that one only becomes obligated in *Elokai neshamah* and *"ha-ma'avir sheinah..."* after sleep during the night, even if the blessings are about one's personal experience. We have already seen in *birkat ha-Torah* and *al netilat yadayim* that nighttime sleep may have a different quality than daytime sleep in *halakhah*. In light of this, one is advised to consult with his or her own halakhic authority before deciding whether or not to follow this line of reasoning.

141 Especially in light of the logical difficulties that come with trying to differentiate between the different *birkhot ha-shachar*, it would appear that

Finally, those who choose to wake early rather than staying awake late while studying must know whether they should recite these blessings even if they wake up before *alot ha-shachar*, as was the case with *al netilat yadayim* and *birkat ha-Torah*, or whether they should wait until after *alot ha-shachar* to recite these blessings. *Peri Chadash*[142] writes that if one wakes up in the middle of the night but intends to go back to sleep before *alot ha-shachar*, he should wait until the morning to recite *Elokai neshamah*. This implies that if one does not plan to go back to sleep, it would be permissible to recite this blessing even before *alot ha-shachar*. *Shulchan Arukh*[143] explicitly writes that one who wakes up before *alot ha-shachar* should recite all the morning blessings except "*asher natan la-sekhvi vinah....*"

Blessing for *Tzitzit*

It is likely that those who stay awake all night also remain dressed in their daytime clothing, including their *tzitzit*, throughout the night. This creates an issue with reciting the blessing on *tzitzit* the next morning. Should one say a new blessing on wearing *tzitzit* when he has been continuously wearing them without interruption since the previous morning when he last said the blessing? It should be noted that men who wear a *tallit* every day generally do not recite the blessing on *tzitzit* even when they do not wear their *tzitzit* overnight. For such men, this topic is a non-issue. Therefore, the following discussion is most relevant for those who only wear *tzitzit* (*tallit katan*) but not a *tallit* (*gadol*).

First, we must clarify whether the ability to recite the blessing on *tzitzit* actually depends on sleep. *Shulchan Arukh*[144] writes that one who sleeps in his *tzitzit* should still recite the blessing on these in the morning, despite never taking them off. *Magen Avraham*[145] explains the logic of this ruling through the following principle: night is a time of exemption from the *mitzvah* of *tzitzit*, and thus passing of the night creates an interruption in the fulfillment of the *mitzvah* of *tzitzit*. Note that *Magen Avraham* does not mention sleep as an interruption to the fulfillment of the *mitzvah* in his explanation. Were sleep an important factor in this discussion, it would have been easier to explain the logic of *Shulchan Arukh* by saying that sleep created the obligation for a new blessing in the morning even though the person at hand slept in his *tzitzit*. We see that the need to recite a new blessing on one's *tzitzit* in the morning when he wore them through the night is based upon the status of the

one would be justified in relying on *Arukh Ha-Shulchan* and reciting the blessings oneself.
142 *Orach Chayyim* 46:1.
143 *Orach Chayyim* 47:13.
144 *Orach Chayyim* 8:16.
145 8:21.

mitzvah of *tzitzit* at night and not the status of *tzitzit* worn during sleep. Therefore, since *Shulkhan Arukh* requires one who slept in his *tzitzit* to recite a blessing, we can safely assume he would also require one who is awake all night, wearing his *tzitzit*, to recite a blessing.

The only authority who suggests otherwise is *Arukh Ha-Shulchan*.[146] He argues that the basis of *Shulchan Arukh*'s requirement of a new blessing in the morning after sleeping in one's *tzitzit* is that sleeping through the night is considered an interruption in the fulfillment of the *mitzvah*. According to his logic, one who stays awake and dressed all night would not require a new blessing, since nighttime alone is not a sufficient interruption to require a new blessing. Since *Arukh Ha-Shulchan* is a solitary opinion on this matter, this topic will be discussed under the assumption that sleep is not relevant to the question at hand.[147]

Whether there is a need for a new blessing for one who wears his *tzitzit* overnight hinges on two questions. First, does the *mitzvah* of *tzitzit* apply during the night? Regarding this there is virtually unanimous agreement that it does not.[148] Second, what does it mean that the *mitzvah* of *tzitzit* does not apply at night? Rambam[149] explains that one's obligation to wear *tzitzit* is only during the day, regardless of whether one is wearing daytime or nighttime clothes. Others, most notably Rabbeinu Tam[150] and Rosh,[151] argue that the nighttime is not a categorical exemption from the *mitzvah* of *tzitzit*, but rather it is the clothing of the night that is exempt. Pajamas do not need *tzitzit* even during the day, and daytime clothing requires *tzitzit* even when worn at night. Ran[152] proposes a third opinion that compromises between the two extremes. He rules that one is only obligated in the *mitzvah* of *tzitzit* when it is daytime *and* one is wearing daytime clothing. Pajamas are exempt even during the day, and daytime clothing is exempt when worn at night.[153]

---

146 *Orach Chayyim* 8:23.
147 Even if *Arukh Ha-Shulchan* is correct, it would not change the *halakhah* for one who stays awake all night, since as we will see, virtually all contemporary authorities agree that even one who slept overnight in his *tzitzit* should not recite a new blessing in the morning based on the principle of *safek berakhot lehakel*.
148 *Tur, Orach Chayyim* 18:1; *Shulchan Arukh, Orach Chayyim* 18:1; Rambam, *Hilkhot Tzitzit* 3:7; Rosh, *Hilkhot Tzitzit* 1.
149 *Hilchot Tzitzit* 3:7–8.
150 *Tosafot, Menachot* 40b s.v. *mi-shum kesut laylah*.
151 *Hilkhot Tzitzit* 1. Also quoted in *Tur, Orach Chayyim* 18:1.
152 *Kiddushin* 14b in *dappei ha-Rif*, s.v *eizo*.
153 There is debate as to where Rashi stands on this issue. See Rashi *Shabbat* 27b s.v. *le-kesut* and *Zevachim* 18b s.v. *perat*, which both indicate that Rashi agrees with Rosh. But see also Rashi *Menachot* 40b s.v. *hakhi garsinan*, which indicates that Rashi agrees with Rambam. *Hagahot Maimoniyot* (*Hilkhot Tzitzit* 3:7) believes Rashi agrees with Rosh. *Beit Yosef* (*Orach*

At first glance we can infer that according to Rambam and Ran, who both agree that nighttime is a categorical exemption from the *mitzvah* of *tzitzit*, the passage of night should create an interruption to the fulfillment of the *mitzvah* and be cause for a new blessing in the morning even for one who wore his *tzitzit* overnight.[154] On the other hand, according to Rabbeinu Tam and Rosh who believe it is only night clothing that is exempt and not nighttime itself, it would seem that one who wore his *tzitzit* all night should not require a new blessing in the morning since there was never any time of exemption to create an interruption in the fulfillment of his *mitzvah*.

While this analysis holds true for Rambam and his camp, there is a difficult responsum of Rosh[155] that challenges this approach. In his responsum, Rosh was directly asked the question of whether one who sleeps in his *tzitzit* needs to remove his *tzitzit* in the morning and put them back on later in order to obligate himself in the blessing, or if one is already obligated in the blessing and removing the *tzitzit* is unnecessary. Rosh answers that one is already obligated to make a new blessing, and removing the *tzitzit* is not required.[156]

Chayyim 18), though, quotes *Hagahot Maimoniyot* as saying that Rashi agrees with Rambam. *Sha'ar Ha-Melekh* (*Hilkhot Tzitzit 3:7*) attempts to resolve the contradiction by claiming that Rashi really agrees with the Ran.

154 This is strongly implied in Rambam *Hilkhot Tzitzit* 3:8.

155 *Teshuvot Ha-Rosh* 2:13.

156 He proves this based on a statement in the Gemara (*Menachot* 43a). The Gemara there says that R. Yehudah used to make *tzitzit* for his wife to wear, implying that he believed *tzitzit* is not a time-bound *mitzvah* and thus implying that nighttime is not an exemption from the *mitzvah* of *tzitzit*. The same R. Yehudah, the Gemara adds, also would recite a new blessing every morning when he put on his *tzitzit*. The Gemara then asks if nighttime is not an exemption from *tzitzit* and therefore according to R. Yehudah there is never a time of exemption to interrupt one's fulfillment of the *mitzvah* of *tzitzit*, why should R. Yehudah recite a new blessing in the morning? The Gemara answers that R. Yehudah subscribed to the opinion of Rebbe who taught that every time one puts on his pair of *tefillin* he should recite a new blessing, even though he had already said a blessing earlier that day and there was no time of exemption between the two blessings. Rashi interprets that the Gemara first assumed that since R. Yehudah did not believe there was a time of exemption to interrupt one's fulfillment of the *mitzvah*, there should be no new blessing for putting on *tzitzit* in the morning, even when one did not wear them at night. The conclusion of the Gemara is that *tzitzit* actually require a new blessing every time one dons them, even though there is no time of exemption, just like *tefillin* require a new blessing each time one dons them during the day. The implication for Rashi is that if one wears his *tzitzit* all night, there would be no new blessing in the morning. Rosh, however, assumes that nobody would ever think that one is not required to recite a new blessing when putting on *tzitzit* after a time of not wearing them, even if that time is exempted from

This responsum of Rosh is difficult to understand. It seems to contradict what he writes in his *Hilkhot Tzitzit*, which implied that one should not require a new blessing every morning if he wears his *tzitzit* all night, as explained above.[157] In an attempt to reconcile these two sources there are two major approaches to understanding Rosh that can be found in the later commentaries.

The first is to reject Rosh's responsum in favor of his writing in *Hilkhot Tzitzit*. *Tur* is the first authority who likely took this approach.[158] *Tur* writes that one who sleeps in his *tzitzit* overnight should not recite a new blessing in the morning. *Beit Yosef* explains that the basis for

the *mitzvah*. Therefore, he interprets that the Gemara is asking why R. Yehudah would need to recite a new blessing every morning in the case that he wore his *tzitzit* all night, since night is not a time of exemption. The conclusion of the *Gemara* is that the assumption of the question is correct, and R. Yehudah only recited a new blessing in the morning because he did in fact remove his *tzitzit* at night. Rosh derives from here that according to the accepted opinion that nighttime is in fact exempted from the *mitzvah* of *tzitzit*, one should require a new blessing in the morning even if one wore his *tzitzit* all night.

157 The logic of Rosh's derivation in his responsum is difficult to understand. The simplest way to explain the derivation is that Rosh is making a two-step argument. The first is his assumption that within the view of R. Yehudah, that there is no nighttime exemption from the *mitzvah* of *tzitzit*, the determining factor in whether one must recite a new blessing in the morning is whether one wore his *tzitzit* overnight. If one wore his *tzitzit* overnight, there would be no blessing since there is no interruption, and if he did not wear his *tzitzit* overnight he would recite a new blessing even though there was no time of exemption. However, this is all within the view of R. Yehudah. If, on the other hand, there is in fact a categorical exemption from the *mitzvah* of *tzitzit* at night, whether or not one wore the *tzitzit* overnight would no longer be the determining factor in the need for a new blessing. Instead, the main factor would be the simple fact that the nighttime exemption itself creates the interruption in the fulfillment of the *mitzvah*. This interruption occurs whether or not a person physically wears his *tzitzit*. In this way the Gemara becomes a direct proof for the notion that whether one wore his *tzitzit* overnight is not a significant factor in determining the need to recite a new blessing in the morning. From here, the second step in Rosh's argument is to explain why this is so. Why is it that if nighttime is exempted from the *mitzvah* of *tzitzit*, it no longer matters whether one wears his *tzitzit* overnight? The simplest explanation is that the exemption is a categorical one for the nighttime that applies even when one is wearing daytime clothing with daytime *tzitzit*. Therefore, nighttime itself creates an interruption, because even one who was wearing his *tzitzit* was not doing so in fulfillment of any *mitzvah*. This would, essentially, be Rambam's view. The problem with this simple explanation, of course, is that Rosh explicitly wrote in his *Hilkhot Tzitzit* that the exemption at night applies to nighttime clothing only, and not nighttime itself.

158 *Tur, Orach Chayyim* 8:16.

this ruling of the *Tur* is Rosh's *Hilkhot Tzitzit*[159] which states that one is obligated to wear *tzitzit* with day clothing even during the night. It is therefore logical that nighttime does not create an interruption to the *mitzvah* of *tzitzit*. However, as *Beit Yosef* points out, this ignores Rosh's own ruling in his responsum. *Bach*[160] defends the ruling of *Tur* by essentially arguing that Rosh's responsum should be ignored in favor of his rulings in *Hilkhot Tzitzit*.[161] *Taz*[162] essentially repeats *Bach*'s analysis in his commentary on *Shulchan Arukh*, and adds the possibility that Rosh wrote his responsum at a time when he accepted Rambam's interpretation of nighttime being a categorical exemption from *tzitzit*, but changed his ruling by the time he wrote his *Hilkhot Tzitzit*.

Similarly, *Derishah*[163] argues that the Rosh's responsum was written to a questioner who subscribed to the view of the Rambam that nighttime is a categorical exemption to the *mitzvah* of *tzitzit*. Rosh wrote the responsum for that particular individual, and was merely explaining that those who accept the Rambam's view should recite a new blessing in the morning even after wearing their *tzitzit* overnight. Rosh himself, however, would not require a new blessing in accordance with the simple understanding of his *Hilkhot Tzitzit*.

The second approach to understanding Rosh's opinion is to accept the responsum as a valid source of Rosh's final opinion and attempt to

159 *Hilkhot Tzitzit* 1.
160 *Orach Chayyim* 8:15.
161 The reason for this is that he believes that Rosh himself in *Hilkhot Tzitzit* (*siman* 20) quotes Rashi's explanation of the Gemara in *Menachot* 43b and does not offer the interpretation that he himself gives in his responsum. (It should be noted that the part of Rashi's explanation that Rosh quotes is ambiguous and does not definitively say that the Gemara's initial question was asking why R. Yehudah should need a new blessing even when he had not worn his *tzitzit* overnight.) Once Rosh reads the Gemara like Rashi, *Bach* argues that Rosh can no longer use this Gemara as proof that one who wore his *tzitzit* overnight must recite a new blessing. Thus, if the two sources of Rosh's opinion contradict each other openly, they are irreconcilable and one must choose one or the other. For *Bach*, Rosh's opinion in *Hilchot Tzitzit* is more logical. According to this explanation, the conclusion of the Gemara that R. Yehudah needed a new blessing only when putting on his *tzitzit* after a period of not wearing them, whether that be day or night, applies to us as well. Although R. Yehudah believed that nighttime is not exempt from *tzitzit* and we do not accept his opinion, Rosh's understanding of the nighttime exemption, namely that it only applies to night clothing, makes nighttime itself no more of an interruption for Rosh than it is for R. Yehudah. Therefore, if one wears his *tzitzit* overnight, according to *Bach*, he is certainly not obligated to recite a new blessing in the morning because as long as he wore his daytime clothing overnight, there was no interruption to the fulfillment of the *mitzvah*.
162 *Orach Chayyim* 8:15.
163 *Orach Chayyim* 8:4.

reconcile the two sources together. R. Yosef Karo is the most prominent authority to take this approach.[164] He reconciles the two sources by explaining that even though daytime clothing is still obligated in *tzitzit* at nighttime, as Rosh ruled in *Hilkhot Tzitzit*, since the idea of nighttime is the cause of the exemption of night clothing from *tzitzit*, passage through the night is itself enough of an interruption to create a need for a new blessing in the morning, as Rosh ruled in his responsum. R. Yosef Karo also cites Rambam[165] in his commentary, and notes his surprise at *Tur* for ruling that one does not require a new blessing in the morning, which he believes to be in opposition to both Rambam and Rosh.

Arukh Ha-Shulchan[166] suggests an alternative way to reconcile the two sources. He argues that consistent with his *Hilchot Tzitzit,* Rosh did not view nighttime to be an interruption, and therefore a person who stays awake all night wearing his *tzitzit* should not recite a new blessing in the morning. Rosh required a new blessing in the responsum only because that dealt with a situation where the person *slept* in his *tzitzit* overnight. Although night itself is not an interruption, sleeping during the night is an interruption that creates a need for a new blessing.[167]

In terms of the final *halakhah*, we have seen that *Tur*[168] rules that one should not recite a new blessing in the morning. *Bach* and *Taz* agree. *Shulchan Arukh*[169] rules that one should recite a new blessing.[170] *Mishnah Berurah*[171] writes that because of this debate it is best to avoid saying a blessing that may be unnecessary. Instead, one should have in mind that his blessing on his *tallit* should cover his *tzitzit* as well. *Arukh Ha-Shulchan*[172] rules that this is a case of *safek* and therefore

---

164 *Beit Yosef, Orach Chayyim* 8:16. He also accepts the opinion of the responsum of Rosh in *Shulchan Arukh, Orach Chayyim* 8:16.

165 *Hilchot Tzitzit* 3:7.

166 *Orach Chayyim* 8:23.

167 As mentioned at the beginning of this section, *Arukh Ha-Shulchan* is the only authority who considers sleep an important factor in this discussion.

168 *Hilkhot Tzitzit* 8:16.

169 *Orach Chayyim* 8:16.

170 This ruling, however, may be logically problematic. In *Beit Yosef* to *Tur Orach Chayyim* 18:1 s.v. *katuv*, he rules in accordance with Rambam's understanding of the nighttime exemption. He does so because he claimed that Rashi also agreed with Rambam, and because we are lenient in cases of *safek berakhah* (doubtful blessings) to not require a blessing when wearing *tzitzit* at night even in day clothing. However, it is not at all clear that Rashi agreed with Rambam (see footnote 153 above). Furthermore, if the impetus for his ruling was leniency in situations of doubtful need for a blessing, then applying that same principle to the case of one who wears his *tzitzit* overnight should require R. Yosef Karo to rule that one should not recite a new blessing in the morning.

171 8:42.

172 *Orach Chayyim* 8:23.

one should be lenient and not recite a new blessing. It is safe to assume that both authorities would agree that ideally one who does not wear a *tallit* should hear the blessing on *tzitzit* or *tallit* from somebody who is obligated to recite it, with the intention that this should count as his own blessing.

It is clear that the majority opinion among the early authorities is that one should not recite a new blessing. Therefore, the later authorities suggest subsuming this blessing under the blessing for *tallit*, if one wears one, hearing the blessing from somebody else, or simply not reciting the blessing altogether. However, those who exclusively follow the rulings of *Shulchan Arukh* should recite a new blessing in the morning.

For those who do recite a new blessing there is also a question of whether one needs to physically move the *tzitzit* on his body when reciting the new blessing in the morning. *Shulchan Arukh*[173] writes that it is a good thing for one to move his *tzitzit* when reciting the blessing.[174]

Finally, there is the situation where one does not stay awake all night, but instead wakes up before *alot ha-shachar*. In this situation, *Hagahot Maimoniyot*[175] writes in the name of the *Sefer Ha-Terumot* that one should put on his *tzitzit* without reciting a blessing when he wakes up. Once it is late enough in the morning, he should recite the blessing and move his *tzitzit* while keeping them on his body. Rama[176] rules according to this view, and *Arukh Ha-Shulchan*[177] agrees as well.

---

173 *Orach Chayyim* 8:16.

174 *Taz* (*Orach Chayyim* 8:16) questions why *Shulchan Arukh* merely suggests that one should move his *tzitzit* in this scenario, when in other situations the movement of the *tzitzit* during the blessing is a requirement. For example, in the case where one puts on *tzitzit* during the day but wishes to defer his blessing to a later time, he must move his *tzitzit* on his body when reciting that blessing. He explains that this situation is unique in that the movement of the *tzitzit* is not needed to clarify that your intention is to begin fulfillment of the *mitzvah* at the time of the blessing rather than at some earlier point when you first put on the *tzitzit*. When one wore his *tzitzit* through the night, his intention is obvious because there is no earlier point that the *tzitzit* were put on since the previous day's blessing. *Beit Yosef* and *Bach* (*Orach Chayyim* 8:16) ask the similar question of why movement of *tefillin* is a requirement when reciting the blessing while on *tzitzit* it seems to be just a suggestion. The most compelling answer is that of *Bach*, who writes that the movement of the *tefillin* makes it as if one is just donning his *tefillin* at the time of movement. With *tzitzit*, however, this cannot be said since he does not wish to ignore the fact that he was wearing his *tzitzit* before recitation of the blessing, he simply wishes to start his official fulfillment of the *mitzvah* with his recitation of the blessing. Therefore, the movement is not necessary with *tzitzit*.

175 On Rambam *Hilchot Tzitzit* 3:8.

176 *Orach Chayyim* 8:16.

177 *Orach Chayyim* 8:23.

Taz[178] notes that unlike the movement of the *tzitzit* for one who wears them all night, which is just a recommendation, in this scenario the movement of the *tzitzit* is actually a requirement since it needs to be clarified that one's intention is not that the blessing should refer to the time when one put on the *tzitzit* while it was still nighttime.

Keriat Shema al Ha-Mitah

One final topic to discuss is the latest time at night one is able to recite the bedtime *shema*. If one stays awake all night but has the opportunity to go to sleep in the morning, after *alot ha-shachar*, should he or she still recite the bedtime *shema*? Does one recite the bedtime *shema* whenever one's major sleep for a given day happens to be, or can it only be recited within certain time limits?

Biur Halakhah[179] writes that if one goes to sleep after *alot ha-shachar*, one should not recite the bedtime *shema* because the blessing of *ha-mappil*, said at the beginning of the bedtime *shema*, was established to only be said at nighttime. Besides for the blessing of *ha-mappil*, the paragraph of *shema* which is part of the bedtime *shema* should also not be read after *alot ha-shachar* since that is already time for the morning *shema* and it is not ideal to fulfill the morning *shema* without the usual blessings that come before and after it. *Biur Halakhah* also adds that he is unsure about a situation where a person is going to sleep slightly before *alot ha-shachar*. He wonders whether that person should still recite the bedtime *shema* because he or she is within the prescribed time limits, or whether he or she should refrain from reciting it since the fulfillment of that blessing, falling asleep, is unlikely to happen before *alot ha-shachar*.[180]

Summary

For a person who stays awake all night:
1. After *alot ha-shachar*, one should go to the bathroom and then wash one's hands in the normal fashion with the blessing afterwards.
2. If possible, one should listen to *birkat ha-Torah, Elokai neshamah*, and *ha-ma'avir sheinah* from another person, having in mind that his or her blessing should fulfill one's own obligation.
3. If it is too difficult to find another person from whom to hear the blessings, there is the option of using *Ahavah Rabbah* as one's *birkat*

---

178 *Orach Chayyim* 8:17.
179 *Orach Chayyim* 239, s.v. *samukh le-mitato*.
180 It is actually a debate among the authorities whether the blessing of *ha-mappil* is recited for one's individual sleep, or whether it refers to *minhago shel olam* of the idea of sleep at night in general. This is part of why it is unclear whether one should recite the blessing right before *alot ha-shachar* as well.

ha-Torah, so long as one learns or reads a few verses of Torah after *shacharit*. If one does not wish to use *Ahavah Rabbah*, one may recite the regular *birkat ha-Torah* on one's own.

4. If one took a nap during the day before staying awake all night, one should certainly say *birkat ha-Torah* on one's own in the morning.

5. If it is too difficult to find another person from whom to hear *Elokai neshamah* and *ha-ma'avir sheinah*, there is debate whether one should recite the blessings on one's own. This can be discussed with one's own *posek*, but leading authorities have endorsed both the option to say them on one's own and the option to not say them. Although we normally avoid blessings that may not be necessary or appropriate, in this case there may be some *poskim* who rely on those opinions that these blessings should be said nonetheless.

6. If a person wears a *tallit gadol*, he should have in mind that his blessing on that should cover his *tzitzit*. If a person only wears *tzitzit* and not a *talit gadol*, and he wore his *tzitzit* overnight he should attempt to hear the blessing on *tzitzit* from another person. If this is too difficult, he should not recite a blessing on *tzitzit* in the morning.

7. If a person ends up having time to sleep, he or she should only recite the bedtime *shema* if going to sleep before *alot ha-shachar*.

For a person who wakes up before dawn:

1. If one is waking up for the day, even though it is before *alot ha-shachar*, one should wash one's hands with the blessing when one wakes up. There is no need to repeat this blessing after *alot ha-shachar*, though one should wash one's hands without a blessing after *alot ha-shachar*. There are some authorities who believe one should be careful to keep one's hands clean from the time one initially washes them until *shacharit*.

2. If one goes back to sleep after washing one's hands with the blessing, one should wash one's hands without a blessing when one wakes up the second time.

3. One should put on his *tzitzit* when he wakes up without saying the blessing. If one wears a *talit gadol*, the blessing on that will cover his *tzitzit*. If not, he should wait until the earliest time for the *mitzvah* of *tzitzit*, and then recite the blessing. He should move the *tzitzit* on his body immediately after reciting the blessing (without removing them from his body).

4. One can choose to wait until *alot ha-shachar* to recite the *birkat ha-Torah*, or to recite it when one wakes up. Certainly if one will be involved in any type of Torah study one should recite it when one wakes up.

5. Even if one goes back to sleep later in the night one does not need to repeat the *birkat ha-Torah* when one wakes up for the second time.

6. If one does not plan to go back to sleep again, one does not need to wait until after *alot ha-shachar* to recite *Elokai neshamah* and the *birkhot ha-shachar*, though he should not recite "*ha-noten la-sechvi vinah…*" until after *alot ha-shachar*, in accordance with the ruling of *Shulchan Arukh* noted above.

For a person who sleeps in a way that qualifies as sheinat keva *and wakes up in the early part of the night and stays awake for the remainder of the night:*

1. One should wash one's hands without the blessing when one wakes up the first time. After *alot ha-shachar* one should use the bathroom and then wash one's hands with a blessing again.
2. There is debate regarding whether this person needs to recite a new *birkat ha-Torah* or not, but most authorities hold that one does. One should have in mind that one's blessing will cover the entirety of the next day, even if one goes back to sleep later in the night. One then does not need to repeat the blessing in the morning.
3. If one is not going back to sleep later in the night, one does not need to wait until after *alot ha-shachar* to recite *Elokai neshamah* and the *birkhot ha-shachar* (except "*ha-noten la-sekhvi vinah…*"), though it might be preferable to wait rather than reciting them so early in the night.

Chapter 6

The Earliest Time for *Shacharit*

Matthew Schaikewitz, MD

O ne of the most commonly encountered questions among those who rise early for work is how early one is allowed to recite *shacharit*, the morning prayer service. This question becomes especially relevant for students on their clinical rotations and for residents who must be at the hospital early in the morning. In this chapter we will analyze how students and residents may best fulfill the morning obligation to pray when they must be present at the hospital early in the morning.[1] We will briefly discuss the different *zemanim*, halakhic times, during the morning hours that will be referenced throughout the remainder of the chapter. Next, we will identify each segment of the morning service and discuss the earliest time it can be recited. Finally, we will close with a summary and offer practical advice in light of our findings.

A Brief Introduction to the Morning *Zemanim*: *Ammud Ha-Shachar, Mi-Sheyakkir and Hanetz Ha-Chammah*

In this chapter, we will discuss specific times in the morning when individual parts of the morning prayer service may be recited. In chronological order, the *zemanim* are: *ammud ha-shachar*, dawn; *mi-sheyakkir*, literally, "when one can distinguish"; and *hanetz ha-chammah*, sunrise. These terms will be further explained in the forthcoming paragraphs.

---

1   Some material in this chapter will contain advice that is more practical for men than for women. The following chapter discusses how these *halakhot* apply to women.

Ammud ha-shachar is around the time when the eastern sky begins to light up.[2] The Gemara explains that an average person can walk a distance of four *milin* during the time between *ammud ha-shachar* and *hanetz ha-chammah*.[3] Assuming, as does *Shulchan Arukh,* that it takes 18 minutes for an average person to walk one *mil,*[4] *ammud ha-shachar* occurs 72 minutes before *hanetz ha-chammah*. However, the assumption that a person can walk one *mil* in 18 minutes is debated.[5] There is also a debate whether *ammud ha-shachar* occurs at a fixed number of minutes before *hanetz ha-chammah* in all parts of the world and for each day of the year, or whether this time fluctuates based on distance from the equator as well as day of year.[6] According to those who maintain the time fluctuates based on location, the correct time of *ammud ha-shachar* can be obtained each day through astronomical calculation based on the degrees of the sun below the horizon.[7]

2 *Mishnah Berurah* (58:18) and *Biur Halakhah* (58 s.v. *mi-she'alah ammud ha-shachar*) explain that there is a *zeman* called *he'ir penei ha-mizrach,* when the eastern sky lights up. According to *Magen Avraham* (89:2) and others, *ammud ha-shachar* and *he'ir penei ha-mizrach* are two separate times, and *ammud ha-shachar* occurs a short time before *he'ir penei ha-mizrach*. According to Gra (*Shenot Eliyahu, Berakhot* 1:1 s.v. *Rabban Shimon ben Gamliel omer*) and others, these *zemanim* refer to the same time in the morning.
3 *Pesachim* 94a.
4 *Orach Chayyim* 459:2.
5 *Biur Halakhah* (459 s.v. *havei revi'it sha'ah*) writes that the time to walk one *mil* according to some is 22.5 minutes and according to others is 24 minutes. According to *Iggerot Moshe* (*Orach Chayyim* 4:6), Gra (*Biur Ha-Gra, Orach Chayyim* 459 s.v. *ve-shiur mil*) holds that the time it takes to walk one *mil* is 22.5 minutes, and *Chok Ya'akov* (*Orach Chayyim* 459:10), as explained by *Tiferet Yisra'el* (*Yakhin, Pesachim* 3:21; *Hilkheta Gevirta, Pesachim* 3:2), maintains that it could take up to 23 minutes.
6 *Biur Halakhah* (261 s.v. *she-hu*) explains that *Peri Megadim* (*Eshel Avraham* 261:9) uses a fixed number of minutes when calculating the four *milin* from sunset until nighttime. He writes that according to Gra (*Biur Ha-Gra, Orach Chayyim* 261:2 s.v. *she-hu*), calculations in the Gemara based on *milin* were only meant to be used during the months of *Nissan* and *Tishrei* (when the amount of daylight and nighttime are equal) and for the latitude of Babylonia. According to Gra, therefore, the calculation of *ammud ha-shachar* changes based on location and time of year.
7 If one assumes that in *Bavel* on a day when daytime and nighttime hours are equivalent that *ammud ha-shachar* occurs 72 minutes before *hanetz ha-chammah*, this corresponds to a certain amount of visible light in the sky which corresponds to a specific number of degrees of the sun below the horizon. This turns out to be when the sun is 16.1 degrees below the horizon (www.myzmanim.com). In order to determine when the same amount of light is present at other locations and at different times of year, we can calculate the time corresponding to when the sun is 16.1 degrees below the

The second term, *mi-sheyakkir*, can refer to two distinct times in the morning: *mi-sheyakkir bein techeilet le-lavan*, the time when one can distinguish between blue and white, or *mi-sheyireh et chaveiro be-richuk arba ammot ve-yakirenu*, the time when one can recognize an acquaintance a distance of four *ammot* away. Most authorities maintain these times are equivalent.[8] Whereas the calculation of *ammud ha-shachar* is derived mathematically from the Gemara as described above, determination of *mi-sheyakkir* has traditionally occurred by the assessment of qualified rabbis as they used natural light to determine when they could distinguish between blue and white or recognize an acquaintance. This method has led to variation in the assessment of the timing of *mi-sheyakkir*, ranging from 66 to 35 minutes before *hanetz ha-chammah*.[9] As with *ammud ha-shachar*, there is also a debate whether one should use a fixed number of minutes before *hanetz ha-chammah* to determine *mi-sheyakkir* or if it should be based on degrees of the sun below the horizon.

The final relevant time we will reference is *hanetz ha-chammah*, or sunrise, which occurs when the sun begins to shine its rays on the mountaintops.[10]

Because alculating these *zemanim* is complicated, it is suggested that one follow printed calendars and tables to know when *ammud ha-shachar*, *mi-sheyakkir*, and *hanetz ha-chammah* occur on any individual day.[11] In certain extenuating circumstances, it is possible that some *poskim* would allow relying on times not listed on the calendar which would make it easier to pray before starting an early rotation at the hospital. One is advised to speak to a halakhic authority to know when leniencies might apply.

---

      horizon. 16.1 degrees is the standard calculation of *ammud ha-shachar* used by www.myzmanim.com.

8   Yerushalmi *Berakhot* 1:2 records that these times are identical. This view is adopted by Ramban (*Milchamot Hashem, Berakhot* on *dappei ha-Rif* 8b, s.v. *aval be-shel shacharit*). See *Beit Yosef* (*Orach Chayyim* 58 s.v. *ve-chen katav*) for more opinions espousing this view. *Mishnah Berurah* (*Orach Chayyim* 58:2) writes this as well. However, Rabbeinu Yonah (*Berakhot* 4b in *dappei ha-Rif*, s.v. *amar Abaye*) assumes these times are different, and it appears *Arukh Ha-Shulchan* (*Orach Chayyim* 58:8) assumes these times are different as well.

9   A review of the different opinions can be found in R. Gil Student's *Posts Along the Way, Volume 1: Shuls* (Yashar Books, 2009, pp. 17–19; also available online at http://hirhurim.blogspot.com/2008/01/earliest-time-for-tal-lis-and-tefillin.html), as well as http://www.myzmanim.com/read/sources.aspx.

10   *Mishnah Berurah* 89:1.

11   One excellent resource which provides these times is the website MyZmanim (www.myzmanim.com).

Netilat Yadayim[12]

One who wakes up before *ammud ha-shachar* should wash one's hands and may recite the blessing.[13] In this scenario, authorities question whether *ruach ra'ah*, an evil spirit, descends on the hands after this time before *ammud ha-shachar*, thus necessitating re-washing of the hands after *ammud ha-shachar*. Rama,[14] therefore, advises that the hands should be washed again without a blessing after *ammud ha-shachar*.

Asher Yatzar and Elokai Neshamah

Rosh[15] writes that these blessings can be recited before *ammud ha-shachar*. *Beit Yosef*[16] cites Rosh and others that agree, and this appears to be the *halakhah*.[17]

Birkat Ha-Torah

There exists a debate between *rishonim* regarding recitation of *birkat ha-Torah* if one wakes up in the morning and studies Torah before *ammud ha-shachar*. Rosh[18] rules that one in this situation should recite the blessings because sleep creates a break between one day and the next. Rabbeinu Tam[19] rules that the blessings on the Torah are in effect from

---

12 This topic and the next three (*Asher Yatzar* and *Elokai Neshamah*, *Birkat Ha-Torah*, and *Tallit Gadol* and *Tallit Katan*) are discussed in greater detail in Chapter 5.

13 Rosh (cited in *Tur, Orach Chayyim* 47) writes that if one wakes up to learn Torah before *ammud ha-shachar* one should nevertheless recite the blessing over washing the hands.

14 *Orach Chayyim* 4:14. *Ishei Yisrael* (p. 20) writes that one who arises before *ammud ha-shachar* should wash hands immediately, and if one is ready to pray (does not need the restroom) the blessing should be recited then. If one is not ready to pray, one should wash hands after using the restroom and then make the blessing. If these washings took place before *ammud ha-shachar*, he writes that one should wash again three times without a blessing.

15 Cited in *Tur, Orach Chayyim* 47.

16 *Orach Chayyim* 47 s.v. *katav adoni avi z"l*.

17 *Shulchan Arukh, Orach Chayyim* 46:1 writes that one who awakes from sleep should recite *Elokai neshamah*, implying even if one wakes up before daytime.

18 *Berakhot* 1:13 and cited by *Tur, Orach Chayyim* 47.

19 *Tosafot Berakhot* 11b s.v. *she-kevar*.

morning to morning, and should therefore be delayed until *shacharit*.[20] *Shulchan Arukh*[21] rules like Rosh that one should recite *birkat ha-Torah*.

Tallit Gadol and Tallit Katan

In reference to a garment with *tzitzit* attached, the Torah writes *"u-re'item oto u-zekhartem et kol mitzvot Hashem,"* "You will see it and remember all of the commandments of Hashem."[22] Based on the words "you will see it," the Gemara[23] deduces that a *kesut laylah*, a nighttime garment, does not require *tzitzit*, as the garment cannot be seen at night. However, there is a debate among *rishonim* regarding the nature of this exemption. Rambam[24] writes that any garment worn at night is exempt from *tzitzit*. Rosh[25] and Rabbeinu Tam[26] disagree and write that this exemption relates more to the particular article of clothing than to the time of day the clothing is worn. In their opinion, a daytime garment is obligated in *tzitzit* even if worn at night, while a nighttime garment is exempt from *tzitzit* even if worn during the day. Ran[27] takes into account both considerations, namely the type of garment and also the time of day it is being worn. He writes that the only time a garment needs *tzitzit* attached is when a daytime garment is being worn during daytime hours.

The opinions of both Rambam and Rosh are cited by *Tur*.[28] *Shulchan Arukh*[29] also cites the opinions of both Rambam and Rosh, and does not favor one opinion over the other.[30] Regarding the blessing, Rama[31] invokes the principle of *safek berakhot lehakel*, we are lenient with regard to blessings in a case of doubt. Since we are in doubt whether to follow Rambam or Rosh, we should be lenient and only recite the blessing when indicated according to both authorities. Therefore, one should

20 See *Beit Yosef Orach Chayyim* 47 s.v. *ve-hamashkim ba-boker* for additional *rishonim* who debate this question.
21 *Orach Chayyim* 47:13.
22 Numbers 15:39.
23 *Menachot* 43a. This is taught in a Beraita in support of the opinion of R. Shimon to explain why the *mitzvah* of *tzitzit* is a time-bound, positive commandment such that women would be exempt.
24 *Hilkhot Tzitzit* 3:7.
25 *Hilkhot Tzitzit* 1, printed in the end of Gemara *Menachot*.
26 *Menachot* 40b, s.v. *mishum kesut laylah*.
27 *Kiddushin* 14b in *dappei ha-Rif*.
28 *Orach Chayyim* 18.
29 *Orach Chayyim* 18:1.
30 In *Beit Yosef* (*Orach Chayyim* 18 s.v. *katav*) he writes that practically he favors the opinion of Rambam, but in *Shulchan Arukh* he cites the opinions of both Rambam and Rosh.
31 *Orach Chayyim* 18:1.

only recite the blessing on the *tzitzit* during the daytime on a garment designated for daytime use.

Determination of Daytime with Respect to *Tzitzit*

Given that we only recite a blessing on the *tzitzit* when wearing a garment during the daytime, we must determine when daytime is with regard to *tzitzit*. Rambam[32] writes that the blessing can be recited after *mi-sheyakkir*, the time when one can distinguish the blue threads from the white threads of the *tzitzit*. *Beit Yosef*[33] cites the opinion of Rambam and explains that although this time is not explicitly written with regards to *tzitzit*, perhaps Rambam learned it from the discussion in the Gemara regarding the earliest time to recite *shema*.[34] Rabbeinu Yonah[35] also writes that it is possible that the *mitzvah* of *tzitzit* begins at *mi-sheyakkir*. Mordekhai[36] writes that, based on the verse *u-re'item oto*, the *mitzvah* begins after *ammud ha-shachar*.[37]

Shulchan Arukh[38] writes that one can recite the blessing as early as *mi-sheyakkir*. Rama[39] writes that if one wears the *tzitzit* after *ammud ha-shachar*, some say one can make a blessing at that time (even though it is before *mi-sheyakkir*), and he writes that this is the common practice. *Mishnah Berurah*[40] cites multiple authorities regarding the practical *halakhah*, and advises that one should avoid reciting the blessing before *mi-sheyakkir*. He writes, however, that if the blessing was even recited before *ammud ha-shachar*, one would not need to repeat the blessing later, because perhaps the law is in accordance with Rosh that a daytime garment is obligated in *tzitzit* even at night. *Arukh Ha-Shulchan*[41] takes a more lenient approach. He reasons that *tzitzit* is similar to

---

32 *Hilkhot Tzitzit* 3:8.

33 *Orach Chayyim* 18 s.v. *mah she-katav ha-Rambam*.

34 See also *Biur Ha-Gra, Orach Chayyim* 18:3 s.v. *me-eimatai* who learns the source for Rambam from *Menachot* 43b.

35 *Berakhot* 4b in *dappei ha-Rif* s.v. *amar*. He understands that the time that one can recognize a friend from four *ammot* away is a different time than when one can distinguish between the blue and white of the *tzitzit*, and he offers both times as possibilities for the earliest time for the *mitzvah* of *tzitzit*.

36 *Megillah* 801.

37 He is quoting this as the opinion of Raavyah, and he agrees. Raavyah explains that while other *mitzvot* dependent on daytime hours should not begin until a later time (usually *hanetz ha-chammah*), since the verse regarding *tzitzit* says *u-re'item oto*, one can begin the *mitzvah* at an earlier time, which he argues must be *ammud ha-shachar*.

38 *Orach Chayyim* 18:3.

39 *Orach Chayyim* 18:3.

40 *Orach Chayyim* 18:10.

41 *Orach Chayyim* 18:9.

other daytime *mitzvot* which should ideally be performed after *hanetz ha-chammah* but can still be fulfilled after *ammud ha-shachar* (see below, for instance, regarding *shemoneh esrei*). Therefore, he rules that if one is wearing *tzitzit* just after *ammud ha-shachar*, one makes the blessing at that time. R. Moshe Feinstein maintains the blessing should not be made until after *mi-sheyakkir*.[42]

Tefillin

In practice, *tefillin* are not worn at night. There is a debate in the Gemara and *rishonim*, however, regarding how this law is derived and whether it is a Torah or rabbinic law. The Gemara[43] notes that the Torah, in a section discussing Passover-related *mitzvot* as well as the *mitzvah* of *tefillin*, states that "this statute" shall be observed *mi-yamim yamimah*, "from year to year." While the plain meaning of this phrase refers to observing the *mitzvah* for eternity, the use of the word *yom*, day, suggests that the *mitzvah* is to be performed only during the day. However, the Gemara cites a debate regarding to which "statute" the verse refers. R. Yosi Ha-Gelili understands the verse to refer to the *tefillin*, and the reference to daytime teaches that, according to Torah law, the *tefillin* are only worn during the day and not at night. According to R. Akiva, this verse refers to the Passover sacrifice, and he understands that Torah law permits donning the *tefillin* at night. However, even R. Akiva does not appear to permit donning the *tefillin* at night in practice, as evidenced by the following story in the Gemara.[44] Ravina was sitting before R. Ashi, and it became dark and R. Ashi put on his *tefillin*.[45] Ravina asked R. Ashi if he was wearing the tefillin to protect them, and R. Ashi answered that he was. However, Ravina realized that R. Ashi was not actually wearing them to protect them, and he understood that R. Ashi holds that the law is one can wear them at night, but we do not teach this law to others.[46] Although R. Ashi appears to hold that one can wear *tefillin* at night, per R. Akiva, he nevertheless does not advise this in practice.

42 *Iggerot Moshe, Orach Chayyim* 4:6.
43 *Menachot* 36b.
44 The story is related in *Menachot* 36b shortly after the debate between R. Yossi Ha-Gelili and R. Akiva is cited, and appears to support the view of R. Akiva.
45 This is consistent with the text of the Gemara we have and according to Rashi (s.v. *ve-im leshomran*). However, other *rishonim* (Rif, *Hilkhot Tefillin* 9a and Rosh *Hilkhot Tefillin* 17) had a variant text which states that R. Ashi did not put on *tefillin* after dark but merely kept them on from beforehand from when it was still daytime. According to this text, it is more problematic to don *tefillin* at night than to keep them on from before.
46 The Talmudic phrase is *halakhah ve-ein morin ken*.

Interpretations of *Menachot* 36b

Rashi understands the practice of R. Ashi that we advise others to avoid wearing *tefillin* at night because one may inadvertently fall asleep in them and thereby defile them.[47] *Tosafot* write that we rule according to R. Akiva and R. Ashi that, according to Torah law, *tefillin* can be worn at night, but there is a rabbinic decree to refrain from wearing them at night lest one fall asleep while wearing them.[48] Rif[49] and Rosh[50] also write that the law is in accordance with R. Ashi. Rambam,[51] however, disagrees with these *rishonim* and rules in accordance with R. Yosi Ha-Gelili that, according to Torah law, the time for putting on *tefillin* is during the day and not at night.

Tur[52] writes that according to Torah law one can wear *tefillin* at night, but one should nevertheless not put them on at night.[53] *Shulchan Arukh*[54] similarly writes that it is forbidden to put on *tefillin* at night lest one fall asleep in them. *Mishneh Berurah*[55] explains that although we maintain that Torah law permits wearing *tefillin* at night, rabbinic law forbids it.

Earliest Time to Put On *Tefillin* under Normal Circumstances

It emerges from our discussion that according to rabbinic law one should not, under normal circumstances, put on *tefillin* at night. We will see shortly that exceptions to this rule do exist. Under normal circumstances, the earliest time of the day one is allowed to put on *tefillin*

---

47 *Menachot* 36b s.v. *ve-ein morin ken.* He only explicitly states that one may fall asleep in them, but the implication is that one will pass gas when asleep and thereby defile the *tefillin.*
48 *Menachot* 36b s.v. *ve-shamarta et ha-chukah ha-zot le-moadah.*
49 *Hilkhot Tefillin* 9a, found in the back of Gemara *Menachot.*
50 *Hilkhot Tefillin* 16, found in the back of Gemara *Menachot.*
51 *Hilkhot Tefillin* 4:10.
52 *Orach Chayyim* 30.
53 *Tur*, based on the variant text explained above, interprets R. Ashi as referring to a case where one had *tefillin* on before nighttime and kept them on into the night. In this case, it is not technically forbidden to keep wearing the *tefillin*, but *ein morin ken.* However, the case where one initially lays *tefillin* at night is explicitly forbidden. This formulation of the law, with the distinction between initially placing the *tefillin* versus keeping them on from beforehand, is similarly written by *Shulchan Arukh, Orach Chayyim* 30:2.
54 *Orach Chayyim* 30:2.
55 30:4.

is stated clearly in the Gemara[56] by Abaye as the time one can recognize an acquaintance from a distance of four *ammot*. This opinion is not debated in the Gemara and it is accepted by the *rishonim*[57] and *Shulchan Arukh*.[58] Rabbeinu Yonah[59] writes that the reason the *mitzvah* of *tefillin* begins at this time is based on the verse: "Then all the peoples of the earth will see that the Name of Hashem is proclaimed over you, and they will revere you."[60]

The Case of Early Travel

The Gemara[61] cites a Beraita which indicates that in certain circumstances *tefillin* may be worn even earlier than *mi-sheyakkir*. It states that if a person wakes up early in the morning to travel and fears that the *tefillin* will become lost, he can put them on, and when the proper time arrives he may touch the *tefillin* and recite the blessing. This Beraita is cited by Rif[62] and Rosh[63] as the *halakhah*. However, they both mention the case of early travel without requiring the fear of the *tefillin* becoming lost. It is possible that their text of the Beraita lacked this stipulation.[64] In any event, it appears that Rif and Rosh understand that the concern that one will fall asleep wearing the *tefillin* at night is not a factor when one wakes up early to travel.

Tur[65] writes in the name of Rosh that if one must travel, he may put on the *tefillin* before *mi-sheyakkir*, and after *mi-sheyakkir* he may touch the *tefillin* and make the blessing. *Tur* also quotes the opinion of Rabbeinu Peretz that the blessing can be made immediately upon wearing them even though it is still night.[66] *Shulchan Arukh*[67] rules that if one wants

56 *Berakhot* 9b.
57 Rambam, *Hilkhot Tefillin* 4:10; Rif, *Hilkhot Tefillin* 9a; Rosh, *Hilkhot Tefillin* 17.
58 *Orach Chayyim* 30:1.
59 *Berakhot* 4b in *dappei ha-Rif*, s.v. *amar Abaye le-tefillin ka-acherim*.
60 Deuteronomy 28:10.
61 *Menachot* 36a.
62 *Hilkhot Tefillin* 8b.
63 *Hilkhot Tefillin* 16.
64 See *Beit Yosef* (*Orach Chayyim* 30 s.v. *ve-im tzarikh lelech la-derekh yakhol lehanicham kodem zemanam be-lo berakhah*) who appeared to have a version of the Beraita consistent with Rif and Rosh.
65 *Orach Chayyim* 30.
66 *Beit Yosef* (*Orach Chayyim* 30 s.v. *ve-haRabbeinu Peretz katav keivan de-kayma lan de-laylah zeman tefillin hu*) writes that Rabbeinu Peretz understood that the Beraita is in accordance with the opinion that nighttime is not the time for *tefillin* on a Torah level. He understands that according to the opinion that nighttime is a time for *tefillin* from the Torah perspective, the blessing can be recited even at night in cases of early travel.
67 *Orach Chayyim* 30:3.

to travel early in the morning, he may put on the *tefillin*, and when the correct time arrives, he may touch the *tefillin* and recite the blessing. *Shulchan Arukh* adds that in this scenario, there is no concern that he will fall asleep wearing the *tefillin*, since he has left his home to travel. *Mishnah Berurah*[68] comments that this leniency applies to one traveling by foot or riding an animal but would not apply to one traveling in a wagon, as the fear that he may fall asleep still exists.

R. Moshe Feinstein[69] addresses a case where one is at work all day and is unable to put on *tefillin* during the day, but he could put on *tefillin* before *ammud ha-shachar* (and will be able to pray later without *tefillin*). He writes that in this scenario, one should put on *tefillin* before *ammud ha-shachar*, and can even recite the blessing[70] at this time, in part because one will not take the *mitzvah* seriously if a blessing is not recited.[71]

Birkhot Ha-Shachar

Rosh[72] writes that one who wakes up before *ammud ha-shachar* can recite all of *birkhot ha-shachar* except for the blessing of *ha-noten la-sekhvi vinah* which should be recited during the day. This view is accepted by *Tur*[73] and *Shulchan Arukh*.[74] *Mishnah Berurah*[75] writes that according to most *acharonim*, even the blessing of *ha-noten la-sekhvi vinah* can be recited before daytime, but he cites those who maintain that ideally one should not do this.

---

68 30:14.
69 *Iggerot Moshe*, Orach *Chayyim* 1:10.
70 In an earlier *teshuvah* (*Iggerot Moshe*, Orach *Chayyim* 1:10), R. Feinstein advises that it is better for a *talmid chakham* to refrain from saying the blessing at this time, as there is no concern that he will take the *mitzvah* less seriously. However, in a *teshuvah* written many years later (*Iggerot Moshe*, Orach *Chayyim* 4:6) he writes that is possible that even the *talmid chakham* should recite the blessing to avoid taking the *mitzvah* less seriously.
71 R. Feinstein takes into account the opinion of Rabbeinu Peretz as cited by *Tur* above. He also writes that the variant text utilized by *Tur* and *Shulchan Arukh* does not conform to the text possessed by the majority of *rishonim*. According to the text possessed by most *rishonim*, the story about R. Ashi teaches that there is no technical prohibition to lay *tefillin* at night, but *ein morin ken*.
72 Cited by *Tur*, *Orach Chayyim* 47.
73 *Orach Chayyim* 47.
74 *Orach Chayyim* 47:13.
75 47:31.

Korbanot

Rosh[76] writes that *parshat ha-tamid* should be recited after dawn because its recitation is in place of the sacrifice which took place during the day. *Tur*[77] rules in accordance with Rosh and writes that ne should recite all the *parshiyot ha-korbanot* during the daytime. *Shulchan Arukh*[78] also rules that the *parshiyot ha-korbanot* should be recited during the daytime. *Mishnah Berurah*[79] adds that the *mishnayot* recited following the *parshat ha-tamid* should also be recited during the daytime as they also take the place of the sacrifices. However, he writes[80] that *parshat ha-kiyor* and *parshat terumat ha-deshen* can be recited before daytime. If one is pressed for time, he allows recitation of all the *korbanot* while it is still night.[81]

Pesukei De-Zimra

The earliest time for reciting this portion of the *tefillah* is not delineated in the Gemara and appears to be a debate between later authorities. Many authorities maintain that if one pressed for time *pesukei de-zimra* can be recited before *mi-sheyakkir*,[82] and others write that it can even be recited before *ammud ha-shachar*.[83]

Birkhot Keriat Shema

Initially, one might suspect that the earliest time one can recite the blessing of *shema* should follow the earliest time for reciting *shema* itself, which will be described below. Indeed, Rashba writes that in a pressing situation one may recite both *shema* and its blessings – including the blessing of *yotzer or* – after *ammud ha-shachar*.[84] Rashba explicitly includes the blessing of *yotzer or* which refers to the creation of

---

76 Cited by *Tur, Orach Chayyim* 47.
77 *Orach Chayyim* 1 and *Orach Chayyim* 47.
78 *Orach Chayyim* 1:6 and 47:13.
79 47:32.
80 1:17.
81 1:17 in the name of *Peri Megadim*.
82 *Biur Halakhah* (58 s.v. *zeman keriat shema*) writes that ideally one should recite *pesukei de-zimra* after *mi-sheyakkir* while wearing *tallit* and *tefillin*, but in a time-pressing situation one can recite until *barkhu* before *mi-sheyakkir* and then put on *tefillin* and continue with the blessings of *shema*. R. Ovadia Yosef writes in *Yechavveh Da'at* 2:8 that *pesukei de-zimra* should not be recited before *ammud ha-shachar*.
83 *Ishei Yisra'el* (p. 156) writes that it is permitted to recite *pesukei de-zimra* before *ammud ha-shachar*. See footnote 48 there for various opinions.
84 Rashba *Berakhot* 8b s.v. *u-le'iynan keriah* and s.v. *ketzaro shel davar*.

light, stating that there is enough light outside after *ammud ha-shachar* to recite this blessing. This view is adopted by *Shulchan Arukh*[85] as well. However, *Magen Avraham*[86] writes that one should not recite the blessing of *yotzer or* until after the time one can distinguish between blue and white (*mi-sheyakkir*), and this view is supported by Gra,[87] *Pri Megadim*,[88] and *Mishnah Berurah*.[89] These authorities maintain, however, that in a pressing situation the other blessings of *shema* may be recited after *ammud ha-shachar*.[90]

Shema

The command to recite *shema* daily is Biblical in origin, as the phrase in the first paragraph of *shema* itself attests that it should be recited "when you lie down and when you rise."[91] The Gemara infers from here that there is a Biblical obligation to recite *shema* each morning and night.[92] This verse which teaches the obligation to recite *shema* is also used by the Gemara to teach the appropriate times for its recitation. Hence, regarding the morning recitation, the Mishnah and Gemara set out to define the time of day when most people arise from sleep,[93] and there is a parallel discussion regarding the nighttime *shema* as well.[94]

The First Talmudic Source: *Berakhot* 9b

The Mishnah[95] cites a debate regarding the earliest time *shema* may be recited. The first opinion states that the earliest time is when one can distinguish between *tekhelet*-colored wool and white wool, while R. Eliezer holds the earliest time is when one can distinguish between

---

85 *Orach Chayyim* 58:3.
86 *Orach Chayyim* 58:5.
87 *Orach Chayyim* 58:3 s.v. *ve-gam shappir*.
88 *Eshel Avraham, Orach Chayyim* 58:5 s.v. *mikri*.
89 58:17.
90 They maintain that the blessings of *shema* may be broken up if necessary, such that *yozter or* is postponed until after *mi-sheyakkir* while the other blessings can be recited together with *shema* after *ammud ha-shachar*. See footnote 159 below.
91 Deuteronomy 6:6–7.
92 *Berakhot* 2a.
93 Rabbeinu Yonah (*Berakhot* 4b in *dappei ha-Rif*, s.v. *me-eimatai korin et shema be-shacharit*) writes explicitly that the Mishnah's discussion of the earliest time to recite the morning *shema* is dependent on when people begin to wake up in the morning.
94 *Berakhot* 2a.
95 *Berakhot* 9b.

tekhelet-colored wool and leek-colored wool.[96] *Tekhelet* is a blue dye derived from a sea creature called *chilazon*, and the color of leek is a green-blue color. The first opinion of the Mishnah maintains the time to recite *shema* is earlier than according to R. Eliezer, as it takes less light to distinguish between blue and white than to distinguish between blue and green. The Gemara, commenting on this Mishnah, lists additional opinions regarding the earliest time to recite *shema*.[97] One of these times, attributed to the opinion of *Acherim*, is that the morning *shema* can be recited from the time one can recognize his friend[98] a distance of four *ammot* away.[99] R. Huna says that the *halakhah* is in accordance with *Acherim*, while Abaye maintains one should recite the morning *shema* like the *vatikin*, the devout ones.[100] The Gemara describes that the *vatikin* would recite *shema* just before sunrise in order to be able to say *shemoneh esrei* right at sunrise.

Most authorities maintain that the amount of light to distinguish between blue and white is the same as the amount of light to recognize a friend four *ammot* away.[101] Thus, according to the conclusion of the Gemara, R. Huna maintains the earliest time to recite *shema* is *mi-sheyakkir*, while it appears that Abaye holds the earliest time is just before *hanetz ha-chammah*. However, there is a debate among *rishonim* whether R. Huna and Abaye are indeed arguing, or if Abaye agrees one

96 One might wonder why the Mishnah formulates the times in this manner, especially given the fact that it is trying to determine the time when people arise from bed. Ramban (*Milchamot Hashem, Berakhot* 2b in *dappei ha-Rif*) writes that we are indeed trying to determine the time when people rise in the morning. He references the Gemara in *Menachot* 43b which links the time for reciting the morning *shema* with the ability to see the *tzitzit*. The Gemara bases this on the verse which we recite as part of *shema* (Numbers 15:39): "And you shall see it and remember all the commandments of Hashem." Among many other interpretations of this verse, the Gemara infers that the time to recite the morning *shema* is linked to the time one can see the strings of the *tzitzit*, which are composed of white and blue strings. Thus, the Gemara understands that the verse "and you shall see it" is used to inform us when to assume that most people are rising from bed in the morning.

97 *Berakhot* 9b.

98 *Tosafot* (*Berakhot* 9b s.v. *acherim omrim ad she-yireh chavero*), based on the Yerushalmi, comment that the friend cannot be a very dear friend because he would be recognized even in the middle of the night, but rather it must be an acquaintance that one knows but is not too familiar with.

99 *Ammot* are a measurement of arm-breadths. Four *ammot* is approximately the length of six to eight feet.

100 Rashi ad loc s.v. *vatikin* describes them as people of humility who cherish *mitzvot*.

101 See footnote 8 above.

can recite *shema* from *mi-sheyakkir* but he is stating that the ideal time is just before sunrise.[102]

The Second Talmudic Source: *Berakhot* 8b–9a

The next source we will analyze implies that one can recite *shema* even before *mi-sheyakkir*. The Gemara discusses two versions of a statement made by R. Shimon ben Yochai.[103] In one version, he permitted the nighttime *shema* to be recited before *ammud ha-shachar* and the morning *shema* after *ammud ha-shachar*. The Gemara explains that the morning *shema* can be recited after *ammud ha-shachar* because starting at this time people begin to rise from bed. In the next version of the statement, he permitted the nighttime *shema* to be recited before *hanetz ha-chammah* and the morning *shema* after *hanetz ha-chammah*. In reference to both versions separately, R. Yehoshua ben Levi rules in accordance with R. Shimon ben Yochai.

The ruling which emerges from this Gemara is that according to one version, the morning *shema* can be recited after *ammud ha-shachar*, while the other version implies that *shema* should not be recited until after *hanetz ha-chammah*. The simple understanding is that these two versions represent opposing views and disagree with one another. In other words, the first version views the period between *ammud ha-shachar* and *hanetz ha-chammah* as a time when people wake up, while the second version views this time period as a time when people are asleep. One opinion in *Tosafot*[104] interprets the Gemara in this way, and *Tosafot* rule in accordance with the version permitting the morning *shema* to be recited after *ammud ha-shachar*.[105] However, another explanation of *Tosafot*[106] and most *rishonim*[107] view these two versions as complementary and understand that the time period between *ammud*

---

102 Rosh (*Berakhot* 1:10), Rabbeinu Yonah (*Berakhot* 4b in *dappei ha-Rif*, s.v. *tanya*), Tosafot (*Berakhot* 9b s.v. *le-keriat shema ke-vatikin*), and Rashba (*Berakhot* 8b s.v. *ketzaro shel davar*) state that there is no debate between R. Huna and Abaye, but rather Abaye is stating the ideal time while R. Huna (and R. Yehoshua ben Levi, see discussion below about *Berakhot* 8b–9a) is stating the less ideal but nonetheless allowed time. *Beit Yosef* (*Orach Chayyim* 58 *u-mah she-katav rabbenu ve-chen katav ha-Rambam*) writes that Rambam and Rif assume there is a debate between R. Huna and Abaye, and they rule that ideally one should follow the opinion of Abaye.

103 *Berakhot* 8b–9a.

104 *Berakhot* 8b s.v. *lo le-olam leilya hu* and 9b s.v. *le-olam yemama hu*.

105 *Tosafot* 9b s.v. *le-keriat shema ke-vatikin*.

106 *Berakhot* 9a s.v. *le-olam yemama hu*, second answer.

107 Rif (*Berakhot* 2a); Rashba (commentary to *Berakhot* 8b s.v. *ketzaro shel davar*); Rambam (*Hilkhot Keriat Shema* 1:10 and 1:12); Rosh (*Berakhot* 1:9); Ramban (*Milchamot Hashem* in *dappei ha-Rif Berakhot* 2a); and *Tosafot* (*Berakhot* 9a s.v. *le-olam yemama hu*, second answer).

ha-shachar and *hanetz ha-chammah* can be considered a time when people are asleep and also a time when people wake up. Therefore, they rule that one could recite both the evening and morning *shema* during this time period.[108]

At first glance this Gemara stands in opposition to the previously cited Mishnah and Gemara which permit reciting the morning *shema* no earlier than *mi-sheyakkir*. Because of this contradiction, *Tosafot*[109] on this Gemara comment that although this Gemara seems to say that one can recite the morning *shema* after *ammud ha-shachar*, it must not mean immediately after this time, but rather that one must wait some time, until at least after *mi-sheyakkir*. However, most *rishonim*,[110] including *Tosafot* to *Berakhot* 9b,[111] understand that one could fulfill the obligation to recite the morning *shema* even immediately after *ammud ha-shachar*. These *rishonim* view the opinions of R. Yehoshua ben Levi (*Berakhot* 8b–9a) and R. Huna and Abaye (*Berakhot* 9b) as complementary, and formulate the practical ruling as follows: one should ideally recite the morning *shema* just before *hanetz ha-chammah* like the *vatikin* (per Abaye). The next best time is from *mi-sheyakkir* until *hanetz ha-chammah* (per R. Huna). If this is not possible, many rule that one has still fulfilled the *mitzvah* by reciting *shema* in between *ammud ha-shachar* and *mi-sheyakkir* (per R. Yehoshua ben Levi). These *rishonim* list early morning travel as an example when one is permitted to recite *shema* immediately after *ammud ha-shachar*.

Further Characterizing the Circumstances when *Shema* Can Be Recited Immediately after *Ammud Ha-Shachar*

While the Gemara *Berakhot* 8b–9a implies that for travel, *shema* can be recited immediately after *ammud ha-shachar*, this implication is challenged by a Beraita.[112] According to the Beraita, one who wakes up early to travel can fulfill the *mitzvot* of *shofar*, *lulav*, and *megillah*, and later when the time for *shema* arrives it may be recited. Certainly, one cannot fulfill the *mitzvot* of *shofar*, *lulav*, and *megillah* before the day begins at *ammud ha-shachar*, and yet the Beraita implies that at this time, immediately after *ammud ha-shachar*, *shema* may not be recited. This Beraita

---

108 Rosh (*Berakhot* 1:9) writes that one could not recite both the nighttime and morning *shema* during this time period on a given day, as this is a contradiction.

109 *Berakhot* 8b s.v. *lo le-olam leilya hu*.

110 Rif (*Berakhot* 2a–2b), Rashba (*Berakhot* 8b s.v. *u-le'inyan keriah shel shachar*), Rambam (*Hilkhot Keriat Shema* 1:12), Rosh (*Berakhot* 1:9), and *Tosafot* (*Berakhot* 9a s.v. *le-olam yemama hu* second answer).

111 s.v. *le-keriat shema ke-vatikin*.

112 Gemara *Berakhot* 30a.

is troubling for the majority of *rishonim* quoted above who maintain that *shema* may be recited immediately after *ammud ha-shachar* in cases of travel.

Beit Yosef[113] cites multiple *rishonim* who explain that there are different types of travel. According to Rashba,[114] permission is granted to recite *shema* immediately after *ammud ha-shachar* only when the travel is dangerous because of thieves or wild animals. In this case, since one cannot concentrate even on the beginning of *shema* if one recites it while traveling,[115] it is permitted to recite *shema* immediately after *ammud ha-shachar*, before traveling. However, the Beraita is discussing a case in which travel is not complicated by wild animals or thieves. In this case, since one will be able to concentrate on *shema* even during the travel, one must wait until at least after *mi-sheyakkir* to recite *shema*. Rabbeinu Yonah[116] writes along these lines as well. He states that one could only recite *shema* immediately after *ammud ha-shachar* when the caravan is in a rush and will not wait for one to say *shema* when the ideal time arrives. However, if the caravan is not in a rush and one will be able to recite *shema* during the ideal time while en route, that would be preferred. *Beit Yosef* also quotes the opinion of Mahari Abuhab who understands *Tur* in a similar manner. *Tur*[117] writes that a person who needs to travel (*"she-tzarich lehachzik ba-derekh"*) can recite *shema* immediately after *ammud ha-shachar*. The word *lehachzik* means "to grip," and Mahari Abuhab argues that this language implies that one could only recite *shema* at this time when one is forced to rush in one's travels in a way that would preclude reciting *shema* in the proper way at the ideal time.

Despite this analysis, Rif[118] and Rambam[119] rule that even if one was not in a pressing situation but rather chose to recite *shema* at this time for convenience, one nevertheless fulfills the obligation to recite *shema* if it was recited after *ammud ha-shachar*. *Tur* also writes that one who recited *shema* before *mi-sheyakkir* fulfills the obligation as long as it was recited after *ammud ha-shachar*.[120] However, *Tur* adds that one should not become accustomed to this. *Beit Yosef*[121] understands the caveat of *Tur* as stemming from logic since the dispensation to recite *shema* immediately after *ammud ha-shachar* was only granted

---

113 *Orach Chayyim* 58 s.v. *mi she-hu anus.*
114 *Berakhot* 8b s.v. *u-le'inyan pesak.*
115 More specifically, from the beginning of *shema* until the words *"al levavekha."*
116 *Berakhot* 2b s.v. *i nami.*
117 *Tur Orach Chayyim* 58.
118 *Berakhot* 2b.
119 *Hilkhot Keriat Shema* 1:12.
120 *Orach Chayyim* 58.
121 *Orach Chayyim* 58 s.v. *mah she-katav rabbeinu ve-hu she-lo yehe ragil la'asot ken.*

in pressing situations. *Bach*[122] writes that the caveat of *Tur* appears to emerge from the Gemara.[123] He suggests that in a case when one can avoid reciting *shema* immediately after *ammud ha-shachar* but chooses to do so anyway, this should only happen infrequently, as in once per month. However, he adds that if one is in a pressing situation even on a frequent basis one may recite *shema* immediately after *ammud ha-shachar* each time because one has no other option.

The Ruling of *Shulchan Arukh* and Later Authorities

Shulchan Arukh[124] writes that the time to recite *shema* begins at *mi-sheyakkir*, but the most ideal time is just before *hanetz ha-chammah*. He continues that one who is subject to circumstances beyond one's control could recite *shema* immediately after *ammud ha-shachar*.[125] He uses travel as an example of such circumstances, but rules like Rashba and Rabbeinu Yonah that the travel must be such that one cannot concentrate even on the beginning of *shema*[126] if one were to recite it in the ideal time. He adds that if one recited *shema* immediately after *ammud ha-shachar* even without being a case of pressing circumstances, one has still fulfilled the obligation. *Mishnah Berurah*[127] rules in favor of *Bach* that one should only recite *shema* in between *ammud ha-shachar* and *mi-sheyakkir* as infrequently as once per month if it is avoidable, but if one is frequently in a pressing situation it is permissible even on a frequent basis.

Semikhut Geulah Le-Tefillah

The principle of *semikhut geulah le-tefillah*, the juxtaposition of redemption and prayer, refers to the practice of reciting *shema* and its blessings (which includes the blessing "*ga'al yisra'el*," referring to Hashem as the

---

122 *Orach Chayyim* 58 s.v. *u-mah she-katav ve-hu she-lo yehe ragil la'asot ken*.

123 The Gemara (*Yoma* 37b) relates that one who recites *shema* with the people in the *mishmar* (group of *kohanim* responsible for the priestly activities in the Temple) does not fulfill his obligation. Surely the *kohanim* were reciting *shema* after dawn, and yet the Gemara describes that one who joins them does not fulfill his obligation. *Bach* (*Orach Chayyim* 58 s.v. *u-mah she-katav ve-hu she-lo yehe ragil la'asot ken*) suggests that according to *Tur*, the Gemara refers to one who recites *shema* at this time on a daily basis and the Gemara teaches that it is forbidden to become accustomed to reciting *shema* at this time. Rather, suggests *Bach*, it is only permitted on occasion, as in once per month, unless one has no other option.

124 *Orach Chayyim* 58:1–4.

125 The halakhic term used by *Shulchan Arukh* is *anus*.

126 Until "*al levavekha*." However, Rama (*Orach Chayyim* 89:8) understands concentration is only needed for the first verse.

127 *Orach Chayyim* 58:19.

Redeemer) immediately before shemoneh *esrei* (known in the Gemara's parlance as "*tefillah*," "prayer"). The Gemara[128] praises a person who performs *semikhut ge'ulah le-tefillah*, and generally one should avoid breaking this practice. Whether or not a person should split the segments of *shacharit* in order to pray at the proper time before going to work will depend on the particular circumstances related to that case and should be posed individually to a qualified halakhic authority.

Shemoneh Esrei

The *shemoneh esrei* is the central part of the three daily prayer services. The origin of this prayer is subject to a debate in the Gemara.[129] Initially the Gemara writes that R. Yossi ben R. Chanina maintains it was established by the patriarchs Avraham, Yitzchak, and Ya'akov, while R. Yehoshua ben Levi maintains it was established by the Men of the Great Assembly and patterned after the sacrifices in the Temple. In the conclusion of the Gemara, however, both opinions maintain that the prayers were patterned after the sacrifices. R. Yosi ben R. Chanina posits that the patriarchs initially established the prayers, but the rabbis later patterned the timing of their recital after the sacrifices of the Temple.

Timing of the Morning Sacrifice in the Temple

Thus, the *shemoneh esrei* we say each morning is patterned after the morning sacrifice that was brought daily in the Temple. Therefore, in order to determine the earliest time one is permitted to say the *shemoneh esrei*, it seems logical to search for the earliest time the morning sacrifice was permitted to be slaughtered. Two separate *mishnayot* will shed light on this question. The first describes the protocol on *Yom Kippur* for determining when to begin the morning sacrifice in the Temple. The Mishnah[130] describes how the *kohanim* would only begin the morning sacrifice after determining that the entire eastern sky had lit up.[131]

128 *Berakhot* 9b.
129 *Berakhot* 26b.
130 Mishnah *Yoma* 3:1.
131 The Mishnah describes that during the morning of the *Yom Kippur* service, an administrator would say to the assembled *kohanim*: go out and see if the time for slaughtering the morning sacrifice has arrived. If it had arrived, the person who saw it would say "*barkai*," meaning that the first shimmer of light was visible in the sky. The Mishnah then writes that Matityah ben Shmuel says: all of the eastern sky has lit up. There are two general approaches to understanding the opinion of Matityah ben Shmuel:
   1. Rambam (Commentary to Mishnah, *Yoma* 3:1) and R. Ovadiah me-Bartenura (commentary to *Yoma* 3:1) write that there is a debate between the first opinion of the Mishnah and Matityah ben Shmuel.

There is a debate whether this is the same time as *ammud ha-shachar*, or whether *ammud ha-shachar* occurs earlier when only a small amount of light is visible in the sky.[132] According to either view, this time is certainly before *hanetz ha-chammah*.

The second Mishnah discusses the timing of *mitzvot* which should be performed during the daytime.[133] The Mishnah lists daytime *mitzvot* such as reading the *megillah* and performing circumcision, and states that ideally they should be performed after *hanetz ha-chammah*, but if they were performed from *ammud ha-shachar* the obligation has been satisfied. This Mishnah does not explicitly mention the morning sacrifice, but this *mitzvah* is also dependent on the daytime.[134] In combination, these two *mishnayot* demonstrate that the morning sacrifice, after which the morning prayer service is patterned, was permitted to be slaughtered in the Temple starting from *ammud ha-shachar* or perhaps only after the entire eastern sky was lit up, but certainly before sunrise.

Talmudic Sources and Opinions of *Rishonim*

Despite the fact that the morning sacrifice could have been slaughtered well before sunrise, the Gemara[135] is quite clear that the ideal time to say *shemoneh esrei* in the morning is just after *hanetz ha-chammah*. To

---

The first opinion maintains the slaughtering began at an earlier time when the sky just begins to light up, whereas Matityah ben Shmuel requires the later time, when the entire eastern sky is lit up. Rambam (Commentary to Mishnah ibid. and *Mishnah Torah, Hilkhot Temidin U-Musafin* 1:2) rules in accordance with Matityah ben Shmuel.

2. Rashi (*Menachot* 100a s.v. *Matityah ben Shmuel*) and Tosafot (*Menachot* 100a s.v. *Matityah ben Shmuel omer*) understand that Matityah ben Shmuel was the administrator of the lots in the Temple and is functioning in this role in the Mishnah. After one *kohen* would say "*barkai*," Matityah ben Shmuel would ask: has the whole eastern sky lit up?

According to both explanations of this Mishnah, the conclusion is that the slaughtering took place only after the entire eastern sky lit up.

132 See *Biur Halakhah* (89 s.v. *ve-im hitpallel me-she'alah ammud ha-shachar*) for extensive discussion. Among other opinions cited there, he writes that *Magen Avraham* maintains that *ammud ha-shachar* occurs when a small amount of light begins to shine in the eastern sky, whereas *he'ir penei ha-mizrach* requires more light in the eastern sky. However, he writes that according to Gra, whenever authorities refer to *ammud ha-shachar* they actually mean that the entire eastern sky has lit up.

133 *Megillah* 2:4.

134 Rashi (*Yoma* 28a s.v. *zeman ha-shechitah*) learns that slaughtering of sacrifices should take place during the day based on the verse in Leviticus 19:6, "on the day of your slaughtering."

135 Gemara *Berakhot* 26a and 9b.

support this ruling, the Gemara[136] cites the verse,[137] "They will fear you with the sun."[138]

Several *rishonim* understand that while the ideal time to pray is at *hanetz ha-chammah*, one has fulfilled the obligation if one prayed after *ammud ha-shachar*. Rosh[139] writes this, and he explicitly makes the connection to the morning sacrifice in the Temple as proof that praying after *ammud ha-shachar*[140] fulfills the obligation. The ruling of Rosh is echoed by *Tur*.[141] *Tosafot* also imply that the morning prayer can begin after *ammud ha-shachar*.[142] Rambam[143] writes that the ideal time is with *hanetz ha-chammah*, but in a pressing situation it is permitted to pray after *ammud ha-shachar*.

Practical Law

Shulchan Arukh[144] rules that the ideal time for *shemoneh esrei* is at *hanetz ha-chammah*, but if one prayed from *ammud ha-shachar*[145] one has fulfilled one's obligation. In a pressing situation, he writes that one is permitted to pray after *ammud ha-shachar*.

136 Gemara *Berakhot* 9b.
137 Psalms 72:5.
138 One could suggest that this time is also considered ideal based on the previously cited Mishnah that daytime *mitzvot* should be performed after *hanetz ha-chammah*.
139 *Berakhot* 4:1.
140 His language is *mi-she'alah barak ha-shachar ve-he'ir penei ha-mizrach*, when the shimmer of the morning comes up and the west is lit up. As mentioned above, it is debated whether *ammud ha-shachar* and *he'ir penei ha-mizrach* are separate times. See *Biur Halakhah* (*Orach Chayyim* 89 s.v. *ve-im mitpallel mi-she'alah ammud ha-shachar*) and *Arukh Ha-Shulchan* (*Orach Chayyim* 89:11).
141 *Orach Chayyim* 89.
142 *Berakhot* 30a s.v. *avuha*.
143 *Hilkhot Tefillah* 3:1,7.
144 *Orach Chayyim* 89:1,8.
145 Using similar language to Rosh, he writes that one has fulfilled the obligation if said after *ammud ha-shachar ve-he'ir penei ha-mizrach*. As mentioned above, it is debated whether *ammud ha-shachar* and *he'ir penei ha-mizrach* are separate times. See *Biur Halakhah* (*Orach Chayyim* 89 s.v. *ve-im mitpallel mi-she'alah ammud ha-shachar*) and *Arukh Ha-Shulchan* (*Orach Chayyim* 89:11). Practically, authorities seem to permit saying *shemoneh esrei* after the calculated times for *ammud ha-shachar* that appear in published calendars, and do not distinguish between *ammud ha-shachar* and *he'ir penei ha-mizrach*. See, for instance, *Iggerot Moshe* (*Orach Chayyim* 4:6).

The Remainder of *Shacharit*

After *shemoneh esrei, shacharit* continues with *tachanun*, the Torah reading (on certain days of the week), *ashrei, la-menatzei'ach, u-va le-tziyyon, aleinu, shir shel yom*, and other prayers according to one's custom. If one was praying at a time when it was already permitted to say *shema* and *shemoneh esrei*, then it would seem permissible to continue with the remainder of *shacharit*.

A question which might face students and residents is whether certain segments of the remainder of *shacharit* may be skipped. Ideally, these segments of *shacharit* should be said in their entirety. However, R. Ovadia Yosef[146] writes based on R. Natronai Gaon[147] and other authorities that *tachanun* is not a formal requirement, and when time is very pressed one can skip *tachanun*. *Arukh Ha-Shulchan*[148] writes that initially *tachanun* was instituted as an optional prayer, but nowadays it has become accepted by the Jewish people as a standard part of prayer and is therefore similar to a formal obligation.

The importance of reciting *ashrei* at this point is highlighted by the Gemara[149] which states that a person who recites this prayer three times daily is guaranteed to be a *ben olam ha-ba*, a person deserving of the World to Come. The Gemara[150] also states that one of the prayers upon which the world stands is *kedushah de-sidra*, a reference to the *kedushah* recited during *u-va le-tziyyon*.[151] Based on these teachings, R. Ovadia Yosef[152] emphasizes the importance of saying these prayers.[153] He also emphasizes the importance of the Torah reading as this enactment was instituted by Moses and his prophets, and it was expanded by Ezra and his court.

Summary

Based on our discussion above, the following table summarizes the earliest times the components of *shacharit* may be recited:

---

146 *Yechavveh Da'at* 2:8.
147 Cited by *Tur, Orach Chayyim* 131.
148 *Orach Chayyim* 131:2.
149 *Berakhot* 4b.
150 *Sotah* 49a.
151 Rashi (*Sotah* 49a s.v. *a-kedushah de-sidra*) explains that this prayer was established so that all of Israel would study Torah daily by reading Torah verses and their Aramaic translation. And since this is the practice of all Jews, learned and unlearned alike, it has two elements that make it precious – *kedushat Hashem* and Torah learning.
152 *Yechavveh Da'at* 2:8.
153 While he is willing to allow skipping of *tachanun* when necessary, he does not generally allow skipping these segments of *shacharit*.

Tallit / Tefillin	Introductory Tefillot	Shema	Shemoneh Esrei
	May wash *netilat yadayim*[a]		
	May recite *asher yatzar* and *Elokai neshamah*, *birkat ha-Torah*, and all *birkhot ha-shachar* <u>except</u> *ha-noten la-sekhvi vinah* (SA)[b]		
	May recite *korbanot* and associated *mishnayot* if pressed for time; may recite *parshat ha-kiyyor* and *parshat terumat ha-deshen* (MB)		
	May recite *pesukei de-zimra* according to some opinions		
AMMUD HA-SHACHAR			
May recite blessing on *tallit* (Rama, AS) May don *tefillin* without *berakhah* (SA)[c]	May recite all *birkhot ha-shachar* (SA) May recite *korbanot* and associated *mishnayot* (SA) May recite *pesukei de-zimra* if pressed for time (*Biur Halakhah*)	May recite *birkhot keriat shema* (SA) except *yotzer or* (MA, PM, Gra, MB) May recite *shema* in pressing situation only if reciting it later will impede concentration (SA)	May recite *shemoneh esrei* in pressing situation (SA)[d]
MI-SHEYAKKIR			
Ideal time for wearing and reciting blessings on *tallit/tefillin* (SA, MB)	May recite *pesukei de-zimra*	May recite all *birkhot keriat shema* May recite *shema*, ideally immediately before *hanetz ha-chammah* (SA)	May recite *shemoneh esrei* in pressing situation (SA)[d]
HANETZ HA-CHAMMAH			
			Ideal time for *shemoneh esrei* (SA)[d]

Guide to abbreviations: *SA – Shulchan Arukh*; *MA – Magen Avraham*; *MB – Mishnah Berurah*; *PM – Peri Megadim*; *AS – Arukh Ha-Shulchan*.

[a] Rama rules that one should wash one's hands again after *ammud ha-shachar*.
[b] *Mishnah Berurah* writes that according to most *acharonim* even the blessing of *ha-noten la-sekhvi vinah* may be recited before daytime, but he cites those who maintain that ideally one should not do this.
[c] R. Moshe Feinstein recommends reciting a *berakhah* when donning *tefillin* even before *mi-sheyakkir*.
[d] Once one was permitted to pray the earlier parts of *shacharit*, the remaining prayers from *tachanun* until the end of *shacharit* may be recited.

Ruling of *Mishnah Berurah*

Biur Halakhah[154] discusses the earliest time a person is permitted to recite *shacharit* in a time-pressing situation. He writes that a person should try to start *pesukei de-zimra* after *mi-sheyakkir* so that the *tefillin* do not have to be placed between *yishtabach* and *yotzer or*. However, if this is not possible, a person could recite *pesukei de-zimra* before *mi-sheyakkir* without wearing *tefillin*, and after *mi-sheyakkir* he can place the *tefillin* and continue with *yotzer or*. In a separate comment, in reference to a case of travel, *Mishnah Berurah* allows an alternative practice of wearing the *tefillin* before *mi-sheyakkir* while praying *pesukei de-zimra* and after *mi-sheyakkir* he may touch the *tefillin* and recite the *berakhah* on them.[155]

Ruling of R. Moshe Feinstein

R. Moshe Feinstein describes how a person should pray if he has to rush to work early in the morning.[156] He writes that in a case of pressing need, one may rely on the calculation of *ammud ha-shachar* being 90 minutes before *hanetz ha-chammah*, or possibly slightly earlier.[157] He writes that one who must rush to work is certainly considered in a pressing situation and is permitted to recite *shema* and pray *shemoneh esrei* in between *ammud ha-shachar* and *mi-sheyakkir*. He writes that one should put on *tallit* and *tefillin* so that he does not become accustomed

154 58 s.v. *zeman keriat shema*.
155 *Mishneh Berurah* 89:40.
156 *Iggerot Moshe, Orach Chayyim* 4:6. At the end of the responsum, he writes that his opinion on this matter is novel and requires more thought but would apply to a case of great need.
157 The time duration between *ammud ha-shachar* and *hanetz ha-chammah*, according to the conclusion of Gemara (*Pesachim* 94a), is the time it takes to walk four *milin*. The time it takes to walk one *mil* is debated by the authorities. R. Feinstein summarizes the following opinions on this topic. *Shulchan Arukh* (*Orach Chayyim* 459:2) and *Shakh* (*Yoreh De'ah* 69:25) maintain that this time is 18 minutes, which means *ammud ha-shachar* is 72 minutes before *hanetz ha-chammah*. Gra (*Biur Ha-Gra, Orach Chayyim* 459 s.v. *ve-shiur mil*) holds that one *mil* is 22.5 minutes, making *ammud ha-shachar* 90 minutes before *hanetz ha-chammah*. *Chok Ya'akov* (*Orach Chayyim* 459:10, commentary to *Shulchan Arukh, Orach Chayyim* 459:2), as explained by *Tiferet Yisra'el*, maintains that the time is up to 23 minutes, making *ammud ha-shachar* up to 92 minutes before *hanetz ha-chammah*. R. Feinstein writes that although the duration of time between *ammud ha-shachar* and *hanetz ha-chammah* varies by time and place, we are informed by astronomers that even on short days the time of *ammud ha-shachar* is earlier than this, and in a case of pressing need one can rely on the opinions of Gra and *Chok Ya'akov*.

to praying without them and also to avoid forgetting to wear *tefillin* later in the day. The blessing on the *tallit* should not be recited until after *mi-sheyakkir*, and if he must leave for work before that time, then after *mi-sheyakkir* he should make the blessing on his *tallit katan* wherever he is.[158] Regarding *tefillin*, ideally one should make the blessing after *mi-sheyakkir* if he is still wearing them at that time. However, if he has to leave for work before *mi-sheyakkir*, and he will not have time to wear *tefillin* later in the day, he writes that it is possible he should make the blessing even if he is a *talmid chakham* to avoid degrading the *mitzvah* (as one is less likely to fulfill the *mitzvah* with the proper respect if one does not recite a *berakhah*), and certainly the blessing should be made if he is not a *talmid chakham*.[159]

R. Feinstein also addresses whether one should have intent to fulfill the obligation of *shema* if one must pray before *mi-sheyakkir* but will have time to say *shema* after *mi-sheyakkir* without wearing *tefillin*. He writes that if one must pray before *mi-sheyakkir*, even if one will have time later to recite *shema* after *mi-sheyakkir*, but at the later time he will not be wearing *tefillin*, it is better to have intent to fulfill the *mitzvah* while wearing *tefillin* before *mi-sheyakkir* because of the importance of saying *shema* with *tefillin* and because this person is permitted to say *shema* at this time because of the pressing situation.[160]

Ruling of R. Ovadia Yosef

R. Ovadia Yosef describes how working people should organize an early *minyan* when they must rush to work.[161] They can begin saying *parshat ha-akeidah*, *korbanot*, and *pittum ha-ketoret* 90 minutes before

---

158 See there for elaboration on why he rejects Rama regarding making the blessing after *ammud ha-shachar*.

159 *Ishei Yisra'el* (18:10, p. 177) proposes a similar suggestion for those who must rise early for work. He writes that one may recite *pesukei de-zimra* before *ammud ha-shachar*, and begin with the blessings of *shema* after *ammud ha-shachar* until the conclusion of *shacharit*. However, in contrast to R. Feinstein, he writes that the blessing of *yotzer or* should not be recited until after *mi-sheyakkir*, and therefore it should be skipped during *shacharit* and recited after *mi-sheyakkir* as an individual blessing.

160 *Ishei Yisra'el* (p. 177 footnote 25) explains R. Feinstein as follows: If one will have time after *mi-sheyakkir* to recite *shema* while wearing *tefillin*, he should nevertheless recite *shema* with its blessings after *ammud ha-shachar*, but he should have in mind not to fulfill the *mitzvah* of *shema*, and later, after *mi-sheyakkir*, he should repeat *shema* while wearing *tefillin*. However, if one knows that after praying he will not have time to say *shema* at the proper time while wearing *tefillin*, he should intend to fulfill the *mitzvah* even before *mi-sheyakkir*.

161 *Yechavveh Da'at* 2:8.

hanetz ha-chammah.[162] They should only start *barukh she-amar* after 72 minutes before *hanetz ha-chammah.*[163] They should only wear *tallit* and *tefillin* after finishing *yishtabbach*, as at this point the time of *mi-sheyakkir* will have already passed.[164] Then they continue with *kaddish*, *barkhu*, and *yotzer or* through *shemoneh esrei*. For *shemoneh esrei*, the *chazzan* should begin immediately reciting the first three blessings aloud with *kedushah*, and afterwards all continue the *shemoneh esrei* quietly. If they have more time, they should continue with *vidui*, *tachanun*, and the rest of *shacharit*. If they do not have time, they skip *vidui* and *tachanun* as he maintains that recitation of *tachanun* is not a formal obligation. Afterwards the *chazzan* recites *kaddish*, followed by *ashrei*, *u-va le-tziyyon*, and *kaddish*.[165] On Mondays and Thursdays, even if there is no time to say *vidui*, *tachanun*, *Kel melekh yoshev al kissei rachamim*, and *ve-hu rachum*, they should read from the Torah if possible. After the Torah reading, they recite *kaddish*, *ashrei*, *u-va le-tziyyon*, and the remainder of *tefillah* can be completed while traveling to work.

Application to Medical Students and Residents

Making specific rules for the application of these laws to medical personnel is difficult as the rules will depend on the individual circumstances and should be judged on a case-by-case basis, and all practical questions should be posed to a qualified rabbinic authority. Based on our previous discussion, when one needs to pray early in the morning, there are several questions that should be asked: What time will one need to leave the house? Will he or she be travelling on a bus or other means whereby praying while traveling is feasible? Will there be time to pray in the hospital at some point? Will there be a safe place to leave one's *tefillin* in the hospital if this is necessary?

We have seen in our discussion that if one must go to work early, he or she may pray after *mi-sheyakkir*. If this is not feasible, some authorities permit praying between *ammud ha-shachar* and *mi-sheyakkir*. The greatest challenges to prayer during this time period are the recitation

---

162 It is explained in *Yalkut Yosef* (*Hilkhot Tefillah*, volume 1, commentary to 89:11, p. 70) that R. Yosef allows this in deference to the opinions that *ammud ha-shachar* occurs 90 minutes before *hanetz ha-chammah*.

163 He writes that this is the time of *ammud ha-shachar* according to most authorities and *Shulchan Arukh*.

164 R. Yosef rules here according to *Peri Megadim* that the time of *mi-sheyakkir* is about 6 minutes after *ammud ha-shachar*, i.e., about 66 minutes before *hanetz ha-chammah*.

165 As written above, R. Yosef elaborates on the importance of reciting *ashrei* three times daily as per Gemara *Berakhot* 4b and the importance of *kedushah de-sidra* (part of *u-va le-tzion*) as per Gemara *Sotah* 49a.

of *shema* and wearing *tefillin*, both of which should ideally begin after *mi-sheyakkir*. We have described above the opinion of R. Moshe Feinstein regarding the proper procedure in this scenario.

The calculations of *ammud ha-shachar* and *mi-sheyakkir* are complex and subject to debate. While it is recommended that students and residents use the commonly printed calendars to ascertain these times, it is possible that one could rely on earlier calculations in certain circumstances. The opinion of R. Moshe Feinstein regarding this matter was detailed above.

Nishmat Avraham[166] writes that in principle, one who is busy caring for patients is not obligated in prayer. He cites R. Yitzchak Zilberstein[167] who argues that doctors and nurses who are taking care of patients, even if they are being paid, are considered to be involved in a *mitzvah* which exempts them from other *mitzvot*. However, he cites R. Shlomo Zalman Auerbach[168] who argues that one is obligated to pray if there is time and it is not a burden. Practically, most students and doctors have time to pray *shacharit* in the morning in a way which will not adversely affect their care of patients. If a conflict arises, it is possible that one would be permitted or even obligated to skip *shacharit*. One is advised to speak with a rabbinic authority if this scenario is anticipated. It goes without saying that the obligation to save a life supersedes the obligation of prayer.

166 Hebrew edition, end of *Orach Chayyim* 89, *dinei tefillah le-rofei – sikkum dinim* 5, p. 94.
167 In *Nishmat Avraham*, Hebrew edition, commentary to *Orach Chayyim* 38:8, comment 6, p. 28.
168 Ibid. He specifically addresses wearing *tefillin* and reciting *shema*.

Chapter 7

Prayer Obligations for Women in Medical School

Naomi Schwartz and Sarah Mizrachi

For medical students working long shifts in the hospital, it is often hard to find the time to pray. Female medical students face the same difficulties as male students in this regard. Clinical rotations requiring early presence in the hospital can make davening *shacharit* difficult. While women's time restraints for the components of *shacharit* are generally similar to those of men (see previous chapter), their obligation in prayer itself may be different. In this chapter, we will explore sources for women's obligation in prayer, as well as explanations for some common women's practices. In addition, we will discuss the order of priority for women's prayers when under time constraints. With this understanding, women can navigate their demanding hospital schedules while fulfilling their prayer obligations.

Women's Obligation in Daily Prayer

A woman's obligation in prayer stems from a well-known debate between Rambam and Ramban concerning the halakhic status of prayer, as well as the earliest sources for prayer itself. Rambam considers prayer to be a Torah obligation, stemming from the verse *"va-avadtem et Hashem Elokeichem."*[1] He explains that the meaning of the term *"avodah"* (service of God) can be clarified through another verse, *"u-le'ovdo be-khol levavkhem,"* "to serve Him with all your heart."[2] The Gemara[3] explains that serving God with all of one's heart means serving Him through

1 Exodus 23:25.
2 Deuteronomy 11:13.
3 *Ta'anit* 2a.

prayer. As this obligation can be traced to a Biblical source, Rambam[4] extrapolates that daily prayer is a non-time-bound commandment in which both men and women are obligated. The obligation to pray does not necessitate the recitation of a preset text, but must involve three criteria: praise, request, and gratitude. The set texts and times of prayer were mandated rabbinically, and thus, according to Rambam, did not become an obligation for women. *Magen Avraham*[5] invokes Rambam's stance to explain why many women do not recite *Shemoneh Esrei* on a daily basis, instead opting to fulfill the obligation of prayer when they perform *Netilat Yadayim* by including a request with their prayer in order to contain all three aspects.

Ramban,[6] however, believes that these Biblical verses are not the source of the obligation to pray. He considers the above verses to be only indirect references to prayer, extrapolated by Chazal through an *asmakhta* (Biblical allusion), and therefore, prayer constitutes only a rabbinic obligation. As the command itself is rabbinic, and the laws of the set texts and times of prayer are as well, Ramban considers them all to be equal components of the obligation of prayer. Although in his view prayer is a time-bound commandment, Ramban believes that it applies to both men and women, because of his interpretation of a statement in the Gemara. The Gemara[7] writes that women are obligated in prayer because "*rachamei ninhu,*" the purpose of prayer is to appeal for mercy, which both men and women need in equal measure. *Mishnah Berurah*[8] writes that most authorities follow Ramban, such that women, like men, are obligated to recite *Shemoneh Esrei* twice a day, during *shacharit* and *minchah*. He adds that women are not obligated in the third *ma'ariv* prayer, as *ma'ariv* began as an optional prayer that most men accepted as an obligation, whereas women never did.

This debate is a key factor in whether women must pray *shacharit* and *minchah* as men do, or whether they can satisfy their requirement though a small declaration of prayer once a day. However, there is another consideration involved in the obligation of women in prayer, regarding the care of small children and those who are ill. Children have the status of an ill person,[9] and thus, those caring for them are exempt from certain obligations. Generally, *halakhah* dictates that one who is busy fulfilling one obligation need not stop to fulfill another one.[10] This becomes relevant to prayer when it comes to caregivers, who need

---

4   Rambam, *Hilkhot Tefillah* 1:1–2.
5   106:2.
6   *Hassagot Le-Sefer Ha-Mitzvot, Mitzvat Aseh* 5
7   *Berakhot* 20b.
8   106:4.
9   See Rama 276:2 and 328:17.
10   *Sukkah* 26a.

not abandon their charges to observe other commandments.[11] Women who are taking care of small children (and those who are caring for those who are actually ill, such as those working in the hospital) may be exempt from prayer entirely for this reason, if praying would compromise care. In these cases, many women rely on Rambam's position and recite a small prayer, allowing them to fulfill some level of prayer despite their time constraints.

Shema

As *keriat shema* during prayer is a time-bound commandment, limited to a certain time period after sunrise, women are not obligated to recite it.[12] However, women are required to fulfill the non-time-bound commandment of "accepting the yoke of Heaven," which can be easily accomplished by reciting the first verse of *shema*. Therefore, *Mishnah Berurah*[13] writes that it is proper to teach women to recite this first line of *shema* daily. However, women are not required to recite the *berakhot* before *shema*,[14] as these *berakhot* are connected to the time-bound commandment, rather than the acceptance of God's supremacy.

The *berakhot* after *shema* ("*emet ve-yatziv*" and onwards) are not related to the time-bound commandment of *shema*, but instead have another purpose. *Mishnah Berurah*[15] writes that women should be encouraged to recite these *berakhot* because they exist in order to be "*somekh ge'ulah le-tefillah*," to connect redemption (the *berakhah* of *ga'al Yisra'el*) to prayer (*shemoneh esrei*). These paragraphs connect the *shemoneh esrei* prayer (which women are obligated to recite) to discussion of the Exodus from Egypt, a commandment that women should fulfill as well.

Pesukei De-Zimra

According to R. Akiva Eiger,[16] the purpose of *pesukei de-zimra* is to prepare for prayer (i.e., *shemoneh esrei*). Therefore, if women are obligated in *shemoneh esrei*, they should be obligated in *pesukei de-zimra* as well. However, *Arukh Ha-Shulchan*[17] disagrees, and writes that women are not required to recite *barukh she-amar* or *yishtabbach*. He writes that because their purpose is mainly to praise God, women may recite

11 R. Shlomo Zalman Auerbach, cited in *Nishmat Avraham, Orach Chayyim* 4:38.
12 *Shulchan Arukh* 70.
13 106:4.
14 *Mishnah Berurah* 70:2.
15 106:4.
16 *Orach Chayyim* 52:1; cited by *Mishnah Berurah* 70:2.
17 *Orach Chayyim* 70:1.

these prayers as Miriam did by the splitting of the sea, but there is no requirement to do so.

Birkhot Ha-Shachar and Birkat Ha-Torah

When describing the general obligation of *birkhot ha-shachar*, *Mishnah Berurah*[18] explains that their purpose is to allow man to benefit from the world. He writes that in order to enjoy anything from this world, man must say a blessing on it first, which he can fulfill through these *berakhot*. While *Mishnah Berurah* does not specifically mention women in this case, *Shulchan Arukh*[19] clearly states that women recite "*she-asani kirtzono*," an alternate form of one of these blessings. This implies that women were reciting all of *birkhot ha-shachar*. However, elsewhere *Mishnah Berurah*[20] is less clear about women's obligation in these blessings, writing that it would depend on whether or not they are considered time-bound commands. *Aruch Ha-Shulchan*[21] explicitly rules that women should be obligated in *birkhot ha-shachar*, as the subjects of the blessings apply to them as well.

Regarding *birkat ha-Torah*, *Shulchan Arukh*[22] explicitly writes that women should recite it. *Biur Halakhah*[23] explains this statement by saying that, although women do not have the same obligation of Torah study as men, they are still required to learn the Torah laws that apply to them, and thus, they should recite the blessing on learning Torah each day. He also adds that women are required to recite daily *korbanot* the same way they are obligated in prayer, and as *korbanot* consist of Torah verses, women should recite the blessing on learning Torah before reciting *korbanot*. However, other *poskim* disagree, and interpret *Shulchan Arukh*'s statement simply as granting permission to say the blessings, rather than a declaration of obligation.[24] Gra[25] explains that it cannot be an obligation, because women do not have the general requirement of learning Torah, and therefore they cannot be obligated in a blessing that states "and He commanded us to be engrossed in the words of his Torah."

18 46:1.
19 *Orach Chayyim* 46:4
20 70:1.
21 *Orach Chayyim* 70:1.
22 *Orach Chayyim* 47:14.
23 47:14.
24 *Shulchan Arukh* generally rules, in accordance with the practice of Sefardim, that women do not recite *berakhot* on *mitzvot* for which they are not obligated to perform, even if they perform the *mitzvot* electively. Therefore, in this case, he is explaining why it is permitted to recite a *berakhah*.
25 *Orach Chayyim* 47:14.

Priorities in Women's Prayer When under Time Constraints

When women are pressed for time, they may omit some of the prayers. Based on the principles we have outlined above, the practice of *tefillah* in such situations differs for Ashkenazic and for Sefardic women.

For Ashkenazic women, who should recite both *shacharit* and *minchah* based on the views of *Magen Avraham*[26] and *Mishnah Berurah*,[27] there is a hierarchy to the order of the prayers that should be recited when pressed for time, based on which prayers have the strongest indication of obligation. These prayers should be recited in the order listed in the *siddur*, but they are listed below in priority from most to least important for women.[28]

1. *Shemoneh esrei* (see above, "Women's Obligation in Daily Prayer")
2. The first verse of *shema* and the line "*barukh shem kevod malkhuto le-olam va-ed*" (see above, "*Shema*")
3. *Emet ve-yatziv* (see above, "*Shema*")
4. *Barukh she-amar*, *ashrei*, and *yishtabbach* (see above, "*Pesukei De-Zimra*")
5. *Birkhot ha-shachar* and *birkat ha-Torah* (see above, "*Birkhot Ha-Shachar* and *Birkat Ha-Torah*")
6. Blessings before *shema* (see above, "*Shema*")
7. The entire *shema* (see above, "*Shema*")
8. The entire *pesukei de-zimra* (see above, "*Pesukei De-Zimra*")

Sefardic women follow the ruling of Rambam, discussed above, that only one *tefillah* is required each day. R. Ovadia Yosef recommends that women ideally recite the *shemoneh esrei* of *shacharit*, prefaced by *birkhot ha-shachar* and *birkat ha-Torah*, as well as the first verse of *shema*. Because the blessings before and after *shema* and the blessings of *pesukei de-zimra* are not mandated for women, the practice of many Sefardic women is not to recite these blessings or to recite them without God's name;[29] this should be discussed with one's halakhic advisor. If one is very busy in the morning, then because there is no specific need to recite *shacharit* over any other *tefillah*, one can recite *minchah* or *arvit* instead.[30]

---

26   *Orach Chayyim* 106:2.
27   106:4.
28   *Halikhot Bat Yisra'el* 2:3.
29   See *Yalkut Yosef, Otzar Dinim Le-Ishah U-Lebat*, 8:2 (pp. 86–100).
30   *Yalkut Yosef, Otzar Dinim Le-Ishah U-Lebat*, 9:1 (p. 104).

Chapter 8

Reciting *Berakhot* in a Hospital Setting

Rabbi Ephraim Meth

B*erakhot* are, symbolically, face-to-face encounters with Hashem. We address Hashem in second person, *"atah,"* "you," as we would someone standing opposite us. In this respect, *berakhot* are similar to *shemoneh esrei* and *keriat shema*.[1] Consequently, they require a dignified setting and focused mindset. In this chapter, we will discuss the laws regarding reciting *berakhot* in a hospital, where a healthcare worker might be in a setting which may not be appropriate for the recitation of a *berakhah*.

In addition, we will discuss a common situation for healthcare workers, that of moving from place to place after reciting a *berakhah* on food. We will discuss whether a new *berakhah* must be recited if one is no longer in the location where one recited the first *berakhah*.

Reciting *Berakhot* in Undignified Settings

The laws concerning dignified and undignified settings are derived hermeneutically from the Biblical discussion of proper battlefield conduct. Jewish military camps must conform to certain standards of cleanliness and dignity, since Hashem accompanies Jewish soldiers to battle. In particular, soldiers must cover their feces after defecating, "so that their camp can be holy."[2] From this verse, we derive that it is inappropriate to meet Hashem in proximity to uncovered feces, but it is not problematic to meet Him within sight of transparently covered feces.[3] Moreover,

---

1 *Mishnah Berurah* 76:2.
2 Deuteronomy 23:15.
3 *Berakhot* 25b.

the Torah[4] writes, "He should not see in your midst any nakedness." From this we derive that it is inappropriate to meet Hashem wherever nakedness is visible (whether covered transparently or uncovered), but it is permissible to meet Him where nakedness is invisible, even if it is in close proximity to the meeting.

The Gemara notes that certain objects (e.g., chamberpots) are Biblically equivalent to feces, while others (e.g., urine) are only rabbinically equivalent to feces. Similarly, the Gemara defines the scope of what does and what does not constitute "nakedness." Interestingly, however, the Gemara does not supply us with the precise hermeneutical derivations for these definitions, perhaps because the Torah intended them to be derived via the aesthetic-spiritual intuition of the Masoretic sages rather than via formal hermeneutic rules.

Similarly, Chazal considered it self-evident that we must concentrate on our *berakhot*, and therefore enacted legislation forbidding us to recite *berakhot* in settings that may distract us. In particular, they were concerned that men might be distracted by inappropriate thoughts about women.

What should one do in an undignified setting?

Ideally, one should remove oneself to the nearest dignified setting before reciting the *berakhah*. If the *berakhah* is on food, one should begin eating immediately following the *berakhah*, and one may then continue eating even in the undignified setting.[5]

One may recite *berakhot* when his or her body faces perpendicularly (more than ninety degrees) to an offensive object such as excrement, urine, or genitalia.[6] A man may close his eyes and recite *berakhot* opposite insufficiently attired women.[7] Women may recite *berakhot* even with their eyes open opposite insufficiently attired women.[8] When adherence to these rules would result in damaged health or severe financial loss, one may sometimes be lenient in consultation with a competent halakhic authority.

Under many circumstances, it is better to eat without a *berakhah* than to recite one's *berakhah* in a place where reciting *berakhot* is halakhically forbidden.[9] If one accidentally recited a *berakhah* in a place where reciting *berakhot* is forbidden, one sometimes must repeat the *berakhah*.[10] If the *berakhah* was recited on food, one sometimes may

---

4   Deuteronomy ibid.
5   *Mishnah Berurah* 84:7.
6   *Mishnah Berurah* 75:29.
7   *Mishnah Berurah* 75:1.
8   *Mishnah Berurah* 75:8.
9   *Mishnah Berurah* 62:8–9.
10 *Mishnah Berurah* 75:4; 185:5.

not continue eating. A competent halakhic authority should be consulted.

One should learn how to ignore, at will, distracting images (e.g., television screens) and sounds (e.g., radio, public announcement systems). One should spend a few moments before each *berakhah* tuning out all distractions.[11] One should spend a few moments before each *berakhah* ascertaining that his or her environs are suitably dignified.[12]

Which settings are insufficiently dignified?

Rooms designated for people with unclothed genitals (e.g., bathrooms, pool or gym locker rooms, delivery rooms, urological surgery rooms, etc.) are considered undignified.[13] When the designated area of the room is cordoned off by a curtain, one may recite *berakhot* in the rest of the room.

Any place that smells of human excrement or urine or vomit is considered undignified, up to a four *ammot* distance (approximately seven feet) from where the smell ceases.[14] One may not recite *berakhot* in such places even when the smell is neutralized by air freshener or by a mask. However, when the excrement is properly covered, and the smell is neutralized, one may recite *berakhot*.[15]

Any place with uncovered excrement or urine is considered undignified.[16] Therefore, any place with an uncovered catheter or commode is likely to be considered undignified.[17] Metal, glass, or ceramic commodes may not be problematic when empty, as these materials are less absorbent and thus are not considered inherently undignified when they are completely empty. Plastic receptacles are also not problematic when empty, as long as they do not smell.[18]

Any place where genitalia are visible (even when transparently covered) is considered undignified.[19] This does not apply to genitalia of boys under nine years of age or girls under three.[20] Any place where insufficiently attired women are visible is undignified.[21] The standards of attire probably do not differ between hospital patients and others.

11 *Mishnah Berurah* 75:17.
12 *Mishnah Berurah* 185:5.
13 *Shulchan Arukh, Orach Chayyim* 84:1. One may recite *berakhot* in rooms sometimes used for people with uncovered genitalia, as long as those rooms were not specifically designated as such (*Mishnah Berurah* 84:3).
14 *Shulchan Arukh, Orach Chayyim* 83:1; *Nishmat Avraham* 76:1.
15 *Nishmat Avraham, Orach Chayyim* 87:6.
16 *Shulchan Arukh, Orach Chayyim* 76.
17 *Shulchan Arukh, Orach Chayyim* 87:1.
18 *Nishmat Avraham, Orach Chayyim* 87:3.
19 *Shulchan Arukh, Orach Chayyim* 75:4.
20 *Mishnah Berurah* 75:23.
21 *Shulchan Arukh, Orach Chayyim* 75:1.

One should not recite *berakhot* within line-of-sight of non-Jewish religious symbols.[22]

Reciting a New *Berakhah* After Moving to a New Location

A common situation for healthcare workers involves moving from place to place, for example, during rounds. Suppose one recites a *berakhah* before eating a snack. Does one have to recite an additional *berakhah* after moving to a new location? The following paragraphs will analyze this question from conceptual, textual, and finally practical angles.

Conceptually, this question requires us to establish criteria for determining when two acts of eating are deemed continuous and when they are deemed discontinuous. Three types of factors contribute to continuity and to discontinuity. First, a person's thoughts and intentions can forge a bond of continuity between two acts of eating. For this reason, when one intends to eat while moving, one's intentions sometimes render all of one's acts of eating continuous. (For instance, one who begins a meal by reciting *ha-motzi* at home and continues in his or her car needs not recite a new *berakhah*, provided that he or she intended from the outset to eat in both locations.[23]) Conversely, when a person consciously or subconsciously intends to not eat any more (such as when one washes *mayim acharonim*), acts of eating performed before the genesis of this intention and acts of eating performed after this intention may be deemed discontinuous.[24] Second, when two acts of eating take place in similar environs (either under the same roof or within the same four walls), the similarity forges a bond of continuity between those acts. Conversely, when two acts of eating take place in radically different contexts (e.g., one indoors and the second outdoors), they may be considered disconnected. Third, halakhic requirements or lack thereof can determine whether two acts of eating are continuous or discontinuous. Hence, acts of eating food which requires a *berakhah acharonah* in the place where it was eaten are more likely to be continuous, since the eater is obligated to return to his or her original location and conclude the meal with a *berakhah acharonah*. In contrast, acts of eating food which does not require a *berakhah acharonah* in the place where it was eaten are more likely to be discontinuous, since the eater has fewer obligations binding him or her to the original act of eating and the original location. For this reason, also, when 72 minutes elapse between two acts of eating (and hence one is neither obligated

---

22 *Shulchan Arukh, Orach Chayyim* 94:9; *Mishnah Berurah* 94:30.
23 *Mishnah Berurah* 178:42.
24 *Shulchan Arukh, Orach Chayyim* 179:1.

nor permitted to recite a *berakhah acharonah* on the first act of eating), both acts require a *berakhah rishonah*, since the eater has fewer obligations binding him to his original act of eating.

With these ideas in mind, we will approach the sources which discuss this issue. The Gemara[25] mentions three cases, two of which require a new *berakhah*, and one which does not. First, one who moves from place to place in the midst of his meal needs not recite a new *berakhah*. Second, one who moves from house to house must recite a new *berakhah*. Third, one who moves from one side of a tree to the other side must recite a new *berakhah*. *Beit Yosef* explains that in the first situation, all acts of eating took place within the same four walls, and hence are considered continuous, whereas in the latter two cases, the acts of eating did not take place within the same four walls (presumably, the tree under discussion is growing outdoors), and hence are considered discontinuous.

Mishnah Berurah[26] expands the range of cases. Two corners of one room, or two rooms underneath one roof, or two stories within one house are considered "from place to place," writes *Mishnah Berurah*, and hence do not require two separate *berakhot*, since these three cases definitely are not "from house to house." The definition of separate locations with respect to *berakhot* may differ from that in other areas of *halakhah*. For example, with regard to *kiddush* (where the *Shabbat* meal must take place in the house where *kiddush* was recited), some authorities consider two rooms or two stories halakhically equivalent to two houses.[27] However, regarding *berakhot*, the criteria for establishing continuity between two acts of eating are more liberal, and therefore two rooms or two stories are considered belonging to a single house.

Finally, let us analyze the practical ramifications of the above discussions. *Beit Yosef*[28] and *Mishnah Berurah*[29] emphasize that ideally, one should make a *berakhah acharonah* before leaving any location, and a *berakhah rishonah* before beginning to eat at a new location, lest one forget upon arrival at his or her new location to recite a *berakhah acharonah*. This does not violate the injunction against *berakhah she-einah tzerikhah* (an unnecessary *berakhah*), since the extra *berakhot* are necessary to avoid potentially forgetting the *berakhah acharonah*.[30] If one is justly confident that he or she will not forget, or if one is unable to recite a *berakhah acharonah*, under most circumstances one who arrives at a new location needs not recite a new *berakhah*. A new *berakhah* need not be recited if any of the following five conditions apply:

25 *Pesachim* 101b.
26 *Mishnah Berurah* 178:22, *Biur Halakhah* s.v. *be-vayit*.
27 *Biur Halakhah* ibid.
28 *Orach Chayyim* 178.
29 Introduction to *siman* 178.
30 *Mishnah Berurah* 178:35.

1. They were eating food that requires either a *ha-motzi* or a *mezonot*.[31]
2. They left people who were participating in their meal at their original location, and they return to that original location to finish their meal. (This condition is not satisfied if one wishes to continue his or her meal in a new location.[32])
3. They are still in the same room where their meal began.[33] Here are some examples of how this rule may apply in a hospital:
   - The box-shaped corridors of hospitals are considered a single room, as long as the corridors' continuity is not interrupted by walls or doors.
   - Private rooms off the corridor are separate from the corridor, as are walled stairways and walled greeting/waiting areas.
   - Nurses' stations that are separated from the corridor by permanent tall desks are probably not considered separate rooms.
   - It is possible that any two locations under a single roof are considered to be "in the same room."[34] Two hospital buildings connected by an enclosed bridge or an underground tunnel are probably considered to be under a single roof. An underground parking lot or a driveway that runs underneath a wing of a building is probably also considered to be under the same roof as its building. It is unclear whether or not an awning that protrudes from the wall is considered to be under the same roof as its building.
4. They are under the same roof as their original location, and they can see from their present location a place where they previously ate part of their present meal.[35]
5. They are under the same roof as their original location, and they intended to eat while moving when they began their meal.[36] If one is uncertain whether or not he or she intended to eat while moving, it is safe to assume that he or she did so intend.

In fact, people need to recite a new *berakhah rishonah* only if they stepped outside (even onto a balcony or porch), and even then only if they left nobody behind, and even then only on non-*ha-motzi*, non-*mezonot* foods.

---

31 Rama, *Orach Chayyim* 178:2. Although *Shulchan Arukh* (ad loc) rules that in such a case, one must still recite a new *berakhah*, Sefardic practice in this case is to follow the ruling of Rama against *Shulchan Arukh* because of the principle of *safek berakhot lehakel*. See *Yalkut Yosef, Netilat Yadayim U-Berakhot, siman* 178, footnote 1.
32 Ibid.
33 *Mishnah Berurah* 178:9.
34 *Biur Halakhah* ibid.
35 *Mishnah Berurah* 178:12.
36 Ibid.

Chapter 9

Working in the Hospital on *Chol Ha-Mo'ed*

Jerry Karp, MD, PhD

While some medical school programs may understand and accommodate an observant Jewish student's request to be excused from classes or clerkships on *Shabbat* or *yom tov*, and some residency programs might accommodate *Shabbat* or *yom tov*, the same is often not true with regard to *chol ha-mo'ed*. For this reason, it is prudent to examine whether it is permitted for a medical student or resident to work on *chol ha-mo'ed* in the hospital. In this chapter, we will discuss two avenues of possible leniency with regard to this question.[1]

The Prohibition of *Melakhah* on *Chol Ha-Mo'ed*

Although it is often thought that there is no prohibition of performing *melakhah* on *chol ha-mo'ed*, as there is on *Shabbat* or *yom tov*, this is incorrect. Indeed, the Gemara[2] states that it is prohibited to perform *melakhah* on *chol ha-mo'ed*, just as on *Shabbat* or *yom tov*. However, the Gemara adds that Chazal were empowered by the Torah to define the exact parameters of which *melakhah* would be prohibited on *chol ha-mo'ed* and which would be permitted.[3] Because of this flexibility granted to Chazal, there are five categories of *melakhah* which are permitted on *chol ha-mo'ed*:[4]

1   An excellent work which can be consulted for more detail about the laws of *chol ha-mo'ed* is R. Dovid Zucker and R. Moshe Francis' *Chol HaMoed* (New York: Mesorah Publications, 2009).
2   *Chagigah* 18a.
3   There is a debate among the *rishonim* as to whether the prohibition of performing *melakhah* on *chol ha-mo'ed* is a Torah prohibition or a rabbinic prohibition. See *Beit Yosef* (*Orach Chayyim* 530).
4   *Mishnah Berurah* 530:1.

1. *davar ha-aved – melakhah*, which, if not performed over *chol ha-mo'ed*, will lead to a loss;
2. *melakhah* necessary for the preparation of food or other physical needs (*okhel nefesh*) in celebration of the *chol ha-mo'ed* or *yom tov;*
3. *melakhah* performed by a worker who has no food to eat and who therefore needs the money given as compensation for the work;
4. *melakhah* performed for public needs; and
5. any *ma'aseh hedyot*, work which requires no expertise, for the purpose of fulfilling a *chol ha-mo'ed* or *yom tov*-related need.

We will explore two specific avenues, based on these categories, that might permit a medical student or resident to work in the hospital on *chol ha-mo'ed*.

Davar Ha-Aved

As noted, one category of dispensation for performing *melakhah* on *chol ha-mo'ed* is *davar ha-aved, melakhah* which, if not performed over *chol ha-mo'ed*, will lead to a loss. According to *Magen Avraham*,[5] this dispensation applies even if one is unsure whether a loss will result if the *melakhah* is not performed.[6] However, there are several limits to this dispensation. In particular, *Shulchan Arukh*[7] notes, based on the Mishnah,[8] that one may not intentionally save *melakhah* for *chol ha-mo'ed* since that is a convenient time to perform the *melakhah*. Additionally, *Shulchan Arukh*[9] adds, based on the Gemara,[10] that one should not perform *melakhah* that involves significant exertion. Finally, the dispensation is only granted when there is an anticipated loss of

---

5   *Orach Chayyim*, beginning of 537, citing *Maharshach* responsa 1:113. It should be noted that *Chayyei Adam* (106:5) disagrees with this assertion, but many *poskim* appear to adopt *Magen Avraham*'s position as normative.

6   According to *Machatzit Ha-Shekel* and *Peri Megadim* (ad loc), the basis of *Magen Avraham*'s extension of the dispensation of *davar ha-aved* even to a case of uncertain loss is based on his assumption that the prohibition of *melakhah* on *chol ha-mo'ed* is only rabbinic (see footnote 3), and since in a case of uncertainty with respect to rabbinic law (*safek de-rabbanan*) we are lenient, one can perform *melakhah* for a *davar ha-aved* even in a case of uncertainty. However, *Biur Halakhah* (537 s.v. *davar ha-aved*) argues that this is a problematic assertion, since several *rishonim* who believed that *melakhah* on *chol ha-mo'ed* is prohibited by the Torah still believe that one may be lenient in a case of uncertainty. Rather, he argues, one can be lenient whenever the uncertainty is substantively grounded (*matzui*).

7   *Orach Chayyim* 537:16.

8   *Mo'ed Katan* 12b.

9   *Orach Chayyim* 537:2.

10 *Mo'ed Katan* 2a.

one's current assets, but not when not performing the *melakhah* would lead to a loss of profit.[11]

This category of dispensation is the halakhic basis for those who go to work on *chol ha-mo'ed*. The halakhic justification is that if one does not go to work, one may be fired from his or her job, and this would lead to loss of what one currently has – one's job. This reasoning is supported by R. Ovadia Yosef,[12] R. Moshe Feinstein,[13] R. Shlomo Zalman Auerbach and R. Yehoshua Neuwirth.[14] It should be noted that these authorities caution that one should preferably schedule one's vacation to take place during *chol ha-mo'ed*, although R. Feinstein permits one to take vacation during the summer instead if one has a specific reason for preferring vacation at that time of year.

Based on this reasoning, it would appear that a resident would be permitted to work on *chol ha-mo'ed*, as a resident who is absent without justification risks dismissal from the program. It may be that a medical student would be permitted to attend a clerkship during *chol ha-mo'ed* if there is a concern that the student's grade for the clerkship would be adversely affected if he or she were to be absent. Especially since the student will be absent during *yom tov*, the student may be justifiably concerned that the clerkship or site director, or one's attending physician, might be averse to the student missing even more days of the clerkship for *chol ha-mo'ed*. One's grade for the clerkship might be considered part of one's current assets, rather than potential profit, since the grade will be assigned regardless at the end of the clerkship.

Medicine on *Chol Ha-Mo'ed*

Even if there were no *davar ha-aved* involved, there may be another avenue for leniency, namely, that *melakhah* is permitted on *chol ha-mo'ed* for medical treatment. The Tosefta[15] notes that it is permitted to perform blood-letting for an animal on *chol ha-mo'ed*, and more generally, all medical treatment is permitted for an animal on *chol ha-mo'ed*. Moreover, the Tosefta[16] writes that one may imbibe certain potions on *chol ha-mo'ed*, ostensibly for the purpose of medical treatment. This

11 *Shulchan Arukh* 537:1, based on the Mishnah in *Mo'ed Katan* (2a).
12 *Yalkut Yosef*, Mo'adim, pp. 512.
13 Cited in R. Dovid Zucker and R. Moshe Francis' *Chol HaMoed* in the appendix, in R. Feinstein's cited rulings, section 18.
14 *Shemirat Shabbat Ke-Hilkhatah* 67:11.
15 *Mo'ed Katan* 2:11, Lieberman edition.
16 *Mo'ed Katan* 2:10, Lieberman edition.

ruling is codified by Rif,[17] Rambam[18] and Rosh.[19] *Tosafot*[20] raise the possibility that the medical treatment permitted for an animal on *chol ha-mo'ed* would be limited only to treatment that does not require the performance of *melakhah*. One might have thought that this statement in the Tosefta would still be novel, since even medical treatment which does not require *melakhah* is prohibited on *Shabbat* and *yom tov*, as Chazal prohibited it due to the concern that one might grind the herbs required for medicine, thus violating *Shabbat*. However, *Tosafot* point out, giving medicine to an animal is *not* prohibited on *Shabbat* and *yom tov*, since we assume that Chazal were not concerned that one would grind herbs to produce animal medication. Therefore, the Tosefta must be permitting even providing medical treatment to an animal which requires the performance of *melakhah*.

Me'iri[21] explicitly notes that if medical treatment for an animal is permitted on *chol ha-mo'ed*, even if *melakhah* is involved, medical treatment for people is certainly permitted on *chol ha-mo'ed*. In fact, the Yerushalmi[22] quotes the Tosefta with a slight emendation, stating explicitly that one may blood-let or perform medical treatment for either animals or people on *chol ha-mo'ed*. Thus, *Tur*[23] and *Shulchan Arukh*[24] codify that all medical treatment for people is permitted on *chol ha-mo'ed*.[25] Two reasons are offered for this dispensation. One explanation, offered by *Peri Megadim*,[26] is that medical treatment is permitted on *chol ha-mo'ed* since it is considered a *chol ha-mo'ed*-related need (*tzorekh ha-mo'ed*), which is permitted on *chol ha-mo'ed*. An alternative explanation, first offered by Me'iri[27] but later noted by *Nishmat*

---

17 *Mo'ed Katan* 4a.
18 *Hilkhot Yom Tov* 8:15.
19 *Mo'ed Katan* 1:20.
20 *Mo'ed Katan* 10b s.v. *ve-ein mone'in*.
21 *Mo'ed Katan* 10b s.v. *mekizin*.
22 *Pesachim* 4:8.
23 *Orach Chayyim* 532.
24 *Orach Chayyim* 532:2.
25 *Nishmat Adam* (110:2) and *Biur Halakhah* (531 s.v. *kol adam*) argue that one who is not ill at all, but rather has a local pain, may not perform *melakhah* (or have *melakhah* performed on one's behalf) for the purpose of medical treatment, although one may still take medication (as opposed to *Shabbat* and *yom tov*, when one may not take medication even when this does not involve *melakhah*). See R. Dovid Zucker and R. Moshe Francis' *Chol HaMoed*, appendix section 6, for a longer discussion of this issue. In any case, the overwhelming majority of patients in the hospital are considered ill, and thus this question is largely irrelevant in a hospital setting.
26 *Eshel Avraham* 532:2.
27 *Mo'ed Katan* 10b s.v. *mekizin*.

Adam,[28] is that this is considered a *davar ha-aved*: one's health is one's most important asset, and it is essential that one's health not deteriorate.

Based on this dispensation, it would appear that there is an additional avenue to permit a medical student to attend a clerkship or for a resident to work on *chol ha-mo'ed*. Since the work performed is part of medical treatment for the patient, this work would appear permitted on *chol ha-mo'ed*. Indeed, *Shulchan Arukh* rules that if a *melakhah* is permitted on *chol ha-mo'ed*, it is also permitted for another person to do the *melakhah* on the first person's behalf.[29]

Note About Writing on *Chol Ha-Mo'ed*

Although we have shown two possible avenues for leniency in this case, it should be apparent that when it is easy to avoid performing *melakhah* on *chol ha-mo'ed*, this would be preferable. One area in which this is particularly relevant is that of writing, which is prohibited on *chol ha-mo'ed* like any other *melakhah*. As noted, it would appear that writing is permitted if needed for medical treatment on *chol ha-mo'ed*. However, several authorities, including R. Yehoshua Neuwirth,[30] R. Yosef Shalom Elyashiv,[31] R. Ovadia Yosef,[32] and R. Yehudah Henkin[33] believe that it is completely permitted to type on a computer on *chol ha-mo'ed*. R. Neuwirth and R. Yosef explain that typing is permitted since the writing is not permanent.[34] Therefore, if the hospital uses an electronic medical record, it would seem preferable for the medical student or resident

---

28 110:2.
29 There is some debate about whether the person performing the *melakhah* is permitted to receive payment for his or her services. Rama (*Orach Chayyim* 542:1) cites *Kol Bo* (*siman* 60) who permits one to receive payment for *melakhot* performed in a case of *davar ha-aved*. Thus, if medical treatment is considered *davar ha-aved*, it would be permitted for a physician to receive payment for rendering services. Indeed, R. Shlomo Zalman Auerbach (cited in *Nishmat Avraham, Orach Chayyim* 532:1) rules that a physician may indeed receive payment for medical treatment on *chol ha-mo'ed*. However, *Biur Halakhah* (542 s.v. *ve-davar ha-aved*) is unsure whether this dispensation should apply even to *davar ha-aved*. In any case, given that medical students are not paid for services, there should be no halakhic concern for students working at the clerkship site. Similarly, residents are paid on a per annum basis and so they are not specifically paid for their work on *chol ha-mo'ed*.
30 *Shemirat Shabbat Ke-Hilkhatah* 66:55.
31 Cited in *Mevakshei Torah* p. 473, 85; also cited in R. Dovid Zucker and R. Moshe Francis' *Chol HaMoed*, p. 90, footnote 43.
32 *Yabbia Omer, Orach Chayyim* 8:48.
33 *Benei Banim* 3:45.
34 Perhaps the same is true of writing which is only needed for a short period of time, such as lab values that are jotted down for presenting to an attending

to avoid writing on paper, if possible, and to write only on the electronic medical record or into a cell phone or other electronic device. Obviously, if this is inconvenient, regular writing would appear to be permitted as well, though one could consider using a *shinui* if doing so is feasible.

Conclusion

As discussed here, there appear to be two possible avenues for leniency in allowing medical students and residents to work in the hospital on *chol ha-mo'ed*. First, residents would certainly risk severe consequences including dismissal if they do not work on *chol ha-mo'ed*. Similarly, if a medical student is concerned that his or her grade might be negatively impacted by not attending clerkships during *chol ha-mo'ed*, this might be a *davar ha-aved*, which is permitted on *chol ha-mo'ed*. Secondly, medical treatment is inherently permitted on *chol ha-mo'ed*, and thus *melakhah* performed by the resident or student in the hospital will likely be permitted in any case. Obviously, a resident or student should refer his or her specific situation to a qualified halakhic advisor who can comment regarding whether these dispensations might be applicable.

---

or before recording electronically, although this author is not aware of any similar suggestion by prominent *poskim*.

Chapter 10

Mourning Periods in the Jewish Calendar

Jerry Karp, MD, PhD

Although many halakhic concerns for medical students and residents surround the observance of *Shabbat* and *yom tov*, the periods of mourning on the Jewish calendar can also generate challenges for the observant Jewish student or resident. In this chapter, we discuss several issues that may arise during the mourning observances of *sefirat ha-omer* and the three weeks between 17 Tammuz and *Tishah Be-Av*.

Shaving during *Sefirat Ha-Omer* and the Three Weeks

Although various demonstrations of mourning are practiced during the time of *sefirat ha-omer* and during the three weeks between 17 Tammuz and *Tishah Be-Av*, one that often concerns the medical student or resident is the prohibition of shaving during these time periods. Students and residents might worry that not shaving in observance of these mourning periods may demonstrate lack of professionalism to their supervisors, and might adversely affect their evaluations and clerkship grades. We will briefly discuss the origins of the prohibition upon shaving during these mourning periods as well as various positions regarding whether one may be lenient in cases of need.

Of these two periods, the mourning period between 17 Tammuz and *Tishah Be-Av* was established earlier, during the time of the Mishnah and Gemara. The Mishnah[1] states that during the week of *Tishah Be-Av*, as a demonstration of mourning, it is prohibited to cut one's hair. *Shulchan Arukh*[2] records this ruling, but Rama[3] notes that

1   *Taanit* 26b.
2   *Orach Chayyim* 551:3.
3   *Orach Chayyim* 551:4.

Ashkenazim have the practice to abstain from cutting hair even earlier, starting on 17 Tammuz. *Shulchan Arukh*[4] also notes that there is no distinction between cutting one's hair and shaving one's beard, as these are both prohibited during this time of mourning.

During the Middle Ages, the custom to mourn during *sefirat ha-omer* became prevalent. Although the *ge'onim* only prohibited marriages during this time of the year, the custom to avoid getting a haircut or shaving was adopted later, and is noted by *Tur*[5] and *Shulchan Arukh*.[6]

This leaves the question of whether one may shave if one faces a possible loss otherwise. Two possible avenues of leniency have been suggested by contemporary authorities. R. Moshe Feinstein[7] permits shaving both during *sefirat ha-omer* and during the three weeks between 17 Tammuz and *Tishah Be-Av* if one needs to do so for work, as he argues that the custom was not intended to apply if it would lead to financial loss. He notes, though, that shaving is absolutely prohibited during the week of *Tishah Be-Av*, even in such a situation, as this is not a custom but is recorded as a ruling in the Mishnah and Gemara. One might discuss with a halakhic advisor whether one might be permitted to shave given one's personal situation.

Another lenient view is that of R. Joseph B. Soloveitchik,[8] who proposed that the mourning during both the period of *sefirat ha-omer* and the period of the three weeks is likened to the mourning during the twelve months following the loss of a parent. For this period of twelve months, *Shulchan Arukh*[9] rules that one may shave if one has grown one's beard long enough that a friend would scold him for letting his beard grow. Although Rama[10] states that the length of time one would have to be unshaven to reach this threshold is three months, R. Soloveitchik notes that the common custom is to rely on those who are more lenient with regard to shaving a beard, as a beard grown for even a short period looks unkempt on a person who is normally clean-shaven.[11] Therefore, he rules that one is similarly permitted to shave one's beard during *sefirat ha-omer* as well as during the period of the three weeks.[12]

4   *Orach Chayyim* 551:12.
5   *Orach Chayyim* 493.
6   *Orach Chayyim* 493:2.
7   *Iggerot Moshe, Orach Chayyim* 4:102.
8   Cited in *Nefesh Ha-Rav* p. 191.
9   *Yoreh De'ah* 390:4.
10 Ibid.
11 See *Noda Be-Yehudah, mahadura kamma, Orach Chayyim* 14; *Gesher Ha-Chayyim* 21:11(4).
12 R. Aharon Lichtenstein argues that since there is room for leniency with regard to shaving during *sefirat ha-omer*, one is *obligated* to do so on Friday, in preparation for *Shabbat*, as having a clean-shaven face is a form of *kavod Shabbat*, honoring the *Shabbat*. He notes that the *mitzvah* of

However, R. Soloveitchik notes that the period of mourning from *Rosh Chodesh Av* until after *Tishah Be-Av* is likened to the thirty days following the passing of a relative, during which haircuts and shaving are absolutely prohibited, even if one's friend would scold him. Therefore, shaving is still prohibited during this time period.

Observance of *Tishah Be-Av*

Introspective mourning is an integral part of the *Tishah Be-Av* observance. However, for the medical student and resident, whose classes and obligations do not recognize this day, it is necessary to navigate the observance of the day given one's obligations. We will discuss whether engaging in activities which are part of one's medical school obligations are permitted on *Tishah Be-Av*.

Working in the Hospital on *Tishah Be-Av*

It is often difficult or impossible for medical students or residents to request an absence on the day of *Tishah Be-Av*. Even if one could request to be absent, a student might be concerned that this would have a negative impact on his or her evaluations, and a resident might worry about asking for an additional day of accommodation especially if other more prioritized observances are accommodated. Is it permitted for the medical student or resident to work in the hospital on *Tishah Be-Av*?

The Mishnah[13] states that whether working on *Tishah Be-Av* is permitted is dependent on where one lives. If one lives in an area where the custom is to refrain from work on *Tishah Be-Av*, one must abstain from work; if one lives in an area where the custom is to work on *Tishah Be-Av*, one may work. The Mishnah adds that a Torah scholar should not work in either case, and R. Shimon ben Gamliel proclaims that one ought to conduct oneself as a Torah scholar and therefore not work. Many authorities quote R. Ovadiah Bartenura,[14] who explains that the reason for the custom is that one must spend *Tishah Be-Av* focusing on mourning, and if one works, this will detract from one's mourning. It should be noted that although the Gemara labels this as a custom, the Gemara elsewhere[15] states that if one does work on *Tishah Be-Av*, one will not see any blessing emanating from this work. The implication, suggests *Magen Avraham*,[16] is that even if one lives in a place where the

---

honoring *Shabbat* overrides the mourning customs of *sefirat ha-omer*. See "Shaving in Honor of Shabbat During the Omer," online at http://etzion.org.il/en/shaving-honor-shabbat-during-omer.
13   *Pesachim* 54b.
14   *Pesachim* 4:5 s.v. *talmidei chakhamim*.
15   *Ta'anit* 30b.
16   554:27.

custom is to work on *Tishah Be-Av*, this work will not be blessed. It is evident that the question of working on *Tishah Be-Av* is a serious one.

Beit Yosef[17] writes that the custom in all Jewish communities of which he is aware is to refrain from working on *Tishah Be-Av*. Rama[18] states that the custom is to refrain from working until *chatzot*, midday. *Magen Avraham*[19] adds that based on R. Ovadiah Bartenura's explanation of the custom, one must also refrain from working on the night of *Tishah Be-Av* since one is required to mourn during that time as well. *Arukh Ha-Shulchan*[20] notes a more lenient custom, that one should refrain from working until after the recitation of *kinot*. He attributes this leniency to the difficulty of earning a living at the time. He adds that since this is the custom, it cannot be prohibited, as the prohibition of working on *Tishah Be-Av* in any case is based on local custom. Still, he notes that it is ideal to refrain from working until after *chatzot*.

It should be noted that the discussion regarding working on *Tishah Be-Av* is not about the performance of *melakhah* that would be prohibited on *Shabbat* or *yom tov*. Indeed, Rama[21] writes that work that does not take time, such as lighting a candle or tying a knot, is permitted on *Tishah Be-Av*. These actions are clearly prohibited on *Shabbat* and *yom tov*. However, as noted, the prohibition of working on *Tishah Be-Av* is not about the performance of *melakhah*, but about avoiding distraction from mourning. Therefore, one may perform quick *melakhah* such as turning on a light on *Tishah Be-Av*, since this does not distract from mourning.[22]

While it would appear that the prohibition to work on *Tishah Be-Av* before *chatzot* is established in our time, *Shulchan Arukh*[23] rules that just as on *chol ha-mo'ed*,[24] one is permitted on *Tishah Be-Av* to perform work that is needed to prevent a loss (*davar ha-aved*). This is the basis of the common practice on *chol ha-mo'ed* for those who are unable to avoid working on *chol ha-mo'ed* to go to work: if there is a concern that not going to work will result in losing one's job after *chol ha-mo'ed*, one is permitted to go to work. The same is true, therefore, on *Tishah Be-Av*. This would appear to the basis of a dispensation for medical students and residents to work in the hospital on *Tishah Be-Av*. If there is a concern that not doing so might adversely affect one's evaluation or job, it would appear that this is considered a *davar ha-aved* which would justify attending the clerkship.

17 *Orach Chayyim* 554.
18 *Orach Chayyim* 554:22.
19 554:23.
20 *Orach Chayyim* 554:21.
21 *Orach Chayyim* 554:22.
22 See *Magen Avraham* 554:23.
23 *Orach Chayyim* 554:23.
24 See Chapter 9.

In any case, it is apparent that, if at all possible, one should avoid working on *Tishah Be-Av* until after *chatzot*. Even if one must work on *Tishah Be-Av*, one should still remember that the purpose of refraining from work is to focus one's attention on mourning. Therefore, one should attempt to find time on *Tishah Be-Av*, when there is a respite from work, to engage in mourning by reciting *kinot*, listening to a recorded lecture about *Tishah Be-Av*, or reflecting on the themes of the day.

Studying on *Tishah Be-Av*

Although studying for an exam on *Tishah Be-Av* is not explicitly discussed in any contemporary source known to this author, it would appear that two issues must be addressed. First, as with working on *Tishah Be-Av*, studying would appear to detract from one's ability to focus on mourning. Indeed, there are many rulings in *acharonim* prohibiting pleasurable or even mundane activities that distract one from mourning. For example, *Shulchan Arukh*[25] prohibits taking a stroll on *Tishah Be-Av* since one might come to levity, and *Mishnah Berurah*[26] cites *Shelah*[27] who writes that one should not walk with a group on *Tishah Be-Av* since one might have mundane conversations, and one should only discuss the themes of *Tishah Be-Av* during the day. *Shulchan Arukh*[28] also rules that one should not prepare food until after *chatzot*, and *Levush*,[29] who also cites this *halakhah*, explains that it is because one should not spend time performing activities that will distract one from the remembering the events of *Tishah Be-Av*. More similar to our case, *Arukh Ha-Shulchan*[30] rules that a mourner should not read secular books, especially if he or she enjoys reading them. *Piskei Teshuvot*[31] concludes that one should not read secular books on *Tishah Be-Av* before *chatzot*[32] so as not to distract from mourning. However,

25 *Orach Chayyim* 554:21.
26 559:41.
27 *Ta'anit, Ner Mitzvah*, s.v. *nohagim be-khol makom*.
28 *Orach Chayyim* 559:10.
29 *Orach Chayyim* 559:10.
30 *Yoreh De'ah* 384:9.
31 554:1.
32 He does not explain the reasoning for limiting the prohibition to the period before *chatzot*. See R. Moshe Harari's *Mikra'ei Kodesh, Ta'anit* section 3, ch. 7, footnote 58, who cites this and argues that the distinction is difficult. Presumably, the distinction is similar to that noted by *Levush*, who only prohibits preparing food before *chatzot* because this period is designated for introspection and mourning, whereas the period after *chatzot* appears to be more lenient in this regard (as evidenced also by the fact that one may work after *chatzot*). R. Harari agrees that the period after *chatzot* allows for leniency when there is a pressing need, but he is discussing

one might argue that if studying is required on *Tishah Be-Av*, and one is concerned that if one does not study on *Tishah Be-Av*, one's performance on an exam will be considerably worse, studying constitutes a *davar ha-aved*, and is permitted just as work is permitted. If this is the case, then it would appear that one should limit studying to the period after *chatzot* if at all possible. Clearly, if one can study before or after *Tishah Be-Av* instead, this would be mandated.

The Prohibitions of *Tishah Be-Av*

Washing Hands and Using Soap and Hand Sanitizer

Although washing one's hands or body is prohibited on *Tishah Be-Av*, *Shulchan Arukh*[33] permits washing hands if they are dirty, or if one has used the restroom; *Mishnah Berurah*[34] explains that this is because only washing for pleasure is prohibited, but washing for cleanliness is permitted. Thus, washing one's hands for infection control in the hospital is permitted on *Tishah Be-Av*.[35] Similarly, using hand sanitizer on *Tishah Be-Av* does not constitute a form of prohibited anointing on *Tishah Be-Av* because this prohibition is also limited to anointing for pleasure.[36]

Greeting Patients

As part of routine patient care, the medical practitioner greets each patient and asks how the patient is feeling. On *Tishah Be-Av*, however, *Shulchan Arukh*[37] rules that one may not greet another; *Mishnah Berurah*[38] notes that this prohibition includes saying "good morning." If a patient greets the observant Jewish practitioner, *Shulchan Arukh*[39] permits responding in kind, though with a graver tone. If appropriate, a possible alternative for the practitioner would be to begin the conversation by asking how the patient is feeling this morning. In this vein, R. Gavriel Zinner[40] notes that asking how someone is feeling

---

reading secular books when there is no pressing need, so perhaps he might agree that when one is studying for a test, and studying on *Tishah Be-Av* is urgently needed, there is room for leniency.

33 *Orach Chayyim* 554:9.

34 554:19.

35 R. Gavriel Zinner (*Nitei Gavriel, Bein Ha-Metzarim* 70:14) explicitly rules that physicians may wash their hands on *Tishah Be-Av* for infection control.

36 *Shulchan Arukh, Orach Chayyim* 554:15.

37 *Orach Chayyim* 554:20.

38 554:41.

39 Ibid.

40 *Nitei Gavriel, Bein Ha-Metzarim* 76:9–10.

on *Tishah Be-Av*, as well as visiting the sick, are certainly permitted on *Tishah Be-Av*.[41]

Sitting before *Chatzot*

Shulchan Arukh and Rama[42] cite the custom not to sit on a chair during the morning of *Tishah Be-Av*; according to *Shulchan Arukh*, this custom lasts until *minchah*, whereas according to Rama, it lasts until after *shacharit* and the recitation of *kinot* have concluded, which *Magen Avraham*[43] notes is a reference to the time after *chatzot*, midday. However, there are several situations in which a medical student or resident may need to sit if he or she is required to work in the hospital before *chatzot*. We will examine when there might be grounds for leniency.

There is debate among twentieth-century *poskim* as to whether one is permitted to sit on a moving vehicle on *Tishah Be-Av*. R. Yosef Shalom Elyashiv,[44] R. Ephraim Greenblatt,[45] and R. Chaim Pinchas Scheinberg[46] permit this. R. Greenblatt adds that he was told that R. Avraham Yishayahu Karelitz, author of *Chazon Ish*, rode in a taxi on *Tishah Be-Av*. R. Elyashiv's reasoning is that the prohibition of sitting applies only when the sitting functions as a form of pleasure, but not when one is sitting for another reason such as safety. Similarly, R. Gavriel Zinner[47] rules that one who performs *hagbahah* on the Torah at *shacharit* may sit down, just as *Derishah*[48] rules that a mourner who performs *hagbahah* may sit. He also rules that a *sandak* may sit at a *berit milah*.[49] On the other hand, R. Shlomo Zalman Auerbach[50] rules that one should preferably stand while traveling on a bus on *Tishah Be-Av*, if possible.

It would appear that if the medical student or resident needs to sit in order to perform medical procedures (e.g., performing a pelvic exam), those who permit sitting when not for pleasure would perhaps permit

41 R. Mordechai Eliyahu (cited in R. Moshe Harari's *Mikra'ei Kodesh*, *Ta'anit* section 3, ch. 7 footnote 79) also permits asking another individual how he or she is feeling, suggesting that this is a lesser version of greeting and thus permitted on *Tishah Be-Av*. R. Avigdor Nebenzahl (cited by R. Harari, ibid) permits asking a sick person how he or she is feeling, but not others.
42 *Orach Chayyim*, 559:3.
43 559:3.
44 Cited in *Torat Ha-Yoledet*, ch. 48, footnote 17.
45 *Rivevot Ephraim* 1:382.
46 Cited in *Rivevot Ephraim*, ibid.
47 *Nitei Gavriel*, *Bein Ha-Metzarim* 60:19 and footnote 32; 68:10.
48 *Yoreh De'ah* 384:2.
49 *Nitei Gavriel*, *Bein Ha-Metzarim* 68:10.
50 *Halikhot Shlomo*, *Tishah Be-Av*, 15:6.

this as well. However, there appears to be no room for leniency in a situation where one wishes to sit down to avoid awkwardness when others are sitting, and certainly not for comfort.

Chapter 11

Tzniut and Operating Room Attire

Batya Zuckerman, MD

While attire worn to the hospital is usually up to the discretion of clinical clerks (within the boundaries of professionalism), there are some instances where it becomes necessary to wear specific items of clothing for particular clerkships. This situation is most often encountered in the operating room where maintaining a sterile environment is absolutely critical. Students and operating room staff are asked to wear scrubs, which consist of a mask; a cap worn over the hair; a short-sleeved, V-neck top; pants; and shoe covers. For women who are accustomed to wearing higher necks, longer sleeves, and/or skirts, wearing scrubs in the operating room may present some practical challenges. It must be kept in mind that the guidelines for modest clothing may vary depending on which halakhic authority is consulted. Furthermore, the issues with individual clothing items discussed may not all be considered equally important.

Sources for Modest Dress

In addressing the challenges of wearing scrubs in the operating room, we will briefly discuss the teachings of the Gemara which highlight the importance of modest dress. The Mishnah[1] rules that there are some instances in which a husband is exempt from fulfilling the monetary obligations listed in the *ketuvah* to his wife upon dissolution of the marriage. Among these is the case where his wife "weaves in the marketplace." The Gemara there explains that this is because of the potential for her to expose her arm while weaving. While this case is related more to laws of the *ketuvah* than to dictums of modesty, it nevertheless sheds

---

1   *Ketubot* 72a.

light on the importance of proper attire in the public setting. In a similar fashion, the Gemara elsewhere[2] discusses the body parts of a woman that are considered to be *ervah*, private areas. These include *tefach* (a particular measure of usually-covered skin), *shok* (the thigh), *se'ar* (hair), and *kol* (voice). The Gemara relates that exposure to these types of *ervah* precludes the woman's husband from reciting *keriat shema*. From this Gemara as well, though the focus is on a man's obligation to recite *shema*, a sense of appropriateness of a woman's dress is brought to the fore. Rambam[3] and *Shulchan Arukh*[4] codify these two laws.

Contemporary authorities stress the importance of modest dress as well. R. Moshe Feinstein[5] discusses the permissibility of wearing particular garments with regard to the prohibition of *malbushei nochrim*, clothes unique to non-Jews. At the end of his responsum, he states that women must avoid wearing immodest clothes regardless of whether they would violate this particular prohibition. R. Ovadia Yosef[6] discusses the permissibility of a store selling sleeveless garments to women with regard to the prohibition of *lifnei ivver*, causing another Jew to sin. In that discussion, he cites various Biblical verses[7] that speak to the impermissibility of immodest dress. He focuses in particular on exposure of the arms, shoulders, chest, and back.

Wearing Clothing from the Opposite Sex

Another potential concern of wearing scrubs in the hospital is the prohibition of *begged ish*, the Biblical prohibition[8] for a woman to wear the garments of a man. However, it is clear from the Gemara and later authorities that a unisex garment is not subject to this prohibition. The Gemara[9] relates the story of the wife of R. Yehuda who made some woolen garment that both she and her husband would wear. Maharsha[10] notes that this was not a violation of *begged ish* because it was a unisex garment. In a similar vein, *Ohalei Ya'akov*[11] rules that the prohibition of *begged ish* only applies to garments whose styles are unique to men. Because hospital scrubs are worn by men and women, they are not subject to this prohibition.

2   *Berakhot* 24a.
3   *Hilkhot Keriat Shema* 3:16; *Hilkhot Ishut* 24:12.
4   *Orach Chayyim* 75; *Even Ha-Ezer* 115:4.
5   *Iggerot Moshe, Yoreh De'ah*, 1:81.
6   *Yechavveh Da'at*, 3:67.
7   Such as Ezekiel 20:25, Deuteronomy 23:10, Deuteronomy 23:15, and Leviticus 21:18.
8   Deuteronomy 22:5.
9   *Nedarim* 49b.
10   *Chiddushei Aggadot*, ibid.
11   *Siman* 70.

Practical Suggestions

We offer these practical guidelines as a starting point for developing an approach to hospital attire that is within the bounds of professionalism, recognizing that standards for modest dress may vary within the Orthodox community. It is useful to keep in mind that when actually "scrubbed in" to a surgery, the sterile gown should be sufficient to satisfy all *tzniut* concerns, as the gown worn in the operating room covers the whole torso and is loose-fitting. Many times, however, when just observing a surgery, only sterile scrubs are worn but without a gown. In these scenarios, the following advice may be useful:

1. One way to cover the neckline in an otherwise low-cut top is to wear two scrub tops, the bottom one backwards and the top one normally.
2. For those wearing the scrub shirt and pants, larger-sized scrubs generally avoid pants legs from being too form-fitting and cover as much of the arm as possible.
3. Married women, who cover their hair, can wear a scarf/*tichel* under the surgical cap.
4. If one feels that a practical solution might conform to one's halakhic standards but might be less than ideal, one might consider waiting until it is absolutely necessary to change into surgical garb.
5. One should remember always to maintain the sterile environment expected in the operating room setting.

Hopefully, through keeping these ideas in mind, as well as the ever-encompassing *"shivviti Hashem le-negdi tamid,"* "I place God before me always,"[12] it will be possible to navigate these issues correctly and comfortably.

---

12 Psalms 16:8.

Chapter 12

Mikveh Issues during Rotations and Residency

Becky Epstein, MD

Of the various halakhic issues that female medical students and residents can encounter during rotations and residency, questions of *niddah* are often among the most complicated due, in part, to the complex elements and consequential nature of the *halakhot* of *niddah*.

After a woman who is a *niddah* completes the *shivah nekiyyim* ("seven clean days") during which she has ensured there is no recurrent blood), she must immerse herself in the *mikveh* for the final stage of her purification process. A woman should perform the *tevilah* (immersion in the *mikveh*) after nightfall, exactly one week after she begins counting her *shivah nekiyyim*. For example, a woman who begins counting her *shivah nekiyyim* Sunday evening immerses in the *mikveh* the following Sunday night.

For several reasons, it is a priority for a woman to immerse in the *mikveh* on time. First, if a woman delays her *tevilah*, she will delay the important *mitzvot* of *peru u-revu* (having children)[1] and *onah* (marital relations between husband and wife). Additionally, by waiting to go to the *mikveh*, it may become more difficult for a woman to conceive, if she remains a *niddah* while she is ovulating. However, while it is important for a woman to immerse in the *mikveh* the night that she completes her *shivah nekiyyim*, there may be certain scenarios that arise during third- and fourth-year rotations and residency that make it difficult or impossible to do so.

A common situation is when a female medical student or resident is on overnight call during the night she would ordinarily immerse in the *mikveh*. Although in the winter months it may be possible for a woman to immerse in the *mikveh* after nightfall before her shift begins, this

1   *Shulchan Arukh, Yoreh De'ah* 197:2.

option is often unavailable in the summer months, when night call may begin before nightfall. The other options for when one can – and should – immerse in a *mikveh* generally depend on whether she will be on night call for additional nights, subsequent to her "ideal" *mikveh* night.

If a woman is unable to immerse in the *mikveh* on at the ideal time, the *poskim* discuss three other times when she could immerse: the seventh day before nightfall, any subsequent night, or any subsequent day.

Under normal circumstances, it is prohibited to immerse in the *mikveh* on the seventh day before nightfall.[2] The Gemara[3] explains that such immersions are not allowed out of concern that it will create a *safe*k (a situation of doubt). Rashi explains that this refers to a case in which a woman who immerses in the *mikveh* on the seventh day has marital relations with her husband before nightfall and finds blood immediately afterwards. Such blood retroactively discounts her *shivah nekiyyim*, which are not complete until nightfall of the seventh day, rendering her immersion invalid. Her marital relations with her husband on the seventh day, then, will have violated the Torah prohibition of cohabiting while a woman is a *niddah*.

There are some *poskim*[4] who believe, based on the explanation in the Gemara, that seventh day *mikveh* immersions may be allowed under extenuating circumstances. If a woman truly needed to immerse before nightfall of the seventh day, it could be permissible as long as she does not see her husband until after nightfall. Because the woman would not see her husband until her *shivah nekiyyim* are complete, it would be impossible to create a situation in which a woman will have mistakenly had marital relations while she is a *niddah*, thus alleviating the Gemara's concern. *However, it is important to note that this* pesak *is particularly controversial, and is not agreed upon by all* poskim.[5]

A more widely-accepted option for a woman to immerse in the *mikveh*, if she cannot do so on her ideal *mikveh* night, is on the next possible night (i.e., the eighth night).[6] However, if a woman is unable to immerse in the *mikveh* on the seventh night *and* on the eighth night, can she immerse on the eighth day before nightfall, or must she wait until the ninth night? An eighth-day immersion is not as problematic as a seventh-day immersion because a woman who immerses on the eighth day has already completed her *shivah nekiyyim*. Therefore, the scenario described in the Gemara would occur. Nonetheless, the Gemara[7] states that daytime immersions are *always* problematic due to *serakh*

---

2   *Shulchan Arukh, Yoreh De'ah* 197:3.
3   *Niddah* 67b.
4   *Lechem Ve-Simlah* (*Simlah* 197:5) and *Sidrei Taharah* 197:9.
5   Of note, the practice is cited approvingly by R. Moshe Feinstein (*Iggerot Moshe, Yoreh De'ah* 3:60).
6   *Niddah* 67b.
7   Ibid.

bittah, concern that a woman's daughter may see her mother return from the *mikveh* during the day and incorrectly conclude that daytime immersions are permissible, even on the seventh day. *Shulchan Arukh*[8] therefore concludes that a woman should ideally not immerse before nightfall on *any* day.

However, there is still more room to be lenient for eighth-day immersions than for seventh-day immersions, since the only concern is *serakh bitah* but there is no concern that a woman will violate the more severe prohibition of having marital relations while a *niddah*. Thus, Rambam[9] and *Shulchan Arukh*[10] agree that if a woman cannot immerse in the *mikveh* at night (e.g., if it is dangerous to travel to the *mikveh* at night), she can immerse during the eighth day or afterwards. Importantly, a daytime immersion is only allowed if the woman will also not be able to immerse on the following night. So, for example, a woman who cannot immerse in the *mikveh* on the seventh, eighth and ninth nights may immerse on the eighth or ninth day, but must wait until the tenth night to immerse in the *mikveh* if she has not already done so on the eighth or ninth day.

The following is a brief outline of possibilities available to a female medical student or resident who has night call and needs to immerse in the *mikveh*. Her options are based on the halakhic discussions above, and may differ depending on her specific night call schedule.

NOTE: The outline below should *not* be used to resolve halakhic questions independent of a *posek*. One must always consult with one's *posek* before deciding when to immerse in a *mikveh* in such scenarios, especially since not every *posek* will allow all of these leniencies and every scenario is different. This discussion is solely meant to introduce to the reader the basic options of *tevilah* in these cases so that they may recognize a halakhic question when it arises and ask it intelligently.

A. *A woman is on night call for only one night (her "ideal" mikveh night):*
   1. *Tevilah* can be pushed off until the next night (i.e., the eighth night from when she began counting her *shivah nekiyyim*).
   2. Some *poskim* may allow the woman to immerse in the *mikveh* on the seventh day before nightfall. She must, however, go directly from the *mikveh* to her shift at the hospital, as she is not allowed to see her husband until after nightfall.[11]
B. *A woman is on night call for more than one night (her "ideal"* mikveh *night, plus any consecutive nights which follow it):*

8   *Yoreh De'ah* 197:3.
9   *Hilkhot Issurei Biah* 4:8.
10 *Yoreh De'ah* 197:4.
11 See *Simlah* 197:5 and *Sidrei Taharah* 197:9. Again, this *pesak* is not accepted by all *poskim*, and therefore is a particular matter of dispute.

1. *Tevilah* can be pushed off until the next night that she is able to attend the *mikveh*.
2. The woman can immerse in the *mikveh* on the eighth day before nightfall, or any subsequent day in which she will not be able to immerse in the *mikveh* that night. For example, if a woman has night call on the seventh, eighth, ninth and tenth nights from when she began counting her *shivah nekiyyim*, she may immerse in the *mikveh* on the eighth, ninth or tenth day before nightfall.[12]

Due to the disputed nature of the issues involved, it is imperative that a woman consults with her *posek* before relying on any of the possible options mentioned above. With her *posek*'s guidance and advice, she will hopefully be able to immerse in the *mikveh* at a time which is both halakhically acceptable, as well as personally comfortable for her.

---

12 See Rambam (*Hilkhot Issurei Biah* 4:8) and *Shulchan Arukh* (*Yoreh De'ah* 197:4); see also *Darkhei Teshuvah* 197:33 and *Avodat Ha-Gershuni* 20.

Section III
Interacting with Patients

Chapter 13

Physical Contact between Men and Women for Health Professionals

Jeremy Miles, MD

The prohibition on physical contact between men and women is a common halakhic predicament that arises in various environments. For medical students and health professionals, however, this issue is fraught with many new complexities and questions. Notwithstanding everyday concerns that arise for students, such as shaking hands with classmates, for students in their clinical education and for healthcare practitioners, questions about physical exams and interactions with patients emerge, which obscure matters even further. This chapter will first present a broad analysis of the topic and then relate this background to the dilemmas that occur throughout medical school and in healthcare settings.

A. The Prohibition in the Torah, *Rishonim* and *Acharonim*

The source of the prohibition of physical contact between men and women is derived from the end of the verse, *"lo tikrevu legallot ervah,"* "Do not come near in uncovering their nakedness."[1] In Talmudic language, the term *ervah* (plural: *arayot*) is used to refer to a person with whom sexual relations are forbidden. Based on the peculiar language of this verse, commentators explain that not only "revealing the nakedness," i.e., having sexual relations with an *ervah,* is prohibited, but even becoming close, *tikrevu,* is forbidden, to both men and women.[2] What

1 Leviticus 18:6.
2 See Rashi ad loc, s.v. *lo tikrevu.*

is included in the category of "*tikrevu*" is relatively ambiguous and has been the source of debate among various authorities.

Rambam[3] writes that one who kisses or hugs an *ervah* "*be-derekh ta'avah*," in an amorous fashion, or has any form of pleasurable sexual contact, is liable to receive lashes. It is evident from Rambam's statement that the prohibition of contact with an *ervah* is Biblical in origin. That said, Rambam's statement could be interpreted in numerous ways and has been a source of debate among later commentators. The central point of contention of these later arguments is the phrase "*be-derekh ta'avah*." Does this phrase signify that only amorous touch is prohibited, but non-amorous touch is permitted? Or is any sort of physical contact between a man and woman considered "*be-derekh ta'avah*"?

Ramban[4] disagrees with Rambam's interpretation of the verse. He believes that the verse is outlining the general prohibition of intercourse with an *ervah* and not mere physical contact. In his preferred explanation, he posits that the prohibition of contact is only a rabbinic inference deduced from the word *tikrevu*.

Thus, both Rambam and Ramban postulate that there is a prohibition of physical contact between sexes based on the verse in the Torah. However, they argue with regard to the severity of such a prohibition. Furthermore, although Rambam and Ramban discuss the source of the prohibition of physical contact, they hardly elaborate on its scope or practical applications. Yet, later *poskim* have elucidated many of these issues using the words of the Rambam and Ramban as a basis in adjudicating these matters.

Commenting on Rambam, *Beit Yosef*[5] affirms that touching one's wife who is in a state of *niddah* would be prohibited, even if she were deathly ill.[6] *Beit Yosef* considers this point in the context of whether it is permissible for a man to take the pulse of his sick wife who is also a *niddah*. The reason why *Beit Yosef* prohibits this, despite the general rule that almost all prohibitions are suspended for *pikuach nefesh*, saving a life, is because this case would fall under the category of *avizrayhu*. *Avizrayhu* is a term used in the Gemara when an act is similar to one of the three cardinal sins (murder, illicit sexual relations and idolatry) which one may not violate even in a *pikuach nefesh* situation, but does not exactly fit into the category.[7] Although *Beit Yosef*

---

3   *Issurei Biah* 21:1. Cf. *Sefer Ha-Mitzvot, lo ta'aseh* 353.
4   *Hasagot* on *Lavin* in *Sefer Ha-Mitzvot*, 353.
5   *Yoreh De'ah* 195.
6   *Beit Shmuel* (*Even Ha-Ezer* 20:1) and *Torat Shelamim* (*Yoreh De'ah* 195: 15) agree with *Beit Yosef*'s interpretation of Rambam.
7   *Beit Yosef*'s understanding that physical contact is included in the category of *avizrayhu* is not obvious. One could argue that contact is still Biblically prohibited but not to the extent of being categorized with the three cardinal sins.

is discussing a scenario between a husband and wife where there are added stringencies, his reasoning would apply even to non-married men and women. *Beit Yosef* bases his position on Rambam, quoted above, that physical contact is Biblically prohibited. However, he neither elaborates on Rambam's phrase *"be-derekh ta'avah"* nor does he differentiate between different forms of physical contact. Consequently, according to *Beit Yosef*, all forms of touch are prohibited on a Biblical level, regardless of one's attitudes or intentions.

However, *Shakh*[8] understands Rambam's position differently. He suggests that, even according to Rambam, there is only a Biblical prohibition of physical contact when done *"be-derekh ta'avah ve-chibbat biah,"* touch performed in a sexual manner. In *Beit Yosef*'s scenario though, the contact is certainly not *"be-derekh ta'avah"* and therefore would be permissible in a medical context.[9] Moreover, *Shakh* emphasizes that there is an accepted custom of all Jewish doctors to take pulses and perform other medical procedures on women, even if they are married (and thus considered *ervah*).[10] Hence, according to *Shakh*'s interpretation of Rambam, physical contact is Biblically prohibited only when done in a matter of *chibah*, in an affectionate fashion, which excludes such contact needed to take the pulse of a woman.

Nevertheless, it is still unclear how to interpret *Shakh*'s arguments. Does he believe that physical contact in which there is no *chibah* is absolutely permitted? Or, even though he maintains that it is Biblically permitted, is there still a rabbinic prohibition banning all forms of physical touch? R. Moshe Feinstein provides both explanations of *Shakh* in two separate responsa, as will be discussed below. R. Ovadia Yosef[11] interprets *Shakh* as stating that there is still a rabbinic prohibition. Similarly, R. Yosef quotes *Kereiti U-Peleiti*[12] and R. Chaim Pelagi[13] who also believe that there is nonetheless a rabbinic prohibition with all physical contact, regardless of the form or the intent.

---

8   *Yoreh De'ah* 195:20.
9   This case involves a husband and wife and, therefore, the additional elements of *niddah* and *harchakot* (additional prohibitions that apply to a husband and wife while she is a *niddah*) must be addressed as well. Since the wife in this scenario is a *choleh she-yesh bo sakkanah*, dangerously ill, *pikuach nefesh* applies and these other halakhic issues are ignored. Yet, if this case did not involve a husband and wife, *Shakh* would hold that physical contact is permissible, even absent *pikuach nefesh* considerations, because there is no *derekh chibah ve-ta'avah* involved.
10   *Semag* (*Lavin* 126) writes similarly that one only incurs lashes, indicating that the prohibition is Biblical, when the contact was *be-derekh ta'avah ve-chibbat biah*.
11   *Taharat Ha-Bayit* vol. 1, 38.
12   *Yoreh De'ah*, 195:20.
13   Responsa *Lev Chayyim*, 2:4.

The discussion thus far has highlighted the main areas of dispute among early commentators with respect to the global prohibition of physical contact. We observe three different outlooks on the nature of physical contact with *arayot*. First, according to Ramban, contact is a rabbinic prohibition, which brings with it relative flexibility in handling various situations. Second, according to *Beit Yosef*'s analysis of Rambam, physical contact is a Biblical prohibition subsumed under the category of *avizrayhu* and all forms of physical contact are included. Third, according to *Shakh*'s view of Rambam, only contact which is "*derekh chibah ve-ta'avah*" is Biblically prohibited, while other forms of contact are still rabbinically prohibited.

B. Shaking Hands

Medical school is similar to other types of graduate schools and business scenarios in that there is intermingling between men and women. The classic scenario of physical contact during the years of medical school is shaking hands with members of the opposite sex. Whether this is permissible or not depends on several nuances that will be discussed below.

While shaking hands is obviously a form of physical contact, it is not clear whether it is encompassed in the prohibition of physical contact. In order to answer this, we need to ask two questions: 1) Is the act of shaking hands considered *derekh chibah*? 2) If shaking hands is not *derekh chibah*, is it then permitted to shake hands with members of the opposite sex, or is there still a categorical prohibition on contact even when not *derekh chibah*? These questions are very difficult to answer as they depend somewhat on sociological and cultural considerations. Yet, many *poskim* in the past century have had to confront these persistent concerns and have provided solutions to many of these questions.

R. Yaakov Kanievsky,[14] the Steipler Gaon, believes that shaking hands with members of the opposite sex is a Biblical prohibition, as per the position of Rambam. R. Kanievsky argues that no person in modern times can shake the hand of a person of the opposite sex without any affection or desire involved. He contrasts modern man to the *amora'im* of the Gemara who had physical contact with women yet had no illicit thoughts or feelings from those encounters.[15] Therefore, according to R. Kanievsky, there are forms of touch, which theoretically would be allowed if there were no *derekh chibah*, as there is evidence in the Gemara of scenarios where physical contact was allowed because there was no *chibah* among the people involved. However, nowadays, it is impossible for there to be physical contact between sexes without

---

14 *Karyana De-Igreta*, 162-163; cited by *Nishmat Avraham, Even Ha-Ezer* 20.
15 *Ketubot* 17a, *Shabbat* 13a.

chibah. Moreover, he writes that even if a woman initiates a handshake, it would be prohibited to reciprocate under any conditions, even if it would lead to her embarrassment. R. Kanievsky argues that his position reflects that of *Chazon Ish. Chazon Ish,* as cited by R. Kanievsky,[16] states that any physical contact between an unmarried man and woman falls under the category of *avizryahu,* concurring with the position of *Beit Yosef.* Consequently, shaking hands has the status of *yehareg ve-al ya'avor,* such that one must give up one's life in order to avoid transgressing this prohibition, and according to *Chazon Ish* and R. Kanievseky, one must give one's life to avoid shaking hands with a member of the opposite sex.

R. Moshe Feinstein discusses this topic in four responsa. In one responsum,[17] R. Feinstein writes that there are "*yirei Hashem*" who shake the hands of women and rely on the fact that it is not "*derekh chibah ve-ta'avah.*" He disagrees with this view and insists that it is difficult to rely on this assumption. Elsewhere,[18] R. Feinstein is more emphatic in his position and writes that it is absolutely prohibited to shake a woman's hand because it is *derekh chibah.* Furthermore, in another responsum,[19] R. Feinstein rules that it is permissible to sit next to a person of the opposite sex on a train or bus, even though there will presumably be physical contact, because it is not *derekh chibah ve-ta'avah.* R. Feinstein bases his explanation on *Shakh* who, as stated above, declares that the prohibition of physical contact only applies when it is *be-derekh chibah ve-ta'avah.* R. Feinstein interprets *Shakh,* in this responsum, as postulating that physical contact is outright permitted if it is not *derekh chibah.* However, in a fourth responsum,[20] R. Feinstein understands *Shakh* in a different manner. He deduces from *Shakh* that there is still a rabbinic prohibition of physical contact between men and women, even if there is no *chibah.* The only way that physical contact could be permitted, R. Feinstein suggests, is when there is no *chibah* and there is an additional factor that mitigates any potential illicit act or thought. One example of this is "*avidatayhu taridi,*" one who is engaged in one's work. When someone is involved in his work, there is a lower likelihood of unfavorable outcomes to occur. This is how R. Feinstein justifies *Shakh*'s explanation about the everyday occurrence of Jewish doctors taking the pulses of women. Since the act itself is not "*derekh chibah ve-ta'avah,*" and the doctors are focused in their work, there is no worry that physical contact would lead to anything else and therefore is permitted.

16 *Karyana De-Igreta,* 162–163; cited by *Nishmat Avraham, Even Ha-Ezer* 20.
17 *Even Ha-Ezer* 1:56.
18 *Orach Chayyim* 1:113; *Even Ha-Ezer* 4:32(9).
19 *Even Ha-Ezer* 2:14.
20 *Yoreh De'ah* 3:54.

What emerges from these various responsa is that R. Feinstein affirms that only physical contact that is *derekh chibah* is Biblically prohibited, yet contact which is not *derekh chibah* is a matter of dispute between two responsa of R. Feinstein. Nevertheless, R. Feinstein himself felt that shaking hands is considered *derekh chibah* and thus is prohibited.

In line with R. Feinstein, several *poskim* agree that shaking hands in a normal fashion is *derekh chibah*, and therefore attempt to provide practical solutions to this dilemma. R. Joseph B. Solveitchik has been quoted as stating that if one would shake a person's hand like a "dead fish," i.e., let the other person do the act of touching, it would not be considered *derekh chibah*.[21] Similarly, R. Mordechai Willig has been reported to advise to shake hands in a very firm manner so that there is no *chibah* involved.[22] Therefore, according to both R. Soloveitchik and R. Willig, it follows that one should avoid initiating a handshake with a member of the opposite sex and should only shake hands when the other person initiates.

However, R. Hershel Schachter asserts that handshaking is not *derekh chibah*.[23] R. Schachter quotes a responsum of R. Chaim Berlin, the Netziv's son, who concurs with this idea as well.[24] In addition, R. Schachter claims[25] that even though R. Feinstein prohibited handshaking in writing, R. Feinstein's students told him personally that R. Feinstein was lenient in practical situations. What emerges is that R. Schachter agrees with R. Feinstein's understanding of the prohibition of physical contact (as articulated in at least one responsum cited above), yet believes that handshaking is not included in the prohibition.

In a medical school environment, many scenarios could arise that would put these ideas into practice. One such case would be when a student is meeting a fellow student or professor for the first time. Can the student extend his or her hand first or does he/she need to wait until the other party initiates? Can he/she even shake the person's hand at all? According to R. Kanievsky and *Chazon Ish*, one would not be allowed to shake the person's hand, no matter the circumstance, as they believe every form of touch is *derekh chibah*. R. Feinstein, presumably, would concur because he believes that shaking hands is considered *derekh chibah*. However, R. Willig and R. Soloveitchik would permit shaking hands with a classmate or a professor, if the classmate/professor initiates and the handshake is performed in a specific manner such that there is

---

21 Rabbi Aryeh Leibowitz delineates many of these positions in a lecture available online at http://www.yutorah.org/lectures/lecture.cfm/773078.

22 Ibid.

23 R. Schachter's lecture on this topic is recorded and available at http://www.torahweb.org/audio/rsch_100508.html.

24 Ibid.

25 In a recording available online at http://www.yutorah.org/lectures/lecture.cfm/773851.

no *chibah*. R. Schachter, on the other hand, states that handshaking is not considered *derekh chibah* and, accordingly, is permitted between men and women. R. Schachter understands *Shakh* as asserting that once *derekh chibah* is not a concern there is no rabbinic prohibition and therefore handshaking is halakhically permissible. Consequently, not only is shaking hands with the opposite sex permitted but even initiating is allowed, assuming it is done in a proper fashion.[26]

Even if one argued that handshaking is not defined as *derekh chibah*, there are many *poskim*,[27] as discussed above, who believe that there still is a rabbinic injunction against all forms of touch. That said, one could argue that even according to those *poskim*, in a scenario where a student or professor initiates a handshake, he or she would be allowed to recipro-cate. This is because of the dictum "*gadol kevod ha-beriyot she-docheh et lo ta'aseh she-ba-Torah*," great is human dignity in that it overrides any prohibition from the Torah.[28] Although this phrase implies that all prohibitions are disregarded in situations of *kevod ha-beriyot*, where human dignity is at stake, the Gemara eventually limits this dictum to rabbinic prohibitions, while it does not apply to most Torah prohibi-tions. In any case, since a person would presumably be embarrassed or insulted if one did not return a handshake, one could potentially apply the rule of "*kevod ha-beriyot*" in this circumstance and allow shaking hands, even though there is an existing rabbinic prohibition. In fact, R. Yaakov Kamenetsky[29] explores this scenario and poses the possibility of allowing handshaking when embarrassment is an issue, yet he admits that further analysis is needed.

C. Physical Contact in the Context of Physician Training

One of the more unique concerns that arise in medical school is in the context of physician training. During the early years of medical school, medical students learn how to perform a physical exam. Students learn these techniques and skills by practicing on each other, which inevitably involves physical contact. The nature of the contact during a physical exam is quite different than a mere handshake. The added level of inva-siveness prompts additional questions that do not pertain to shaking hands.

---

26 R. Schachter believes that it is permitted to initiate a handshake, but only in circumstances that require one to do so.

27 R. Yosef, *Kereiti U-Peleiti* and R. Chaim Pelagi.

28 *Berakhot* 19b.

29 *Emet Le-Ya'akov* to *Shulchan Arukh*, p. 405.

There is very little discussion in classical sources regarding physical contact in these contexts. As a result, it becomes quite challenging when categorizing these other forms of touch with regard to the prohibition. Nonetheless, one factor that can conceivably be employed as a basis for leniency is the setting in which the contact is taking place. Although the type of physical contact is a major determinant of whether something is defined as *derekh chibah* or not, the context of such contact is also a key component. If the physical contact is done in a professional setting with the appropriate mindset one could argue that this renders the contact not to be *derekh chibah*. As Rambam writes, only contact which is performed in a framework of *"ta'avah"* is forbidden. That said, this consideration is not definitive and must be analyzed further.

The physical exam involves various forms of touch such as palpation, percussion and feeling for various pulses. With regard to taking a pulse, *Shakh*,[30] as discussed above, notes that it has been the custom for centuries for Jewish male doctors to take the pulses of female patients. While it could be that *Shakh* held this view only regarding physicians who were involved in *pikuach nefesh*, it is apparent that *Shakh* assumed that taking a pulse is not *derekh chibah*. Thus, *Shakh*, according to those who understood there being no rabbinic prohibition, would allow this in context of training as well. In fact, R. Feinstein, who in one responsum[31] interpreted *Shakh* as stating that a rabbinic prohibition does persist with regard to touch which is not *derekh chibah*, still admits that when there are other factors at play, such as *"avidatayhu taridi,"* one who is engaged in one's work, then *Shakh* would render touch which is not *derekh chibah* to be permissible. The Gemara[32] understands this idea to mean that when one is involved in his professional duties, illicit thoughts will not arise and therefore something that would technically be prohibited in one context can be permitted in another. In this setting, one can contend that training is a form of "work" and therefore creates a scenario where one can be lenient. R. Kanievsky, on the other hand, presumably would prohibit these forms of contact, irrespective of the context, due to the assumed illicit thoughts that one could not prevent. Additionally, R. Kanievsky quoted *Chazon Ish* as stating that any form of touch is *avizrayhu* and has the status of *yehareg ve-al ya'avor*, such that one must give up one's life rather than violate the prohibition. Therefore, even in a context of learning and training, these scenarios would be considered prohibited. Regarding the opinions of R. Soloveitchik, R. Willig and R. Schachter, the main question at play would be whether these forms of touch are objectively considered *derekh chibah* or not. R. Soloveitchik and R. Willig, who believe that

30   *Yoreh De'ah* 195.
31   *Yoreh De'ah* 3:54.
32   *Bava Metzia* 91a.

shaking hands in a normal fashion is *derekh chibah*, would presumably view these forms of touch as *derekh chibah* as well. Yet, it is unknown whether they factor in the context or if *"aviditayhu taridi"* plays a role in the discussion. These questions apply similarly to the opinion of R. Schachter as well.

D. Physical Contact in the Hospital Setting

While the scenarios discussed above certainly apply in the later years of medical school, novel complexities arise as students enter their clinical rotations. During the later years of medical school, students rotate through various specialties in hospitals or primary care clinics. These clinical experiences are mainly educational as students apply their medical knowledge to the real life setting. That said, medical students can be quite influential in the care of patients. Medical students and physicians are involved in performing physical exams and comforting patients during their stay, both of which generate halakhic questions.

As discussed above, the physical exam presents itself with various questions. While the dispensation of performing a physical exam in the context of training would undoubtedly apply in this scenario, there is even more of a reason to be lenient. When dealing with patients there might be an added element of *pikuach nefesh* or *safek* (uncertain) *pikuach nefesh*. According to most authorities, if the patient is defined as dangerously ill[33] or there is uncertainty as to whether the patient is dangerously ill, it would then not only be permitted to perform a physical exam or anything else that involves physical contact, but obligatory. However, those who believe that physical contact is included in the category of *avizrayhu* of the prohibition of illicit relations, and therefore would be included in *yehareg ve-al ya'avor*, would argue that it would still be prohibited to touch a person of the opposite sex in this case. Furthermore, even if *pikuach nefesh* is not a factor, there are still leniencies, as discussed above, with regard to a physical exam, which can be applied in this scenario as well, such as *"aviditayhu taridi"* or lack of *derekh chibah*.

An additional question that materializes in these clinical settings is that of comforting patients in need. Most people who find themselves in the hospital are in a precarious state, full of anxiety and distress. Although the main goal of the medical team is to treat the patient, comforting him or her is an important facet of patient care. Medical students, as part of a medical team, have the advantage of spending an ample amount of time with patients, more than attending physicians and residents. Accordingly, medical students can play a critical role in tending to the psychological care of patients. With all this in mind, an

---

33   See Chapter 20 for a discussion of how different patient types are classified.

incident may occur where a medical student or physician perceives that a patient would benefit greatly from holding his or her hand or putting an arm around the patient's shoulder. The question is whether it is permissible for a student or physician to comfort a patient of the opposite sex in this manner.

This scenario is a bit more complex as the act of touching in this case is not just a means to a diagnosis or for medical knowledge but is for comfort and consolation. Although one's intent in this case is not sexual in nature, it is nevertheless affectionate touch. Additionally, even if this form of touch is considered affectionate, does it fall into the category of "*derekh chibah ve-ta'avah*"? *Nishmat Avraham*[34] cites R. Yehoshua Neuwirth who posits that a physician is allowed to calm a patient of the opposite sex by holding the patient's hand or head if he or she is in pain or scared. *Nishmat Avraham* does not expound on the reasoning for this dispensation of R. Neuwirth. One could argue that this scenario is permitted either due to "*aviditayhu taridi*" or because there is no *chibah* in this context. He does not differentiate between different types of patients and thus, it is unclear whether *pikuach nefesh* is playing a role in this case. Because R. Neuwirth does not differentiate between different types of patients, it would appear that a medical student or physician would be permitted to comfort a patient of the opposite sex through these means. R. Hershel Schachter concurs with this view.[35]

Conclusion

The subject of physical contact in the context of medical school and in the hospital is quite multifaceted. This is true not only because the milieu of medical school and healthcare practice creates these intricate circumstances but also because these matters are very difficult to classify. Nevertheless, it is important to elucidate these dilemmas no matter how complex they seem to be. In brief, while this chapter introduces the prohibition of physical contact and the halakhic questions that arise, it is imperative to emphasize that this discussion is only meant to broach the many questions that emerge and is in no way meant to adjudicate personal halakhic questions. Every scenario is unique and should be dealt with the appropriate *yirat shamayim* and with the advice of a personal halakhic advisor.

---

34 *Yoreh De'ah* 195.
35 In a recording available at http://www.yutorah.org/lectures/lecture. cfm/773851.

Chapter 14

Lifnei Ivver: When Best Practice Conflicts with Religious Practice

Rabbi Yair Hindin

Over the past number of decades, trends towards openness and acceptance have taken a stronghold in American society.[1] In many ways, these trends have brought significant benefits to the American Jewish community. Religious rights and protection for public religious expression are just two such positive outgrowths of current liberal trends. At the same time, however, the sacrosanct value of tolerance presents challenges for any faith group, and Orthodox Judaism is no exception. Broadly put, there is little tolerance when a practitioner's religious values place any limit upon that which the practitioner can present or perform for the patient, client, etc. More specifically, the tension between the "best practice" in a particular field and religious beliefs or laws is one example of this challenge.

"Best practice" is that which a particular field has determined to be the most ethical and appropriate approach to a problem. At times, a professional organization, such as the American Medical Association (AMA) or the American Psychological Association (APA), recommends certain practices as "best practices" and an individual practitioner bound by these standards may be subject to loss of professional

---

1   Pew Research Center, Social and Political Attitudes, http://www.pewforum. org/2015/11/03/chapter-4-social-and-political-attitudes/. Immanuel Kant, Religion Within the Limits of Reason Alone (New York: Harper & Row, 1960), pp. liv–lvii. Emil Fackenheim, Encounters Between Judaism and Modern Philosophy (Philadelphia: Jewish Publication Society, 1973), ch. 2, offers a Jewish perspective to this issue. Moving from Western philosophy to American society, Henry Steele Commager's The American Mind (New Haven: Yale University Press, 1967), pp. 19–21, discusses the realities in contemporary American society.

license or legal action if these approaches are disregarded.[2] While often these standards align, or at least do not conflict, with religious practice, there are a number of ways in which "best practice" can conflict with normative Orthodox Jewish practice, namely *halakhah*. This conflict can manifest itself in any one of four categories: offering professional advice, enabling a violation of Jewish law, passively allowing a violation of Jewish law, or actively supporting a violation of Jewish law. For example:

- *Professional Advice:* Best practice may call upon a doctor to recommend sterilization or contraceptive methods for a patient in cases which violate *halakhah*. Another example may be when best practice dictates that a clinician encourage homosexual behavior or offer advice on ways that make a homosexual relationship more sustainable, which is antithetical to *halakhah*.
- *Enabling:* Writing a prescription for certain forms of non-halakhic contraception or distributing condoms may be best practice in certain situations but may conflict with *halakhah*.
- *Passively Allowing:* Withholding CPR for a patient who has a non-halakhic DNR (do not resuscitate) order may be considered best practice even when it contradicts *halakhah*. More generally, best practice may be to stop the administration of lifesaving acts in certain scenarios whereas *halakhah* would require continued intervention.
- *Actively Engaging:* In certain scenarios best practice may require performing a procedure, such as providing assistance during an abortion, even when it opposes *halakhah*. An anesthesiologist may be called upon to assist a non-halakhic abortion.

Three areas of *halakhah* are relevant to our topic: *Lifnei ivver*, the prohibition against placing a stumbling block in front of a blind person; *mesayye'a*, supporting a sinner; and *dina de-malkhuta dina*, the obligation to follow the law of the land. Of these three, the first and second areas will occupy the focus of this chapter.

Lifnei Ivver

The prohibition of *lifnei ivver* appears in the Torah: "You should not curse the deaf, *nor put a stumbling block before the blind*, but you should fear your God: I am the Lord."[3] While most commentators believe that the specific scenario described in this verse is prohibited,[4]

---

2   Mary Hermann and Barbara Richter Herlihy, "Legal and ethical implications of refusing to counsel homosexual clients." *Journal of Counseling and Development*, Vol. 84, 2006, pp. 414–418.
3   Leviticus 19:14.
4   *Minchat Chinukh* (*Mitzvah* 232, s.v. *ve-hu ke-over al mitzvat ha-melekh ve-ein lokin*) discusses the possibility that the literal meaning of the verse may not be included within the Biblical prohibition.

i.e., placing a physical stumbling block in front of someone who lacks sight, the Gemara offers two additional, less literal, understandings. The first describes a prohibition against offering bad advice to someone who is "blind," unaware of the details, of a particular matter. For example, intentionally offering bad financial advice is included within this understanding of *lifnei ivver*. A second understanding of *lifnei ivver* offered by the Gemara is enabling someone to sin. For example, a doctor who advises a non-halakhically-sanctioned abortion may violate this prohibition. Thus the verse reads as follows: it is prohibited for someone to assist an individual who is "blind" to the correct path of Torah observance to commit an act of sin. While both interpretations are relevant to our topic, this chapter will focus on the second interpretation.

Dependent or Independent Prohibition

An issue that may initially appear theoretical but indeed has practical significance is whether the prohibition to cause another to sin is an outgrowth of the specific prohibition which one is encouraging, or a separate, general prohibition of *lifnei ivver*, unconnected to any specific prohibition. One practical illustration of this distinction may relate to the moment when one violates *lifnei ivver*. Does one violate *lifnei ivver* when one "places" the stumbling block, i.e., when one facilitates the sin, or only when the "blind person" stumbles, when the sin is committed? If the prohibition is linked to the specific sin which one encourages another to commit, one is more likely to assume that *lifnei ivver* is violated at the moment the sin is actually committed. According to this approach, one can only violate *lifnei ivver* if the sin being facilitated actually occurs. If there is only a general prohibition of *lifnei ivver*, then we are likely to view the placing of the stumbling block as the moment of the violation of the prohibition. Additionally, the violation can occur even if the actual sin being facilitated never occurs. Thus, according to this first approach, if it is unlikely that the sin will ultimately be committed or perhaps even if it will occur indirectly, there may be more room for leniency. For example, if a Jewish doctor recommends a procedure, guided by best practice, but knows the patient will likely not undergo this procedure, perhaps understanding the prohibition of *lifnei ivver* as linked to the specific sin violated may create room for leniency.

Another practical manifestation of these two perspectives may emerge when dealing with rabbinical prohibitions. Does one violate a Biblical or rabbinic prohibition of *lifnei ivver* when one facilitates a rabbinic prohibition? Initially, one might assume that when the Torah describes the prohibition of *lifnei ivver*, it is irrespective of the "type" of stumbling block and thus one always violates a Biblical prohibition. Yet, it would be strange for one to violate a Biblical prohibition for facilitating violation of a rabbinic prohibition. This question may also be rooted in the nature of the *lifnei ivver* discussed above. If *lifnei ivver* is considered to be an extension of the sin one facilitates, then one could only violate a rabbinic prohibition for facilitating a rabbinic prohibition. If, however, *lifnei ivver* remains its own distinct violation, then it may not matter what type of violation is being facilitated: any facilitation incurs a Biblical prohibition. In general, there are some leniencies which exist when dealing with rabbinic prohibitions and thus determining what type of prohibition one is violating, Biblical or rabbinic, is of great significance. For example, a situation in which one is unsure if a violation of *lifnei ivver* will occur as a result of one's actions, a case of *safek*, may demonstrate the relevance of the aforementioned discussion. One is generally permitted to engage in a scenario of *safek* when dealing with a rabbinic violation. However, if the *safek* relates to a Biblical violation, one is prohibited from engaging in such a situation. Thus, determining the level of the violation in a case of *lifnei ivver*, Biblical or rabbinic, is of great import.

A final question which may hinge upon this distinction relates to whether one can encourage sinning when there may be long-term halakhic value in doing so. For example, R. Shlomo Zalman Auerbach[5] discusses the permissibility of giving a Jewish guest food when there is concern that this individual will not recite a *berakhah*. He concludes that this is permissible since although in the short-term, the individual will eat without reciting a *berakhah*, viewed through a long-term perspective, a positive relationship between the guest and the host may bring the guest closer to Jewish observance. R. Aharon Lichtenstein explains the logic of this approach to be rooted in R. Auerbach's understanding of *lifnei ivver*. If a given violation of *lifnei ivver* is linked to the sin one is facilitating, then the moment the violation occurs, in this case the eating of the food without a *berakhah*, one would violate the prohibition of *lifnei ivver*. However, understanding the prohibition as a general one may enable one to detach the violation of *lifnei ivver* from the prohibition one has facilitated and adopt an approach in which *lifnei ivver* is violated at a later point. This understanding, according to R. Lichtenstein, affords certain leniency and may serve as the halakhic basis for R. Auerbach to permit giving food to someone who will not say a *berakhah*. If ultimately, even in the distant future, one's guest is more likely to observe *mitzvot*, one might be permitted to cause that guest to commit a prohibition in the short term.

Relating this to our discussion, one may ask if a practitioner, for example, may enable or facilitate a sin in a particular situation if it is reasonable to assume that in the long run this will lead to decreased Torah violation. Understanding the prohibition of *lifnei ivver* as a global

5   *Minchat Shlomo* 35.

prohibition unconnected to any specific prohibition may allow for a long-term view which may permit this approach.

The Likelihood of Sinning

The Gemara[6] discusses the scenario of handing a cup of wine to a *nazir*, an individual who has taken a vow not to drink wine, or handing *ever min ha-chai*, flesh from a live animal prohibited to non-Jews under the seven Noahide laws, to a non-Jew. Commenting on this discussion, Rashi[7] states that this is prohibited, "*shema yavo lishtot*," "lest [the *nazir*] come to drink." The implication from Rashi is that even if the *nazir* will not likely drink the wine, passing the *nazir* wine falls under the prohibition of *lifnei ivver*.[8] *Tosafot*[9] disagree and understand the Gemara to be presenting a scenario in which the *nazir* is likely to drink the wine.[10] Ritva,[11] in a different context, states that one only violates the prohibition of *lifnei ivver* when one is certain the sin will occur through one's facilitation. *Shulchan Arukh*[12] adopts the approach of *Tosafot* and requires a high likelihood that once facilitated, the sin is going to occur.[13]

R. Chaim Fischel[14] quantifies the element of "likelihood" discussed by the *rishonim* and *Shulchan Arukh*. He claims that it is permissible to facilitate a sin when there is a 50% chance that a sin will not occur. Facilitating in a scenario in which the chance of a sin occurring is greater than 50%, a scenario which he describes as having *raglayim le-davar*, significant indications that the sin will occur, is rabbinically prohibited. One only violates a Biblical prohibition of *lifnei ivver* when one is certain the sin will occur. These divisions are quite relevant to our topic, since often the potential sin a doctor or clinician may enable may possess a less-than-50% chance of occurring.

Notwithstanding the ruling of *Shulchan Arukh*, several *poskim* place limitations on the ability to rely upon the possibility that the sin might not occur.

6   *Avodah Zarah* 6a–6b.
7   Ad loc s.v. *lo yoshit*.
8   Rosh (*Avodah Zarah* 1:2 s.v. *tanya*) adopts this position as well.
9   Ad loc s.v. *minayin*.
10   The text of *Tosafot* reads, "*mishum de-mistama, le-mishtei ka ba'ei lei,*" "Because in all likelihood, for the purpose of drinking, he [the *nazir*] wants it."
11   *Avodah Zarah* 22a s.v. *chada ve-od ka'amar*.
12   *Yoreh De'ah* 151:1.
13   *Shevet Ha-Levi* (*Yoreh De'ah* 62) rules leniently when the resulting transgression will not definitely occur, in accordance with *Shulchan Arukh*'s ruling.
14   *Machaneh Chayyim* 1:47.

- R. Eliezer Waldenberg[15] writes that even if there is doubt as to whether the sin will occur, *Shulchan Arukh* would only be lenient when one's act of facilitating is indirectly linked to the sin which occurs. For example, if one were to hand non-kosher food to an observant Jew, it is only after that observant Jew decides to eat the food and thereby violate *halakhah* that the sin occurs. In such a case, one has only facilitated indirectly and thus one has not violated *lifnei ivver*. However, if one's act of facilitating is directly linked to the sin, then even if there was doubt initially whether the sin would occur, one has still violated *lifnei ivver*. As an example, R. Waldenberg points to a case of lending without witnesses.[16] In such a case, it is possible the borrower will forget about the loan and swear falsely, albeit mistakenly, that there was never any loan. The borrower does not make a conscious decision to swear falsely, and the only cause of this violation of *halakhah* was the initial loan without witnesses. Although there may have been some doubt as to whether the borrower would forget about the loan and swear falsely initially, since the false oath occurred as a direct outgrowth of the initial loan, the borrower would violate *lifnei ivver* in such a case.

- R. Shlomo Zalman Auerbach[17] advances a distinction between giving another person something that is inherently permissible but which could be used for a prohibition, like a house, and giving something that can be directly used for a prohibition, such as an animal that could plow a field during *shemitah*. When one gives an object that is inherently permissible, one may rely upon the possibility that it will not be used for a prohibition, whereas when one gives an object that could be used directly for a prohibition, there must be a high likelihood that it will not be used for sin. This distinction is supported by Ritva's[18] explanation for the permissibility of giving money to an uneducated Jew who may use the money to purchase forbidden foods. Ritva states that since the money is not inherently forbidden, any doubt that the sin will occur is sufficient to avoid the prohibition of *lifnei ivver*.

- Drawing from the comments of a number of *rishonim*,[19] R. Ovadia Yosef[20] suggests that even if there is a likely possibility that the sin will not occur, one should not rely upon this possibility absent any need or benefit. One example is a store owner who sells immodest clothing thus enabling women to dress immodestly. Although the store owner might be enabling women to sin, there is a chance that

15 *Tzitz Eliezer* vol. 4, 5:3.
16 *Bava Metzia* 75b.
17 *Minchat Shlomo, mahadura tinyana* (2–3), 100:3.
18 *Avodah Zarah* 63a s.v. *omer adam le-chamarav u-lepoalav*.
19 Ramban, Rashba, Ritva and Ran on the Gemara in *Gittin* 61a.
20 *Yechavveh Da'at*, 3:67.

the clothes will not be worn immodestly (e.g., they will be worn as undergarments), and since there is financial gain to the store owner, one may rely upon this possibility and sell the garments. However, in a case where there is no benefit to the facilitator, for example lending the immodest clothing, one should avoid lending the clothing lest one violate the prohibition of *lifnei ivver*.

The ability to rely upon a possibility that a sin will not occur is especially relevant when one is not dealing with the Torah prohibition of *lifnei ivver*, but with the rabbinic prohibition of *mesayye'a*, facilitating a sin. Although the details of *mesayye'a* will be discussed below, put simply, merely supporting a person who is engaged in sin, such as lending a helpful hand to a woman who is grinding flour from grains harvested during the *shemitah* year, is rabbinically prohibited.[21] However, according to the understanding of many *rishonim*, even the slightest possibility that one's support will not result in sin is sufficient to avoid violating this rabbinic prohibition. For example, Rabbeinu Tam[22] claims that one is allowed to lend a cooking utensil to a woman known to violate the laws of *shemitah* since one can make the claim, albeit very farfetched, that she may use this utensil to count coins. Thus, this rabbinic extension of *lifnei ivver*, *mesayye'a*, appears not to apply in cases where there is even a minute chance the violation may not occur.

Taken together, it is clear that although almost any action could potentially facilitate a sin, most authorities understand that an action only violates the prohibition of *lifnei ivver* if there is a high likelihood that it will actually facilitate a sin. This may offer doctors and clinicians significant room for leniency. If, for example, a patient is seeking a second opinion, or the advice being offered is theoretical or general, even if it would result in the patient or client transgressing, the doctor or clinician may not violate *lifnei ivver*. One specific example, prescribing contraception may be permissible due to the assumption, however farfetched, that they may be used in situations which are permissible.

Enabling Additional Violations of a Prohibition

A variation of this discussion is a situation in which one enables another person to commit additional prohibitions, when that individual was already violating the prohibition without any assistance. This situation is of great relevance to medical professionals; for example, if this were permitted, one could prescribe prohibited forms of contraception to a couple who already has them. *Tosafot*[23] contend that such facilitation

---

21 *Gittin* 61a.
22 *Gittin* 61a s.v. *mashelet ishah le-chavertah*.
23 *Avodah Zarah* 14b s.v. *makom she-nahagu she-lo limkor ein mokhrin*.

does violate *lifnei ivver*, while Ritva[24] claims that it does not. The position of *Tosafot* is adopted by several later *acharonim*, including *Beit Shmuel*.[25] *Minchat Yitzchak*[26] cites the position of *Kehilot Ya'akov* regarding a situation in which one purchases a newspaper from a company owned by Jews. If one's subscription will increase the number of newspapers produced or the hours the company is open on *Shabbat*, *Kehillot Ya'akov* contends that one violates a Biblical prohibition of *lifnei ivver*, consistent with the position of *Tosafot*.

It is possible that this debate hinges upon the question of whether the prohibition of *lifnei ivver* is connected to the specific prohibition violated or a separate, independent, prohibition. If *lifnei ivver* is viewed as a violation of the specific prohibition which one has facilitated, causing another person to violate more prohibitions should be prohibited as well. Castrating five animals, the prohibition described in the *Beit Shmuel*, is worse than castrating two animals. However, if *lifnei ivver* is a standalone prohibition, it might possess its own unique set of rules, including the possibility that there is no prohibition to cause another to commit additional prohibitions if that individual was already capable of committing the prohibition once.

Lifnei Ivver and *Mesayye'a*

"Two Sides of the River"

An important distinction appears in the Gemara[27] regarding which cases of facilitation violate *lifnei ivver*. If one hands a *nazir* wine that was otherwise inaccessible, for example, if the *nazir* and the wine were located on opposing sides of a river (*trei avrei de-nahara*), one violates the Biblical prohibition of *lifnei ivver* since one enables the *nazir* to sin. But if one hands the *nazir* wine that the *nazir* could have accessed himself or herself, for example, wine which was located on the same side of the river (*chad avra de-nahara*), one does not violate the Biblical prohibition since one is only playing an auxiliary role in the *nazir*'s sin.

Significant debate surrounds the exact parameters of the first situation, *trei avrei de-nahara*. Rashi[28] explains that this phrase refers to situations in which the sin could not have occurred without the help of the enabler. It is not Biblically prohibited to enable a sinner when the sin is anything short of "impossible" to do without one's help. However, other commentators extend the Biblical prohibition to cases in which

24 *Avodah Zarah* 6b s.v. *talmud lomar ve-lifnei ivver lo titten mikhshol*. Me'iri (6a. s.v. *kol mah she-ne'esar lanu*), subscribes to this position as well.
25 *Even Ha-Ezer* 5:18.
26 3:79.
27 *Avodah Zarah* 6a–6b.
28 Ad loc s.v. *de-kayma be-trei avrei*.

the sinner would have had to expend effort or purchase the prohibited item had there been no support.[29] *Ketav Sofer*[30] appears to understand the logic of this second approach to be rooted in chance. Once there is some amount of effort required to sin, physical or financial, there is a greater chance that the potential sinner may not violate the prohibition. Thus, facilitating in such a case is downgraded to a rabbinic prohibition.

Rambam[31] expands the category of *trei avrei de-nahara* to include a case of simply increasing someone's chances of sinning. He states that if an individual is prone to weakness in a certain area, such as a Jewish thief, selling this individual weapons, which will increase the likelihood of theft, falls under the Biblical violation of *lifnei ivver*. Building upon this idea of Rambam, *Chazon Ish*[32] states that convincing someone to sin or weakening his or her resolve not to sin violates *lifnei ivver*. For example, praising a fine wine in the presence of a *nazir* determined not to drink wine, who subsequently drinks, would be a violation of *lifnei ivver*.

"One Side of the River"

The Gemara explicitly states that a scenario of *trei avrei de-nahara*, "two sides of the river," violates *lifnei ivver*. However, the Gemara does not discuss the prohibition, if any, in a case of *chad avra de-nahara,* "one side of the river," when the wine is readily accessible and another individual hands this wine to the *nazir*. Some authorities[33] rule that there

---

29 Me'iri ad loc s.v. *kol mah she-ne'esar lanu*. Also see *Chavvot Ya'ir* (185) who more specifically defines what extra "effort" would create *trei avrei de-nahara*. In the context of a discussion about selling *sha'atnez*, clothes containing a forbidden mixture of wool and linen, to a non-observant Jew, he states that should the purchaser have to travel by boat or land to attain similar clothes, or even if clothes are accessible without a journey but the clothing is not sized properly, such situations would deem a case to be *trei avrei de-nahara*. Thus, facilitating in such cases would violate the Biblical prohibition of *lifnei ivver*.

30 *Yoreh De'ah* 83. He writes that once there is physical or financial effort required to violate a particular prohibition, "Perhaps he will not want to be burdened."

31 *Hilkhot Rotze'ach U-Shemirat Nefesh* 12:14.

32 This position is quoted in *Minchat Yitzchak* (3:79) as well. *Chazon Ish* bases his position on *Mo'ed Katan* 17a which discusses the scenario of hitting one's adult children. Such behavior violates *lifnei ivver* and, according to *Chazon Ish*, is rooted in the fact that doing so weakens the adult child's will to not violate the commandment of honoring one's parents.

33 See Rabbeinu Yerucham's *Toledot Adam Ve-Chavah, netiv* 17 *chelek* 6 (p. 160 column 1), and *Turei Even, Megilah* 21a and *Chagigah* 13a.

is no prohibition in such a case.[34] A slight variation of this approach is that while no formal prohibition exists, such behavior is inappropriate. Me'iri[35] calls the behavior of the facilitator *serach mesayye'a*, "akin to (the rabbinic prohibition of) supporting (sinners)." Mordekhai[36] concludes that while one has not violated *lifnei ivver* in this case, one has not acted properly and instead is *chayyav lehafrisho me-issur*, "required to separate this individual from sin."

Most commentaries, though, are of the opinion that *chad avra de-nahara* is rabbinically prohibited.[37] Ritva[38] states that if the potential sinner asks for the prohibited object to commit a sin, even if the object is accessible, facilitating such a situation is prohibited. Ritva, and many others, direct our attention to a concept called *mesayye'a*, already discussed in the Mishnah.[39] The Mishnah permits one to lend baking utensils to a woman suspected of using food grown during the *shemitah* year, which is prohibited, for baking. However, actively baking *with* her is rabbinically prohibited due to the decree of *mesayye'a*, "supporting (sinners)." The lending scenario is permissible, according to the Gemara, only because of a leniency rooted in fostering the value of

---

34 This position emerges from a simple reading of the Gemara in *Avodah Zarah* 6a–6b. The Gemara presents two reasons for the prohibition of selling animals to non-Jewish idol worshippers three days prior to their festival: causing the idol worshipper to praise a foreign deity, or causing the idol worshipper to use the animal for idol worship. In either case, one is violating the sin of *lifnei ivver*. The Gemara searches for a practical difference between these explanations and concludes that in a case in which the idol worshipper has additional animals, selling an animal is still problematic according to the first concern but not according to the second concern. Thus, in a case of *chad avra de-nahara*, when the idol worshipper has other animals to use for idol worship, providing support does not appear to violate *lifnei ivver* at any level. The logic of this position may be that in a case of *chad avra de-nahara*, the help provided to the sinner is either non-existent or insignificant: *lifnei ivver* only applies when not helping makes a meaningful difference.

35 *Avodah Zarah* 6b s.v. *kol mah she-ne'esar*.

36 *Hagahot Mordekhai, Shabbat* 450.

37 Ran, *Avodah Zarah* 1b in *dappei ha-Rif*, s.v. *deika nami*; Tosafot, *Shabbat* 3a s.v. *bava de-reisha patur u-mutar*; *Minchat Shlomo* 35. In response to the logic of the position which does not find any prohibition in a case of *chad avra de-nahara* (presented in footnote 37), these commentaries may claim that not helping in case of *chad avra de-nahara* may lower, however minimally, the chances of the sin occurring; or that even if one's support will not have a practical impact on chances of the sin occurring, one is required, rabbinically, to not support a sinner no matter what; or the rabbis wanted one to make a statement, through inaction, of one's opposition to the sin which will occur.

38 *Avodah Zarah* 6b s.v. *talmud lomar*.

39 *Gittin* 61a.

darkhei shalom, "ways of peace." However, it appears according to the Gemara that both situations in theory fall under the rabbinic prohibition of *mesayye'a.*

Ritva[40] notes some degree of leniency when confronted with a case of *chad avra de-nahara.* Drawing from the Gemara,[41] Ritva states that if there is any residual benefit to the facilitator in a case of *chad avra de-nahara,* such as making money off a sale, Chazal allowed for leniency and did not prohibit facilitating in such a situation. However, this exception only holds true providing that the sin is not definitely going to occur. For example, selling an ox to a Jew who may use it to plow during the *shemitah* year is permissible since the facilitator, the seller, is gaining financially and the sin is not definite. However, says Ritva, if there were no benefit, such as a loan, this case would be prohibited.

Another broad sweeping exception to the category of *chad avra de-nahara* emerges from a comment by R. Moshe Feinstein.[42] In response to a question about the permissibility of renting a wedding hall to a couple who will have mixed dancing at their wedding, R. Feinstein differentiates between giving someone the prohibited item (e.g., non-kosher food) and giving an item which can be used for sin (a wedding hall which may host mixed dancing). He states that *mesayye'a* may not apply to the second category since it would be illogical to apply this prohibition so broadly. If it did, R. Feinstein claims, one would not be able to lend or give any item to any Jew suspected of sinning.

Additional leniencies regarding *mesayye'a* are raised by R. Yaakov Ettlinger.[43] Drawing from *Chavvot Ya'ir,*[44] he distinguishes between assistance provided prior to the sin, for which the prohibition of *mesayye'a* does not apply, and support while the sin is occurring, for which one does violate *mesayye'a.* Another similar leniency limits the application of *mesayye'a* to assistance that will certainly lead to a sin, or assistance in a situation where the other individual has expressed a desire to sin; assistance which will not definitely lead to sin does not violate *mesayye'a.*[45]

---

40   *Gittin* 61a, s.v. *mashelet ishah.*
41   *Avodah Zarah* 15b.
42   *Iggerot Moshe, Yoreh De'ah* 1:72.
43   *Binyan Tzion, siman* 15.
44   *Siman* 185. Furthemore, *Yad Malachi* (361), *Biur Ha-Gra* (151:8) and Netziv (*Meishiv Davar,* vol. 2, 31–32) all raise a similar leniency, that assistance prior to the sin does not violate *mesayye'a.*
45   Both leniencies offer additional ways of reconciling the positions of *Tosafot* in *Masekhet Avodah Zarah* and *Masekhet Shabbat. Masekhet Shabbat* is discussing a case in which the sin is in the process of occurring, and hence *Tosafot* state that *mesayye'a* applies. *Masekhet Avodah Zarah* is discussing a case in which the sin is not actually in the process of occurring and hence,

An important debate relevant to our discussion surrounds whether *mesayye'a* applies to non-Jews. *Tosafot* in *Avodah Zarah*[46] indicate that *mesayye'a* applies neither to Jews nor non-Jews in a case of *chad avra de-nahara*, while *Tosafot* in *Shabbat*[47] conclude that the concept of *mesayye'a* applies to Jews but not to non-Jews. Rama,[48] in discussing whether one may sell animals to non-Jews if they may be used for idol worship, when the non-Jews already have access to these animals (a case of *chad avra de-nahara*), writes that some opinions view this as permissible while others are strict. *Shakh*[49] explains that the two positions differ regarding whether *mesayye'a* is prohibited at all. However, he offers a third possibility: that *mesayye'a* applies to Jews but not to non-Jews. He argues that *Tosafot* in *Avodah Zarah* believe that there is a prohibition of *mesayye'a*, but that it does not apply to non-Jews,[50] who are the subject of discussion in that Gemara.

R. Moshe Feinstein[51] explains *Shakh*'s position by noting that Chazal prohibited Jews from engaging in behavior that can lead a fellow Jew to sin, but did not demand those exacting standards when relating to a non-Jew. This difference is rooted in the unique standard of interdependence that exists between Jews, known generally as *arvut*.[52]

Some commentators[53] believe, unlike *Shakh*, that the two positions cited by Rama are specifically regarding a non-Jew, and the debate is regarding whether *mesayye'a* applies to non-Jews.[54] If *mesayye'a* does apply to non-Jews, as would be the position of the strict view cited by

---

according to *Tosafot*, there is no violation of *mesayye'a*. See the ensuing discussion for further elaboration on this tension.

46 Ad loc, s.v. *minayin she-lo yoshit adam kos yayin le-nazir*.

47 3a, s.v. *bava de-reisha patur u-mutar*.

48 *Shulchan Arukh, Yoreh De'ah* 151:1.

49 Ad loc, *siman* 6 s.v. *yesh omerim*.

50 As well as a *mumar*. The details of *mumar* with regard to *lifnei ivver* will be discussed below.

51 *Iggerot Moshe, Yoreh De'ah* 3:90.

52 This approach suggests that the prohibition of *mesayye'a* is not necessarily related to *lifnei ivver*, but a separate prohibition which furthers *arvut*. Those who believe that *mesayye'a* applies to non-Jews may reason that *mesayye'a* is an outgrowth of *lifnei ivver*, and thus has the same scope as *lifnei ivver* has.

53 *Hagahot Ha-Gra, Yoreh De'ah* 151:8.

54 Gra notes that this approach appears to conflict with the simple understanding of the Gemara in *Avodah Zarah* (6a–6b). Gra appears to resolve this conflict by claiming that the rabbinic decree of *mesayye'a*, while generally applying to non-Jews, does not encompass cases in which there is any level of doubt that the non-Jew will violate the prohibition with the Jew's support. Therefore, the Gemara is dealing with a case of both *chad avra de-nahara*, i.e., *mesayye'a*, as well as a case in which there is some level of doubt.

Rama, that would present a considerable stringency in the laws of *lifnei ivver*.

Another wrinkle in this discussion relates to whether *mesayye'a* applies to a *mumar*, a non-believing Jew.[55] According to *Shakh*,[56] *mesayye'a* does not apply to a *mumar*, while *Magen Avraham*[57] rules that *mesayye'a* does apply. *Dagul Me-Revavah*[58] makes a radical suggestion: he explains that according to *Shakh*, a *mumar* is no different from any Jew who intentionally violates a prohibition. One who intentionally violates a prohibition cannot be subject to the *halakhah* of *mesayye'a*. Therefore, one can support a Jew who knowingly violates a prohibition in violating that prohibition.

A final important discussion regarding *chad avra de-nahara* emerges from a nuanced debate between *Penei Moshe*[59] and *Mishneh Le-Melekh*.[60] If a potential sinner can commit a sin only through the assistance of someone who is prohibited to offer this assistance, is such a case considered *chad avra de-nahara* or *trei avrei de-nahara*? For example, if a *nazir* can only access wine through the help of Reuven violating *lifnei ivver*, is Shimon's handing the wine to the *nazir* considered a Biblical violation of *lifnei ivver*, in the category of *trei avrei de-nahara*, or a rabbinic violation of *lifnei ivver*, *chad avra de-nahara*? The operative question is whether *chad avra de-nahara* indicates only that the potential sinner already has a practical means of accessing the sin, or that those means are also halakhically permissible.

Penei Moshe argues that if the sinner has any other way of committing the sin, even if it entails another person's violation of *lifnei ivver*, this downgrades the violation of *lifnei ivver* to a rabbinic prohibition. *Mishneh Le-Melekh* disagrees and views help that violates the prohibition of *lifnei ivver* to be halakhically insignificant such that the case is categorized as *trei avrei de-nahara*. R. Yitzchak Weiss[61] significantly limits the practical import of this debate. He suggests that *Mishneh Le-Melekh* agrees with *Penei Moshe* in a case in which the facilitator is unaware that what he or she is facilitating is prohibited or is unaware of the entire category of *lifnei ivver*. Thus, if a *nazir* can only access the

---

55 The exact definition of a *mumar*, particularly in our modern context, is complex. *Biur Halakhah* (*Orach Chayyim* 608:2 s.v. *aval im mefurash ba-Torah*) states that the obligation to rebuke a fellow Jew does not apply to someone who (1) violates *Shabbat* publicly or (2) commits a sin as an act of rebellion. *Minchat Yitzchak* (3:79) appears to extend this definition to the topic of *lifnei ivver*.
56 *Yoreh De'ah* 151:6.
57 *Orach Chayyim* 347:4.
58 *Yoreh De'ah* 151:6.
59 2:105.
60 *Hilkhot Malveh Ve-Loveh* 4:2 s.v *ke-derekh she-asur*.
61 *Minchat Yitzchak* 3:79.

wine through a Jew who does not know about *lifnei ivver* or does not know that a *nazir* is prohibited to drink wine, another Jew only transgresses a rabbinic violation of *lifnei ivver* by handing wine to this *nazir*. This debate has tremendous practical relevance which will be discussed below.

With regard to practical *halakhah*, many authorities follow the position of *Mishneh Le-Melekh*[62] while others have adopted the position of *Penei Moshe*.[63] When confronted with the pressures of "best practice," an accepted norm in the field, there are *poskim* who allow adopting the more lenient position of *Penei Moshe*.[64]

Application to Specific Clinical Scenarios

We will conclude by applying the principles discussed thus far to a number of relevant clinical scenarios where a tension between *lifnei ivver* and "best practice" exists. Although it is impossible to discuss all possible scenarios of conflict that do or will exist, we will discuss a number of common scenarios.

Abortions

Many *poskim* discuss the scenario in which a woman wishes to undergo an abortion that is not halakhically sanctioned, or wishes to receive a referral for such an abortion. This woman can easily receive assistance from many non-religious Jewish or non-Jewish doctors. Even according to the position of *Mishneh Le-Melekh*, detailed above, if there are non-Jews willing to offer the referral or provide support to the doctor performing the abortion, such a case would be treated as *chad avra de-nahara,* a case of *mesayye'a,* and thus rabbinically prohibited. As we mentioned earlier, *mesayye'a* does not apply to non-Jews and non-observant Jews, and furthermore there are numerous leniencies which apply to *mesayye'a* even with regard to observant Jews, creating many potential exceptions. Thus, numerous leniencies may exist when a doctor or nurse is confronted with this specific scenario.

---

62 These include the *Benei Chayi* (*Choshen Mishpat* 34, *Hagahot Beit Yosef* 7), *Chida* (*Darkhei Yosef, Choshen Mishpat* 9:3), and *Minchat Chinukh* (232:3). R. Yitzchak Yaakov Weiss (*Minchat Yitzchak* 3:79) states that the majority of *poskim* adopt the position of the *Mishneh Le-Melekh*.

63 These include *Kenesset Ha-Gedolah* (*Yoreh De'ah* 159, *Hagahat Ha-Tur* 11), *Ketav Sofer* (*Yoreh De'ah* 83), and *Machaneh Chayyim* (*Orach Chayyim*, 2:18).

64 See R. Yosef Zvi Rimon ("Lifnei Ivver Lo Titein Mikhshol, Part 1," http://etzion.org.il/en/you-shall-not-place-stumbling-block-blind-part-1), who also cites the authorities noted in footnotes 65 and 66.

R. Yitzchak Zilberstein[65] addresses a case in which an obstetrician knows that upon providing information about a birth defect, a woman will seek an abortion. He quotes R. Yosef Shalom Elyashiv who adopts the position of *Mishneh Le-Melekh* and concludes that enabling in such a case is a Biblical violation of *lifnei ivver.*[66] Such an analysis is limited to cases in Israel when the other doctors are Jewish and would thus violate *lifnei ivver,*[67] but when non-Jewish doctors are readily available, even *Mishneh Le-Melekh* would consider such a case *chad avra de-nahara.* Thus, offering a referral for a non-halakhically-sanctioned abortion or supporting the doctor performing an abortion for a non-Jew or even a non-observant Jew would be permitted. Even if the patient were an Orthodox Jew, since the potential violation in these cases is rabbinic, *mesayye'a,* one may be able to use the leniencies discussed regarding an intentional sinner to permit assisting in an abortion in this case.

In the context of this discussion, R. Zilberstein considers an interesting and very relevant scenario. What if following *halakhah* and not a clear "best practice" will cause a doctor to lose his or her job? R. Zilberstein argues[68] that *lifnei ivver* does not require one to give up his or her job. He cites Maharil Diskin[69] who rules that providing support in a case in which a *nazir* demands wine and threatens to hurt this individual, who is on the other bank of the river, should this person not support the sin, is not considered *lifnei ivver.* He explains that support under duress is not considered "placing a stumbling block" and thus incurs no violation. Our case, states R. Zilberstein, is similar and facilitating a sin when the alternative is losing one's job is considered support under duress and thus not prohibited.

DNR (Do Not Resuscitate)

R. Moshe Feinstein addresses a case of doctor responsible for implementing a DNR order which is in violation of *halakhah.*[70] He argues that such a case is *chad avra de-nahara* since there are many non-Jewish

65 *Shiurei Torah Le-Rofe'im,* 248:2, p. 266.
66 Regarding the possibility of having a non-Jewish doctor offer the information about the birth defect, since non-Jews are not bound by *lifnei ivver,* R. Zilberstein comments that while in this case the non-Jewish doctor would not violate *lifnei ivver,* the doctor would violate murder of a fetus even though it is not being done directly, since indirect murder is prohibited as well.
67 There is no prohibition of *lifnei ivver* for non-Jews. This may indicate that *lifnei ivver* is a standalone prohibition, since otherwise each of the seven Noahide laws would have a prohibition of *lifnei ivver.*
68 *Shiurei Torah Le-Rofe'im,* 248:2, p. 269.
69 *Kuntras Acharon* 5:145.
70 *Iggerot Moshe, Yoreh De'ah* 4:54.

doctors who can implement this DNR. Therefore, giving the order for a non-Jew is theoretically permissible since there is no rabbinic prohibition of *mesayye'a* with regard to non-Jews. However, his advice is to remove oneself from the situation. When the patient is a Jew, R. Feinstein forbids implementing a DNR order which runs counter to *halakhah* and even requires the doctor to spend significant funds to ensure the patient can be kept alive for as long as possible. He concludes by noting that if differentiating between Jews and non-Jews would lead to *eivah*, hatred,[71] a doctor should provide similar care to non-Jews. Based on earlier discussion, one could imagine justifying ordering a non-halakhic DNR for a non-observant Jew, yet R. Feinstein makes no such distinction.

Handing Forms to a Non-Observant Doctor on *Shabbat*

R. Eliezer Waldenburg[72] deals with handing forms to a non-observant Jewish doctor on *Shabbat* with the knowledge that this doctor will violate *Shabbat* to complete them. He specifically addresses the case of a female nurse handing the forms and concludes that for a woman such a case is permissible. He notes that this case is *chad avra de-nahara*, since the doctor can obtain the forms without the help of the female nurse, and proceeds to base this position on a number of interesting assumptions. First, he cites the opinion that understands the basis of the prohibition of *chad avra de-nahara*, also known as *mesayye'a*, to be rooted in the concept of *arvut*, Jewish interdependence.[73] He then cites views that believe that *arvut* may not apply to women. Although he is hesitant about each assumption, he is willing to rule leniently since this case is quite common and hard to avoid. Additionally, he notes, the fact that it is not certain that the doctor will violate *Shabbat* by completing the forms offers additional room for leniency.

Although he does not discuss a male nurse, it appears that he would conclude that such a case is not permitted. However, when dealing with a non-observant Jew, there may be additional leniencies.

Summary

Placing limits upon another's ability to act is often at odds with contemporary social and cultural norms. Religion, however, by definition, demands and limits specific behaviors. Furthermore, Judaism places a

---

71 The exact definition will not be discussed here. Whether it refers to hatred alone or specifically to actionable hatred, i.e., life-threatening danger, is subject to significant discussion. For more discussion, see R. Dov Karoll, "Laws of Medical Treatment on Shabbat," *Verapo Yerape*, vol. 1 (2011), pp. 211–230. See also the discussion in Chapter 20.

72 *Tzitz Eliezer* 9:17, chapter 11.

73 See discussion above in the section titled "One Side of the River."

great value on ensuring the proper behavior of fellow coreligionists as well as all humankind. This value is concretized by the Biblical prohibition of *lifnei ivver* and its rabbinic extensions. Understandably, knowing the contours of this prohibition is of great value for proper Torah observance: to help one navigate the complex waters of mandated actions (or inaction) which respond to and impact those around us. One arena in which the prohibition of *lifnei ivver* is of particular relevance is that of medicine. Healthcare professionals' behaviors, almost by definition, impact those around them. At times, this impact is at odds with *halakhah* and must be avoided. Here, we sought to highlight and analyze some of the central issues pertaining to *lifnei ivver* in hopes of offering healthcare professionals a way to begin thinking about the tensions between contemporary practice and halakhic demands.

While our ultimate hope is for the world to be an *"agudah achat la'asot retzonekha be-levav shalem,"* a unified society that serves Your will wholeheartedly,[74] we recognize that until that point, a delicate balance between religious freedom and religious observance must be met and knowing the nuances of *lifnei ivver* offers us a critical first step.

---

74 From *U-Va Le-Tzion* at the end of the *Shacharit* prayers.

Chapter 15

Maintaining Patient Dignity During Rounds

Yona Saperstein, MD

A few years ago, I was in a foreign country in a medical ethics program for medical students, and part of our program included geriatric rounds. One time during geriatric rounds, the attending took us into a female patient's room, told us the patient's illnesses, and mentioned that the patient had dementia. The attending then proceeded to lift up the patient's gown to show us her feeding tube, and we all watched the patient grimace uncomfortably. Then, while the patient was still uncovered, the attending proceeded to engage us in a discussion as to whether it was ethical to keep her alive.

Rounds are a mainstay of medical education during the clinical years of medical school and during residency. During rounds, the entire team, consisting of the attending, residents, students and any other relevant staff members such as social workers or pharmacists visit the patients, discuss the patients' medical and personal issues, examine the patient and discuss treatment plans. Rounds are necessary for the treatment team, as they are an efficient method to ensure that the entire team is aware of each patient's current status, and they are a good forum for the entire team to discuss physical exam findings and treatment plans. Rounds are also an educational experience for the medical students; students are often involved in the discussions and learn in a hands-on manner how to identify symptoms and treat illnesses.

While the inclusion of medical students in rounds is an integral part of medical student education, two halakhic issues are relevant to the student taking part in rounds: *gilui sod*, the prohibition of revealing private information, which is a category of *lashon ha-ra*, prohibited slander; and *malbin penei chaveiro be-rabbim* (literally, one who whitens one's friend's face in public), the prohibition of embarrassing one's fellow in public, which might be violated while exposing a patient in front of the whole team. Mitigating these prohibitions is the fact that in order to effectively treat a patient, everyone involved in patient treatment must be aware of all of the health issues and examination findings of the patient. However, if there are students and trainees who are not actively involved in treating the patient and are participating in rounds to learn, these two issues remain: revealing confidential information about patients might constitute *gilui sod*, and exposure of a patient in front of students might constitute *malbin penei chaveiro be-rabbim*.

Also of importance is the fact that students at different levels of training have different levels of responsibility in patient care. This varies not only according to the student's level of training, but also varies across different specialties and hospital locations. The aforementioned halakhic issues tend to be less significant when involving more advanced students in a specialty where the student is an active member of the team, and more significant in a setting where the student participates in rounds but does not actively participate in patient care after rounds.

The first halakhic issue related to rounds is that of *gilui sod*, the prohibition of revealing private information. The Torah[1] prohibits slander using the words "*lo telekh rakhil.*"[2] The Gemara[3] states that one who reveals secrets is in violation of the prohibition of slander, based on a verse in Proverbs[4] which equates revealing secrets with slander. Additionally, the Gemara[5] states that one is not allowed to divulge personal information about his fellow without explicit permission. From this, we learn that there is a prohibition to reveal personal information to others.

Interestingly, R. Eliezer Waldenberg[6] rules that talking about other patients' confidential health information during rounds in front of trainees does not constitute a violation of *gilui sod*. He gives a two-pronged argument for why it is permitted to discuss confidential patient information in front of trainees. His first argument is that it is implicitly understood on the part of the patient and the physician that patient information will be discussed in front of trainees. Even if the physician and patient sign a document of confidentiality, divulging the information to trainees does not represent a breach of confidentiality, considering that the implicit understanding on the part of the patient and physician is that information will be discussed with the entire team, including the students. R. Waldenberg's second argument is that even

1   Leviticus 19:16.
2   The exact translation of these words is subject to dispute – see Rashi and Ramban on 19:16. However, all authorities agree that this verse refers to the prohibition of slander; see *Ketuvot* 46a, and *Sanhedrin* 30a and 31a.
3   *Sanhedrin* 31a.
4   11:13.
5   *Yoma* 4b.
6   *Tzitz Elizezer* 13:81.

trainees, who are not actively involved in patient care, may have some valuable input during rounds which can help the patient, and therefore, discussion of confidential patient information even in front of trainees can assist in adequate patient care.

The second halakhic issue related to student rounds is that of *malbin penei chaveiro be-rabbim*, the severe prohibition of embarrassing one's fellow in public.[7] R. Waldenberg[8] writes that there is indeed a concern of embarrassing the patient by exposing him or her in front of the trainees in the healthcare team who are not actively involved in patient care. He suggests but immediately rejects the notion that one might be allowed to embarrass a patient in public if this is a necessary step in teaching the next generation of doctors. He quotes a statement of *Netziv*[9] about the Biblical dermatological disease of *tzara'at*. The Torah states that *tzara'at* can only be diagnosed by a *kohen*, and *Netziv* derives from the Torah's use of the word *lehorot*, "to teach," in conjunction with the law of *tzara'at*,[10] that the *kohen* who diagnoses the patient does so with other trainee *kohanim* at his side, in order to train the other *kohanim* in the art of diagnosing *tzara'at*. From this, we can suggest that it would be permissible to publicly expose a patient in order to teach medical students, if it is a necessary step in teaching the students. However, *Netziv* concludes his comment by explaining that the end of the verse, "This is the law of one who is afflicted with *tzara'at*," teaches that the only instance in which one may embarrass a patient for the purpose of educational instruction is with regards to *tzara'at*; it is not permissible in any other circumstance. Therefore, we must conclude that exposure of a patient in front of students might constitute *malbin penei chaveiro be-rabbim*, and there is no room to allow embarrassment of the patient for the purpose of educational instruction.

R. Waldenberg[11] concludes that in order to avoid the issue of embarrassing a patient in front of the students, the patient should be asked explicitly if he or she would feel comfortable with students being brought into the room. In this way, it is not embarrassment of the patient if the patient allows himself or herself to be exposed in front of the students. However, if the patient responds that he or she is not comfortable with students in the room, R. Waldenberg rules that students may not be brought into the room; otherwise, there would be a violation of publicly embarrassing the patient.

7   The Gemara (*Bava Metzia* 58b) states that embarrassing one's friend in public is tantamount to murder. The Gemara (ibid, 59a) also quotes R. Shimon bar Yochai who says that one should go as far as to jump in a furnace in order to avoid embarrassing one's friend in public.
8   *Tzitz Eliezer* 13:81.
9   *Ha'amek Davar*, Leviticus 14:55.
10 Leviticus 14:57.
11 13:81.

Chapter 16

Reciting *Meshanneh Ha-Beriyot*

Jerry Karp, MD, PhD

T he unique training experienced by medical students and residents affords them the opportunity to have religious experiences which the average observant Jew does not. One of these might occur when the medical student or resident encounters a patient who, tragically, has an unusual deformity. In this situation, the student or resident might be able to recite a special *berakhah*:

בָּרוּךְ אַתָּה ה' אֱ-לֹהֵינוּ מֶלֶךְ הָעוֹלָם מְשַׁנֶּה הַבְּרִיּוֹת:

Blessed are You, God, our LORD, *Master of the Universe, Who makes the creatures different.*[1]

We will discuss the parameters of when and how this *berakhah* may be recited.

Origin

The Gemara[2] states that one who sees a person with a congenital deformity should recite the *berakhah* of *meshanneh ha-beriyot*. Although another statement cited by the Gemara suggests that one should recite a different *berakhah* upon seeing a person with a deformity, that of "*Barukh... dayyan ha-emet*" ("Blessed are You... the True Judge"), the Gemara concludes that *dayyan ha-emet* is to be recited only upon seeing someone with an acquired deformity, whereas one should recite *meshanneh ha-beriyot* upon seeing someone with a congenital deformity. The recitation of this *berakhah* is codified in *Shulchan Arukh*.[3]

---

1 This translation appears in the Koren Sacks Siddur (Jerusalem: Koren Publishers, 2009).
2 *Berakhot* 58b.
3 *Orach Chayyim* 225:8.

Types of Deformities

The Gemara specifies several deformities for which one should recite the *berakhah*, including people with especially pigmented skin, midgets, or people with unusual figures. However, *Chayyei Adam*[4] observes that we are not accustomed to recite this *berakhah*. He concludes that nowadays we are more accustomed to seeing people with deformities, and so they are less striking to us.[5] As *Shulchan Arukh*[6] notes that one only recites the *berakhah* upon the first time seeing an individual with a given deformity, since only then is the individual's appearance striking, *Chayyei Adam* extrapolates that the *berakhah* is not recited upon seeing individuals whose deformities are commonly seen.[7] Thus, it would appear that the *berakhah* is primarily recited upon seeing a particularly striking deformity. This is an unusual situation for the average person, but is much more likely to occur for a medical student or resident, who sees many patients across a wide cross-section of medical disciplines, some of which might have striking congenital abnormalities.

Frequency of Recitation

As noted, *Shulchan Arukh*[8] rules that the *berakhah* is only recited the first time that the deformity is seen. Rama cites a differing custom to recite the *berakhah* if at least thirty days have passed since the last time one has seen a similar deformity.[9] *Mishnah Berurah*[10] advises a compromise, whereby if one sees an individual with a similar deformity at least

4   63:1.
5   Perhaps this is because of the advent of modes of transportation that allow people to see many more others over the course of a lifetime, including those with deformities or disabilities, than one might have seen centuries ago.
6   *Orach Chayyim* 225:9.
7   R. Moshe Steinberg ("*Shinui min be-androginos*," *Assia* vol. 1, p. 142) asks whether a *mohel* recites the *berakhah* of *meshanneh ha-beriyot* upon performing the circumcision of an *androginos*, a child born with the reproductive organs of both a male and a female. He notes that under normal circumstances, one certainly does not recite *meshanneh ha-beriyot* upon a deformity that is covered and unseen; the *berakhah* is not recited upon a deformity whose existence is known but is not currently seen. R. Steinberg questions whether one recites a *berakhah* upon such a deformity when one can see it, such as a *mohel* performing a circumcision. Presumably, this question is also relevant for those in the medical profession. R. Steinberg does not provide a conclusive answer to the question.
8   *Orach Chayyim* 225:9.
9   This is the interpretation of *Magen Avraham* (225:19) and *Mishnah Berurah* (225:31).
10   225:30.

thirty days after the previous instance, one should recite the *berakhah* without God's name.

Sensitivity toward the Individual

Especially upon meeting an individual with a deformity, it is of utmost importance to display heightened sensitivity toward the patient's feelings and possible insecurities. Indeed, R. Shlomo Zalman Auerbach[11] notes, as should be obvious, that one must be careful to recite the blessing surreptitiously so that the individual with the deformity will not be hurt by seeing someone recite the *berakhah* upon him or her. The Gemara's grouping of this *berakhah* with another *berakhah* acknowledging tragic circumstances, *barukh dayyan ha-emet*, suggests that this *berakhah* might serve to heighten our sensitivity toward the plight of the *berakhah*'s subject.[12] This theme is especially appropriate for medical students and residents, who constantly strive to become more sensitive toward patients and their needs and struggles.

11 Cited in *Nishmat Avraham, Orach Chayyim* 225:1.
12 It should be noted, however, that the *berakhah* may not be primarily intended to acknowledge the subject's plight. The Gemara prescribes the recitation of the same *berakhah* upon seeing a remarkable animal such as a monkey or elephant, a case where the *berakhah* is obviously not intended to evoke sympathy. On this basis, when Ra'avad (cited in *Tur, Orach Chayyim* 225) wrote that the *berakhah* is not recited upon seeing a subject for whom one has no sympathy, *Bach* (*Orach Chayyim* 225), *Magen Avraham* (225:18) and *Taz* (*Orach Chayyim* 225:1) concluded that Ra'avad must be referring to the *berakhah* of *dayyan ha-emet*, which is intended to evoke sympathy, but not the *berakhah* of *meshanneh ha-beriyot*, which is recited regardless of sympathy. Nonetheless, the Gemara's grouping of the two *berakhot* together certainly suggests that both *berakhot* could be vehicles toward expressing sympathy for the subject.

Chapter 17

Treating a Near-Death Patient

Eric Kupferstein, DO

Medical students and residents in the course of their training encounter patients who are gravely ill and actively dying. In *halakhah*, a near-death patient is referred to as a *goses*. In this chapter, we will discuss the unique laws pertaining to this type of patient which will be useful for observant Jewish students and doctors to learn.

Who is a *Goses*?

We must begin by defining exactly who qualifies as a *goses*. A vague definition is offered by Rambam,[1] who writes that a *goses* is "one whose death rattle can be heard,"[2] i.e., who is breathing his or her last breaths. Likewise, Rama[3] gives a vague definition, stating that a *goses* is one who, "when about to die, brings up sputum into his throat as a result of chest tightness." It is indicative from Rama that the death of a *goses* is imminent. However, Rama writes that a *goses* can also, in theory, be conscious and able to talk.

A more concrete definition is provided by *Tur*,[4] who writes that if a *goses* were to remain in his or her state for three days, it can be assumed that he or she has died and the relatives should begin sitting *shivah*. *Perishah*[5] deduces from this comment that a *goses* is defined as one who is sick to the extent that his or her prognosis is no longer than three days. Other definitions include that of Rosh,[6] who writes that a *goses*

1   *Peirush Ha-Mishnayot, Arakhin* 3:1.
2   R. Yosef Kafich (translation of *Peirush Ha-Mishnayot* ad loc) translates Rambam's comments as "one whose throat's sound can be heard at the time of death."
3   *Even Ha-Ezer* 121:7.
4   *Yoreh De'ah* 339.
5   Ibid.
6   *Mo'ed Katan* 3:97.

has three or four days to live. R. Moshe Feinstein[7] agrees to the definition based on a prognosis no longer than three days, but asks what if the patient lives longer than three days._R. Feinstein concludes that, in such a case, it is more likely that a mistake was made in assessing the patient to begin with. A *goses*, he writes, is halakhically assumed to die within three days, and although in theory it is possible for the patient to live longer, the vast majority of such patients will die within three days. It is more likely, writes R. Feinstein, that those who evaluated the patient were wrong in declaring the patient a *goses*.

With the advent of modern medicine, classifying a patient as a *goses* has become more complicated than ever. Various medical interventions can extend the life of any dying patient. R. G. A. Rabinowitz[8] writes that a patient can still be considered a *goses* even if he or she lives longer than three days as a result of medical interventions, if the original prognosis was that of a *goses*. On the other hand, R. Shlomo Zalman Auerbach[9] argues that a terminally ill patient cannot be classified as a *goses*, because of the various medical interventions available. Furthermore, Dr. Avraham Steinberg[10] writes that over the years the clinical signs that indicate a *goses* have been forgotten and the overall process of dying has changed in modern medicine due to various interventions. He quotes R. Feinstein[11] who writes that we are no longer experts in defining a *goses* in a practical manner. Likewise *Nishmat Avraham*[12] writes that a clear definition of a modern day *goses* is difficult to suggest. However, he does offer a loose but practical definition: a *goses* is "a patient who has reached the terminal stage of his or her illness and for whom nothing further can be done, and who has been defined, after halakhic consultation, as being in the category of DNR (do not resuscitate)." *Nishmat Avraham* also notes that when he consulted with R. Shlomo Zalman Auerbach about the definition of a *goses*, R. Auerbach responded, "You are the doctor." Regardless of the definition, *Nishmat Avraham* writes that once the status of *goses* has been reached, the *halakhot* of *goses* apply even if the patient lives longer than the original prognosis.

Halakhic Status of a *Goses*

A *goses* is considered alive in all regards, as is codified in *Shulchan Arukh*.[13] All types of legal implications are included in this statement, such as the permissibility of giving a *get* or the wife of a *kohen* eating

7   *Iggerot Moshe, Choshen Mishpat* vol. 2, 75:5.
8   R. G. A. Rabinowitz, *Halakhah U-Refuah*, vol. 3, p. 102.
9   Cited in *Encyclopedia Hilkhatit Refu'it*, s.v. *noteh lamut* (2), footnote 16.
10   *Encylopedia Hilkhatit Refu'it*, s.v. *noteh lamut* (2), section 2.
11   *Iggerot Moshe, Choshen Mishpat* vol. 2, 73:3.
12   *Yoreh De'ah* 339:1(1), p. 450.
13   *Yoreh De'ah* 339:1.

terumah.[14] Furthermore, one is obligated to set aside *Shabbat* laws to treat the patient if his or her condition can be treated.[15] Nevertheless, the Gemara[16] states that the majority of *gosesim* will die. This too has halakhic implications, for example, whether a *kohen* can be in the room with a *goses*.[17] Even though the *goses* will likely die very soon, it is forbidden, writes Rama,[18] to do anything to hasten his or her death. *Shulchan Arukh*[19] lists many actions that are forbidden because they may hasten the patient's death, such as closing the eyes of the patient; in fact, one who closes the eyes of a *goses* prior to the actual death is called a murderer. Rama adds that merely moving the *goses* from his or her place is forbidden as this may hasten death. Indeed, the Mishnah[20] compares a *goses* to a flickering candle that is extinguished once someone touches it, just as touching a *goses* hastens death. However, Rama permits removing an impediment to the patient's death. For example, salt that is preventing the soul from departing[21] may be removed from the patient. *Bach*[22] adds that not only are physical actions forbidden but even causing emotional pain to the *goses* is forbidden, e.g., bringing in a coffin. *Bach* quotes Rivash[23] who adds that even actions performed out of the *goses*'s sight that may cause emotional pain are forbidden, lest the patient find out. However, *Bach* disagrees with this stance and rules that only actions in the presence of the *goses* can be forbidden.

There are instances when moving the *goses* is permitted. Moving the patient for the sake of medical treatment that will extend his or her life is permitted. R. Akiva Eiger,[24] discussing a case in which a fire broke out in the house of the *goses*, rules that the *goses* should be removed

14 R. Feinstein (*Iggerot Moshe, Choshen Mishpat* vol. 2, 75:5) acknowledges that according to some opinions, a *goses* can only be presumed alive if one is in the *goses*'s presence – otherwise one must assume that the *goses* has died. However, R. Feinstein insists, from a medical perspective, the patient is certainly considered alive and should be dealt with accordingly.

15 *Birkei Yosef* commenting on *Orach Chayyim* 329:4.

16 *Gittin* 28a.

17 See *Shulchan Arukh, Yoreh De'ah* 339:1 and the various commentaries there for further discussion.

18 *Yoreh De'ah* 339:1.

19 Ibid.

20 *Semachot* 1:4.

21 According to *kabbalah*, salt has protective powers and can protect from death. Rama therefore discusses a case where the patient has salt as a means of ensuring that the soul stays with the patient, thus preventing death. However, a more practical scenario is replacing a blood pressure medication (e.g., dobutamine, norepinephrine, etc.) in a hypotensive patient who is artificially being kept alive as a result of the medication. See *Nishmat Avraham, Yoreh De'ah* 339:7, p. 494.

22 *Yoreh De'ah* 339.

23 Responsa 114.

24 *Yoreh De'ah* 339:1.

from the house. R. Yehoshua Neuwirth[25] states that medical treatment may be administered to the *goses* regardless of whether he or she is conscious, even if this requires additional movement, since the patient may wake or may be more aware of his or her environment than assumed. *Nishmat Avraham*[26] reiterates that there is no question that anyone who is treating, helping or saving the *goses* is permitted to touch/move him or her as necessary. He goes so far to say that even a *kohen* is obligated to treat the *goses* if he thinks he can save the patient's life, even if the *kohen* is unsure whether the patient has died already. Even if another non-*kohen* doctor is present, the *kohen* doctor must enter the room and help.[27] On the other hand, if it is certain that no medical intervention will help this patient and that he or she has reached the status of a *goses*, then the above prohibitions regarding touching/moving the patient take effect.

Practical Issues for the Medical Student and Resident

Practicing Procedures on the *Goses*

Medical students are required to learn basic procedures such as physical exams, blood drawing, obtaining arterial blood gases, and others. Many patients are reluctant to be "practiced upon" and often patients who are less likely to resist qualify as *gosesim*. Granted, the student certainly has no intention to harm the patient, but the question remains: may unnecessary procedures be performed on a *goses*? R. Yitzchak Zilberstein[28] writes that it is forbidden for any physician or healthcare staff member to practice procedures on a *goses* even if the *goses* has given permission in advance. He states that one should rebuke those who do practice such procedures. *Nishmat Avraham*[29] writes more specifically that once it is established that the patient is a *goses*, routine blood pressure, temperature, pulse and the like should not be taken (even by fully trained professionals) as the results will not alter the treatment/prognosis of the patient and the additional movement may cause stress to the *goses*. However, if the patient is conscious and will notice that routine care has ceased, and this will cause the patient to despair, then these procedures should be performed with care to avoid causing emotional distress to

25 Cited in *Nishmat Avraham, Yoreh De'ah* 339:3, p. 481.
26 Ibid.
27 This is based on the principle (Yerushalmi *Nedarim* 4:2) that *lo mi-kol adam zokheh lehitrape'ot*, the patient may not merit to be saved from any given person, i.e., there is no way to predict which doctor will be successful in treating the patient, so we do not prevent any doctor from treating the patient, even if another doctor can treat the patient in a way that might involve fewer halakhic complications.
28 *Sefer Assia*, vol. 5, pp. 80–81.
29 *Yoreh De'ah* 339:3, p. 481.

the patient. Certainly these guidelines pertain to the medical student as well. The medical student should thus certainly not practice physical exams or any other procedure on the *goses*.

Moving the *Goses*

Of course, in instances when moving the *goses* may save his or her life or at least extend it, movement would be mandated. Even when nothing more can be done for the patient, exceptions can be made to the law against moving a *goses*. R. Shlomo Zalman Auerbach[30] explains that the ruling of *Shulchan Arukh* not to move a *goses* applies only to moving the patient for no reason or for the benefit of a non-seriously ill patient. However, if the *goses* must be moved so that another seriously ill patient can be treated, body parts of the *goses* such as his or her arm, or the *goses*'s bed, may be moved. Obviously, care should be taken to avoid unnecessary stress on the *goses*. R. Shmuel Wosner[31] rules similarly that the main prohibition regarding a *goses* is moving the body itself rather than the bed on which the patient is resting. For example, in an emergency room where multiple patients are blocking each other, and one patient must be transferred to the intensive care unit immediately but is being blocked by a *goses*, the *goses*'s bed may be moved. R. Wosner reasons that since much concern is given to avoid causing stress to the *goses,* and it is only a remote possibility that this may hasten death, moving the *goses* is permitted to save another patient's life. This is not comparable to removing an instrument from the mouth or the body of the *goses* to be used in another patient, which is not allowed. Another scenario in which the *goses* may be touched is stroking the hand of a *goses* who may be frightened in order to give emotional support. However extreme movement, like a mother taking her child, who is a *goses*, into her arms, would not be permitted.

Cleaning a *Goses*

While unnecessary movement of the *goses* is prohibited, may the *goses* be cleaned or have his or her linen changed, even if these activities are not necessary for medical treatment? *Nishmat Avraham*[32] writes that all nursing care that is necessary for the physical and mental comfort of the patient, such as washing, cleaning him or her and changing of the bed linen must be done.

---

30 Cited in *Nishmat Avraham, Yoreh De'ah* 339:3, p. 481.
31 *Assia*, vol. 55 (5754), pp. 43–45, reprinted in *Sefer Assia* vol. 11, pp. 10–11.
32 *Nishmat Avraham, Yoreh De'ah* 339:1 (C).

Behavior Near the *Goses*

Ma'avar Yabok[33] cautions that one should be careful not to engage in idle chatter near a *goses*. Likewise, one should not eat or drink around the *goses*.[34] People standing around the bedside of the *goses* should either pray in repentance or speak words of Torah with the *goses*. *Shulchan Arukh*[35] rules that the *goses* should not be left alone, rather one should always remain at the bedside of the patient; Rama adds that it is a *mitzvah* to remain at the patient's bedside. R. Akiva Eiger[36] adds that if there is no one else who can care for the *goses* according to Jewish law, then one should remain at the bedside even if this means missing *zeman tefillah*.

At the time of departure of the soul, there are many different customs as to what should be done.[37] These include lighting candles, opening a window, reciting Psalms and other prayers, and annulment of vows. Furthermore, it is proper to gather ten men to be present as the soul departs. Many of the above-mentioned customs are not pertinent to the medical student as they are more relevant to family members who remain at the bedside throughout. However, the medical student should be cognizant of his or her behavior while tending to the *goses* and should recognize the customs that religious families practice at the time the patient reaches the status of *goses*.

Preparing a Death Certificate

While it may be beneficial to the medical team to begin preparing the death certificate and other documents regarding the patient's death prior to the actual death, this may cause emotional distress to the patient. The permissibility of this practice should thus be dependent on the debate between *Bach* and Rivash as mentioned above. According to *Bach*, so long as these documents are not prepared in front of the patient and the patient will not be aware of such documents, this is permissible. Rivash would disagree due to concern that the patient may become aware of the documents, leading to additional emotional distress. According to Rivash, not only would preparing such documents be prohibited, but any preparation for death would be prohibited for the same concern.

---

33 *Siftei Renanot* chapter 4.
34 This practice is cited by R. Leopold (Yekutiel Yehudah) Greenwald (*Kol Bo al Aveilut*, pp. 22–23) from the practices of the Chevra Kadisha of Nikolsburg.
35 *Yoreh De'ah* 339:4.
36 Ibid.
37 See R. Avraham Steinberg's *Encyclopedia Hilkhatit Refu'it*, s.v. *noteh lamut* (2), who cites various practices; see also Chapter 18 for more details.

Conclusion

The medical student and resident will inevitably come across patients that can be considered *gosesim*. In today's era of modern medicine, the definition of a *goses* has become complicated, but as cited above from R. Shlomo Zalman Auerbach, a doctor can determine which terminally ill patients qualify. Once a patient reaches this stage, all unnecessary stressors should be avoided, including unnecessary blood draws and physical exams. However, any procedure that can be done to extend the patient's life would certainly be permitted as the patient is still considered to be alive. Likewise, the emotional support and dignity of the patient should be preserved. One should, as always, consult a qualified halakhic advisor with regard to any complex questions that one may encounter.

Chapter 18

Providing Care for the Deceased

Rabbi Joshua Brown, MD

The immediate moments after the passing of a loved one are often filled with tremendous sorrow, sadness and confusion for family members and friends. Healthcare providers have the unique opportunity to be present at the bedside during this most vulnerable time and to help comfort those who are in pain. In addition, healthcare workers, with deference to the family members, can help to perform the initial postmortem care rituals in a sensitive and respectful manner. Medical students, who are often less busy than attending physicians and residents, are uniquely suited to assist family members. Occasionally, after a Jewish patient on the floor passes away, a family member may ask an observant Jewish member of the healthcare team what is to be done next within the Jewish tradition.

In this chapter, we outline a step-by-step approach to how postmortem care is to be conducted followed by a brief discussion and analysis of the rituals.[1]

---

1   Many of the rituals discussed in this chapter are based heavily on customs that have been practiced by *chevra kadisha* groups. This author discussed many of those customs with R. Elchonon Zohn, president of the National Association of Chevra Kadisha. R. Zohn informed this author of many customs that are listed in this chapter for which no source is cited. An excellent source which summarizes many customs practiced after the passing of a hospital patient is R. Jason Weiner's *Guide to Observance of Jewish Law in a Hospital*, New York: Kodesh Press, 2012. Another source of information about terminal illness and bereavement in *halakhah* is R. Aharon Levine's *Zikhron Me'ir*.

Part 1: Initial Steps of Care

Instructions

1. Record time of death and make sure family knows the exact time.
2. Wait twenty minutes before proceeding with the care.
3. Contact *chevra kadisha*.
4. Encourage the healthcare team to fill out the death certificate as soon as possible in order to expedite release of the body and permit burial.

Discussion

The time of death according to Jewish law is a heavily debated issue. To simplify matters, we will assume that the deceased in this discussion is someone who has undergone cardiac death.[2] In such a case, one should ideally wait twenty minutes after the patient has been pronounced dead before proceeding with the formal postmortem rituals. The reason for waiting is that there is a prohibition of touching or moving a *goses*, a person who is on the brink of death, lest one expedite the death through these actions. Therefore, to avoid these issues, one should wait twenty minutes to ensure that the patient is truly deceased.[3] The time of the patient's death should be recorded and communicated to the family members in order for them to note the day of commemoration, since the time on the death certificate is not always exact. In addition, the *chevra kadisha* that the family plans on using should be contacted as soon as possible to expedite their arrival. Local community synagogues and Jewish funeral homes will have information about which *chevra kadisha* a family member may contact.

Part 2: Next Steps

Instructions

1. Do *not* tear garments.
2. Encourage family members to say *"Barukh Dayan Ha-Emet,"* "Blessed is the God of Truth," without using God's name. The formal blessing will be done at the funeral.
3. Family members should also be encouraged to say two verses:

---

2   Issues involving brain death and organ donation are outside the scope of this chapter.
3   *Gesher Ha-Chayyim*, 3:2(1).

ה' נָתַן וה' לָקַח יְהִי שֵׁם ה' מְבֹרָךְ:

Hashem gave, Hashem took; May the name of Hashem be blessed.[4]

הַצּוּר תָּמִים פָּעֳלוֹ כִּי כָל-דְּרָכָיו מִשְׁפָּט אֵ-ל אֱמוּנָה וְאֵין עָוֶל צַדִּיק וְיָשָׁר הוּא:

The Rock – perfect is His work, for all His paths are justice;
God of faith without iniquity, righteous and fair is He.[5]

Discussion

Shulchan Arukh,[6] based on the Gemara,[7] rules that anyone present at the time the soul departs is obligated to rend his or her garments (colloquially known as "tearing *keriah*"). Rama[8] argues and writes that one should tear *keriah* "before the face of the deceased has been sealed," which is interpreted as prior to the burial of the deceased. Although the custom used to be in accordance with *Shulchan Arukh*, nowadays we follow the opinion of Rama and delay the practice until the funeral for a variety of reasons.[9] Some suggest that tearing *keriah* must be done in a precise manner and therefore tearing *keriah* is delayed until the funeral when an expert is available for assistance.[10] It is also a tremendous merit for the soul to depart in the company of other people. Therefore, in order not to discourage people from attending the bedside, anyone present at the time of passing is exempted from tearing *keriah*. This law especially benefits physicians who would have to continuously tear their garments if the initial law were still in practice.

The family is encouraged to say "*Barukh Dayan Ha-Emet*," without mentioning God's name or kingship ("*melekh ha-olam*"), as the full blessing is intrinsically linked to the tearing of one's garments, now performed at the burial.[11] Nevertheless, at the moment the soul departs, all who are present should be encouraged to recite the passages mentioned above, as a way to affirm one's faith, and to acknowledge that the death of a loved one is a matter of God's will and is not comprehensible to the human mind.

---

4   Job 1:21.
5   Deuteronomy 32:4.
6   *Yoreh De'ah* 339:3.
7   *Mo'ed Katan* 28a.
8   *Yoreh De'ah* 340:1.
9   See *Gesher Ha-Chayyim*, 4:1(9).
10   See *Gesher Ha-Chayyim*, 4:1(6).
11   See *Gesher Ha-Chayyim*, 4:1(7). He adds (4:1(5)) that if the deceased is one's rabbi with whom he learned all his Torah, then indeed, one does tear *keriah* and recite "*Barukh Dayan Ha-Emet*" with God's name.

Part 3: Care of the Body

Instructions

1. The eyes and mouth of the body should be closed. Often the mouth is unable to be closed, and one is advised to take gauze and wrap it over the head and under the chin to make sure it is shut. This is done is out of respect for the body. Some cite an additional reason for this practice, namely to prevent air from entering the body and causing it to swell which can expedite the decomposition process.[12]
2. The body, including the face, should be covered in a white sheet.[13] The covering is done for several reasons. One reason is so that onlookers will not lose respect for the deceased whose features have now changed. Another is that covering the face may prevent the soul from experiencing pain because the deceased is unable to respond and defend itself to any accusation. In addition, the Gemara[14] states that looking upon the face of a deceased person causes one to forget one's learning.[15]
3. Raise the head so that it is elevated above the rest of the body.[16]
4. Straighten hands and fingers as much as possible out of respect for the body.[17]
5. Tie the feet together, either by tying the two big toes together, or by tying the ankles together. This practice as well as the following one are done preemptively, to prevent damage to the extremities when the body is transferred and moved.[18]
6. Tie the hands together over the stomach. It is important not to place the hands across the chest since this mimics a non-Jewish custom.
7. There is an ancient custom to put the body on the floor.[19] One reason suggested for this custom is that this keeps the body cool. Another reason cited is that a stone floor (which was the usual layout of homes) does not transfer impurity, and therefore putting the body

---

12 R. Chaim Binyamin Goldberg's *Mourning in Halachah*, p. 52; *Gesher Ha-Chayyim* 3:2(2); see *Shabbat* 151b.

13 The *halakhah* states that the body should also be undressed. The *chevra kadisha* will perform this ritual outside the hospital setting at a more appropriate location.

14 *Horayot* 13b.

15 *Mourning in Halachah*, pp. 50–51; *Gesher Ha-Chayyim* 3:1(1). Based on *Ma'avar Yabok* 43:9.

16 *Gesher Ha-Chayyim* 3:2(1).

17 This custom is based on the Midrash (*Sifrei, Haazinu, piska* 339) which notes that both Moshe and Aharon straightened their hands before dying. See *Gesher Ha-Chayyim* 15:2(7).

18 *Mourning in Halachah*, p. 52, citing *Zivula Batrayta* 1:2(1).

19 *Ma'avar Yabbok, Siftei Renanot* chapter 9; *Gesher Ha-Chayyim* 3:2.

(which is impure) on the floor avoids the transfer to other objects. A third reason cited is that placing a body on the floor symbolizes the punishment of stoning; thus, this act should serve as atonement for sins committed during the deceased's lifetime so that the deceased should not be further punished in the World to Come.[20] Nowadays, due to hospital protocol and in deference to other patients, this practice is often unable to be performed. However, if the deceased is in a private room and there is no hospital prohibition, then this custom should be followed.

Setting Aside Items for Burial

A member of the *chevra kadisha* will sometimes detach the patient from hospital equipment and ensure that the appropriate items will be buried. There are many instances, however, where the *chevra kadisha* will not be able to oversee this process. Thus, healthcare workers have an opportunity to assist with setting aside the following items:

- Any device which has an internal pathway to the body such as Foley catheters, gastrointestinal tubes, chest tubes, or any central or peripheral lines should not be removed and instead should be removed by the *chevra kadisha* prior to burial.[21] The reason for this is that these devices, if not removed appropriately, will most likely cause bleeding, and any blood should be buried with the body based upon the verse, "For blood is the essence of life."[22] This even includes blood that spills after the patient is already deceased. In addition, blood that contributes to the patient's death (such as blood from a hemorrhage) should be collected and buried along with the patient. Other bodily fluids, however, do not need to be buried with the patient.
- An endotracheal tube in the mouth should be removed so that it does not distort the shape of the mouth. An endotracheal tube in the nose should be left. If the endotracheal tube has blood on it, it should be sent along with the body for burial in any case.
- Dentures should be buried with the person and either left in the mouth or sent along with the body. The reason is that anything artificial which replaces a body part, such as dentures, should be buried with the deceased.[23] However, an item which functions simply to enhance an already functioning body part, such as a hearing aid, does not get buried.

---

20 *Gesher Ha-Chayyim* 3:2(1).
21 *Gesher Ha-Chayyim* 9:3(4); *Nitei Gavriel, Hilkhot Aveilut* vol. 1, 44:10.
22 Leviticus 12:23.
23 See *Shulchan Arukh* and Rama, *Yoreh De'ah* 349:2; *Gesher Ha-Chayyim* 8:8–9.

Part 4: Management of the Room

Instructions

1. There is a custom to light a candle in the room,[24] based on a verse, "The candle of God is the soul of man."[25] Lighting candles is not allowed in a hospital as they constitute a fire hazard; however, this practice should be performed if a person dies elsewhere. There is no custom to light electric candles in the hospital setting.
2. There is a custom to open the windows in the room.[26] This is done in order to keep the room cool, as well as to delay the body from decaying. Some suggest mystical reasons for opening windows, such as to create a path for the departing soul to reach the heavens, or to drive away harmful spirits.[27] Another reason is to spill out exposed water (see next section). Nowadays, in a hospital setting, it may not be possible to open the windows which may be permanently shut. In addition, opening a window can lead to a cold draft of air which may be uncomfortable to other patients sharing the room. Out of respect for them, this practice is not done in the hospital setting.
3. One should pour out any water that is open and exposed to the air.[28] In the past, the water was customarily poured outside an open window to surreptitiously[29] alert others in the surrounding area that someone had passed away. Neighbors would then come and visit the mourners, while *kohanim* would be warned from entering. Nowadays, based on kabbalistic reasons,[30] one should pour out any exposed water into a sink.

Part 5: Guarding the Body (*Shemirah*)

It is a *mitzvah* to guard the body of the deceased (*shemirah*), to the point that one is exempt from all other commandments.[31] Even a *kohen* who is a mourner for this deceased and responsible for the burial is permitted to be in the room and watch over the body.[32] The Gemara[33] clarifies that *shemirah* was mainly instituted to guard the body from being attacked

24 *Gesher Ha-Chayyim* 2:3(3).
25 Proverbs 20:27.
26 *Gesher Ha-Chayyim* 2:3(4).
27 *Mourning in Halachah*, p. 50.
28 *Shulchan Arukh, Yoreh De'ah* 339:5.
29 One is not supposed to explicitly share news of an individual's passing; see *Shakh, Yoreh De'ah* 339:9.
30 *Taz, Yoreh De'ah* 339:4.
31 *Shulchan Arukh, Yoreh De'ah* 341:6.
32 *Shulchan Arukh, Yoreh De'ah* 373:5; *Mourning in Halachah*, p. 55.
33 *Berakhot* 18a.

by rodents and insects. Nowadays, this concern is not applicable in modern hospital rooms, and certainly not in a hospital morgue, which is a sterile environment. In addition, nurses and other hospital personnel are continuously moving between hospital rooms and their presence can satisfy the basic *shemirah* requirement.[34] Thus, while it may be a worthy act of kindness, *shemirah* in a hospital setting is not an absolute obligation.

The major reasons to perform *shemirah* even in the hospital setting are based upon kabbalistic ideas that it provides comfort for the soul since the soul is aware of what is occurring. Some point to a kabbalistic notion that a person's soul is in flux until the body is buried, and since the body is emptied of the soul at that time, harmful spirits might enter the body; thus, guarding the body serves a critical purpose by preventing this.[35] In a more practical sense, knowing that someone is actively watching the body brings peace of mind to the mourners. Certainly, if a medical student or resident has time and is not needed elsewhere, then it is reasonable and respectful to stay with the body and recite Psalms.

Part 6: Reciting Psalms

One can easily assist family members in reciting chapters of Psalms. If the family members do not read Hebrew, they can be encouraged to recite Psalms in whichever language they know best. Specifically, the chapters customarily read include 16, 17, 23, 91, 121, and 130.

Conclusion

After the passing of a Jewish patient, healthcare practictioners, and especially medical students who may have more time to spend with the family, are empowered to assist the patient's family in observing traditional Jewish rituals following the departure of the soul. Facilitating the observance of some of the customs delineated above allows healthcare practitioners to have a meaningful impact on Jewish patients and their families not only in life, but also in the crucial minutes and hours after their passing.

---

34 See *Iggerot Moshe, Yoreh De'ah* 1:225.
35 *Gesher Ha-Chayyim* 5:4(4).

Chapter 19

Practicing Procedures on Deceased Patients

Yona Saperstein, MD

Stories are not uncommon of medical residents and other staff being asked to practice medical procedures on patients who have recently died. Certain procedures – such as proper techniques in intubation or chest compression – are easier to perform on patients who are not responsive or even deceased. Much discussion emerges from these incidents relating to the emotional and legal issues involved. In this chapter, we will focus primarily on the halakhic perspective – does Jewish law allow practicing intubation or other procedures on deceased patients?

Multiple halakhic issues arise with regard to practicing procedures on deceased patients. The first is the issue of *hana'ah* (benefit) from a dead body. The Gemara prohibits deriving benefit from a dead body, and we will discuss whether practicing procedures on dead bodies is considered benefit. The second issue is that of *nivul ha-met* (desecration of a dead body). We will discuss whether our specific case is considered desecration of the body. Lastly, we will discuss whether the benefit of having doctors well-trained to perform the procedures constitutes *pikuach nefesh* (saving of a life), as they will be able to use those skills in the future to save the lives of others. In cases of *pikuach nefesh*, almost all of the Torah prohibitions can be set aside in order to save a life.

Hana'ah (Benefit) From Dead Bodies

What is Considered *Hana'ah*?

The issue of *hana'ah*, or gaining benefit from a dead body, is discussed in the Gemara,[1] which rules that there is a prohibition to benefit from

---

1   *Sanhedrin* 47b.

a dead body or shrouds which have been placed on the dead body. For instance, wearing the shrouds or selling the body or the shrouds would constitute prohibited benefit. Whether practicing intubation on a dead body is considered benefit, thereby making it prohibited, is contingent on a parallel discussion as to whether or not dissecting a human body for the purpose of autopsy or medical instruction is considered benefit. The question is: is using a cadaver for the purpose of gaining knowledge considered prohibited benefit, or is only physical benefit considered prohibited benefit?[2] A majority of contemporary authorities, including R. Shlomo Zalman Auerbach[3] and *Nishmat Avraham*,[4] claim that dissecting a human body in anatomy lab is considered benefit, and is therefore subject to this prohibition. R. Auerbach[5] even goes as far as to rule that it is considered benefit to gaze at a dissected cadaver, and it is therefore prohibited to gaze at a dissected cadaver even if one doesn't actively dissect the cadaver. However, R. Tzvi Pesach Frank[6] posits that although autopsies are considered desecration of a dead body, they are not considered a form of benefit. Additionally, when R. Moshe Feinstein[7] discusses dissection of bodies, he only mentions that it constitutes a prohibition of desecrating the body and does not mention that there is a prohibition of benefit involved. In a later responsum,[8] when R. Feinstein discusses benefit from a dead body, he lists several cases in which the prohibition of benefiting from a dead body has been violated, all of which include using cadaveric components for medicinal or curative purposes, rather than using the cadaver to gain information. We see that there is a fundamental dispute among modern halakhic authorities as to whether using cadavers to gain information is included in the category of the prohibition of benefit from the cadaver.[9] The permissibility of intubating a dead patient would seem to hinge on this discussion: according to those who consider dissection a form of benefit because gaining knowledge from a cadaver would constitute benefit, intubating a dead patient to practice skills is also considered benefiting from the cadaver and is subject to

---

2   Prohibited physical benefit, classically, is when one uses the flesh or organs of the cadavers, such as in the case of organ procurement. All agree that using organs is considered benefit. Inserting a tube in the trachea during intubation, however, does not necessarily involve use of the physical body in the same manner, but instead would only serve to enhance the technique of the practitioner.

3   *Minchat Shlomo, mahadura tinyana,* 97.

4   *Nishmat Avraham, Yoreh De'ah* 349:2(1A), p. 517.

5   *Minchat Shlomo, mahadura tinyana,* 97.

6   *Har Tzvi, Yoreh De'ah,* 278.

7   *Iggerot Moshe, Yoreh De'ah* 2:151.

8   *Iggerot Moshe, Yoreh De'ah* 1:229.

9   For further discussion about this topic, see Chapter 2.

this prohibition, while according to R. Frank and R. Moshe Feinstein, practicing intubation is not considered benefit and is therefore allowed.

Cadavers of Jews and Non-Jews

Even if one were to assume that practicing intubation is considered a prohibited form of benefit, based on the view of R. Auerbach, the question arises as to the scope of the prohibition of benefit from a dead body. While all authorities agree that the prohibition of benefit from a dead body applies to a Jewish body, there is considerable discussion as to whether this prohibition also applies to a non-Jewish body. The Gemara[10] uses a *gezeirah shavah*, an exegetical method in which a common word in two different verses related to two different topics teaches that the two topics share a common theme, to derive the prohibition of benefit from a cadaver. The Gemara points out that when Miriam died, the Torah uses the word "*sham*,"[11] which is also used when the Torah teaches us about idols[12] and the law of *eglah arufah*, the calf whose neck is broken in a situation of an unsolved murder.[13] The Gemara explains that just as one may not derive benefit from idols or the *eglah arufah*, one may similarly not benefit from a dead body. The discussion as to whether or not one is prohibited to benefit from a non-Jewish cadaver is based on the fact that the Gemara learned this law from a verse about Miriam, and subsequently this law might not apply to a non-Jewish body.

Despite the teaching from the Gemara, *Shulchan Arukh*[14] states that one is prohibited to benefit from a dead body and its shrouds, whether the cadaver is from a Jewish person or not. However, *Pitchei Teshuvah*[15] states that according to *Shulchan Arukh*, there is a difference: it is Biblically prohibited to benefit from a Jewish cadaver, but it is only rabbinically prohibited to benefit from a non-Jewish cadaver. Therefore, *Pitchei Teshuvah* allows use of non-Jewish cadaveric components, such as medicines, to treat a sick person, even if his or her life is not in danger. Furthermore, *Shakh*[16] quotes many earlier authorities who believe that there is absolutely no prohibition of benefitting from a non-Jewish corpse. R. Shlomo Zalman Auerbach[17] allows dissection of non-Jewish cadavers despite the fact that he considers dissection a form of benefit. He explains that in order to teach students medicine, we can rely on the opinions of

10 *Sanhedrin* 47b.
11 Numbers 20:1.
12 Deuteronomy 12:2.
13 Deuteronomy 21:4.
14 *Yoreh De'ah* 349:1.
15 349:1.
16 *Nekudat Ha-Kesef, Yoreh De'ah*, 349.
17 Cited in *Nishmat Avraham, Yoreh De'ah*, 349:1(1), p. 513.

Shakh and all others who allow benefit from non-Jewish bodies, especially considering that even the stringent opinions hold that it is, at most, a rabbinic prohibition.

Application to Procedures on Dead Patients

Concerning practicing procedures on dead patients, there is debate among halakhic authorities as to whether it is considered a prohibited act of benefit from a dead body if one gains information from it. Even if one argues that gaining information from a dead body is considered benefit, there is a debate as to whether there is a prohibition of benefit from a non-Jewish body, and R. Shlomo Zalman Auerbach would allow dissecting a non-Jewish body in anatomy lab for the purpose of medical instruction. Therefore, from the perspective of prohibited benefit, there is room to allow practicing a procedure on a non-Jewish dead body. Next we will analyze how desecration of cadavers affects our discussion.

Nivul Ha-Met (Desecration)

What is Considered Desecration?

The second issue related to practicing procedures on deceased patients is the prohibition of *nivul ha-met*, desecration of a dead body. The source of this law is the verse in the Torah[18] which describes the treatment of a criminal who is subject to death by stoning. The verse states that one who is subject to death by stoning is hanged, but the corpse must be buried within the day because it is degrading for the body to remain hanging overnight. From this we learn the prohibition of desecrating a dead body.

While an autopsy is clearly considered *nivul ha-met*, it is not as clear whether the same will apply to practicing intubation. To understand the distinction, we will examine why conducting an autopsy is a violation of *nivul ha-met*. While one might think it would be permitted to perform an autopsy, the Gemara[19] rules that there is a prohibition of *nivul ha-met* if one examines a murder victim to see if he or she was a *tereifah* (an individual with a particular pathology which would normally be fatal within a year). The Gemara prohibits this act of *nivul ha-met* even though it may save the murderer's life in court, given that a murderer is not killed by the court if he or she kills a *tereifah*. The act of examining for these pathologies often involves cutting through the skin and examining the lungs and intestines. From this we see that an autopsy-style examination is considered *nivul ha-met*.

---

18   Deuteronomy 21:23.
19   *Chullin* 11b.

It is not as clear if performing a procedure which does not involve cutting the body open is also considered *nivul ha-met*. A cursory reading of the relevant passage in the Gemara[20] would imply that any procedure, even one which does not involve cutting open a cadaver, is considered *nivul ha-met*. The Gemara is discussing a case in which there is a monetary dispute over the property of a thirteen-year-old child who died, and part of the dispute is whether the child has reached puberty, in which case he would be considered an adult. The Gemara says that it would be considered *nivul ha-met* to examine the pubic area of the body. At first glance, this would imply that it is a violation of *nivul ha-met* to simply expose a dead body without cutting it open, and therefore, intubating a dead body would certainly be considered *nivul ha-met*. However, R. Moshe Feinstein[21] re-interprets the passage in the Gemara, and says that the only issue involving *nivul ha-met* in the above case is re-opening the casket in which the child has already been buried. Simply exposing a cadaver which has not yet been buried, without cutting it open, is not considered *nivul ha-met* according to R. Feinstein. It would appear that intubating a dead patient is less degrading than cutting the body open, but more degrading than exposing the patient, and it is therefore unclear how R. Feinstein would view intubation. Importantly, R. Shlomo Zalman Auerbach[22] rules that intubating a dead body is not considered *nivul ha-met*.

Nivul Ha-Met of Non-Jewish Bodies

Even if we argue in favor of the cursory reading of aforementioned passage in the Gemara, and assume that performing procedures on a dead body is considered *nivul ha-met*, or if we argue that practicing procedures is serious enough to be considered *nivul ha-met* even according to R. Moshe Feinstein, there is an additional discussion as to whether the prohibition of *nivul ha-met* applies only to Jews or also to non-Jews. The prohibition of *nivul ha-met* is derived from the prohibition of prolonged hanging of one who is subject to stoning, and only Jews are subject to the punishment of stoning; therefore, it can be argued that the prohibition of *nivul ha-met* only applies to Jewish bodies.

Although there is no explicit discussion in *Shulchan Arukh* as to whether *nivul ha-met* applies to non-Jewish bodies, one passage in the Gemara[23] seems to illustrate the permissibility of *nivul ha-met* to a non-Jewish body. The Gemara recounts an incident in which the students of R. Yishmael burned a woman who was sentenced to burning by

---

20 *Bava Batra* 154a.
21 *Iggerot Moshe, Yoreh De'ah*, 2:151.
22 Cited in *Nishmat Avraham, Yoreh De'ah* 349:2(9), p. 523.
23 *Bekhorot* 45a.

the secular government, and counted her organs in order to learn how many bones are in the human body. *Nishmat Avraham*[24] argues that this story proves that no halakhic prohibition is violated by cutting open the body of a non-Jew. However, R. Shlomo Zalman Auerbach[25] says that it is indeed prohibited to desecrate any body, Jewish or not, but argues that the case in the Gemara is different for one of two reasons. First, the threshold for *nivul ha-met* of a non-Jewish body is higher than that of a Jewish body, so that dissection of a non-Jewish body for the purpose of learning anatomy is not considered *nivul ha-met*. Second, even if dissection of a non-Jewish body for the purpose of learning anatomy is considered *nivul ha-met*, perhaps *nivul ha-met* of a non-Jewish body is permitted for the sake of learning anatomy, just as *hana'ah* from a non-Jewish cadaver is permitted for the sake of learning anatomy.

Is Intubation of a Dead Patient Prohibited Due to *Nivul Ha-Met*?

With regard to practicing intubation on a dead patient who is not yet buried, a cursory reading of the Gemara would imply that it is a violation of *nivul ha-met*, while according to R. Auerbach, practicing intubation on a dead body would not be a violation of *nivul ha-met*. Even if one would argue against R. Auerbach's opinion, there is discussion as to the status of the prohibition of *nivul ha-met* on a non-Jewish body. As we saw previously, there may be three reasons why practicing intubation on a non-Jewish body might be permitted: 1) *Nivul ha-met* may be permitted with regard to a non-Jewish body, as per the argument of *Nishmat Avraham*. 2) Cutting open a non-Jewish body may not be a form of *nivul ha-met*, even if this would be a form of *nivul ha-met* if performed on a Jewish body. 3) We may be permitted to violate *nivul ha-met* of a non-Jewish body if there is a higher purpose involved, such as teaching an intern how to intubate.

Is Gaining Medical Knowledge Considered *Pikuach Nefesh*?

The final issue which pertains to practicing procedures on dead patients is whether the benefit of having doctors well-trained to perform procedures constitutes *pikuach nefesh* (saving a life), as they will be able to use those skills in the future to save the lives of others. If our case constitutes *pikuach nefesh*, it would even be permitted to practice procedures

---

24 *Nishmat Avraham*, Yoreh De'ah 349:1(3), p. 517.
25 Cited by *Nishmat Avraham*, ibid.

on a Jewish body, considering that *pikuach nefesh* would allow us to violate the prohibitions of benefiting from a dead body and desecrating a dead body. R. Yechezkel Landau[26] discusses whether an autopsy can be performed on a Jewish body, and concludes that an autopsy can be performed if there is known to be a living person with a particular illness whose life has a chance of being saved by the information gleaned by the autopsy. However, he does not allow autopsies to be performed with the intention of giving general knowledge to the medical community if there is not currently a reported case of someone whose life can be saved by this autopsy. *Chazon Ish*[27] expands the ruling of R. Landau to allow autopsies if the information gleaned will be able to save the lives of people suffering from an epidemic, even if there is not currently known to be a patient whose life can be saved at this very moment by the information gleaned from the autopsy.

Now that we are aware that there exists a narrowly defined concept of indirect *pikuach nefesh*, that one may violate Torah law in order to glean information to save a sick person or stop an epidemic, the question arises: can we apply this principle one step further to the act of practicing procedures on a dead patient? Can we argue that since there is a patient who would require intubation at any moment, giving the intern the skill to practice intubation is considered *pikuach nefesh* just as performing an autopsy is allowed to benefit a known patient whose life can be saved? Would we consider the commonality of the requirement for intubation as if there was a currently reported case of a patient whose life can be saved by an imminent autopsy? R. Shlomo Zalman Auerbach[28] rules that the connection can indeed be made; he holds that one is allowed to practice intubating a deceased patient, even on a Jewish patient, in order to practice one's intubation skills, considering that at any moment, there will be a patient whose life can be directly saved with intubation, and the case is comparable to R. Landau's scenario of performing an autopsy to save an existing patient with the same disease.

Summary and Similar Cases

R. Shlomo Zalman Auerbach[29] allows interns to practice intubation on deceased patients, even if the patients are Jews. He gives a two-pronged argument in favor of this ruling. His first argument is that the intern's knowledge of intubation is considered *pikuach nefesh*; at any point, there will be a patient in the hospital whose life can be immediately

---

26 *Noda Be-Yehudah*, *mahadura tinyana*, *Yoreh De'ah*, 210.
27 *Ohalot* 22:32.
28 Cited in *Nishmat Avraham*, *Yoreh De'ah* 349:2(9) (p. 523).
29 Cited by *NIshmat Avraham*, ibid.

saved with an intubation, and the commonality of the requirement for intubation is comparable to R. Landau's case of performing an autopsy if there is a known patient whose life can be saved by the autopsy. His second argument is that practicing intubation is not considered *nivul ha-met* considering that it does not involve cutting the body open.[30]

As stated at the outset, this chapter was devoted to exploring the approach to practicing procedures on the recently deceased only from the strict perspective of Jewish law. In the event that performing these procedures would anger family members, co-workers, or hospital administration, one is highly advised to avoid practicing these procedures. Although technically allowed according to *halakhah*, one must be certain to avoid *chillul Hashem* at all costs. In addition, most hospitals have guidelines for students and residents on handling patients who have recently died, and one is certainly encouraged to follow these guidelines.

A more complicated application is the question of practicing procedures on Jewish cadavers which are not invasive, but are not as useful a tool in directly saving a patient's life. One example of this application would be to take a biopsy from a cadaver, either for the purpose of practicing the skills to take a biopsy, or to gain medical knowledge of which it is not known whether this will directly save the life of a patient currently suffering from the same disease. The same would apply to the case of practicing drawing blood from a cadaver. We can extend the logic of R. Auerbach and conclude that practicing non-invasive procedures on a cadaver is not considered *nivul ha-met*. However, according to many authorities, including R. Auerbach himself, gaining medical knowledge from a cadaver would be considered benefit. And unlike the question of practicing intubation, in which a second argument was given that the scenario is considered a case of *pikuach nefesh* due to the prevalence of patients whose lives can be saved with intubation and its comparability to the case of one whose life can be saved with an autopsy, it is

---

30 Interestingly, R. Auerbach does not mention whether practicing intubation is considered benefit from the cadaver. R. Auerbach, as quoted earlier, rules that dissecting a cadaver is considered benefit, and logically, because gaining knowledge from a cadaver is considered benefit, practicing intubation on a cadaver would be considered benefit as well. If R. Auerbach were only to give his second argument, we would still question whether one is allowed to practice intubation on a Jewish cadaver; despite the fact that practicing intubation is not *nivul ha-met*, it would be considered benefit based on his rulings about dissections, and would be prohibited on a Jewish cadaver. However, based on R. Auerbach's first argument, considering that intubation has the status of a direct *pikuach nefesh*, it would be allowed to practice intubation even on Jewish cadavers. It is possible that R. Auerbach does not mention the prohibition of benefit from a dead body when giving this ruling because he would allow practicing intubation on Jewish patients anyway, given his first argument.

not as clear whether we can argue the same with knowledge of biopsies and phlebotomy. R. Moshe Feinstein[31] argues that one is allowed to perform a biopsy on a Jewish cadaver, because it is not a violation of *nivul ha-met*. However, R. Feinstein, as noted earlier, rules that gaining knowledge from a cadaver is not considered benefit. It can be argued that according to R. Auerbach, who holds that dissection of a cadaver is considered benefit, one may only practice phlebotomy or perform a biopsy on a non-Jewish cadaver, based on his argument that one may benefit from a non-Jewish cadaver for an important purpose.

31 *Iggerot Moshe, Yoreh De'ah* 2:151.

Section IV
Residency and *Shabbat*

Chapter 20

Principles of Providing Medical Care on *Shabbat*

Jerry Karp, MD, PhD

Among the chief halakhic issues which face practicing health professionals is how one must conduct oneself with regard to *Shabbat*. Graduating medical students must choose between residency programs that are designed to accommodate *Shabbat* and *yom tov* observance and other residency programs which do not accommodate religious observance. Along the same vein, one who is in a residency program which does not accommodate *Shabbat* observance must do one's utmost to avoid any prohibited *Shabbat* violation. Additionally, practicing physicians are often on call during *Shabbat*, forcing them to navigate the various halakhic issues related to *Shabbat* observance. In this chapter, we will provide an overview of some of the foundational laws related to providing medical care on *Shabbat*. We will not discuss all issues related to this topic; rather we will restrict ourselves to those which are relevant for practicing health care professionals, and particularly medical students and residents.

Pikuach Nefesh on *Shabbat*

Much of the discussion of providing medical care on *Shabbat* revolves around the well-known principle that *pikuach nefesh*, saving a life, overrides *Shabbat* prohibitions. One is permitted, and even obligated, to violate *Shabbat* laws to save the life of another individual. However, the details and scope of this principle are complex, as will be discussed below.

Source

The Mishnah[1] clearly states that one is permitted to violate *Shabbat* to save a life. However, it gives no source for this principle. The Gemara[2] cites numerous opinions for the source that *pikuach nefesh docheh Shabbat*, saving a life overrides *Shabbat*. Several Talmudic sages infer this principle from logical reasoning,[3] while others derive this principle from a Biblical verse.[4] One opinion, offered by R. Shimon ben Menasia, is that we learn that one may violate *Shabbat* to save a life from the

---

1   *Yoma* 83a.

2   *Yoma* 85a–b; the same sources appear in *Mekhilta* (*Ki Tisa, Massekhta De-Shabbata* 1).

3   Three logical arguments are presented in the Gemara:
1.   R. Yishmael notes that one is permitted to kill a burglar in self-defense if one suspects that the burglar is willing to kill in order to prevent being caught. R. Yishmael cites several proofs that killing is a worse sin than *Shabbat* violation, and concludes that if one is permitted to kill in order to save a life, then one is also permitted to violate *Shabbat* to save a life.
2.   R. Akiva notes that if a *kohen* is performing the Temple service at the altar, and elsewhere an individual is about to be executed for a capital crime, he is permitted to pause the Temple service if he can testify that the individual is not deserving of execution. This is ostensibly because saving this individual's life overrides the *mitzvah* of performing the Temple service. Moreover, the Temple service is generally performed on *Shabbat*, indicating that performing the Temple service overrides *Shabbat* observance. Thus, if saving a life overrides the Temple service, and the Temple service overrides *Shabbat* observance, we can conclude that saving a life itself also overrides *Shabbat* observance.
3.   R. Elazar notes that circumcision may be performed on *Shabbat*. Thus, he infers that if circumcision, which only affects one organ, overrides *Shabbat* observance, then saving a life, which affects the entire body, certainly overrides *Shabbat* observance.

4   Besides that of R. Shimon ben Menasia (discussed below), two Biblical verses are suggested:
1.   R. Yosi ben Yehudah derives from *"akh et Shabbetotai tishmoru,"* *"however,* keep my *Shabbat"* (Exodus 31:13) that there is a case in which *Shabbat* need not be observed. This is due to a general principle which states that the word *akh* found in a Biblical verse indicates that a halakhic distinction is to be made. In this case, R. Yosi ben Yehudah assumes that the distinction is between cases in which there is no life at stake and cases in which violating *Shabbat* will allow one to save a life, in which case *Shabbat* violation is permitted.
2.   R. Yonatan ben Yosef derives from *"ki kodesh hi lakhem,"* "for it is holy *to you"* (Exodus 31:14) that *Shabbat* is in our control, rather than *Shabbat* having control over us. Thus, one may violate *Shabbat* to save a life, since otherwise we would be under the control of *Shabbat*.

Biblical verse, *"ve-shameru benei Yisra'el et ha-Shabbat,"* "And the children of Israel will observe the *Shabbat*,"[5] suggesting that one may violate *Shabbat* if it will lead to increased *Shabbat* observance. In particular, R. Shimon ben Menasia formulates a much-cited rule: *"chalel alav Shabbat achat, kedei she-yishmor Shabbatot harbeh,"* "Violate for him one *Shabbat*, so that he will observe many *Shabbatot*." According to R. Shimon ben Menasia, one may violate *Shabbat* to save a life because the saved individual will now be able to observe many *Shabbatot* in the future.[6]

After citing numerous proofs, the Gemara cites Shmuel, who suggests that this principle should be derived from another verse, *"va-chai bahem,"* "And [one should] live by them."[7] This verse teaches that the *mitzvot* are intended to allow us to live by them; Shmuel derives from this that one is not to die because of observance of the *mitzvot*, including *Shabbat*. Rava, a later authority, notes that Shmuel's source is the only one which suggests that one may violate *Shabbat* even if there is uncertainty as to whether a life is in danger. Rashi explains that according to Shmuel, the verse teaches us that we should live by the *mitzvot*, and should not observe *mitzvot* in a way which might lead to death, even if this consequence is not certain to result. Shmuel's source is cited as authoritative by Rambam.[8]

5   Exodus 31:16.
6   Though this reason is not the one which the Gemara cites as authoritative in explaining why one may violate *Shabbat* to save a life, it is cited by later authorities to justify violating *Shabbat* in other situations. One example is Ramban (*Torat Ha-Adam, Sha'ar Ha-Meichush,* Chavel ed. pp. 28–29) who cites Behag as allowing *Shabbat* violation to save a fetus. Ramban explains that although *"va-chai bahem,"* the reason which is cited as authoritative, does not apply here, since the fetus is not yet living, the reason of *"chalel alav Shabbat achat…"* does apply here, since, if born, the fetus will be able to observe future *Shabbatot*. Similarly, *Shulchan Arukh* (*Orach Chayyim* 306:14) rules that one may violate *Shabbat* to rescue a young woman from Christian kidnappers, due to *"chalel alav Shabbat achat…"* (see *Magen Avraham* 306:29): though the woman will not be killed, she will no longer observe *Shabbat* unless she is rescued, so violating *Shabbat* will lead to future *Shabbat* observance. Furthermore, the Gemara elsewhere (*Shabbat* 151b) cites *"chalel alav Shabbat achat…"* as a source to allow *Shabbat* violation if it will lead to future *Shabbat* observance. Some have argued that while the Gemara in *Yoma* does not accept the argument of *"chalel alav Shabbat achat…"* as the primary source that one may violate *Shabbat* to save a life, the Gemara is not rejecting this argument entirely; see *Minchat Asher* (*Ki Tisa*, ch. 4), and R. Gil Student, "Shabbat and Gentile Lives," accessed June 26, 2013, http://www.aishdas.org/student/shabbat.htm.
7   Leviticus 18:5.
8   *Shabbat* 2:3.

Saving the Life of an Individual Who Does Not Observe *Shabbat*

The two sources above seem to imply that violating *Shabbat* might only be permitted if the individual whose life is in danger observes *Shabbat*. R. Shimon ben Menasia's source, *"chalel alav Shabbat achat..."* suggests that one may only violate *Shabbat* if it will lead to future *Shabbat* observance, which would not be the case if the individual at risk does not generally observe *Shabbat*. Similarly, Shmuel's source, *"va-chai bahem,"* suggests that *mitzvah* observance should not cause one to risk one's life, but if the individual in danger does not observe *mitzvot*, one might conclude that we would not be permitted to violate *Shabbat* to save the individual's life. Indeed, *Tosafot*[9] explicitly state that *"va-chai bahem"* applies only to a Jew;[10] it is unclear whether they would apply the source to a non-observant Jew. *Biur Halakhah*[11] writes that *"chalel alav Shabbat achat..."* suggests that one should save a life on *Shabbat* if it will lead to future *mitzvah* observance,[12] but the other sources in the Gemara would allow for violating *Shabbat* regardless of whether it leads to future *mitzvah* observance. Still, *Biur Halakhah* argues that all sources cited in the Gemara would only permit violating *Shabbat* to save the life of a Jew.

Nevertheless, as we will see, the universal practice among observant Jewish doctors (and others) is to save any life on *Shabbat*, regardless of whether the individual is Jewish or not, or whether the individual observes *mitzvot*. The reasons for this practice, which is supported by all prominent contemporary halakhic authorities, will be discussed below.

Non-Observant Jews

The Gemara does not discuss saving the life of a non-observant Jew on *Shabbat*, but based on the above sources, we might conclude that this would not be permitted. Indeed, *Peri Megadim*[13] and *Kaf Ha-Chayyim*[14]

---

9   *Sanhedrin* 74b s.v. *ben noach*; see Maharsha ad loc.
10   Presumably, the reason for this is that the context of the verse is, *"u-shem-artem et mitzvotai... asher ya'aseh ha-adam otam va-chai bahem,"* "and you shall follow My commandments... which if a man performs, he shall live by them." Thus, the law of *"va-chai bahem"* applies only to one who observes the *mitzvot*.
11   *Orach Chayyim* 329 s.v. *ela*.
12   He cites Me'iri (*Yoma* 83a), who allows saving a life on *Shabbat* even if the life will be fleeting, since this will give the individual additional time to repent. According to Me'iri, the source *"chalel alav Shabbat achat..."* allows saving a life on *Shabbat* even if it will lead to future *mitzvah* observance (e.g., repenting), not necessarily *Shabbat* observance.
13   *Mishbetzot Zahav, Orach Chayyim* 328:6.
14   *Orach Chayyim* 329:91.

rule that one may not violate *Shabbat* to save the life of a non-observant Jew on *Shabbat*. *Mishnah Berurah*[15] writes that we do violate *Shabbat* to save the life of a *mumar le-tei'avon*, one who violates commandments for self-gratification, but not to save the life of a *mumar le-hakhis*, one who violates commandments to spite God. We would expect that most non-observant Jews today are in the category of *mumar le-tei'avon*. However, R. Eliezer Waldenberg[16] and and R. Yehoshua Neuwirth[17] argue that *Mishnah Berurah* believes that one who violates *Shabbat* is considered like a *mumar le-hakhis*, and therefore we would not be permitted to violate *Shabbat* to save such a person.[18]

In practice, however, we always violate *Shabbat* to save the life of a non-observant Jew, despite the above authorities' rulings. Later authorities have disagreed with the assertion of *Peri Megadim* for several reasons. First, *Peri Megadim*'s assertion is likely based on the Talmudic statement[19] that if a *mumar le-hakhis*, one who violates commandments in order to spite God, is in danger, one may not save him. Moreover, the Gemara notes elsewhere[20] that one who worships idols or publicly violates *Shabbat* is considered a *mumar le-hakhis*. Thus, it is likely that *Peri Megadim* inferred that if one may not save a *mumar le-hakhis* during the week, then certainly one may not violate *Shabbat* in order to save such a person.

If this is the basis for *Peri Megadim*'s assertion, though, it would allow for the possibility that one may violate *Shabbat* in modern times to save a non-observant Jew's life. Indeed, many contemporary authorities believe that non-observant Jews today are not in the category of *mumar le-hakhis*. Even an authority as early as Rambam[21] argued that the Karaites of his time were not considered *mumarim*, but instead *tinokot she-nishbu*, like "children who were taken captive." Since the Karaites of his time were born to families which already followed Karaite customs, and were thus brought up to believe in Karaite customs, they are less culpable for their actions, and therefore are not in the category of *mumar le-hakhis*. Later, *Chazon Ish*[22] applied this principle toward non-observant Jews of his time. In his discussion of this issue, he explains that one who was born into a non-religious home

---

15   329:9.

16   *Tzitz Eliezer* 8:15, ch. 5.

17   *Halakhah U-Refuah*, vol. 1, pp. 164.

18   *Baddei Ha-Shulchan* (to *Ketzot Ha-Shulchan* 139:5) writes that *Mishnah Berurah* considers one who violates *Shabbat* publicly to be a *mumar le-tei'avon*, and thus we would be permitted to violate *Shabbat* to save the life of such an individual.

19   *Avodah Zarah* 26b.

20   *Chullin* 5a.

21   *Hilkhot Mamrim* 3:3.

22   *Yoreh De'ah* 1:6, 2:19.

is a *tinok she-nishbah*, and therefore the *halakhot* which apply to a *mumar le-hakhis* do not apply to such an individual. He also writes[23] that one is required to violate *Shabbat* to save the life of a non-religious Jew. *Nishmat Avraham*[24] cites numerous authorities who agree with *Chazon Ish*, including R. Yaakov Emden,[25] *Chelkat Ya'akov*,[26] R. Eliezer Waldenberg[27] and R. Ovadia Yosef.[28] All these authorities mandate violating *Shabbat* to save the life of a non-observant Jew.

An alternative basis for disagreeing with *Peri Megadim*'s ruling is suggested by Maharam Schick.[29] He cites *Chatam Sofer*[30] who writes that one may participate in burying a person assumed to be non-Jewish (and wearing a non-Jewish religious symbol around his neck) but found to be circumcised, and thus, in *Chatam Sofer*'s era, likely Jewish. He explains that it is reasonable to assume that the person repented upon realizing that he was about to die, and thus is considered like an observant Jew. On this basis, Maharam Schick disagrees with *Peri Megadim*, saying that a non-observant Jew likely repented when his or her life was endangered, and so we may violate *Shabbat* to save this person's life. He points out that in situations of life-threatening illness, we do not make decisions based on the majority of situations, so even though most people might not repent in this situation, we are allowed to act based on the possibility that the person repented. Moreover, *Chatam Sofer* himself pointed out that in modern times most non-observant Jews are in the category of *mumar le-tei'avon*, and so it is even more likely that such individuals might repent in a life-threatening situation.[31]

---

23 *Yoreh De'ah* 2:26.
24 *Orach Chayyim* 328:6(3), p. 407.
25 *She'eilat Ya'avetz* 1:30.
26 *Orach Chayyim, mahadura batra*, 154. *Chelkat Ya'akov* also argues that there are several other reasons to be lenient and not categorize contemporary non-observant Jews as *mumarim le-hakhis*:
   - One is only considered to be a "public" *Shabbat* violator if one violates *Shabbat* by working in a field (based on *Ittur*, cited in *Beit Yosef, Even Ha-Ezer*, 44).
   - One is not considered a "public" *Shabbat* violator if one would not violate *Shabbat* in front of an important person.
   - One who does not realize the severity of the prohibitions of *Shabbat* is not considered a "public" *Shabbat* violator.
27 *Tzitz Eliezer* 8:15, ch. 5–6.
28 *Yalkut Yosef, Shabbat* vol. 5, p. 291.
29 Responsa *Orach Chayyim* 140.
30 *Yoreh De'ah*, 341.
31 R. Eliezer Waldenberg (*Tzitz Eliezer* 8:15, ch. 5) notes that Maharam Schick only seems to permit saving the life of a *mumar le-tei'avon*, and only when it seems reasonable to assume that the individual repented. However, he suggests that *Chatam Sofer* himself might have been willing to permit saving even a *mumar le-hakhis*, since his comment about the

A final basis for saving the life of a non-observant Jew on *Shabbat* is based on the concept of *eivah*. As we will see concerning saving non-Jews' lives on *Shabbat*, a major factor permitting this is the concern that if an observant Jewish physician does not save a non-Jew's life on *Shabbat*, this will create *eivah*, ill will, which could potentially lead to a non-Jewish doctor not saving the life of a Jewish patient. R. Eliezer Waldenberg,[32] Dayan Yitzchak Weiss,[33] and R. Ovadia Yosef[34] argue that *eivah* applies to non-observant Jewish patients as well, since there is a possibility that if an observant Jewish physician does not care for a non-observant Jewish patient on *Shabbat*, this may lead to a non-observant Jewish physician giving inferior care to an observant Jewish patient in the future.

As a general rule, R. Waldenberg[35] writes that one should assume that any Jewish patient is observant, and even if the patient appears to be non-observant, one should assume that the patient is a *mumar le-tei'avon*, such that saving his or her life on *Shabbat* is permitted. He notes that while most *acharonim* do not permit violating *Shabbat* to save the life of an individual who violates *Shabbat*, it should be permitted in a typical situation since many factors complicate the definition of *mumar le-tei'avon*, including which *melakhot* are performed and in front of how many people, and whether one is only defined as a *mumar* if there is testimony to this effect in a Jewish court. Therefore, he concludes that since we do not need to act based on the majority of situations in cases of life-threatening illness, we must violate *Shabbat* to save the life of a non-observant Jew.

Non-Jews

Just as with non-observant Jews, one would conclude from the sources provided for why violating *Shabbat* is permitted to save a life that this dispensation might not extend to violating *Shabbat* to save the life of a non-Jew, since non-Jews do not observe *Shabbat* or other *mitzvot*.

---

individual likely being a *mumar le-tei'avon* was an afterthought, and his ruling regarding the non-observant Jew seems to have been mentioned without that qualification. Still, *Tzitz Eliezer* is hesitant to allow violating *Shabbat* for a *mumar le-hakhis* according to *Chatam Sofer*, since he is not sure that *Chatam Sofer* would have extended his ruling to *Shabbat* anyway (as Maharam Schick had done).

32   *Tzitz Eliezer* 8:15, ch. 6.
33   *Minchat Yitzchak* 3:20. Dayan Weiss proves that *eivah* applies to non-observant Jews as well from the Gemara (*Avodah Zarah* 26a) which mentions *eivah* with regard to non-scrupulous shepherds (*ro'ei beheimah dakkah*), who are presumably Jewish but not scrupulous in halakhic observance.
34   *Yabbia Omer* 8:38.
35   *Tzitz Eliezer* 8:15, ch. 5.

Indeed, the Mishnah[36] assumes that one may not violate *Shabbat* to save a non-Jew's life. However, today, it is universal practice among observant Jews to violate *Shabbat* to save non-Jews' lives, and contemporary halakhic authorities unanimously support this practice. To understand why this is so, we will examine the history of halakhic discourse on the subject.

The root of this change in practice is the discussion in the Gemara[37] regarding a Jewish midwife delivering a non-Jewish child. The Mishnah states that it is prohibited for a Jewish midwife to birth a non-Jewish child since she will then be responsible for the birth of a child who will eventually worship idols. However, in the ensuing Talmudic discussion, R. Yosef qualifies this ruling and states that if the midwife is offered monetary compensation for her services, she should agree to deliver the child, since not doing so would create *eivah*, ill will.[38] If the midwife were to refuse to deliver the child, even for pay, it would be obvious to the non-Jewish woman that the midwife is refusing because the woman in labor is not Jewish, and this might create animosity. On the other hand, if the midwife is asked to provide her services for free, she could legitimately claim that she is not willing to work for free, and, R. Yosef argues, this would not create animosity toward the Jewish midwife, since her claim is understandable. R. Yosef claimed that this would be true on *Shabbat* as well, but Abaye interjects and rules that the midwife would not be allowed to deliver the non-Jewish child on *Shabbat*, even for pay, since the midwife could legitimately claim that it is the practice for Jewish women only to violate *Shabbat* to deliver Jewish children, but not non-Jewish children; this, Abaye argues, would not create a situation of *eivah*, since the non-Jewish woman would understand and appreciate this logic. It is likely that in Abaye's time, this excuse would have been socially acceptable, such that it would prevent a situation of *eivah*.[39]

Tosafot[40] question the basis for R. Yosef's assumption. Were it not for Abaye's explanation for why there will not be *eivah* as long as the midwife gives an acceptable excuse for not providing her services on *Shabbat*, it would seem that R. Yosef is arguing that one can violate

36 See *Yoma* 83a.
37 *Avodah Zarah* 26a.
38 *Beit Yosef* (*Yoreh De'ah* 154:2) cites Rashba (responsa 1:120) who notes that Ramban himself provided fertility treatments for non-Jewish women so that they could become pregnant, based on R. Yosef's statements in the Gemara. However, *Beit Yosef* also notes that Rabbeinu Yonah strongly disagreed with Ramban and sharply critiqued him, though his reasoning for rejecting R. Yosef's ruling is not explicit.
39 See below for *Chatam Sofer*'s rejection of Abaye's assumption in application to modern times.
40 Ad loc, s.v. *savar*.

Shabbat due solely to *eivah*. This is very surprising: how can a Torah prohibition be suspended because of *eivah*? *Tosafot* suggest that the Gemara must be discussing only a rabbinic prohibition.[41] They explain that the case in the Gemara is one in which the fetus has already been expelled from the uterus, such that removing the fetus is no longer a Torah prohibition. Since, then, birthing in this case is only a rabbinic prohibition, it is reasonable to assume that a rabbinic decree to prevent *eivah* could overrule a rabbinic prohibition. Ritva,[42] however, provides an entirely different answer to this question. He posits that even a rabbinic prohibition would not be suspended to prevent *eivah*. Rather, the Gemara must be discussing a case in which no prohibition, Biblical or rabbinic, is being violated. Thus, Ritva explains, Abaye suggested that the midwife explain that she cannot assist on *Shabbat* not because this is the true explanation, but because it would prevent *eivah*. In fact, the true explanation for why the midwife cannot help is because it is prohibited to help in birthing a non-Jewish woman. Abaye argues that the midwife should provide an untrue explanation of why she cannot deliver the non-Jewish child in order to prevent *eivah*.

It would seem that according to *Tosafot*, one is permitted to violate rabbinic prohibitions to prevent *eivah*, but not Torah prohibitions; according to Ritva, one may not violate even a rabbinic prohibition to prevent *eivah*. Knowing this, we can apply their opinions to our discussion of violating *Shabbat* to save a non-Jew's life. Obviously, if an observant Jew were to refrain from saving a non-Jew's life due to inability to violate *Shabbat*, this would certainly create *eivah*. According to *Tosafot*, it would be permitted for a Jewish physician to violate rabbinic prohibitions on *Shabbat* to save a non-Jew's life, but according to Ritva, the physician would not even be permitted to violate rabbinic prohibitions.

41 More precisely, *Tosafot* write that R. Yosef must be discussing a case where there is no Torah prohibition, but they do not specify that the case still involves a rabbinic prohibition. R. Eliezer Waldenberg (*Tzitz Eliezer* 8:15:6), however, concludes that *Tosafot* intended to argue that there is still a rabbinic prohibition in this case, since *Talmidei Rabbeinu Yonah* (cited in *Sheyarei Kenesset Ha-Gedolah* on *Beit Yosef, Yoreh De'ah* 154:10) write that this case is one in which there is still a rabbinic prohibition, and their language is sufficiently similar to that of *Tosafot* to lead to the conclusion that their opinion is intended to echo that of *Tosafot*. R. Ovadia Yosef (*Yabbia Omer, Orach Chayyim* 8:38) similarly notes the opinion of *Talmidei Rabbeinu Yonah*, and adds that this was also the opinion of *Tosafot Rabbeinu Elchanan*.

42 Ad loc, s.v. *shari*.

Later authorities have debated this question as well. Rambam[43] and *Shulchan Arukh*[44] both rule that one may not assist in delivering a non-Jewish child on *Shabbat*, even when this does not involve any prohibition. However, *Magen Avraham*[45] qualifies *Shulchan Arukh*'s ruling and explains that in a situation in which there might be *eivah*, e.g., when the excuse suggested by Abaye would not be effective, one may assist in the birth as long as it does not involve *Shabbat* violation. *Peri Megadim*[46] questions whether one would be allowed to assist in delivering a non-Jewish child on *Shabbat*, in a case of *eivah*, if it would involve only a rabbinic prohibition. However, *Tosefet Shabbat*[47] and *Kenesset Ha-Gedolah*[48] both permit violating a rabbinic prohibition on *Shabbat* to assist in delivering a non-Jewish child in a case of *eivah*.

Mishnah Berurah,[49] on the basis of *Shulchan Arukh*'s ruling, sharply denounces Jewish physicians who travel on *Shabbat* to save the lives of non-Jews. He notes that even if it is permitted to violate a rabbinic prohibition on *Shabbat* to save a non-Jew's life in a situation of *eivah*, it is certainly prohibited to violate a Torah prohibition, and thus it is strictly forbidden to violate *Shabbat* to save a non-Jew's life.[50]

Despite these sources, it is common practice among observant Jews to violate even Torah prohibitions to save any life on *Shabbat*, whether Jewish or non-Jewish. The earliest source which permits violating Torah prohibitions to save a non-Jew's life is *Chatam Sofer*.[51] He writes that if there is a situation of *eivah* which may lead to endangering a Jewish life, one may violate even a Torah prohibition to assist in the birthing of a non-Jewish woman, as we violate even Torah prohibitions in cases of danger to Jewish lives. Elsewhere,[52] he explains that if a Jewish doctor

43 *Shabbat* 2:12.
44 *Orach Chayyim*, 330:2.
45 *Orach Chayyim*, 330:5.
46 *Eshel Avraham*, ad loc.
47 330:5.
48 Notes to *Tur, Orach Chayyim*, 330.
49 *Orach Chayyim*, 330:5.
50 *Tiferet Yisra'el* (*Avodah Zarah* ch. 2, *Yakhin*, 6) writes that a Jewish midwife or doctor may violate a rabbinic prohibition on *Shabbat* in order to birth a non-Jewish child or in order to save a non-Jewish life, since the government would likely severely punish a midwife or doctor who refused to do so. However, he seems to limit this permission to rabbinic prohibitions only, and notes specifically that one may only cut the umbilical cord because it is considered a *melakhah she-einah tzerikhah le-gufah*. He adds that one should, in any case, cut the cord with a knife, rather than scissors, so as to constitute a *shinui*.
51 *Yoreh De'ah*, 131.
52 *Choshen Mishpat*, 194.

refused to save a non-Jewish life, it would cause hatred of Jews and non-Jewish doctors might refuse to save the lives of Jewish patients.[53]

Similarly, R. Moshe Feinstein[54] argues that in contemporary times, no non-Jew would accept an excuse like that of Abaye for a Jew declining to violate *Shabbat* to save a non-Jew's life. He adds that declining to save a non-Jew's life would endanger the life of the doctor, or more likely, endanger the lives of future Jewish patients, since non-Jewish doctors might refuse to save their lives due to this Jewish doctor's actions. He expresses astonishment at *Mishnah Berurah*'s harsh criticism of Jewish doctors who violated *Shabbat* to save non-Jewish patients' lives. He notes that a Jewish doctor in Russia might have been the only doctor in the area, and would have been severely punished, and likely killed, for refusing to violate *Shabbat* to save a non-Jew's life. R. Feinstein even notes that *Mishnah Berurah*'s printer actually added a note at the bottom of the page explaining that *Mishnah Berurah*'s comments referred only to a Jewish doctor in India; this note itself demonstrates that the printer was concerned about disastrous consequences that might have ensued from *Mishnah Berurah*'s ruling.

R. Feinstein also quotes *Divrei Chayyim*,[55] who writes that he believes the custom of Jewish doctors to violate *Shabbat* to save a non-Jew's life is based on a decree from the Council of Four Lands, the Jewish assembly which governed for Jewish communities in Poland.[56] Since it is surprising that any enactment would have the power to override a Torah prohibition, R. Feinstein concludes that it must have been enacted in an area in which there was no concern for dangerous consequences of a physician refusing to violate *Shabbat* to save a non-Jew's life. However, there was concern that if saving a non-Jewish patient on *Shabbat* were not permitted in that area, the same ruling might be followed in an area in which there was concern of negative repercussions. Therefore, the Council of Four Lands decreed that even in an area in which there was no concern for repercussions of refusing to violate *Shabbat*, it is vital for every Jewish doctor to violate *Shabbat* to save non-Jewish lives so that this same ruling would be followed everywhere. R. Feinstein adds that, nowadays, we would be concerned in *any* area that there could be disastrous consequences if a Jewish doctor refuses to save a non-Jew's life on *Shabbat*, due to the advent of rapid communication. It hardly needs mentioning that, today, with the advent of the Internet and rapid news cycles, the story of a Jewish doctor refusing to

---

53   He cites *Tosafot* (*Gittin* 70a s.v. *Rav Simi*) who note that there is no prohibition for a Jewish doctor to heal a non-Jewish patient. Thus, it would seem that we are more lenient with regard to saving a non-Jew's life than with regard to birthing a non-Jewish woman.

54   *Iggerot Moshe, Orach Chayyim*, 4:79.

55   *Orach Chayyim*, 2:25.

56   See *Encyclopedia Judaica*, 2nd ed., s.v. "Councils of the Lands."

violate *Shabbat* to save a non-Jew's life could travel around the world within minutes.

In a similar vein, R. Yehoshua Neuwirth[57] writes that a Jewish doctor may violate a rabbinic prohibition on *Shabbat* to save the life of a non-Jew, but then cites R. Shlomo Zalman Auerbach[58] who concurs with *Chatam Sofer*'s ruling that one may violate a Torah prohibition to save the life of a non-Jew, especially given the rapid travel of information in our day. R. Auerbach[59] also notes that even if one believes that no one would find out if he or she did not violate *Shabbat* to save the life of a non-Jew (e.g., a convert whose parent loses consciousness and there is immediate danger to life, when no one else is present), such that concern for *eivah* is highly unlikely, one must still violate *Shabbat* to save the non-Jew's life, since one may not always realize the extent to which one is being observed by others.

An additional reason to allow violating *Shabbat* in this case is provided by R. Ovadia Yosef[60] and R. Eliezer Waldenberg.[61] They suggest that since one is only performing a *melakhah* on *Shabbat* to prevent *eivah* that might lead to endangerment of a Jew's life in the future, this defines the physician's actions as *melakhah she-einah tzerikhah le-gufah*, a *melakhah* performed to produce an outcome which is not typically the goal of the *melakhah*. Since most authorities believe that a *melakhah she-einah tzerikhah le-gufah* is prohibited only rabbinically,[62] it would then be permitted even according to *Tosafot* and many other authorities to violate *Shabbat* to save a non-Jew's life. As evidence that this is a case of *melakhah she-einah tzerikhah le-gufah*, they cite Maharik[63] who rules that if one performs a *melakhah* to avoid being murdered by a non-Jew, the *melakhah* is categorized as a *melakhah she-einah tzerikhah le-gufah*.[64] However, R. Moshe Feinstein[65] rejects a broad application of this argument. He explains that a *melakhah* could only be classified as *einah tzerikhah le-gufah* if one does not want the positive outcome for the person for whom he or she is performing the *melakhah* (such as for the non-Jew who is threatening his or her life), but if one wants

---

57 *Shemirat Shabbat Ke-Hilkhatah*, 40:14.

58 Ibid, note 42.

59 Cited in *Nishmat Avraham*, 330:2.

60 *Halakhah U-Refuah* vol. 1, pp. 147–150; *Yabbia Omer, Orach Chayyim* 8:38. In *Yabbia Omer*, R. Yosef notes that this position is not universally accepted.

61 *Tzitz Eliezer*, 8:15, ch. 6.

62 See, for example, *Mishnah Berurah*, 334:84–85.

63 *Siman* 137.

64 See also R. Shlomo Kluger (*Chokhmat Shlomo*, 330:2) who suggests that if one performs a *melakhah* in order to receive monetary compensation, this may also be considered a *melakhah she-einah tzerikhah le-gufah*.

65 *Iggerot Moshe, Orach Chayyim*, 1:121.

that positive outcome, even if he or she would prefer not to perform the *melakhah* on *Shabbat*, this reasoning does not apply.

As is evident, a wide spectrum of contemporary halakhic authorities mandate *Shabbat* violation to save the life of a non-Jew; indeed, virtually all authorities rule unequivocally that one should always violate *Shabbat* to save a life, whether the individual is Jewish or not. However, it should be noted that based on the reasoning of the above authorities, one should not put oneself in a position in which one would be required to violate *Shabbat* to save a non-Jew's life. The only factor which permits *Shabbat* violation to save a non-Jew's life, according to these authorities, is *eivah* which might lead to life-threatening consequences for Jews. It would thus follow that if one can, one should avoid being in this situation altogether, such that no one would ever expect this physician to violate *Shabbat* to save the non-Jew's life, and there will be no *eivah*. Indeed, R. Moshe Feinstein[66] writes that a physician should avoid being on call on *Shabbat*, and if possible, should switch call with another physician so as not to be in the position in which he or she would be required to violate *Shabbat* to save the life of a non-Jew.[67]

Some twentieth-century authorities advanced the possibility that, fundamentally, one may violate *Shabbat* to save the life of a non-Jew, independent of potential consequences of *eivah*. Their arguments are based on the opinion of Ramban[68] that one may violate *Shabbat* to save the life of a *ger toshav*, a non-Jewish individual who has accepted the seven Noahide laws.[69] This might serve as a source to allow one to violate *Shabbat* to save the life of a non-Jew. However, there are several obstacles which need to be surmounted to allow using this source as a basis to permit *Shabbat* violation to save a non-Jew's life:

66 *Iggerot Moshe, Orach Chayyim*, 4:79.
67 In a similar vein, R. Moshe Sternbuch (*Teshuvot Ve-Hanhagot* 3:357) writes that one should avoid working in a hospital in which the patient population is not Jewish, since one would then be putting oneself in a situation in which one would be required to violate *Shabbat* to save the life of a non-Jew.
68 Commentary on Rambam's *Sefer Ha-Mitzvot, Shikhechat Ha-Asin*, 16.
69 Ramban's comment is somewhat ambiguous in this regard. He writes, "We are commanded to save the life of a *ger toshav*, to save him from his misfortune – if he is drowning in a river, or if a boulder fell on him, we must attempt with all our efforts to save him; if he is sick, we must attempt to heal him – and certainly this is the case with regard to our fellow Jew, or a convert, that we are required to do all these for him, and he is included in the law of saving a life, which overrides *Shabbat*..." It is unclear whether this last clause refers only to a Jew or a convert, or to a *ger toshav* as well. Rashbatz (*Zohar Ha-Rakia, mitzvah* 81, note 39) assumes that Ramban included *ger toshav* among those for whom we violate *Shabbat* to save a life.

1. Ramban is the sole authority who takes this position. Rambam,[70] on the other hand, writes that one is required to save a *ger toshav* during the week, but one may not violate *Shabbat* to save the life of a *ger toshav*.

2. The Gemara cites R. Meir who states that a non-Jew becomes a *ger toshav* if he or she pledges in front of a court of three Jews to not worship idols. Though R. Meir's opinion is not normative, and in fact the non-Jew must pledge to keep all seven Noahide laws to become a *ger toshav*, Rambam[71] still rules that the non-Jew must make this pledge in front of a court of three Jews.[72] Since non-Jews today are assumed not to have made such a pledge in front of three Jews, it is difficult to accept that Ramban's ruling applies to contemporary non-Jews.

3. While in most cases it can be safely assumed that any non-Jew does not violate six of the seven Noahide laws – murder, theft, illicit sexual relations, blasphemy, eating from a live animal, and failing to set up a court system – it may be difficult to accept that most non-Jews today do not worship idols. However, many note that Muslims are not considered idol worshippers, since they are monotheists.[73] Furthermore, Rama[74] writes that Christians are not considered idol worshippers, since for non-Jews, worshipping multiple powers which are treated as subdivisions of one entity (*shituf*) is not considered idolatry (though for a Jew, such a belief is considered idolatry and is prohibited).

4. The Gemara[75] states that the law of *ger toshav* applies only when the law of *yovel*, the jubilee year, applies. Since today we do not have *yovel*, it would seem that no non-Jew has the status of *ger toshav*.

Despite all these concerns, several contemporary authorities have argued that non-Jews today can be considered *gerei toshav*. R. Nachum Rabinovitch[76] argues that the *halakhah* follows the opinion of Ramban

---

70 *Shabbat*, 2:12.

71 *Melakhim*, 8:10.

72 *Kesef Mishneh* explains that the *Chakhamim* in the Talmud who argue with R. Meir agree with him that the pledge must be made in front of three Jews.

73 Rambam, *Hilkhot Ma'akhalot Asurot* 11:7; Rashba, *Torat Ha-Bayit Ha-Arokh*, 5:1; *Tur* and *Beit Yosef, Yoreh De'ah* 124; *Shakh, Yoreh De'ah* 124:12; *Taz, Yoreh De'ah* 124:4.

74 *Orach Chayyim*, 156:1; he cites this opinion from Rabbeinu Tam (*Tosafot Bekhorot* 2b s.v. *shema*; Rabbeinu Yeruacham, *Toldot Adam Ve-Chavvah*, 17:5).

75 *Arakhin* 29a.

76 *Melumedei Milchamah*, pp. 146–148; "A Halakhic View of the Non-Jew," *Tradition*, 8:2 (1966), pp. 27–39.

in this matter. Furthermore, he notes that Maharatz Chayes[77] and R. Meir Dan Plotsky[78] believe that a non-Jew is considered a *ger toshav* (with regard to the *mitzvah* of saving the non-Jew's life) even without taking a pledge in front of three Jews. R. Ahron Soloveichik[79] similarly quotes R. Yaakov Emden[80] who believes that contemporary non-Jews are considered *gerei toshav* with respect to some matters, including life-saving; the requirements that *yovel* be in effect and that the non-Jew made a declaration in front of three Jews are relevant only with regard to other, specific *halakhot*. R. Ahron Soloveichik also believes that this is the opinion of the Me'iri,[81] who wrote that there is a difference between the non-Jews of his time and those of Talmudic times who were not *"gedurim be-darkhei ha-dat,"* "restricted by the ways of religion," as well as those authorities who came afterward who espoused similar opinions.[82] Though R. Soloveichik does not directly discuss violating *Shabbat* in writing, he is cited by his students as advocating for violating *Shabbat* to save the life of a non-Jew for fundamental reasons, rather than because of *eivah*.[83] Similarly, R. Joseph B. Soloveitchik and R. Aharon Lichtenstein are both cited as arguing that one should violate *Shabbat* to save the life of a non-Jew for fundamental reasons.[84] It must be stressed that regardless of whether one accepts this position, all contemporary authorities agree that one must violate *Shabbat* to save the life of a non-Jew, regardless of whether one foresees any negative consequences.[85]

---

77 *Kuntras Acharon, Minchat Kena'ot* (in *Kol Kitvei Maharatz Chayes*, p. 1036).

78 *Chemdat Yisra'el, Ner Mitzvah*, 43.

79 *"Be-inyan Mevakrin Cholei Akum Mipenei Darkhei Shalom,"* *Od Yisra'el Yosef Beni Chai.*

80 *She'eilat Ya'avetz*, responsa 1:41. He also notes that even if it were not true that *shituf* is not considered idol worship for non-Jews, Christians living outside of Israel are not full-fledged idolaters since *"minhag avoteihem be-yedehem,"* "they follow the ways of their ancestors." According to this argument, we lower expectations of non-Jews living outside of Israel, and they are not considered accountable for any idolatrous practices they adopt from their parents. R. Soloveichik notes that this is also the opinion of Radvaz (responsa 4:526), and compares this to the opinion of the aforementioned Rambam writing with regard to Karaites.

81 *Avodah Zarah* 26b; *Bava Kamma* 37b; *Bava Kamma* 113a; *Bava Metzia* 59a.

82 *Be'er Ha-Golah, Yoreh De'ah* 266; *Tzemach Tzedek, Yoreh De'ah* 83.

83 See R. Dov Karoll, "Laws of Medical Treatment on Shabbat," *Verapo Yerape* vol. 1, p. 220, footnote 30.

84 R. Dov Karoll, ibid., p. 219.

85 The only possible practical difference between this more fundamental position and the alternative position is that those who permit violating *Shabbat* to save a non-Jew due to *eivah* argue that one should avoid putting oneself

Defining *Choleh She-Yesh Bo Sakkanah*

Based on the discussion in the Gemara cited above, it is clear that one must violate *Shabbat* to save the life of a *choleh she-yesh bo sakkanah*, a dangerously ill patient. However, we must still delineate which types of patients are in this category. *Shulchan Arukh*[86] rules that as long as any doctor believes that a patient is in mortal danger, it is permissible to violate *Shabbat* to save the patient's life. R. Yehoshua Neuwirth[87] rules that if a doctor is unsure whether it is permitted to perform a *melakhah* on *Shabbat* on behalf of a patient who is dangerously ill, one must err on the side of performing the *melakhah*, even if it involves violating a Torah prohibition.

Furthermore, *Shulchan Arukh*[88] rules that we violate *Shabbat* to save a life, even if there is significant uncertainty as to whether the patient is in mortal danger. *Nishmat Avraham*[89] advises that a physician act on *Shabbat* based on how he or she would act during the week: if, during the week, the physician would perform a *melakhah* for a given patient based on a concern that the patient might have a life-threatening illness, the physician should act the same way on *Shabbat*.

Moreover, based on a discussion in the Gemara,[90] *Shulchan Arukh*[91] mandates that even if the patient will only live a short time afterward, we still must violate *Shabbat* to save the patient's life. *Biur Halakhah*[92] cites Me'iri,[93] who explains that we must save the patient's life because he or she will then have additional time to repent. However, he adds that in any case, we hold that the source for saving a life on *Shabbat* is not *"chalel alav…"*, such that one would only be allowed to violate *Shabbat* on behalf of someone who could observe future *Shabbatot*, but *"va-chai bahem…"*, which does not include that qualification. Thus, he notes, one is mandated to violate *Shabbat* to save the life of a patient not required to observe *Shabbat*, such as a deaf-mute person, mentally disabled person, or minor.

---

in a position in which one would be required to violate *Shabbat* to save the life of a non-Jew based on *eivah*. Thus, if one can switch call to avoid being in the hospital, one should do so. It is unclear whether those who permit violating *Shabbat* for more fundamental reasons would require one to avoid being on call on *Shabbat* for this reason.

86 *Orach Chayyim*, 328:10.
87 Cited in *Nishmat Avraham*, introduction to *Orach Chayyim* 328, p. 390.
88 *Orach Chayyim*, 329:3; based on the Mishnah in *Yoma* 83a.
89 Introduction to *Orach Chayyim* 328, pp. 395–396.
90 *Yoma* 85a.
91 *Orach Chayyim*, 329:4.
92 Ad loc.
93 *Yoma* 85a.

Performing Non-Essential *Melakhot*

While one is required to violate *Shabbat* to save a life, there remains a question as to whether one may perform any *melakhah* on behalf of a dangerously ill patient, even one which will not directly affect the patient's life. For example, if a patient requests that the air conditioning in the room be turned on, to provide additional comfort, may one accede to this request? In this case, we assume that the patient's life does not depend on whether the air conditioning is turned on, since in that case it would obviously be permitted to do so.

The Gemara[94] cites R. Hamnuna who rules that a Jew may not perform a *"davar she-ein bo sakkanah"* on behalf of a dangerously ill patient on *Shabbat*, but may ask a non-Jew to perform such an action. Rashi[95] explains that the term *"davar she-ein bo sakkanah"* refers to an action which, if not performed for the patient, will not cause the patient to die, yet the patient is still in need of it. The implication of Rashi's comment is that one may only violate *Shabbat* to perform *melakhot* on behalf of the patient which if not performed may lead to the patient's death. For other *melakhot*, however, one must ask a non-Jew to perform the *melakhah* on the patient's behalf.

However, several medieval authorities offer an alternative approach. *Maggid Mishneh*[96] notes that Rambam prohibits lighting a fire on behalf of a sick person, and interprets this clause to refer to a patient who is not dangerously ill. Thus, he deduces that for a dangerously ill patient, one *may* light a fire on *Shabbat*, even though this is not essential to prevent the patient from dying. This stance is also adopted by Radvaz[97] and *Tashbetz*.[98] However, R. Yosef Karo[99] disagrees, based on Rashi's interpretation of the above statement in the Talmud, and suggests that Rambam must be referring to a patient who is dangerously ill; thus, one may not perform *melakhot* on behalf of a patient who is dangerously ill unless not performing those *melakhot* may cause the patient to die.

---

94 *Shabbat* 129a.
95 Ad loc, s.v. *davar*. See also Ran (*dappei ha-Rif*, 51b, s.v. *davar*).
96 *Shabbat* 2:14, based on the reading of Ra'avad ad loc.
97 4:130.
98 1:54. See also *Biur Halakhah* (*Orach Chayyim* 328, s.v. *kol*), who cites Rabbeinu Gershom (cited in *Or Zarua* 2:108), who rules that one may heat up water on *yom tov* on behalf of a woman who just gave birth (who is classified as a dangerously ill patient). *Biur Halakhah* suggests that Rabbeinu Gershom may hold that one may perform non-essential *melakhot* on behalf of a dangerously ill patient. However, he also raises the possibility that Rabbeinu Gershom believes that heating up water for a woman who just gave birth *is* an essential *melakhah* and is required to prevent the woman from dying.
99 *Kesef Mishneh* ad loc; *Beit Yosef, Orach Chayyim* 328.

Yet, in *Shulchan Arukh*,[100] R. Karo writes that one may perform on behalf of a dangerously ill patient *"kol she-regilim la'asot lo ba-chol,"* literally, anything that one would be accustomed to doing for the patient during the week. *Magen Avraham*[101] infers that one may perform *melakhot* on behalf of a dangerously ill patient if the patient is in need of the *melakhah*, even if the patient will not die if the *melakhah* is not performed. *Mishnah Berurah*[102] agrees with *Magen Avraham's* reading of *Shulchan Arukh*, but in *Biur Halakhah*[103] he cites Rashi and *Beit Yosef* who only permit performing essential *melakhot* on *Shabbat*.[104] He concludes that one should only perform a non-essential *melakhah* for a dangerously ill patient if it is forbidden rabbinically, but not if it is a Torah prohibition. R. Yehoshua Neuwirth[105] rules similarly. Of note, *Mishnah Berurah* also writes[106] that if the *melakhah* is of significant need to the patient, one may perform the *melakhah* on *Shabbat*, even according to Rashi and other stringent authorities.

R. Ovadia Yosef[107] suggests that the debate between Rashi and *Maggid Mishneh* is based on the question of whether a life-threatening situation causes *Shabbat* to be *hutrah*, completely neglected in halakhic considerations, or *dechuyah*, overridden by the situation but still not entirely neglected.[108] As a general rule, if we consider *Shabbat* to be

100 *Orach Chayyim*, 328:4.
101 328:4.
102 328:14.
103 328 s.v. *kol*.
104 He also cites an additional proof for this position. The Mishnah (*Yoma* 82a) states that one may feed a sick person on *Yom Kippur* if doctors explain that it is dangerous otherwise. *Tosafot* (*Shabbat* 128b s.v. *ka mashma lan*), Me'iri (*Shabbat* 128b s.v. *yoledet*) and *Tosafot Yeshanim* (*Yoma* 83a s.v. *choleh*) all emphasize that this is only true in a case where we are concerned that the person will be in danger if he or she does not eat. Other authorities, including Ri and Rabbeinu Tam (cited in *Beit Yosef, Orach Chayyim* 618 s.v. *choleh*), Rashba (responsa 3:14) and Ramban (*Torat Ha-Adam, Sha'ar Ha-Meichush*, Chavel ed., p. 30) also imply that a patient may eat on *Yom Kippur* only if not eating may lead to death. This suggests that one may only violate *halakhah* on behalf of a dangerously ill patient if the action is necessary to prevent the patient from dying. *Biur Halakhah* assumes that one may compare *Yom Kippur* and *Shabbat*, and thus one may only perform essential *melakhot* on behalf of a dangerously ill patient on *Shabbat*.
105 *Shemirat Shabbat Ke-Hilkhatah* 32:33.
106 *Sha'ar Ha-Tziyyun*, note 11.
107 *Yechavveh Da'at* 4:30. He notes that that previous authorities, including *Avnei Nezer* (*Orach Chayyim* 455:5) and *Tzemach Tzedek* (*Orach Chayyim* 38), already suggested that the question of whether one may perform non-essential *melakhot* on behalf of a dangerously ill patient is dependent on whether *Shabbat* is *hutrah* or *dechuyah*.
108 This question has been discussed for centuries and has been suggested as an explanation for numerous debates about the scope of violating *Shabbat* to

hutrah in life-threatening situations, we respond to the situation as if it is not *Shabbat* at all. On the other hand, if *Shabbat* is considered *dechuyah*, then we still respond to life-threatening situations by violating *Shabbat* but the scope of what we may do might be more limited, since we are still cognizant of the presence of *Shabbat*. In applying this question to our discussion, we might suggest that if *Shabbat* is *hutrah* in life-threatening situations, we relate to a patient with life-threatening illness as if it is not *Shabbat*, and thus we may perform even non-essential *melakhot* on the patient's behalf. However, if *Shabbat* is *dechuyah* in life-threatening situations, we might say that only essential *melakhot* are permitted on behalf of a dangerously ill patient, but not *melakhot* which need not be performed to save the patient's life. R. Yosef argues that *Shabbat* is considered *hutrah* in life-threatening situations, and therefore one may perform non-essential *melakhot* on behalf of a dangerously ill patient on *Shabbat*.

In summary, *Shulchan Arukh* rules in accordance with the opinion of *Maggid Mishneh*, that one may perform even non-essential *melakhot* on behalf of a dangerously ill patient, with R. Ovadia Yosef following this ruling as well. In contrast, *Mishnah Berurah* and other later

---

save a life. An early source which seems to suggest that *Shabbat* is *dechuyah* with respect to life-threatening situations is Rambam (*Shabbat* 2:1), who uses the word *"dechuyah"* in his discussion of saving a life on *Shabbat*. Indeed, *Kessef Mishneh* (ad loc) explains that Rambam's intent is that we should avoid violating *Shabbat* when it is possible to save the patient's life without *Shabbat* violation. However, Rambam writes later (2:2) that with regard to a dangerously ill patient, *Shabbat* is *"ke-chol,"* like a weekday, suggesting that he may believe *Shabbat* is *hutrah* with respect to life-threatening situations. Indeed, Rama (responsa 76) assumes that this is Rambam's stance, and several other authorities (including *Arukh Ha-Shulchan*, *Yoreh De'ah* 266:25; *Tzofnat Pane'ach*, *Shabbat* 2:1; *Yechavveh Da'at*, ibid.) suggest that Rambam's intention was that *Shabbat* is *hutrah*, and his use of the word *"dechuyah"* only means that saving a life overrides *Shabbat*; Rambam did not intend to use the word *"dechuyah"* as it is used in later works. Maharam mi-Rotenburg (responsa, Cremona edition, 200; quoted in Rosh *Yoma* 8:14; Rosh responsa 26:5; *Hagahot Mordekhai*, *Shabbat* 466) argues that one should slaughter meat on *Shabbat* to give to a dangerously ill patient, even if non-kosher meat is available, because one may perform any *melakhah* on behalf of a dangerously ill patient on *Shabbat*. He seems to believe *Shabbat* is *hutrah*. Opposing Maharam is Rashba (responsa, 1:689) who argues that *Shabbat* is merely *dechuyah* in life-threatening situations, and therefore one should give the patient non-kosher meat, since eating non-kosher is a lesser violation than slaughtering an animal on *Shabbat*. Ran (*dappei ha-Rif*, 9b, s.v. *u-miha*) also writes that *Shabbat* is *dechuyah* with regard to life-threatening situations, and therefore if one is cooking on *Shabbat* for a dangerously ill patient who will die without cooked food, one may not cook extra food.

authorities including R. Yehoshua Neuwirth rule that one should only be lenient with regard to rabbinic prohibitions, but not Torah prohibitions.

Is It Preferable to Minimize the Level of the Prohibition?

While we have seen that one may, and must, violate *Shabbat* to save the life of a patient whose life is in danger, we might still ask whether one should attempt to minimize the level of prohibition violated. For example, instead of performing the *melakhah* oneself, one might ask a non-Jew to perform the *melakhah* instead, since this is only a rabbinic prohibition. Similarly, one might perform the *melakhah* oneself but with a *shinui*, performing the *melakhah* in a manner in which it is not usually performed, thus also downgrading the level of the act to a rabbinic prohibition. It is obvious that in a case in which these options are not possible, such as when no non-Jew is available or willing to perform the *melakhah*, or when the situation is urgent and any wasted time might decrease the patient's chances for survival, it is prohibited to attempt to downgrade the level of violation and risk the patient's life, and one must perform the *melakhah* oneself in the fastest way possible. However, if the situation is less urgent, and one of the above options is available, must one avail oneself of these options?

It would seem that this question is related to our earlier discussion of whether *Shabbat* is *dechuyah* or *hutrah* in regard to a dangerously ill patient. If *Shabbat* is *hutrah*, and is completely neglected in cases of threat to life, then there should be no need to downgrade the level of the prohibition violated, since there is in effect no prohibition at all. On the other hand, if *Shabbat* is *dechuyah*, and is overridden by the need to save the patient's life but is still considered as a factor in making decisions when possible, then we might require that when possible, one should preferably ask a non-Jew or perform the *melakhah* with a *shinui*.

Asking a Non-Jew
The Gemara[109] states that one should *not* ask a non-Jew to perform *melakhah* in order to save a life on *Shabbat*; rather, the life-saving *melakhah* should be performed by *gedolei Yisra'el*, Jewish leaders. However, there is debate as to the Gemara's reasoning in this statement. *Tosafot*[110] explain that we are worried that the non-Jew may be less concerned with saving the patient's life. In the case discussed in the Gemara, the patient is Jewish, and therefore a non-Jew might be less invested than a Jew in saving the patient's life, perhaps leading him or her to act more slowly and thus endangering the patient's life. One might infer,

109 *Yoma* 84b.
110 Ad loc, s.v. *ela*.

though, that if we are not worried about this, then it would be prefer-able to lessen the degree of *Shabbat* violation by asking the non-Jew to perform the *melakhah*. However, *Kesef Mishneh*[111] writes that accord-ing to Rambam, who rules in accordance with the Gemara's statement, one should not ask a non-Jew to perform the *melakhah* since onlookers might conclude that one may only violate *Shabbat* by asking a non-Jew to perform the *melakhah*, which is certainly not true in urgent cases or cases in which a non-Jew is unavailable. We are meticulously careful about not misleading others with regard to procedure in life-threaten-ing situations, since we do not want people to be overly stringent with regard to *Shabbat*, thus risking a patient's life, and so we avoid asking a non-Jew to perform the lifesaving *melakhah* so that onlookers will know that it is permitted, and mandated, to violate *Shabbat* to save a life. This reasoning is also suggested by Ramban[112] and Ran.[113] In a sim-ilar vein, Rosh[114] writes that we are concerned that people will look for a non-Jew to perform a *melakhah*, thus wasting precious time.

Shulchan Arukh[115] rules that one should not ask a non-Jew to per-form *melakhah* on *Shabbat* to save a life. Rama[116] qualifies this ruling and suggests that if the situation is urgent, one should not ask a non-Jew to perform the *melakhah*, but if there is ample time available, one should ask the non-Jew to perform the *melakhah*, or one should perform the *melakhah* with a *shinui*. However, he notes, if there is con-cern that the non-Jew will perform the *melakhah* more slowly, then one should not ask him or her. *Chayyei Adam*[117] also rules like Rama. In contrast, *Taz*[118] argues vociferously with Rama's opinion, stating that one must not ask a non-Jew to perform the *melakhah* lest onlookers mistakenly believe that one must always ask a non-Jew to perform the *melakhah*. This is also the opinion of *Tosefet Shabbat*,[119] *Shulchan Arukh Ha-Rav*[120] and *Arukh Ha-Shulchan.*[121]

R. Yehoshua Neuwirth[122] rules that one should not ask a non-Jew to perform *melakhah*, since we are worried that the non-Jew may act

111 *Shabbat* 2:3.
112 *Torat Ha-Adam, Sha'ar Ha-Meichush* p. 23.
113 *Shabbat, dappei ha-Rif*, 4b s.v. *ve-ein osin*.
114 *Yoma* 8:14.
115 *Orach Chayyim* 328:12.
116 Based on the opinion of *Or Zarua*, cited in *Shiltei Ha-Gibborim, dappei ha-Rif* 4b, 2.
117 *Hilkhot Shabbat* 68:2.
118 328:5.
119 328:15.
120 328:13.
121 328:7.
122 *Shemirat Shabbat Ke-Hilkhatah*, 32:6.

more slowly. However, he cites *Orechot Chayyim*[123] who writes that if the concern is that the non-Jew may act more slowly, then if the Jew stands nearby and ensures that the *melakhah* is performed with haste, then it would be preferable to ask the non-Jew. R. Eliezer Waldenberg[124] also rules that one should perform the *melakhah* oneself and not ask a non-Jew. He adds that even Rama would agree that only *melakhot* ancillary to the patient's care, such as turning on a light or cooking food, should be performed by a non-Jew, but the patient's direct medical needs should be performed by a Jewish doctor himself or herself. R. Shlomo Zalman Auerbach[125] makes a similar distinction, arguing that *melakhot* related directly to the patient's care should be performed by the Jew himself or herself, while other *melakhot* such as writing laboratory values or turning off the light on the patient's behalf should ideally be performed by a non-Jew.

Performing *Melakhah* with a *Shinui*

In evaluating whether one should preferably perform lifesaving *melakhot* with a *shinui*, we can contrast this situation with the above situation of asking a non-Jew to perform *melakhot*. As we have seen, the two reasons given for not asking a non-Jew to perform lifesaving *melakhot* on *Shabbat* are that the non-Jew might be less invested in saving a Jewish patient's life (*Tosafot*), or that onlookers might mistakenly believe that one must always ask a non-Jew to perform lifesaving *melakhot*, even in urgent situations (Rambam as interpreted by *Maggid Mishneh*; Ramban and Ran). The first reason is certainly not relevant with regard to performing *melakhot* with a *shinui*. On the other hand, one might argue that the second reason is still relevant, and situations might arise when performing lifesaving *melakhot* might lead onlookers to believe that one must always use a *shinui*.

The Gemara[126] discusses lighting a candle on *Shabbat* on behalf of a woman in labor (considered akin to a dangerously ill patient) to calm her. There, the Gemara explains that if more oil is needed, someone may bring the oil, even through the public domain, thus violating *Shabbat*. However, one should preferably carry the oil in one's hands, or if this is impossible, one should carry the oil in one's hair. Rashi[127] and Ramban[128] derive from this statement that with regard to a dangerously ill patient, one should attempt to perform *melakhah* with a *shinui*, if this

---

123 306:13, 328:13; cited in *Shemirat Shabbat Ke-Hilkhatah*, ibid., footnote 16.
124 *Tzitz Eliezer*, 8:15, ch. 2.
125 Cited in *Nishmat Avraham*, introduction to *siman* 328, 4b, p. 393.
126 *Shabbat* 128b.
127 Ad loc, s.v. *be-yad*.
128 *Torat Ha-Adam, Sha'ar Ha-Meichush* p. 30. See also Rashba and Ritva ad loc, s.v. *ein*.

will not further endanger the patient. Similarly, the Mishnah[129] writes that if one forgot to prepare medicine before *Shabbat* on behalf of an infant undergoing circumcision on *Shabbat*, one can grind the medicine by chewing it. Rashba[130] derives from this Mishnah that one should ideally perform *melakhot* for a dangerously ill patient on *Shabbat* with a *shinui*.

Rambam[131] also rules that one should perform *melakhot* for a woman in labor with a *shinui*. However, *Maggid Mishneh*[132] argues that Rambam distinguishes between a woman in labor and other dangerously ill patients. He explains that only for a woman in labor must one perform *melakhot* with a *shinui*, since labor is a natural process and a very small percentage of women in labor die, and so it is not fully comparable to a case of a typical dangerously ill patient, for which one need not use a *shinui* in performing *melakhot*. *Bach*[133] similarly argues that the Mishnah regarding preparing medicine for an infant undergoing circumcision is discussing a case in which the medicine is being prepared before the circumcision, but if the circumcision has already taken place, such that the infant is already considered akin to a dangerously ill patient, one may prepare the medicine without a *shinui*.

Just as Rama rules that one should preferably ask a non-Jew to perform *melakhot*, Rama[134] also rules that if the situation is not urgent, one should employ a *shinui* when performing lifesaving *melakhot*. Others, including *Eliyah Rabbah*[135] and the Vilna Gaon,[136] agree with *Bach*'s reading of the Mishnah, and therefore believe that one need not try to perform the *melakhot* with a *shinui* if possible. R. Yehoshua Neuwirth rules[137] that one should, if possible, perform the *melakhah* with a *shinui*, or should perform the *melakhah* together with another person.[138] However, he also cites R. Shlomo Zalman Auerbach,[139] who advises that if one performs the *melakhah* with a *shinui*, one should announce to onlookers that one need not use a *shinui* if the situation is urgent, and only in non-urgent situations should one try to perform the *melakhah* with a *shinui*.

---

129 *Shabbat* 133a.
130 *Shabbat* 134b, s.v. *ve-heikha*.
131 *Shabbat* 2:11.
132 Ad loc, s.v. *ve-khol*.
133 *Orach Chayyim* 331; *Yoreh De'ah* 266.
134 *Orach Chayyim*, 328:12.
135 331:7.
136 *Biur Ha-Gra, Yoreh De'ah*, 266:10.
137 *Shemirat Shabbat Ke-Hilkhatah* 32:28.
138 That one may minimize the level of prohibition by performing the *melakhah* together with another person is debated; see *Minchat Yitzchak*, 10:30.
139 Ibid., footnote 86.

Treating Non-Life-Threatening Illness on *Shabbat*

Until now, we have discussed only cases in which the patient has a life-threatening condition and treatment may be necessary on *Shabbat* to prevent the patient's death. However, many situations which confront the healthcare professional on *Shabbat* involve patients who are ill but not to a life-threatening extent. As we have emphasized, any situation in which there is even a remote chance of threat to life is classified as a *pikuach nefesh* situation on *Shabbat*, and we violate even Torah prohibitions to prevent the patient from dying. However, when physicians are sure that the patient is in no danger of dying, this dispensation no longer exists. We will now discuss what may be done on *Shabbat* in the care of a *choleh she-ein bo sakkanah*, a patient whose life is not in danger.

Statements in the Gemara

As we will see, there is ample debate among medieval authorities regarding what may be done for a patient whose illness is not life-threatening. To a large extent, this debate is due to various seemingly contradictory statements in the Gemara regarding illness on *Shabbat*. In order to understand the positions espoused by later authorities, we will review these statements in the Gemara and note the ambiguities that arise.

1. *Shabbat* 129a: Asking a Non-Jew
The Gemara quotes R. Hamnuna who states that if a patient is not in danger to life, one can ask a non-Jew to perform *melakhah* on the patient's behalf.[140] This statement is also quoted elsewhere in the Gemara,[141] where it is used to justify the actions of Ameimar, who reportedly assisted a non-Jew in applying medication on his eye on *Shabbat*, but did not apply the medication himself. The Gemara concludes that assisting the non-Jew is not considered sufficiently significant to render Ameimar's actions prohibited.

2. *Avodah Zarah* 28b–29a: The Swollen Eye and Other Local Illnesses
The Gemara states that an *ayin she-maredah*, a swollen eye, may be treated on *Shabbat* even in ways that involve violating a Torah prohibition. Though the Gemara had initially entertained the possibility that only rabbinic prohibitions would be permitted, the conclusion is that even Torah prohibitions may be violated, since eyesight is connected to *uvneta*

---

140 As we noted earlier, this statement is also discussed in the context of performing non-essential *melakhot* on behalf of a dangerously ill patient.
141 *Beitzah* 22a.

de-liba. While the meaning of this phrase is unclear,[142] the import is that a swollen eye may be a life-threatening condition, and therefore one may violate a Torah prohibition to treat this condition just as one would violate a Torah prohibition to treat any life-threatening illness on *Shabbat*.

This Gemara also discusses other local conditions which should be treated on *Shabbat*. The Gemara mentions that the following actions are permissible on *Shabbat*:

- Treating a *makkah shel chalal* (an internal wound)[143]
- Treating lockjaw (*ma'alin oznayim*)[144]
- Moving the *unkeli*,[145] a muscle or cartilage near the heart or stomach[146] which has been dislocated[147]

As with a swollen eye, it is implied that these conditions are life-threatening, and therefore one may violate *Shabbat* to treat them. Conversely, based on the initial discussion of the Gemara, it appears that for a non-life-threatening condition, rabbinic prohibitions may be violated.

---

142 Rashi (s.v. *afilu mishchak ve-ituyei*) explains that *uvneta de-liba* refers to the cardiac muscles, and one may treat a swollen eye on *Shabbat* because eyesight is connected to the heart, i.e., a swollen eye may lead to heart malfunction. *Tosafot* (s.v. *shorayni*), on the other hand, explain that eyesight is connected to the understanding of the heart, and therefore one may treat a swollen eye on *Shabbat*; it is unclear why *Tosafot* believe that this connection between eyesight and the understanding of the heart causes a swollen eye to be a life-threatening condition. For a bibliography of sources which discuss the meaning of this statement in the Gemara, see R. Dr. Avraham Steinberg's *Encyclopedia Hilkhatit Refu'it*, s.v. *ayin*, vol. 6 p. 138, footnote 125. R. Steinberg concludes that it is highly unlikely that the Gemara's understanding of anatomy or physiology in this regard corresponds to that of modern science.

143 Rashi (s.v. *shel chalal*) explains that a *makkah shel chalal* is one which is adjacent to the body cavity, and *Tosafot* (s.v. *makkah shel chalal*) cite an explanation from the Yerushalmi that it refers to a wound inside the body cavity.

144 See Julius Preuss' *Biblical and Talmudic Medicine*, trans. Fred Rosner, New York: Jason Aronson, 2004, pp. 202–203.

145 The meaning of *unkeli* is unclear, and given that the Gemara explains its meaning (as *istumcha de-liba*), it appears that the word was not in common use when the statement in the Gemara was written. Preuss (*Biblical and Talmudic Medicine*, p. 212) discusses several possible meanings of the word.

146 Rashi translates *liba* as heart, while Rabbeinu Chananel translates it as stomach (see Preuss, ibid.).

147 According to Rashi (*Avodah Zarah* 29a, s.v., *istumcha de-liba*), dislocation of this muscle hampers breathing.

3. *Ketuvot* 60a: Drinking Milk from a Goat on *Shabbat*

The Gemara states that someone in great pain may drink milk directly from a goat on *Shabbat*, even though milking a goat is normally prohibited on *Shabbat*.[148] The Gemara continues to explain that milking is permitted in this case because the person is performing the *melakhah* in an atypical fashion, which is thus a rabbinic prohibition, and was not prohibited by the rabbis in cases of great pain.[149]

148 The Gemara explains that the *melakhah* normally violated when milking a goat is *mefarek*, in which something is detached from its source, though the source is not attached to the ground (thus this is not *kotzer*). Rashi notes that this *melakhah* is a *toladah* of the *melakhah* of *dash*, threshing.

149 A similar Gemara in *Yevamot* (114a) relates that Abba Shaul drank milk directly from a goat on *yom tov* when he was ill. Implied is that he would not have done so on *Shabbat*. The Gemara proceeds to challenge Abba Shaul's actions: if Abba Shaul were dangerously ill, he would have been permitted to drink milk from the goat even on *Shabbat*; on the other hand, if there were no threat to life, drinking milk from the goat would have been prohibited both on *Shabbat* and on *yom tov*. The Gemara concludes that Abba Shaul must have been in great pain, and so he reasoned that since the prohibition of *mefarek* is violated in an atypical fashion, which is only a rabbinic violation, the rabbis only prohibited this type of violation on *Shabbat*, when a Biblical prohibition would be punishable by death, but not on *yom tov*, when violation of a Biblical prohibition would be punishable only by lashes. This Gemara seems to directly contradict the Gemara in *Ketuvot*, which suggests that a person in great pain could drink milk from a goat even on *Shabbat*. Several resolutions are offered by the medieval commentators:

- Rabbeinu Tam (*Tosafot Ketuvot* 60a s.v. *gone'ach*; *Tosafot Yevamot* 114a s.v. *Shabbat*; *Sefer Ha-Yashar* 23) explains that the pain Abba Shaul experienced was not due to illness, but to hunger. Thus, he permitted drinking milk from a goat only on *yom tov*, since he reasoned that the rabbis would not prohibit a *melakhah* violated in an atypical fashion on *yom tov*, but they would prohibit such an action on *Shabbat*. However, if Abba Shaul were in pain due to illness, and goat milk were needed for treatment, all would agree that he could drink milk directly from the goat for treatment. A similar answer is offered by Ba'al Ha-Ma'or (*Shabbat, dappei ha-Rif* 61a).

- Ri disagrees with Rabbeinu Tam, noting that if it were true that in cases of illness, one could drink directly from the goat on *Shabbat*, the Gemara in *Yevamot* would have noted, in challenging Abba Shaul's actions, that if he were ill he could have drunk the milk from the goat on *Shabbat*. Therefore, Ri concludes that the two statements in the Gemara represent two differing opinions. This is also the opinion of Rif (*Shabbat, dappei ha-Rif* 61a), Rashba (*Yevamot* 114a s.v. *lo tzerikha* and *Ketuvot* 60a s.v. *mefarek*), and Ritva (*Yevamot* 114a s.v. *ha*).

- Rabbeinu Chananel (cited in Ramban *Ketuvot* 40a s.v. *gone'ach*; Rashba *Ketuvot* 60a s.v. *mefarek*) explains that the Gemara in *Ketuvot* is discussing a case of danger to life, whereas Abba Shaul was not

4. *Shabbat* 148a: Realigning Broken Bones

While the Mishnah[150] records the ruling that one may not realign a broken bone on *Shabbat*, the Gemara records an opposing ruling, that one may realign a broken bone on *Shabbat*. To understand the import of this statement, we must first note that the rabbis generally prohibited providing medical care or taking medicine on *Shabbat*. The reasoning, as explained in the Gemara,[151] is that the rabbis were afraid that since preparing medication often involved grinding, if one were permitted to take medication or provide medical care on *Shabbat*, one might eventually grind medication on *Shabbat*. Therefore the rabbis categorically prohibited taking medicine or undergoing medical procedures on *Shabbat*. However, despite this, the Gemara permits realigning a broken bone on *Shabbat*.

Conclusions from the Statements in Gemara

Based on the Gemara in *Shabbat* 129a, it is clear that for a patient who has an illness which is not life-threatening, one may ask a non-Jew to perform *melakhah*. However, it is unclear whether a Jew may himself or herself violate a rabbinic prohibition in such a case. The statements from the Gemara suggest disparate conclusions on this issue. On the one hand, from the story of Ameimar, who had a non-Jew apply medication to his eye on *Shabbat*, it appears that only a non-Jew may apply medication on *Shabbat*, but a Jew may not do so if the patient's life is not in danger, even though applying medication to the eye (*kochel*) is only a rabbinic prohibition (of using medicine on *Shabbat*).

On the other hand, the Gemara in *Avodah Zarah* implies that were a swollen eye not a case of danger to life, it would be permissible for a person to violate a rabbinic prohibition such as administering medicine on *Shabbat* (though not a Torah prohibition). Similarly, the Gemara in *Shabbat* 148a allows a Jew to realign a broken bone on *Shabbat*, even though this violates the rabbinic injunction against providing medical care on *Shabbat*.

The Gemara in *Ketuvot* is ambiguous with regard to this issue. This Gemara suggests that a person in pain may violate *Shabbat* only by performing a *melakhah* with a *shinui*, which is then only a rabbinic prohibition. This statement is further complicated by the fact that it is debated whether the *melakhah* being discussed, milking a goat, is itself

---

in mortal danger. However, Ramban and Rashba refute this opinion, explaining that the Gemara in *Ketuvot* would not need to state this obvious fact, and there would be no need to invoke the fact that the *melakhah* is performed in an atypical fashion.

150 *Shabbat* 147a.
151 *Shabbat* 53b.

a Torah prohibition or a rabbinic prohibition.[152] If it is a Torah prohibition, then the Gemara is suggesting that one may violate a rabbinic prohibition, such as performing a *melakhah* with a *shinui*, in a case of illness; this conclusion would line up with the statements in *Avodah Zarah* and in *Shabbat* 148a. If milking is a rabbinic prohibition, then the Gemara in *Ketuvot* is suggesting that one may not even violate a rabbinic prohibition for an ill person, as suggested by the Gemara in *Shabbat* 129a, but one may violate a rabbinic prohibition with a *shinui* on behalf of an ill person.

Due to the disparate implications from these statements in the Gemara, there is some debate among the commentators regarding whether a Jew may violate rabbinic prohibitions on behalf of a patient whose life is not in danger. We may now examine the various opinions and how they are reflected in the ruling of *Shulchan Arukh*.

Sakkanat Ever

One explanation offered by the commentators to explain the above discrepancy is that there exists a distinction between illnesses which pose no danger whatsoever and illnesses which pose *sakkanat ever*, imminent danger to a limb or organ. Thus, though the Gemara in *Avodah Zarah* implies that a swollen eye, were it not a danger to life, would still allow for the violation of rabbinic prohibitions, this is an exceptional case since one is in danger of losing the function of the eye. Similarly, one may realign a broken bone on *Shabbat*, even though this violates the rabbinic injunction against medical care on *Shabbat*, since the patient is in danger of losing the function of the limb. However, in the case of illnesses for which there is no imminent danger to a limb, a Jew may not violate even a rabbinic prohibition, and must instead ask a non-Jew to perform *melakhah* on the patient's behalf. This distinction is offered by Ramban,[153] Ritva,[154] Ran,[155] and Rosh.[156]

---

152 The Gemara (*Shabbat* 95a) suggests that milking is a Torah violation. However, this statement is attributed to R. Eliezer, and there is some ambiguity as to whether the opinion of Chakhamim, whose opinion is followed for practical *halakhah*, agrees or disagrees with R. Eliezer on this point. See *Encyclopedia Talmudit*, vol. 7, s.v. *dash*, for discussion of the various viewpoints.

153 *Torat Ha-Adam, Sha'ar Ha-Meichush*. See also *Avodah Zarah* 28b s.v. *ayin*, where Ramban states more generally that a Jew may violate a rabbinic prohibition in any case of illness, even when there is no limb in danger; this position is in contrast to the one expressed in *Torat Ha-Adam*, as will be discussed later.

154 *Avodah Zarah* 28b s.v. *aval*.

155 *Avodah Zarah* 28b s.v. *mai ta'ama*; *Shabbat* in *dappei ha-Rif* 39b.

156 *Avodah Zarah* 2:11.

In contrast to this position, *Tosafot*,[157] Rabbeinu Tam,[158] and Me'iri[159] argue that one may violate even a Torah prohibition in the case of imminent danger to a limb. As proof, *Tosafot* adduce the Gemara regarding a swollen eye, noting that in this case of imminent danger to an organ, one is required to violate *Shabbat*, and thus one can extrapolate that in any case of imminent danger to a limb or organ, one must violate even Torah commandments on *Shabbat*. Rabbeinu Tam and Me'iri also cite the Gemara's ruling regarding a *makkah shel chalal*, explaining that this is a case of imminent danger to a limb, and we can extrapolate from the Gemara that one must violate Torah prohibitions on *Shabbat* in such a case. However, Ra'avyah[160] disagrees with Rabbeinu Tam, pointing out that from the case of a swollen eye we can deduce exactly the opposite point: if one may only violate *Shabbat* in the case of a swollen eye since it is anatomically connected to the heart, and thus may cause life-threatening damage, we can deduce that if risk to an organ or limb will not lead to life-threatening illness, one may not violate *Shabbat*.

Rambam's Stance

While most authorities establish a distinction between illnesses which pose danger to a limb or organ and illness which do not pose such a danger, Rambam[161] never mentions such a distinction, leading to some disagreement as to his position. He states that in cases of illness, one may ask a non-Jew to perform *melakhah* on the patient's behalf. Additionally, he notes that if the patient's needs include actions which are not *melakhot*, a Jew may perform those actions himself or herself on the patient's behalf. Rambam proceeds to list several examples of what may be done on behalf of the patient on *Shabbat*:

- One may ask a non-Jew to apply medication to his eye on *Shabbat* (as per the ruling of Ameimar in *Shabbat* 129a).
- One may treat lockjaw on *Shabbat* (as per the ruling in *Avodah Zarah*).
- One may treat a dislocated *unkeli* on *Shabbat* (as per the ruling in *Avodah Zarah*).
- One may reset a broken bone on *Shabbat* (as per the ruling in the Gemara in *Shabbat* 148a).

Because Rambam does not mention a distinction between cases of danger to a limb and other cases, *Tur*[162] posits that Rambam allows one

157 *Sukkah* 26a s.v. *va-afilu*; also in *Tosafot Ha-Rosh* ibid.
158 Cited in *Or Zarua* 2:180; *Hagahot Maimoniyot, Shevitat Asor* 2:5.
159 *Avodah Zarah* 28b s.v. *kevar*; see interpretation in *Yalkut Yosef, Shabbat* vol. 4, pp. 100–101, footnote 15.
160 Cited in *Or Zarua* and *Hagahot Maimoniyot*, ibid.
161 *Shabbat* 2:10.
162 *Orach Chayyim* 328, as understood by *Beit Yosef* s.v. *aval ha-Rambam*.

to violate rabbinic prohibitions on *Shabbat* for any ill patient, regardless of whether there is a limb in danger. This is because Rambam rules that one may treat lockjaw, a dislocated *unkeli* and a broken bone on *Shabbat*, despite the general rabbinic prohibition of medical care on *Shabbat*, thus suggesting that one may violate rabbinic prohibitions for any ill patient on *Shabbat*. However, *Beit Yosef*[163] questions this approach of *Tur*, noting that Rambam requires one to ask a non-Jew to apply medication to one's eye on *Shabbat*, which suggests that one cannot apply medication oneself, even though this is only a rabbinic prohibition.

A different approach is suggested by *Maggid Mishneh*,[164] who argues that Rambam distinguishes between cases in which the entire body is affected by illness, in which case one may violate rabbinic prohibitions on *Shabbat*, and cases in which only one organ is affected, in which case one may not violate rabbinic prohibitions oneself but must instead ask a non-Jew to perform *melakhah*. Thus, one must ask a non-Jew to apply medication to one's eye, since the illness affects only the eye and not the entire body. As *Beit Yosef* points out,[165] *Maggid Mishneh* assumes that lockjaw, a dislocated *unkeli*, and a broken bone are conditions which affect the entire body, such that Rambam would allow one to violate rabbinic prohibitions to treat them on *Shabbat*. Additionally, it is noteworthy that according to *Maggid Mishneh*, Rambam may hold the opposite view of other authorities in many cases. Most authorities permit violating a rabbinic prohibition in a case of immediate danger to a limb, but not in other cases, while Rambam permits violating a rabbinic prohibition only if the entire body is affected, even if not in a permanently incapacitating way, while he prohibits violating a rabbinic prohibition if one organ is affected, even if its function will be permanently altered or lost if care is not provided immediately.

A final approach is suggested by *Beit Yosef*,[166] who objects to *Maggid Mishneh*'s explanation since Rambam does not seem to distinguish between illnesses which affect the entire body and illnesses which affect one organ. Therefore, he suggests that Rambam makes no distinction between categories of illnesses, but does distinguish between types of rabbinic prohibitions. Rambam only permits one to perform rabbinic prohibitions which are not similar to *melakhot* which are prohibited in the Torah. Thus, one may not apply medication to the eye on *Shabbat*, since this action is similar to the Torah prohibition of writing on *Shabbat*. Similarly, *Beit Yosef* writes, one may not give any medication on *Shabbat* to an ill person, since the prohibition of taking medication on *Shabbat* is based on the concern that one may grind on *Shabbat*,

163 Ibid.; see also *Kesef Mishneh* on *Shabbat* 2:10.
164 *Shabbat* 2:10 s.v. *u-machzirin*.
165 Ibid.
166 Ibid.

which is a Torah prohibition. However, treating lockjaw, resetting the *unkeli* and resetting a broken bone bear no resemblance to any Torah prohibition,[167] and are therefore permitted.

Modern-Day Application

As we will discuss later, *Shulchan Arukh*[168] rules with regard to ill patients in accordance with the opinion of Ramban, and thus, with regard to patients with a limb or organ in imminent danger, *Shulchan Arukh* rules that one may ask a non-Jew to perform *melakhah* or one may violate a rabbinic prohibition. Rama does not disagree with *Shulchan Arukh*'s ruling, and both *Mishnah Berurah*[169] and *Arukh Ha-Shulchan*[170] note that this view also represents the consensus of modern-day halakhic authorities. R. Shlomo Zalman Auerbach[171] adds that this is true even there is uncertainty as to whether the limb or organ is in danger. Furthermore, *Ketzot Ha-Shulchan*[172] extends this ruling to cases in which there is concern that the limb or organ will no longer function as well as it did previously, even if it will not entirely lose its functionality.

However, the category of *sakkanat ever* may be of little relevance to the modern-day physician. R. Eliezer Waldenberg[173] and R. Ovadia Yosef[174] note that modern medicine has shown that most cases of imminent danger to a limb or organ represent imminent danger to the entire body, via infection or other means. Therefore, these cases should instead be categorized as life-threatening illness, for which one is permitted to violate even Torah prohibitions, as we have discussed above.[175] Thus,

---

167 *Beit Yosef* notes that only medical treatment which involves taking medication is sufficiently related to grinding on *Shabbat* such that Rambam would prohibit it.

168 *Orach Chayyim* 328:17.

169 328:57.

170 *Orach Chayyim* 328:18.

171 *Minchat Shlomo* vol. 2, 34:36.

172 Vol. 7, ch.138, *Baddei Ha-Shulchan* 18.

173 *Tzitz Eliezer* vol. 8, ch. 15, 10:9.

174 *Yalkut Yosef, Shabbat* vol. 4, 328:14 (p. 100).

175 In fact, *Bach* (*Orach Chayyim* 328) argues that this is the intention of *Tosafot* and Rabbeinu Tam, who, as discussed earlier, rule that one may violate even Torah prohibitions for all cases of a limb or organ in imminent danger. *Tosafot*'s assertion was so troubling that Rashash (*Sukkah* 26a on *Tosafot* s.v. *va-afilu*) suggested that this statement of *Tosafot* contains an error, and *Tosafot* intended to write that a swollen eye, specifically, is considered like a situation of *pikuach nefesh*, but not danger to any limb or organ. Indeed, Rashash noted, the compiler of *Piskei Tosafot* (*Sukkah* 58) understood *Tosafot* this way. However, *Bach* explains that the assertion of *Tosafot* is merely that situations of danger to one limb or organ tend to endanger the entire body, and therefore necessitate violation even of Torah

if a physician has any reason to be uncertain as to whether a case of a limb or organ in danger may also be life-threatening, the physician must treat the case as that of life-threatening illness and must violate even Torah prohibitions on *Shabbat* if this is necessary to treat the patient. However, in cases in which the physician is sure that the danger to the limb or organ is confined locally, and will definitely not lead to a life-threatening situation, the physician should either ask a non-Jew to perform *melakhah* on the patient's behalf or violate only rabbinic prohibitions.

Choleh She-Ein Bo Sakkanah without *Sakkanat Ever*

While Torah prohibitions are suspended for a patient who is dangerously ill, and rabbinic prohibitions are suspended for a patient whose limb or organ is in imminent danger, these rules do not apply to the case of *choleh she-ein bo sakkanah*, an ill patient who is not in danger. Earlier, we noted some ambiguity in the Gemara with regard to what may be done for these patients. We will now discuss how later authorities rule in this case.

Somewhat uncharacteristically, *Shulchan Arukh*[176] cites four opinions regarding the case of a patient who is not dangerously ill:

1. The most lenient opinion is that of Rashba,[177] who writes that even for a patient who is not dangerously ill, one is permitted to violate a rabbinic prohibition on *Shabbat*. He derives this from the Gemara in *Ketuvot* which permits an ill person to drink milk from a goat on *Shabbat*, since this *melakhah* is being performed with a *shinui*, and is thus no longer a Torah prohibition but a rabbinic prohibition. Rashba does not distinguish between cases of danger to a limb or organ and cases in which no such danger exists; in all these cases, one is permitted to violate rabbinic prohibitions on *Shabbat*. Similarly, *Tur*,[178] as discussed earlier, believes that this is the opinion of Rambam.

2. A more stringent opinion is that of Ran,[179] who writes that for a patient who is not dangerously ill, one may not violate even a rabbinic prohibition on *Shabbat*. One is only permitted to ask a non-Jew to perform *melakhah*. Ran derives this principle from the actions of Ameimar, who asked a non-Jew to apply medication to his eye on *Shabbat*, even though applying medication to the eye is only

---

prohibitions. On the other hand, if there were truly a situation in which only one limb or organ were endangered, and not the rest of the body, it would not be permitted to violate Torah prohibitions in that case.

176 *Orach Chayyim* 328:17.
177 Responsa 3:272.
178 *Orach Chayyim* 328.
179 *Shabbat* in *dappei ha-Rif* 39b, s.v. *u-meha*.

a rabbinic prohibition. This suggests that one may not perform a rabbinic prohibition oneself on *Shabbat* in case of a patient who is not dangerously ill.

3. A middle position is that of Ramban.[180] Ramban notes both of the statements in the Gemara cited by Rashba and Ran, which seem to contradict one another. On the one hand, Ameimar was required to ask a non-Jew to apply medication to his eye on *Shabbat*, and could not do so himself, even though this is a rabbinic prohibition; on the other hand, an ill person is allowed to drink milk directly from a goat on *Shabbat* since the *melakhah* is performed with a *shinui*, downgrading it to a rabbinic prohibition. Ramban explains that for a patient who is not dangerously ill, one may violate rabbinic prohibitions, but only with a *shinui*. Thus, Ameimar could not apply medication to his own eye and was required to ask a non-Jew, which, as noted, the Gemara already stated was always permitted in cases of ill patients. Similarly, with regard to the case in *Ketuvot*, Ramban believes that milking a goat on *Shabbat* is itself only a rabbinic prohibition, and therefore one may milk a goat on *Shabbat* using a *shinui* on behalf of an ill person.

4. *Beit Yosef*, as discussed earlier, argues that Rambam's opinion is more stringent than any of these opinions, since he does not even allow the violation of most rabbinic prohibitions when a limb or organ is in danger, and only permits violating rabbinic prohibitions which are not related to any Torah prohibitions. According to *Beit Yosef*, Rambam believes that in all cases of patients who are not in mortal danger, one may only ask a non-Jew to perform *melakhah* or may violate a rabbinic prohibition which is not related to any Torah prohibition.

Shulchan Arukh rules in accordance with the third opinion, that of Ramban, and Rama does not present a differing opinion. *Mishnah Berurah*[181] notes that this is also the opinion of *Taz*,[182] *Magen Avraham*[183] and Gra,[184] and that it is the predominant opinion of later authorities. Thus, in practice, there are three tiers of patients with regard to *Shabbat* violation: patients who are dangerously ill, for whom any Torah prohibition may be violated; patients who are in imminent danger of losing a

---

180 *Torat Ha-Adam, Sha'ar Ha-Meichush.*
181 328:57.
182 *Orach Chayyim* 328:12. Interestingly, he points out that both *Levush* (*Orach Chayyim* 328:17; see *Eliyah Zuta* 8) and *Bach* (*Orach Chayyim* 328) understood *Shulchan Arukh* to refer to the last opinion, that of Rambam (as interpreted by *Shulchan Arukh* himself), as the third opinion, since it is the third alternative presented to the first opinion of Rashba. He rejects this reading, as does *Magen Avraham*, since it is linguistically difficult.
183 328:14.
184 *Orach Chayyim* 328:17 s.v. *u-lechallel.*

limb or organ, for whom one may ask a non-Jew to perform *melakhah* or violate a rabbinic prohibition oneself; and patients who are ill but not in any danger, for whom one may ask a non-Jew to perform *melakhah* or one may violate a rabbinic prohibition oneself but only with a *shinui*.

Violating a Rabbinic Prohibition without a *Shinui*

While the conclusion of *Shulchan Arukh* is that one may only violate a rabbinic prohibition with a *shinui* on behalf of a patient who is ill, *Chayyei Adam*[185] writes that if one must violate a rabbinic prohibition on behalf of a patient and cannot do so with a *shinui*, it is permissible to violate the rabbinic prohibition without a *shinui*. R. Moshe Feinstein[186] rules in accordance with this opinion and explains that one may do so, if no *shinui* can be performed, because one may rely on the opinion of Rashba as cited in *Shulchan Arukh* that one may violate any rabbinic prohibition on behalf of an ill patient on *Shabbat*. R. Yehoshua Neuwirth[187] cites this opinion as well, ruling that if one cannot perform the action with a *shinui* and cannot find a non-Jew to perform the action, one may then perform the action without a *shinui*.

Violating a Torah Prohibition with a *Shinui*

While most authorities assume that Ramban permits only violating a rabbinic prohibition with a *shinui* on behalf of a patient, some later authorities assume that Ramban permits even violating a Torah prohibition with a *shinui*, even for a patient who is not dangerously ill and who is not in danger of losing a limb or organ.[188] These authorities

---

185 69:12; also cited by *Mishnah Berurah* 328:102.

186 *Iggerot Moshe, Orach Chayyim* 3:53.

187 *Shemirat Shabbat Ke-Hilkhatah* 33:2.

188 While the reason for this reading of Ramban is not clear in most of the authorities who cite the Ramban this way, it is likely as *Ketzot Ha-Shulchan* explans (*Baddei Ha-Shulchan* 134:6): Ramban writes that for an ill patient, one may perform "a *shevut* [rabbinic prohibition] of a *melakhah* performed with a *shinui*." While most understand that this phrase refers to a rabbinic prohibition, derived from a *melakhah*, which is performed with a *shinui*, these authorities read the phrase as referring to a rabbinic prohibition, namely performing a *melakhah* with a *shinui*, i.e., that one may violate a Torah prohibition with a *shinui* since this itself is a rabbinic prohibition. One difficulty with reading the Ramban in this way is that his proof for this ruling is the Gemara in *Ketuvot* which allows a sick person to drink milk from a goat since this act is performed with a *shinui*, and therefore Chazal did not prohibit it in the case of an ill person. According to this reading of Ramban, one must conclude that Ramban believes milking a cow is a Torah prohibition, such that the Gemara is suggesting that an ill person may violate a Torah prohibition with a *shinui*. However, Ramban himself (*Shabbat* 144b s.v. *u-lerabeinu ha-gadol*) writes that milking a cow is a rabbinic prohibition on *Shabbat*. *Eglei Tal* (*Tochen, se'if* 17, note 38:1) appears

include *Eglei Tal*,[189] *Shulchan Arukh Ha-Rav*,[190] *Tehillah Le-David*,[191] and *Ketzot Ha-Shulchan*.[192] R. Shlomo Zalman Auerbach[193] writes that while this is not the majority position, one may rely upon it if no other options are available.

Providing Medical Care to One Who is Not Ill

As mentioned before, Chazal actually prohibited providing medical care on *Shabbat*. This prohibition is independent of any *melakhah* being performed: even if one does not perform any *melakhah* while providing medical care, it is still a rabbinic prohibition to do so on *Shabbat*. The reason for this prohibition is that Chazal were concerned that if one were permitted to administer medical care on *Shabbat*, this might lead one to grind up materials to produce medicine on *Shabbat*, which is a prohibited *melakhah*.[194] Therefore, all medical care and taking medicine is prohibited outright on *Shabbat*. Of course, as we have been discussing until now, this prohibition does not apply in the case of one who is dangerously ill or even ill without any imminent danger to life; it applies only to one who is not ill, such as someone who has a non-incapacitating headache. Therefore, it is unlikely that a healthcare professional would need to be concerned with this prohibition, since hospital patients are often dangerously ill, or if not, they are least in the category of *choleh she-ein bo sakkanah*. However, this prohibition may be relevant if a patient in the hospital is no longer ill and has not yet been discharged. In this case, it would be prohibited to provide any medical care for this patient, even if no *melakhah* or other rabbinic prohibition is being violated.

Special Patient Categories

A number of unique situations occur in a hospital for which the *halakhah* may differ from the standard categories discussed above. We will now briefly review these patient categories and discuss the special *halakhot* that apply to them.

---

to understand that the case in *Ketuvot* is more similar to the *melakhah* of *mefarek*, rendering it similar to a Torah prohibition, and therefore Chazal prohibited violating it in cases of illness unless it is performed with a *shinui*, just as one may violate a Torah prohibition on *Shabbat* with a *shinui* for an ill person.

189 *Tochen, se'if* 18.
190 328:19.
191 328:22.
192 134:4; see *Baddei Ha-Shulchan* 6.
193 Cited in *Shemirat Shabbat Ke-Hilchatah* 33:2, footnote 17*.
194 *Shabbat* 53b.

Psychiatric Illness

Some patients with psychiatric conditions may harbor a danger to themselves or others. For example, a patient with severe depression might be at risk of committing suicide. Alternatively, a patient who has an outbreak of violent behavior could harm or kill others. For this reason, it is generally accepted that patients with psychiatric illness who may pose harm to themselves or others are considered in the category of dangerously ill patients, and one may violate Torah prohibitions on *Shabbat* to prevent a life-threatening situation, even though the disease itself is not directly causing harm to the body. This is the view of R. Moshe Feinstein,[195] R. Eliezer Waldenberg,[196] and R. Ovadia Yosef.[197]

Labor and Childbirth

While it is well-known that one violates *Shabbat* on behalf of a woman in labor, there is a subtle halakhic difference between a woman giving birth and other dangerously ill patients. *Maggid Mishneh*[198] writes that according to Rambam, one must do one's utmost to perform *melakhah* with a *shinui* when assisting a woman in labor on *Shabbat*. As noted earlier, *Maggid Mishneh* believes that one need not generally perform *melakhot* with a *shinui* on behalf of dangerously ill patients. However, he argues that the *halakhah* is different for a woman in labor, since labor is a natural process, rather than a pathological one, and a very small percentage of women in labor die. *Shulchan Arukh,*[199] who generally does not advise using a *shinui* when treating a dangerously ill patient (in contrast to Rama, who, as discussed, advises that a *shinui* be used), rules in accordance with *Maggid Mishneh*, stating that when treating a woman in labor, one should attempt to use a *shinui*. R. Eliezer Waldenberg[200] cites R. Yaakov Emden[201] who emphasizes that *Shulchan Arukh*'s ruling only applies in a case in which the woman is not endangered; if there is a complication or the pregnancy is considered high-risk, one should

195 *Iggerot Moshe, Even Ha-Ezer* 1:65; *Orach Chayyim* 5:18, glosses to *Shulchan Arukh* 306:9; *Orach Chayyim* 1:127.
196 *Tzitz Eliezer* 4:13.
197 *Yabbia Omer*, 8:37. He cites responsa *Admat Kodesh, Yoreh De'ah* 1:6 who permits a psychiatric patient to eat non-kosher meat which doctors claim will cure him.
198 *Shabbat* 2:11 s.v. *ve-khol.*
199 *Orach Chayyim* 330:1; see *Magen Avraham* 330:3 there.
200 *Tzitz Eliezer* 17:65; also cited in *Nishmat Avraham* (recipient of the responsum), *Orach Chayyim* 330:7.
201 *Mor U-Ketziah, Orach Chayyim* 330.

certainly not use a *shinui* and should perform any necessary *melakhah* as quickly as possible.[202]

The Gemara[203] notes that following birth, a woman is still considered in the category of dangerously ill for the following week, and thus a healthcare provider must violate *Shabbat* to perform any *melakhah* which is necessary for her care. Even after this week, she is still considered an ill patient (*choleh she-ein bo sakkanah*) until one month has elapsed since the birth, and therefore one may ask a non-Jew to perform *melakhah* on her behalf or may violate a rabbinic prohibition with a *shinui*.

Fetus

As noted earlier,[204] one reason given in the Gemara for violating *Shabbat* to save a life is that one may violate one *Shabbat* now so that another individual may observe many future *Shabbatot*. On this basis, Ramban[205] cites Behag who allows violating *Shabbat* to save a fetus, since the fetus will eventually be born and be able to observe *Shabbat*. Ramban also proves this ruling from the Gemara[206] which discusses a case of a pregnant woman who dies on *Shabbat* and permits one to bring a knife through the public domain for use in surgically removing the fetus.[207] Ran[208] and Rosh[209] cite Ramban's ruling, but they later disagree, arguing that one may only violate *Shabbat* to save the life of a fetus since endangerment of the fetus may in turn endanger the mother; however, there is no fundamental allowance to violate *Shabbat* to save the life of

---

202 The Brisker Rav (end of commentary to *Yoma* in *Chidushei Maran Riz Ha-Levi Al Masekhtot Yoma Ve-Sukkah Ve-Hilkhot Kiddush Ha-Chodesh*; cited in *Tzitz Eliezer* and *Nishmat Avraham*, ibid.) suggests a similar distinction even for normal pregnancies, arguing that Rambam (*Shabbat* 2:11,13) distinguishes between the period before a woman begins bleeding and afterward: before a woman begins to bleed, we violate *Shabbat* on her behalf but attempt to do so with a *shinui*, whereas once she begins to bleed, we no longer attempt to use a *shinui* when tending to her.

203 *Shabbat* 129a.

204 See footnote 6.

205 *Torat Ha-Adam, Sha'ar Ha-Meichush*; cited in Ritva *Niddah* 44b.

206 *Arakhin* 7a.

207 Ramban cites dissenting opinions who explain that the Gemara permits this because when the mother dies, the fetus inside is considered "born" and therefore one must violate *Shabbat* to save the fetus just as one would for any person; however, in a case in which the mother is alive, these opinions would hold that one may not violate *Shabbat* to save the fetus.

208 *Yoma, dappei ha-Rif* 3b s.v. *ve-katuv*.

209 *Yoma* 8:13.

a fetus. R. Eliezer Waldenberg[210] and R. Yehoshua Neuwirth[211] rule in accordance with Ramban.

Premature Newborns

Shulchan Arukh,[212] based on the Gemara,[213] rules that one may violate *Shabbat* to take care of any of a newborn's medical needs, such as cutting the umbilical cord. However, *Shulchan Arukh* excludes from this any newborn who was born after eight months of gestation, or a newborn whose gestation period was either seven or eight months, if in either case the newborn's hair and fingernails have not completely developed. This exclusion is based on the Gemara[214] which also rules that one may only violate *Shabbat* for the needs of a newborn whose gestation period was either seven months or nine months. Generally, Chazal understood that a newborn whose gestation was seven months or nine months would be viable, but not a newborn whose gestation was eight months. The Gemara elsewhere[215] qualifies this ruling and states that if the newborn after eight months of gestation has developed hair and fingernails, we should assume that the gestation period was actually seven months (and thus the newborn is viable), and the newborn merely delayed in exiting the womb.[216]

---

210 *Tzitz Eliezer* 11:43. He notes that *Shulchan Arukh* does not rule explicitly on this issue. However, he points to *Tur* (*Orach Chayyim* 617), who seems to rule that we violate Torah prohibitions to save the life of a fetus (specifically, with regard to a pregnant woman eating on *Yom Kippur*), implying that he agrees with Behag. There, *Beit Yosef* questions *Tur*'s wording, asking why he rules that this woman can eat lest she *or her fetus* are endangered, since this suggests that it is possible for one's life to be endangered but not the other's. Here, *Beit Yosef* clearly suggests that he agrees with Ran and Rosh as discussed in the main text. R. Waldenberg argues that since *Beit Yosef* did not argue with *Tur*'s ruling, only the reason given (that the mother *or* the fetus could be endangered), this suggests that he agrees with the ruling itself.

211 *Shemirat Shabbat Ke-Hilkhatah* 36:2, 32 foonote 13.

212 *Orach Chayyim* 330:7.

213 *Shabbat* 128b–129b.

214 *Shabbat* 135a.

215 *Yevamot* 80a–80b.

216 Gra (ad loc) argues with *Shulchan Arukh*'s ruling, stating that even if the hair and fingernails are developed, this only permits carrying the newborn (i.e., the newborn is not considered *muktzeh*, as a stillborn fetus would be) and circumcising the newborn on *Shabbat*. One may carry the newborn since carrying a *muktzeh* item is only prohibited rabbinically, and one may circumcise the newborn since this is permitted in any case: if the newborn is considered viable, then his circumcision overrides *Shabbat*, whereas if the newborn is not considered viable, his circumcision is an act which is not considered a *melakhah* (since cutting off skin is only prohibited for live beings). According

Despite *Shulchan Arukh*'s ruling, modern-day authorities allow *Shabbat* violation on behalf of any newborn, regardless of its gestation period or stage of development. R. Ovadia Yosef,[217] Dayan Yitzchak Weiss,[218] R. Shmuel Wosner,[219] and R. Shlomo Zalman Auerbach[220] all permit caring for a premature newborn on *Shabbat* since today, due to the advent of the incubator, a premature newborn often has a good chance of surviving, and so one must violate *Shabbat* for the newborn's medical care. *Nishmat Avraham*[221] cites R. Shlomo Zalman Auerbach who rules that even for a newborn with a developmental defect who cannot survive for more than several weeks, hospital staff should violate *Shabbat* to care for the newborn. Though R. Auerbach acknowledges that by the letter of the law, one may not violate *Shabbat* for such a newborn, he argues that in a hospital setting, one can become easily confused if one tries to distinguish which newborns are capable of thriving for extended periods of time, and therefore if one were to refrain from violating *Shabbat* to care for a newborn who cannot thrive, one would eventually do the same for a newborn who is capable of thriving. Therefore, he rules that hospital staff should care for all newborns the same way, and should violate *Shabbat* on their behalf. He adds that if the newborn had a full gestation, even if it has a developmental defect, one must then, even according to the letter of the law, violate *Shabbat* to care for the newborn.

Conclusion

In this chapter, we have reviewed the *halakhot* relevant to a healthcare professional treating patients on *Shabbat*. While the details are complex, we have seen four major categories: *choleh she-yesh bo sakkanah*, a dangerously ill patient, for whom one may violate any Torah prohibition on *Shabbat*; *sakkanat ever*, a patient who has a limb or organ in imminent danger, for whom one may ask a non-Jew to perform a *melakhah* or one may violate a rabbinic prohibition oneself; *choleh she-ein bo sakkanah*, an ill patient who is not in danger, for whom one may ask a non-Jew to perform *melakhah* or one may violate a rabbinic prohibition oneself with a *shinui*; and a patient who is not ill, for whom one may not violate any prohibition, and furthermore, one may not provide any medical care even if it does not involve any other prohibition. These principles will be very important in subsequent chapters which discuss what a healthcare professional may do on *Shabbat*.

---

to Gra, one may only violate *Shabbat* for the medical needs of this newborn once thirty days have passed, thus retroactively proving viability.
217 *Yalkut Yosef, Shabbat* vol. 4, 330:21 (p. 308).
218 *Minchat Yitzchak* 4:123.
219 *Shevet Ha-Levi* 3:141.
220 Cited in *Shemirat Shabbat Ke-Hilkhatah* 36:12, footnote 24.
221 *Orach Chayyim* 330:20, p. 531.

Chapter 21

Residency Programs and *Shabbat* Accommodation

Jerry Karp, MD, PhD

Perhaps the most difficult decision any medical student must make is selecting a residency program. The student must choose both a medical specialty as well as the hospital where he or she would like to train in order to master that specialty. For the observant Jewish medical student, this decision is significantly complicated by an extra variable – *Shabbat* observance. Most residency programs in the United States require the participating residents to be present in the hospital on *Shabbat* and *yom tov* and do not accommodate the residents' personal religious needs in creating the on-call schedule. Fortunately, a few residency programs are known to accommodate observant Jewish residents by arranging their schedules so they are not call on *Shabbat* and they have vacation over *yom tov*. Still, there are few such programs, and medical students might be hesitant to choose these programs for a number of reasons. Therefore, it is necessary to consider whether a Jewish medical student may apply to and accept a position at a residency program which does not accommodate *Shabbat*.

In this chapter, we will discuss this most crucial question. We will examine the various halakhic problems which may exist in accepting a position at a program which will require one to work on *Shabbat* in a hospital. At the outset, we must emphasize that this decision *cannot* be made by reading a book. One who is considering accepting a residency position which does not accommodate *Shabbat* is strongly advised to consult with a *posek* first. Beyond the decision of choosing a residency program, remaining in contact with a halakhic advisor is necessary to discuss the myriad halakhic questions which will arise once the residency training has begun.

Before reading this chapter, the reader is advised to read the previous chapter which discusses the general halakhic principles which govern violating *Shabbat* on behalf of a patient. As a starting point for our discussion, it is important to emphasize that even if it were permitted for a medical student to accept a residency position that would involve working in the hospital on *Shabbat*, it is absolutely prohibited for a resident to violate *Shabbat* in a manner which is not in accord with the halakhic principles governing illness on *Shabbat*. When a resident works in the hospital on *Shabbat*, he or she must strictly adhere to the *halakhot* of *Shabbat*. Doctors are not exempt from *Shabbat* observance, and though Jewish law does permit, and mandate, *Shabbat* violation in specific circumstances, *the resident must not treat Shabbat in the hospital like any other day of the week*. Several chapters in this book are devoted to the topic of how a resident who works on *Shabbat* in a hospital, if this is permitted at all, must act to ensure the sanctity of *Shabbat*. This is the assumption which underlies the entirety of the following discussion.

Background: Medical Residency in the United States

The Match System

Spots in most U.S. residency programs are controlled by a unique match system, run by the National Resident Matching Program (NRMP). The NRMP employs a computer algorithm that attempts to find an optimal match between medical students and residency programs. Medical students submit a rank order list, in which they list the programs at which they have interviewed and at which they would consider accepting a spot. Each residency program also submits a list of students, in order of preference, whom they would accept in their residency program. The algorithm then considers each student and attempts to place the student in his or her most preferred residency program that still has an available spot. If he or she ranks a program that has no more spots remaining, but he or she was ranked higher by the program than an applicant tentatively matched to the program, the algorithm will replace the tentatively matched student with this student, and then attempt to place the removed student in his or her next most preferred program. This continues until each student has been placed in a program or there are no more programs left to place the student.[1] The match system favors students significantly in that the rank list is confidential, and programs are not allowed to ask students to commit to their programs or to express a preference for their programs in order to receive a spot.[2]

1   National Resident Matching Program, "How the Matching Algorithm Works," available at http://www.nrmp.org/matching-algorithm.
2   National Resident Matching Program, "Match Participation Agreement for Applicants and Programs For the 2014 Main Residency Match," available at http://www.nrmp.org/wp-content/uploads/2017/09/MPA-2018-MRM-Applicants_Programs.pdf.

Several residency programs officially accommodate *Shabbat*, and one can rank on one's list the *Shabbat*-accommodating option at these programs. Other programs do not have an official *Shabbat*-accommodating program, but are known to accommodate *Shabbat*. In these programs, the medical student could discuss *Shabbat* needs with the program director, and arrange that if he or she matches to this program, the program will accommodate *Shabbat* for the student. In some programs, there may be an implicit understanding that the student will express his or her overall preference for this program, and by doing so, the program will agree to rank that student highly so that he or she will be matched to the program, and *Shabbat* can be accommodated. The reason for this course of action is that the program may be wary of ranking highly too many applicants who are interested in *Shabbat* accommodation, since they may all be matched to the program, and the program is unable to accommodate more than a few students' *Shabbat* needs. Therefore, they are interested in ensuring a limited number of applicants requesting *Shabbat* accommodations by suggesting that an indication of preference would be required in order to gain a spot in that program. However, this can be tricky to navigate, since it is illegal, by the rules of the NRMP, for a residency program to ask a student to indicate preference for a program, though it is not illegal for a program to voluntarily express preference for a student, or for a student to voluntarily express preference for a program.[3]

Why Residency Programs Do Not Usually Accommodate *Shabbat*

Unfortunately, most residency programs do not offer *Shabbat* accommodation for the residents in their programs. This may be for one of several reasons. First, the program may be unable to offer *Shabbat* accommodations, since there may be too few residents in the program, and the call schedule may not allow for one resident never to be on call on Friday night or Saturday. Even if such a schedule could be accommodated, it might be unfair to other residents, since Friday night and/or Saturday call may be considered worse than Saturday night or Sunday call, such that allowing one resident to always avoid Friday night or Saturday call would be unfair to the other residents. Second, the program may be able, theoretically, to offer *Shabbat* accommodations, but may not want to make the effort to do so, as it requires more planning than would normally be required by those arranging the schedule. Third, the program may not be aware that medical students may be interested in not working on *Shabbat*. It is often thought that observant Jews may work on *Shabbat* in the hospital, since the job involves *pikuach nefesh*, saving

3   Ibid.

a life. However, as we will see, it is not clear that an observant Jew may work in a hospital on *Shabbat*, and even if this is permitted, it may still be preferable to avoid.

Why Observant Medical Students May Avoid a *Shabbat*-Accommodating Program

Though a medical student may be an observant Jew, he or she may still prefer to apply to a program which does not accommodate *Shabbat*. This may be for any of several reasons. First, in many specialties, no program exists which accommodates *Shabbat*. Such specialties include, but are not limited to, surgery, obstetrics/gynecology, and ophthalmology. A student who is committed to becoming a physician in one of these specialties would have no choice but to accept a spot in a program which does not accommodate *Shabbat*. Second, even in specialties which do have *Shabbat*-accommodating programs, the programs which do not accommodate *Shabbat* may be more prestigious and might offer better training than those programs which offer *Shabbat* accommodations. Such training will make the resident a better future physician, and may also help the resident in being accepted to a desirable fellowship or in being hired to work in a better hospital. The *Shabbat*-accommodating programs may also be in a geographic location where the student would prefer not to work, or may impose unfavorable requirements on students. For these reasons, medical students may be motivated to choose a program which does not accommodate *Shabbat*, even if a *Shabbat*-accommodating program exists.

Practical Constraints in Observing *Shabbat* While Working in a Hospital

Before we discuss the specific halakhic problems with accepting a position at a residency program which will not accommodate *Shabbat*, it is worthwhile to note that even if accepting such a position were permitted, the possibility of observing *Shabbat* while working in a hospital is certainly questionable. As we noted in the previous chapter, there are a number of limitations on what an observant Jewish physician may do on *Shabbat* while treating patients.

Not All *Shabbat* Restrictions Are Waived for Patients

First, though a physician may violate any Torah prohibition on *Shabbat* to prevent a patient from dying, Rama[4] rules that one should perform lifesaving *melakhot* with a *shinui* whenever this does not cause a delay

4   *Orach Chayyim* 328:12.

in care that might endanger the patient. With regard to most patients in a hospital, while their health status may categorize them as *choleh she-yesh bo sakkanah*, dangerously ill patients, it is often the case that the situation is not one of immediate danger, and the doctor would certainly have time to perform *melakhah* with a *shinui*. Thus, a physician working in the hospital on *Shabbat* would be required to consider each action he or she performs and whether the *melakhah* it entails could be performed with a *shinui*. Similarly, if one could accomplish the desired goal by performing a rabbinic prohibition rather than a Torah prohibition, this too would be required of the physician. It goes without saying that if the desired goal could be accomplished without performing any *melakhah* at all, this would also be necessary.

Moreover, if a patient is not dangerously ill, he or she is classified as a *choleh she-ein bo sakkanah*. For such a patient, the physician is only permitted to ask a non-Jew to perform *melakhah* on the patient's behalf, or the physician may perform a rabbinic prohibition but with a *shinui*.[5] The physician may only violate a rabbinic prohibition without a *shinui* if the patient's limb or organ is in imminent danger. These restrictions would severely limit the actions of the physician working in a hospital on *Shabbat*.

Furthermore, there are several routine actions, unrelated to patient care, that a resident may need to perform while in the hospital. For example, a resident may need to walk through electric doors or use an elevator to get from one floor to another, in a case where he or she is not trying to reach a patient but is trying to meet with other staff about administrative responsibilities. Obviously, this is not considered *pikuach nefesh* and there is no dispensation to violate *Shabbat*, even a rabbinic prohibition, in order to perform these actions on *Shabbat*. In order to accurately assess whether one would be able to abide by these restrictions while working in the hospital on *Shabbat*, one should consider spending a weekday in the hospital during one's medical school clerkships, attempting to perform one's daily tasks while abiding by the restrictions which would govern one's actions on *Shabbat*. In this way, the student can decide whether he or she could realistically write notes, respond to other staff, and competently fulfill one's duties under the constraints of *Shabbat* observance.

Mastering *Hilkhot Shabbat*

It should be obvious that one who intends to work in the hospital on *Shabbat* must be very well-versed in the intricacies of the laws of *Shabbat* and how they apply to a physician in a hospital. One must know how one will act when faced with the need to write, type on

5   *Shulchan Arukh, Orach Chayyim* 328:17.

a computer, use an elevator, measure a patient's temperature or blood pressure, and numerous other actions performed by physicians in the course of a normal day at the hospital. Additionally, one who is entering a certain field in which there are specific halakhic issues relevant to that field must be knowledgeable about those issues. For this reason, one who intends to apply for residency programs which do not accommodate *Shabbat* should study these *halakhot* in depth, preferably with a teacher who can answer questions about specific situations that will arise in the medical student's future. Waiting until one is about to start the residency program before learning these *halakhot* is impractical, and will likely lead to the resident being ignorant of these very important *halakhot*.

One Must Abandon One's Career Rather Than Violate *Shabbat*

It is important to consider the possibility that one will be faced with a situation where one will be asked by a superior at the hospital to perform an action which is prohibited on *Shabbat*. For example, one might be asked to write a note in the patient's chart which is only needed to prevent financial liability of the hospital, but which will have no bearing on the patient's current or future health. In such a case, the resident is obligated to decline, presumably explaining that he or she is unable to fulfill this request because it is *Shabbat*. One should consider how one will deal with this situation, what one is comfortable explaining to one's superiors, and to what extent one will be comfortable refusing to fulfill a request from a superior. One who has a timid personality, or one who is too afraid of the possible negative consequences, and will thus accede to the request, should absolutely not accept a position in hospital which will not accommodate *Shabbat*.

If this event ultimately occurs, one will certainly be tempted to accede to the request to avoid creating friction with superiors, possible disciplinary action, or even dismissal from the program, which would certainly destroy one's future career prospects in medicine. However, *Shabbat* observance demands that one politely explain that one cannot fulfill the request since it is *Shabbat*, and offer an alternative that does not violate *Shabbat*. One cannot excuse *Shabbat* violation due to excessive inconvenience or financial loss that could occur from not violating *Shabbat*. Indeed, Rama[6] rules that one is required to spend one's entire fortune in order to avoid violating a negative commandment. Thus, one should obviously make every attempt to politely and tactfully explain the situation and avoid any problems, and if appropriate to suggest a

6   *Orach Chayyim*, 656:1.

satisfactory alternative, but ultimately, one may not violate *Shabbat* in order to avoid an uncomfortable situation, disciplinary action or losing a job.

Halakhic Objections to Accepting a Spot Which Does Not Accommodate *Shabbat*

Having outlined practical halakhic constraints which one must take into account before considering a non-*Shabbat*-accommodating residency position, we will now discuss specific halakhic objections to accepting such a residency position. While we have noted several concerns with working on *Shabbat* in a hospital, we need to consider whether a resident, even making sure not to violate *halakhah* in ways which are not permitted on behalf of an ill patient on *Shabbat*, is allowed to work on *Shabbat* at all. Even if one is committed to observing *halakhah* while working shifts at the hospital, it may still be prohibited to work in the hospital, regardless of what one does, for a number of reasons which we will discuss here.

Violating *Shabbat* to Avoid *Eivah*

As discussed in the previous chapter, the requirement to violate *Shabbat* to save a life is based on one of two Biblical sources, either *"ve-shameru benei Yisra'el et ha-Shabbat,"* or *"asher ya'aseh otam ha-adam va-chai bahem."* In either case, it appears that the Biblical verse would only permit violating *Shabbat* on behalf of another person who observes *mitzvot*. These verses clearly exclude non-Jews who are not obligated in *mitzvot*. However, it is universal practice for Jewish healthcare workers to violate *Shabbat* on behalf of non-Jewish hospital patients. As discussed in the previous chapter, this is understood by most contemporary halakhic authorities to be based on an extension of the concern of *eivah*, ill will, between Jews and non-Jews. While the concept of *eivah* is usually applied only to allow violation of rabbinic prohibitions to prevent ill will between Jews and non-Jews, it is applied in the context of *pikuach nefesh* for non-Jews on *Shabbat* because of a concern for a much more serious *eivah*, namely, ill will between Jews and non-Jews which could lead to endangerment of other Jews' lives. As *Chatam Sofer*[7] notes, if a Jewish doctor refused to save a non-Jewish patient's life on *Shabbat*, this could endanger the Jewish doctor's life, or could endanger the lives of future Jewish patients whose non-Jewish physicians might not be willing to treat them. Therefore, Jewish healthcare workers may even

---

7   *Yoreh De'ah*, 131.

violate Torah prohibitions to save non-Jews' lives on *Shabbat* in order to avoid a situation whereby a Jew's life might be endangered.[8]

While this approach has been embraced by virtually all contemporary halakhic authorities, it suggests some limitations on the dispensation to violate *Shabbat* on behalf of those who do not observe *mitzvot*. Since the dispensation is based on *pikuach nefesh* for other Jews, it would appear that one should avoid being in a situation of treating non-Jewish patients on *Shabbat* so as not to create any situation of *eivah* at all. If the Jewish resident were not in the hospital on *Shabbat*, there would be no expectation from the resident to violate *Shabbat* in order to save the patient, and another non-Jewish resident could treat the patient instead. As a result, the Jewish resident would not be violating *Shabbat*, and there would be no *eivah*. While violating *Shabbat* due to *eivah* concerns is permitted, this would appear to be true only when one found oneself in a situation where *eivah* is a concern, not when one created the situation of *eivah* oneself.

Indeed, R. Yehoshua Neuwirth[9] writes that a Jewish doctor (or resident) working in a hospital with non-Jewish patients *must* switch call with a non-Jewish resident so as not to be in the hospital on *Shabbat*. He notes that one must even be willing to pay the other resident, or agree to take extra shifts during the week, in order to convince the non-Jewish resident to take call on *Shabbat*. Similarly, *Nishmat Avraham*[10] expresses vociferous opposition to Jewish residents working in a hospital with non-Jewish patients on *Shabbat*. He writes that the dispensation of *eivah* may only `be used if one finds oneself in an emergency situation with a non-Jewish person in mortal danger on *Shabbat*, but one may not seek out such situations. He also cites R. Shlomo Zalman Auerbach, R. Yehoshua Neuwirth, and R. Yosef Shalom Elyashiv who agree with this ruling. R. Moshe Sternbuch similarly writes in a responsum[11] that a physician should switch *Shabbat* call with other non-Jewish residents, even offering to pay them in exchange; he writes in another responsum[12] that a Jewish medical student should not accept a residency position which does not accommodate *Shabbat* since he or she will then have to work in the hospital on a consistent basis on *Shabbat*.[13]

8   See the previous chapter for further discussion of this issue as well as a listing of contemporary halakhic authorities who adopt this approach.
9   *Shemirat Shabbat Ke-Hilkhatah* 40:65**.
10 *Orach Chayyim*, 345:1(5–6), pp. 186–188.
11 *Teshuvot Ve-Hanhagot*, 1:864.
12 *Teshuvot Ve-Hanhagot*, 1:871.
13 It is noteworthy that R. Sternbuch points out that there are residency positions in Israel where one would not have to violate *Shabbat* (presumably, he is referring to Shaare Zedek Medical Center in Jerusalem), and therefore Jewish medical students in South Africa (where the responsum was written) may not accept residency positions which do not accommodate *Shabbat*. It

R. Moshe Feinstein[14] also writes about how a Jewish physician should conduct himself or herself on *Shabbat*. While he explains that Jewish doctors may treat non-Jewish patients on *Shabbat* due to *eivah*, he cautions that a Jewish doctor should see to it that he or she is difficult to contact on *Shabbat*, e.g., the doctor's phone number should be unlisted. R. Feinstein adds that a Jewish doctor should try to switch his or her *Shabbat* call in order to avoid being in the hospital on *Shabbat*. If possible, the doctor should specify that his or her day off each week is on *Shabbat*.

Still, it appears that R. Feinstein does not go as far as R. Neuwirth and *Nishmat Avraham*. In a guidebook for Jewish doctors compiled by R. Moshe Tendler and Dr. Fred Rosner,[15] the authors include R. Feinstein's ruling on accepting residencies which do not accommodate *Shabbat*. Asked whether a Jewish medical student should accept the best residency program possible, or a residency program which accommodates the resident's *Shabbat* observance, R. Feinstein responds that the student should accept the residency spot that will provide him or her with the best training possible, at the cost of compromising on the spirit of *Shabbat*. Importantly, R. Feinstein notes clearly that the resident is prohibited from violating *Shabbat* in any way that is not clearly allowed by *halakhah*, as discussed earlier; R. Feinstein simply allows one to work in a hospital on *Shabbat*, keeping the laws of *Shabbat* in their entirety, despite the fact that the resident will be sacrificing the spirit of *Shabbat* to work.

Thus, it appears that R. Feinstein allows one to accept a residency position that does not accommodate *Shabbat*, provided that the resident will be punctilious in *Shabbat* observance. However, R. Feinstein would still insist that any time the resident is scheduled to be on call on *Shabbat*, he or she should make every attempt to switch call with a non-Jewish resident.

---

seems that R. Sternbuch believes that as long as there is some way to learn medicine and become a doctor, regardless of the personal hardship involved in doing so, one is prohibited from putting oneself in a situation where one will violate *Shabbat* due to *eivah*. Interestingly, this implies that there is some value to being able to obtain medical training, such that if, hypothetically, there were no *Shabbat*-accommodating residencies available, one could, perhaps, train in a program which does not accommodate *Shabbat*. However, R. Sternbuch is countering this possibility with another novel but important caveat, which is that if there is any possibility of training without having to violate *Shabbat* due to *eivah*, regardless of how inconvenient, one is required to exercise that option.

14 *Iggerot Moshe* 4:79.
15 Fred Rosner and Rabbi Moses D. Tendler, *Practical Medical Halacha*, New York: Feldheim, 1980, p. 116.

Intentionally Creating a Situation of *Pikuach Nefesh*

As we have described, one is permitted to violate *Shabbat* to save the life of a non-Jew because of considerations of *pikuach nefesh* for the Jewish physician and other Jews who may be endangered if the physician were to avoid treating non-Jews on *Shabbat*. For one who is accepting a residency position, this, in turn, raises an important halakhic concern: is one permitted to intentionally create a situation in which one will be required to violate *Shabbat* for one's own *pikuach nefesh*? It goes without saying that if one finds oneself or another in a situation of danger to life, it is not only permitted, but also a *mitzvah*, to violate *Shabbat* to save a life. But may one intentionally create a situation before *Shabbat* which will necessitate violating *Shabbat* later for *pikuach nefesh*, even if this later violation is permitted?

This question is indeed discussed by medieval and modern authorities. We will examine the source of the possible halakhic problem with intentionally creating a situation of *pikuach nefesh* as well as the opinions of contemporary authorities.

The Gemara and *Rishonim*

The source for the possible halakhic prohibition of intentionally creating a situation of *pikuach nefesh* is one that, at first, seems unrelated to the issue at hand. The Gemara[16] writes that it is prohibited for one to set sail on a ship within three days of *Shabbat*. However, the Gemara qualifies that if one is sailing for the purpose of performing a *mitzvah*, then one may sail even within three days of *Shabbat*.[17]

This passage is somewhat cryptic, since no reason is given for the prohibition. As a result, there are numerous explanations presented by *rishonim* to explain the reason for the prohibition.[18] The explanation

16 *Shabbat* 19a.
17 There is a debate recorded in the Gemara as to whether in this latter case, one must still request from the ship personnel that they not sail on *Shabbat*. However, even according to the opinion that one must make this request, one may still set sail and remain on the ship even if the ship personnel later ignore the traveler's request and sail on *Shabbat*.
18 Besides for the explanations given in the main text, there are several other explanations given in *rishonim*:
    1. Rabbeinu Chananel (ad loc, s.v. *ein mafligin*; also cited by Rif, 7b in *dappei ha-Rif*) and Rabbeinu Tam (cited in *Hagahot Maimoniyot*, *Shabbat* 30:13) explain that the prohibition is due to *techum Shabbat*, the prohibition of traveling more than 2,000 *ammot* on *Shabbat*. Since this is the source of the prohibition, Rabbeinu Chananel explains that it only applies if one is traveling on a body of water which is less than ten *tefachim* deep. This is because the prohibition of traveling more than 2,000 *ammot* on *Shabbat* does not apply in water which is more than ten *tefachim* deep. Rabbeinu Chananel uses this

detail to explain why it was the custom in his time for Jews to sail on the Mediterranean Sea, setting sail even within three days of *Shabbat*. Rabbeinu Chananel does not explain why, according to his reasoning, the prohibition should not apply until three days before *Shabbat*, or in a case where one is performing a *mitzvah*. However, *Bach* (*Orach Chayyim* 248) explains that one may set sail more than three days before *Shabbat* because then, when one leaves the *techum Shabbat*, he is considered *anus*, unable to avoid violating the prohibition. Moreover, in a case of performing a *mitzvah*, Chazal did not prohibit setting sail before *Shabbat* at all. This is because, as *Bach* explains, Chazal generally prohibited leaving the *techum Shabbat*, i.e., traveling more than 2,000 *ammot*, only on dry land, since the Torah only prohibits traveling more than 12 *mil* (a much farther distance than 2,000 *ammot*) on dry land, so Chazal extended this prohibition to include an even shorter distance. In the case of traveling on water, Chazal also extended the prohibition of *techum Shabbat* to 2,000 *ammot* so as not to create a distinction between dry land and water, but did not want to establish this prohibition in a case where one is attempting to perform a *mitzvah*.

2. R. Hai Gaon (cited in *Tashbetz* 4(3):11) and *Tosafot* (ad loc, s.v. *ein mafligin*; also attributed to Ritzva in *Tosafot Eruvin* 43a s.v. *halakhah*) explain that the prohibition is due to the rabbinic prohibition of swimming on *Shabbat*, which was enacted by Chazal to prevent one from making a *chavit shel shayyatin*, a tube that assisted novice swimmers in learning to swim (see *Beitzah* 36b). As an extension of their prohibition on swimming, Chazal also prohibited sailing in a boat before *Shabbat*. *Beit Yosef* (*Orach Chayyim* 248) explains that the prohibition only applies to the three days before *Shabbat* since if one may sail only more than three days before *Shabbat*, one will realize that both sailing and swimming are prohibited on *Shabbat*.

3. Ramban (cited by Ran in commentary to Rif 7b s.v. *tanu rabbanan ha-maflig*) and Rabbeinu Yerucham (*Toledot Adam Ve-Chavah* 12:15) explain that the prohibition applies when the only travelers on the ship are Jews, and non-Jews are sailing the ship, so that it appears that when the non-Jews are violating *Shabbat* while sailing, they are doing so at the behest of the Jews. However, if the majority of those on the boat are not Jewish, it would be permitted for a Jew to sail on the ship since it does not appear that the non-Jews are working on behalf of the Jew.

4. Ritzva (cited in *Tosafot Eruvin* 43a s.v. *halakhah*) explains that Chazal enacted the prohibition lest one lead the boat oneself, thereby carrying an object more than four *ammot* in a *karmelit* area (an intermediate case between that of a public domain and that of a private domain), which is a rabbinic prohibition.

5. Rashbam (cited in *Tosafot* ibid.) explains that the prohibition mentioned in the Gemara is, in fact, only in effect according to the opinion of *Beit Shammai*. *Beit Shammai* holds (*Shabbat* 18a) that one is required to prevent one's possessions from performing *melakhot* on *Shabbat*; thus, for example, *Beit Shammai* rules that one should not

adopted by the most *rishonim*, including Rif,[19] Rambam[20] and Rosh,[21] is that the prohibition is intended to prevent one from becoming seasick during the trip and then being unable to enjoy *Shabbat*, thus failing to fulfill the *mitzvah* of *oneg Shabbat*.[22] Indeed, in his responsa,[23] Rambam writes that the prohibition applies only to one sailing in bodies of salt water, since these cause seasickness, but not to one sailing in bodies of freshwater.

However, an alternative view which is important to our discussion is Ba'al Ha-Ma'or,[24] who explains that the prohibition is based on the fact that sea travel is dangerous, and one will likely be forced to violate *Shabbat* in order to save one's life. Obviously, violating *Shabbat* in this case is permitted. However, if one begins to travel within three days of *Shabbat*, it appears that one deliberately intends to violate *Shabbat*. Therefore, Chazal prohibited one from setting sail within three days of *Shabbat*. As Ba'al Ha-Ma'or notes, the three days before *Shabbat* are designated "*kamei shabbata*," "before *Shabbat*," and so we associate one's actions during these three days as if one is considering how they will affect what will later happen on *Shabbat* itself. However, more than three days before *Shabbat* is not considered "*kamei shabbata*" and so one's actions are not associated with their eventual effect on *Shabbat*. Citing Ba'al Ha-Ma'or, Rivash[25] similarly rules that one may not begin a journey with non-Jews into the desert during the three days preceding *Shabbat*, since the rest of the travelers will want to continue traveling on *Shabbat*, and the Jew will need to violate *Shabbat* to continue

---

put wool in a cauldron on Friday afternoon in order to dye it unless the wool will take up the dye before *Shabbat* begins (*Shabbat* 17b). In a similar vein, *Beit Shammai* does not allow one to board a ship before *Shabbat* if it will violate a prohibition (by leaving the *techum Shabbat*) after *Shabbat* begins. However, we follow the opinion of *Beit Hillel*, who permit one to set up one's possessions to violate *melakhah* after the start of *Shabbat*, and similarly, according to Rashbam, permit one to board a ship before *Shabbat* even if it will travel on *Shabbat*.

19 *Shabbat*, 7b in *dappei ha-Rif*.
20 *Shabbat* 30:13.
21 *Shabbat* 1:38.
22 Based on this reasoning, Rif explains the reasoning behind the two exceptions listed in the Gemara. First, one may sail more than three days before *Shabbat* because the seasickness that results from sailing is likely to last no more than three days. Second, one may sail for the purpose of fulfilling a *mitzvah*, even right before *Shabbat*, because of the classic rule that *osek be-mitzvah patur min ha-mitzvah*, one who is fulfilling a *mitzvah* is exempt from fulfilling a second *mitzvah* (in this case, *oneg Shabbat*).
23 Responsum 308; also cited in *Maggid Mishneh* to *Mishneh Torah* ad loc.
24 *Shabbat* 7b in *dappei ha-Rif*.
25 Responsa, 1:17–18.

traveling with them so that he does not remain alone in the desert, which would be dangerous.

Returning to our case of a medical student choosing a residency program, the question remains whether it is prohibited for a student to accept a position at a program which does not accommodate *Shabbat*. Accepting such a position puts the student in the position of violating *Shabbat* to treat non-Jewish patients, which he or she will be required to do, so as not to endanger himself or herself, or other Jewish patients, as discussed earlier. From the above discussion of the Gemara, we can focus on several key points:

1. Ba'al Ha-Ma'or is the only figure among the *rishonim* who believes that the prohibition of setting sail before *Shabbat* is due to a prohibition of putting oneself in a situation whereby one will be required to violate *Shabbat* due to *pikuach nefesh*. Other *rishonim* understand the Gemara differently, though we cannot know whether this is because they do not believe there is any such prohibition, or because they believe the ruling in the Gemara has an alternative basis. In any event, as we will see, Ba'al Ha-Ma'or is cited by numerous *acharonim* as authoritative in this case.

2. While, with regard to our question, Ba'al Ha-Ma'or seems to be stating a significant stringency, his opinion also carries a significant leniency. As the Gemara noted, the prohibition of setting sail before *Shabbat* does not apply more than three days before *Shabbat*, or in the case of a *mitzvah*. Therefore, it seems that Ba'al Ha-Ma'or is suggesting that one *may* put oneself in a situation whereby one will violate *Shabbat* for *pikuach nefesh* if the situation is one of a *mitzvah*, or if one has arranged this situation more than three days before *Shabbat*. In our discussion of the *acharonim*, we will focus on whether the Ba'al Ha-Ma'or indeed intends this apparent leniency, and whether the *halakhah* is in accordance with this leniency. Furthermore, if the *halakhah* is in accordance with this leniency, we will have to examine whether working in a hospital is considered a situation of performing a *mitzvah*.[26]

---

26 Another possible leniency could be based on the dispensation to create a situation of *pikuach nefesh* more than three days before *Shabbat*. In order to employ such a leniency, one would have to determine whether the resident is considered to have entered this situation of *pikuach nefesh* more than three days before *Shabbat*. This would require a determination of whether we should focus on when the resident accepted the residency position, which is obviously more than three days prior to *Shabbat*; or when the schedule is set, which would likely be three days before *Shabbat*; or when the resident traveled to the hospital, which would be within three days of *Shabbat*. To this author's knowledge, this question has not been explicitly discussed by any halakhic authorities to date.

The Leniency of Ba'al Ha-Ma'or

Shulchan Arukh[27] cites the Gemara and explains that the reason for the prohibition is to enable fulfillment of the *mitzvah* of *oneg Shabbat*, in accordance with the explanation of Rif, Rambam and Rosh discussed above.[28] However, Rama[29] cites the opinion of Ba'al Ha-Ma'or and Rivash that even if the concern of *oneg Shabbat* would not apply, it would still be prohibited to set sail within three days of *Shabbat* if it would be necessary to perform *melakhah* on *Shabbat*, though it is still permitted to set sail more than three days before *Shabbat*. Furthermore, *Shulchan Arukh* later[30] cites the responsum of Rivash, stating that one is prohibited from beginning a voyage into the desert within three days of *Shabbat* since one is putting oneself into a situation of *pikuach nefesh* and will need to violate *Shabbat*. However, he clearly states that it is permitted to begin the voyage more than three days before *Shabbat*.

On the other hand, *Magen Avraham*,[31] *Mishnah Berurah*,[32] and *Arukh Ha-Shulchan*[33] cite two authorities, Radvaz[34] and Mahari ben Lev,[35] who strongly disagree with Ba'al Ha-Ma'or's leniency, which allows one to enter a *pikuach nefesh* situation for a *mitzvah* or more than three days prior to *Shabbat*. Radvaz argues that the other *rishonim* who came after Ba'al Ha-Ma'or did not cite his opinion, and instead suggested other explanations of the Gemara, indicating that they did not agree with Ba'al Ha-Ma'or's leniency. Mahari ben Lev writes that even Ba'al Ha-Ma'or and Rivash did not intend to permit one to set sail more than three days before *Shabbat*, or within three days for the purpose of a *mitzvah*, if one knows with absolute certainty that one will need to violate *Shabbat*. Rather, even in these two exceptional cases, one is only permitted to set sail if there is a possibility, however minute, that one will not violate *Shabbat*. According to Mahari ben Lev, one may not set sail within three days of *Shabbat* if there is even a reasonable possibility that one will need to violate *Shabbat*, but if one is traveling for the purpose of a *mitzvah*, or one leaves more than three days before *Shabbat*, this would be permitted even though there is a "*safek karov le-vadai*," an uncertainty bordering on certainty, that one will need to

27 *Orach Chayyim*, 248:1–2.
28 He also cites the opinion of *Rabbeinu Chananel*, noting that even if one is traveling on a body of freshwater (such that the concern of ruining *oneg Shabbat* does not apply), it is still prohibited to set sail within three days of *Shabbat* if the depth of the water is less than ten *tefachim* (see footnote 18).
29 Ibid.
30 *Orach Chayyim*, 248:4.
31 *Orach Chayyim*, 248:14.
32 248:26; also in *Biur Halakhah*, s.v. *u-posek*.
33 *Orach Chayyim*, 248:11.
34 Responsa, 4:77.
35 Responsa, 2:53.

violate *Shabbat*, but *not* if the situation is one of "*vadai*," certainty, that one will need to violate *Shabbat*.[36]

36 Indeed, based on another comment of Ba'al Ha-Ma'or (*Shabbat* 53b in *dappei ha-Rif*), one might conclude that he did not hold of this leniency himself. He cites Rif (ibid.) who permits bathing a newly-circumcised infant in hot water which had been heated before *Shabbat* or on *Shabbat* itself, since bathing an infant in hot water is necessary for *pikuach nefesh* of the infant following the circumcision. Ba'al Ha-Ma'or, however, draws a distinction regarding when one may heat water of *Shabbat* to bathe a circumcised infant. If one already circumcised the infant and realized that there was no hot water, or the hot water spilled, one may certainly heat water on behalf of the infant since this is a *pikuach nefesh* situation. However, if one has not yet circumcised the infant, one may not heat up water in order to bathe the infant afterward, and the circumcision must be delayed until after *Shabbat*. This is also the opinion of Rashba (*Shabbat* 134b, s.v. *aval*, citing the ge'onim), and R. Yosef Karo (*Kesef Mishneh*, Milah 2:8; *Beit Yosef*, *Yoreh De'ah* 266) argues that it is also the opinion of Rif (ibid.) and Rambam (*Milah* 2:8; responsum 307). Ramban (*Shabbat* 134b, s.v. *aval*) disagrees and argues that the circumcision need not be delayed, and one may heat up water on *Shabbat* before the circumcision. Ba'al Ha-Ma'or's opinion seems to suggest that one may not intentionally create a situation of *pikuach nefesh* on *Shabbat* for which it may be necessary to violate *Shabbat*, even if it will then be permitted to do so. In contrast to the implications of his earlier remark, it seems that here Ba'al Ha-Ma'or argues that this principle is true even when one is performing a *mitzvah*. However, many later commentators explain that Ba'al Ha-Ma'or is indeed consistent, and they suggest several possible distinctions:

1. The simplest understanding, based on the caveat of Mahari ben Lev (see R. Hershel Schachter's *Divrei Ha-Rav*, p. 171), is that Ba'al Ha-Ma'or only permits entering a situation of *pikuach nefesh* for the purpose of a *mitzvah* if it is not certain that there will be a need to violate *Shabbat*, but if one is certain that this will be necessary, such as in this case of heating water for the circumcised infant, Ba'al Ha-Ma'or does not permit entering the *pikuach nefesh* situation.

2. Alternatively, others including *Chatam Sofer* (responsa, 6:97), Netziv (*Ha'amek She'eilah* to She'iltot, Parshat Vayyera 10:9), and the Steipler Gaon (*Kehillot Ya'akov*, Shabbat, ch. 15) explain that the distinction between the two cases is that one is setting sail *before Shabbat*, while one is circumcising the child *on Shabbat*. Ba'al Ha-Ma'or does not allow one to enter a situation of *pikuach nefesh*, even for a *mitzvah*, on *Shabbat*, since this appears as if one is willingly violating *Shabbat*. However, before *Shabbat*, Ba'al Ha-Ma'or lowers the standard for what is considered an appearance of willingly violating *Shabbat*: for a non-*mitzvah*, we consider one who enters a situation of *pikuach nefesh* as if he or she intends to violate *Shabbat*, but for a *mitzvah*, we do not apply this stringency. Netziv adds that even Ramban limits his dispensation to circumcision on *Shabbat*, since circumcision itself overrides *Shabbat*, but Ramban would not allow one to enter a situation of *pikuach nefesh* on *Shabbat* for another *mitzvah*. R. Joseph B.

While *Magen Avraham*, *Mishnah Berurah* and *Arukh Ha-Shulchan* all prohibit putting oneself into a definite *pikuach nefesh* situation even for the purpose of a *mitzvah*, or even more than three days before *Shabbat*, *Eliyah Rabbah*[37] argues that one may put oneself into a definite *pikuach nefesh* situation in either of these cases, and *Shulchan Arukh Ha-Rav*[38] writes that one should not chastise a person who relies on the lenient opinion, though he advises one to be stringent. *Peri Megadim*[39] cites *Eliyah Rabbah*'s ruling, and R. Eliezer Waldenberg[40] interprets this as suggesting that he himself rules like the lenient opinion. Moreover, R. Shlomo Zalman Auerbach[41] and R. Yehoshua Neuwirth[42] write that one may certainly rely on the lenient opinion in certain cases.[43] R. Eliezer

---

Soloveitchik also suggests this distinction between before *Shabbat* and on *Shabbat*. He discusses the topic in a letter written to Dr. Samuel Belkin addressing the question of whether rabbinical students should agree to serve as chaplains in the U.S. army during the Korean War, since they would likely be required to violate *Shabbat* as a result (see *Community, Covenant and Commitment*, ed. R. Nathaniel Helfgot, New York: Ktav Publishing House, 2005, pp. 23–60).

3. Another explanation, offered by R. Joseph B. Soloveitchik (*Community, Covenant and Commitment*, ibid.; *Divrei Ha-Rav* p. 172), is that Ba'al Ha-Ma'or's stringency with regard to circumcision is a unique detail of that *mitzvah*. In particular, circumcision itself does not override *Shabbat* if other ancillary requirements of the circumcision, such as bathing the infant in hot water, cannot be performed without violating *Shabbat*. However, in general, Ba'al Ha-Ma'or's leniency applies to any situation, and generally, one may intentionally enter a situation of *pikuach nefesh* on *Shabbat* if doing so in order to perform a *mitzvah*.

37 248:12.

38 *Orach Chayyim* 248:13.

39 *Eshel Avraham* to *Magen Avraham* 248:14.

40 *Shevitat Ha-Yam* ch. 3, p. 20.

41 *Minchat Shlomo*, 7:2.

42 Cited in *Nishmat Avraham*, *Orach Chayyim*, 248:2, p. 194.

43 In particular, R. Auerbach writes that one is permitted to defend oneself against a robber, even though this might lead the robber to threaten to kill the homeowner, forcing the homeowner to kill the intruder in self-defense. R. Neuwirth argues that in a case of a diabetic woman who, if she became pregnant, would then need to violate *Shabbat* with significantly greater frequency to inject herself with insulin, there is significant room for leniency, especially given the importance of the *mitzvah* of populating the world. *Nishmat Avraham* (ibid.) records that he asked R. Neuwirth how this *mitzvah* would override the prohibition of entering a situation of *pikuach nefesh*, given that *Mishnah Berurah* explicitly mentioned this prohibition in the context of an important *mitzvah*, traveling to Israel: he ruled that one may not set out to travel to Israel before *Shabbat* since one will certainly need to violate *Shabbat*, and one may not enter a certain *pikuach nefesh* situation even for a *mitzvah*. R. Neuwirth replied that the *mitzvah* of populating the world is more important than even that of moving to Israel, and as such all would

Waldenberg[44] seems to rely on the lenient opinion while discussing whether one can perform surgery on Thursday or Friday when it can be delayed safely until after *Shabbat*. He writes that one may perform the surgery even though one will then need to violate *Shabbat* for *pikuach nefesh* reasons, since performing the surgery is a *mitzvah*. He also notes that even if one holds like the more stringent opinion, that one may not enter a certain *pikuach nefesh* situation willingly, even for a *mitzvah*, this stringency is only rabbinic in nature, and perhaps Chazal would have suspended the rabbinic prohibition in a case of great pain experienced by the patient requiring surgery. He argues, citing *Tzemach Tzedek*,[45] that the prohibition is only a rabbinic one[46] since otherwise there should be no distinction between a case in which one is certain one will face a *pikuach nefesh* situation and a case in which one is only nearly certain.[47]

---

agree that this woman could become pregnant. It is unclear, though, which *mitzvah*-related situations R. Neuwirth would include in this dispensation.

44   *Tzitz Eliezer*, 12:43.

45   *Yoreh De'ah* 92.

46   R. Moshe Feinstein (*Iggerot Moshe, Orach Chayyim*, 1:127) also assumes the prohibition is a rabbinic one.

47   R. Hershel Schachter (*Be-Ikvei Ha-Tzon*, ch. 9) argues that the prohibition is, in fact, a Torah prohibition. He explains that the prohibition can be better understood by comparing it to a different area of *halakhah*, that of mixtures of forbidden and permitted food. In this area, there are halakhic differences between solid food and liquid food. The rationale behind these differences is explained by R. Shlomo Kluger (*Cheshek Shlomo* to *Bekhorot* 23b). He notes that when one liquid is mixed in with another liquid, the first liquid is essentially a nonentity since it is indistinguishable. On the other hand, solids are distinct, visible entities, and when one solid is mixed with another solid, the first solid is considered extant and retains its identity to a limited extent. This distinction explains several halakhic differences between solids and liquids. As one example of such a difference, Rama (*Orach Chayyim*, 447:4) notes that if prohibited food falls into permitted food and is less than one-sixtieth of the mixture, the entire mixture is permitted. However, if more prohibited food falls into the mixture, such that the total amount of prohibited food is more than one-sixtieth of the mixture, the status of the mixture depends on whether the food is solid or liquid. If the food is solid, the mixture is prohibited, presumably because the initial prohibited food was never fully nullified but retained its identity, and its identity was "awakened" with the added prohibited food. If the food is liquid, the mixture is permitted, presumably because the initial food lost its identity when it was added to the mixture, and so it cannot be "reawakened" with the addition of new prohibited liquid. A second difference between solids and liquids is that the prohibition of intentionally mixing prohibited food into permitted food to nullify it is a Torah prohibition for solid food according to some authorities (see *Noda Be-Yehudah*, responsa, *Mahadura Tinyana, Yoreh De'ah* 45, and cited in *Pitchei Teshuvah, Yoreh De'ah*,

He also writes elsewhere[48] that he interprets *Shulchan Arukh* and Rama to agree that one may willingly enter even a certain *pikuach nefesh* situation in a case of a *mitzvah* or more than three days before *Shabbat*, and he himself rules in accordance with this leniency.

It would be very important in our discussion to ascertain whether a situation of *mitzvah* allows one to create a situation of *pikuach nefesh* on *Shabbat*. This is because Rama writes[49] that in regard to this question, the scope of what is considered a *mitzvah* is broadened to include even earning a living or going out to greet a friend, and to exclude only one who is going on a trip for pleasure. Certainly, therefore, one who intends to work in the hospital on *Shabbat* would be considered to be performing several *mitzvot*, including saving lives, healing the sick and earning a living. Thus, if one holds like the lenient opinion, it would seem that one would not have to be concerned about willingly entering a *pikuach nefesh* situation on *Shabbat*, while if one holds like the stringent opinion, one would be prohibited to work in the hospital on *Shabbat* since one is willingly entering a case of certain *pikuach nefesh*.

R. Hershel Schachter[50] cites this discussion in reference to choosing a residency program and argues that for this reason, as well as others which will be outlined below, it is prohibited for a medical student to accept a residency position which does not accommodate *Shabbat*. Since the medical student is entering a situation of certain *pikuach nefesh*, given that he or she will be forced to violate *Shabbat* to treat non-Jewish patients in order to avoid creating life-threatening *eivah*, it is prohibited for the medical student to put himself or herself in this situation. This consideration would not apply, however, if the majority of the patients in the hospital were *Shabbat* observers, such that one would

---

99:3; see also Ra'ah, *Bedek Ha-Bayit*, 4:1 s.v. *be-inyan noten ta'am lifgam*), but a rabbinic prohibition for liquid food according to all opinions.

R. Schachter argues that intentionally entering a situation of *pikuach nefesh* on *Shabbat* is similar to mixing solid prohibited food into solid permitted food, since the prohibition of violating *Shabbat* does not disappear entirely when there is a *pikuach nefesh* situation, only that we permit violating *Shabbat* in this situation. Therefore, intentionally entering a *pikuach nefesh* situation on *Shabbat* would be considered a Torah prohibition. R. Schachter adds that the reason there is a distinction between a *mitzvah* situation and a non-*mitzvah* situation, which would appear to suggest that this is a rabbinic prohibition, is that if one is engaged in the performance of a *mitzvah*, we do not consider one to have entered a situation of *pikuach nefesh*, but instead we consider the person to have entered a situation of *mitzvah* performance, that then resulted unintentionally in a *pikuach nefesh* situation which one is not responsible for having caused.

48 *Shevitat Ha-Yam* chapter 3.
49 *Orach Chayyim*, 248:4.
50 *Be-Ikvei Ha-Tzon*, ch. 9.

not be creating a *pikuach nefesh* situation, as the situation already exists regardless of whether the resident will be at the hospital.[51]

Hutrah vs. *Dechuyah*

Another relevant halakhic issue is whether *Shabbat* is considered *hutrah* or *dechuyah* with regard to *pikuach nefesh*. As we have discussed in the previous chapter, there is a longstanding debate in halakhic literature as to whether a life-threatening situation causes *Shabbat* to be *hutrah*, completely neglected in halakhic considerations, or *dechuyah*, overridden but still worthy of consideration whenever possible. Most modern-day halakhic authorities rule that *Shabbat* is considered *dechuyah* in a *pikuach nefesh* situation, such that whenever possible, one should minimize the extent of *Shabbat* violations even in a *pikuach nefesh* situation.

In reference to our topic, one might argue that if indeed *Shabbat* is considered *dechuyah*, this would mean that one may not be in the hospital or on call on *Shabbat* if it is possible for another non-Jewish physician to perform the necessary hospital duties. This would be true regardless of whether the patients in the hospital are Jewish, since with regard to all patients, we attempt to minimize the extent of *Shabbat* violation. R. Moshe Feinstein[52] writes, indeed, that a Jewish physician should avoid being in the hospital or being reachable by potential patients on *Shabbat* if there are other competent non-Jewish doctors who could tend to these patients' needs. He notes that this is actually the crux of the difference between deeming *Shabbat* as *dechuyah* or *hutrah* with regard to *pikuach nefesh*: if *Shabbat* is *dechuyah*, the doctor must treat the patient the same way he or she would treat the patient if *Shabbat*

---

51 Contrast this with the position of R. Shlomo Zalman Auerbach, mentioned earlier, that even if one patient in the hospital is Jewish, it is permissible (and advisable) to work in the hospital on *Shabbat* so as to take better care of this patient, and then, once there, the resident can take care of non-Jewish patients as well due to *eivah* which might escalate to *pikuach nefesh*. Interestingly, R. Schachter notes in an audio-recorded lecture given to observant Jewish nurses (available online at http://www.yutorah.org/lectures/lecture.cfm/773851) that a nurse (and presumably, a resident) may work on *Shabbat* in a hospital which was founded for the purpose of treating Jewish patients. If this is the case, it would be advisable, if one were entering a field in which *Shabbat*-accommodating residencies do not exist, to attempt to secure a spot at a hospital founded on behalf of Jews. Still, as noted below, R. Schachter cites other reasons why a resident should not work in the hospital on *Shabbat*, so he might still prohibit this course of action.

52 *Iggerot Moshe, Orach Chayyim* 4:79.

were *hutrah*, but the doctor must also avoid having any patients come to him or her on *Shabbat* in the first place.[53]

While R. Feinstein clearly states that a Jewish physician should avoid being in the hospital on *Shabbat*, it appears that he does not believe that one must go so far as to not accept a position at a residency program where he or she will be assigned call on *Shabbat*. Indeed, in the same responsum, R. Feinstein discusses what one should do if one is forced to be on call in the hospital on *Shabbat*, implying that he believes one may accept a residency position where one might be in such a position. Additionally, as noted earlier,[54] R. Feinstein is cited by R. Moshe Tendler and Dr. Fred Rosner as ruling that one may accept a residency position at the program where one will receive the best training, provided that one will not violate *Shabbat* in any unauthorized way.

Similarly, R. Shlomo Zalman Auerbach appears not to consider the *dechuyah* position to imply that one should avoid working in a hospital on *Shabbat* in any situation if another physician is available. While he argues (as discussed above) that one must avoid working in the hospital on *Shabbat* if it will mean the violation of *Shabbat* in order to avoid *eivah*, he notes a possible caveat: if there is even one Jewish patient in the hospital, R. Auerbach writes[55] that it is preferable for the Jewish resident to remain in the hospital, since he or she will take better care of the Jewish patient. This does not mean that R. Auerbach permits one to accept a residency position which is not *Shabbat*-accommodating. Indeed, the dispensation seems only to apply if the resident notices on Friday afternoon that there is a Jewish patient in the hospital, and R. Auerbach does not seem to allow one to assume in advance that there will be a Jewish patient in the hospital. However, given that one may remain in the hospital if there is a Jewish patient, even if a non-Jewish doctor could cover the shift, it appears that working in the hospital is not contrary to the *dechuyah* position.[56]

---

53 R. Asher Weiss (*Minchat Asher*, Yitro, ch. 33) writes that even if we accepted the *hutrah* position, a doctor should still avoid working in a hospital on *Shabbat* if possible, since the doctor should attempt to fulfill the *mitzvot* of *Shabbat* to the greatest extent possible.

54 See footnote 15.

55 *Shemirat Shabbat Ke-Hilkhatah*, 40:65**; see notes to this footnote in volume 3.

56 In other contexts, R. Auerbach writes that the *dechuyah* position does not imply that one must avoid violating *Shabbat* at all costs. In particular, R. Auerbach writes (*Shemirat Shabbat Ke-Hilkhatah* 19:20; *Moriah*, Sivan–Tammuz 5731, pp. 10–19) that one is not required to endure major inconvenience in order to avoid violating *Shabbat*. He provides several examples:
   - Hospital staff may cook food for a sick patient on *Shabbat*, rather than give the patients food that they brought for themselves to eat.

R. Hershel Schachter[57] argues that the *dechuyah* position will pose a difficulty to a medical student wishing to accept a residency position which does not accommodate *Shabbat*. He cites *Chatam Sofer*,[58] who writes that a *kohen* may not accept the responsibility to treat dying patients when another competent, non-*kohen* physician can accept this responsibility. *Chatam Sofer* explains that while *pikuach nefesh* overrides the prohibition of a *kohen* coming in contact with the dead, this prohibition is only *dechuyah*, and not *hutrah*, with respect to *pikuach nefesh*. Therefore, in an emergency situation, a *kohen* is certainly permitted to treat a dying patient, even if other physicians are available, since the emergency situation warrants attention from whoever can provide it. However, this license does not allow the *kohen* to accept the responsibility of being the default physician when a patient's life is in danger.[59] R. Schachter concludes from *Chatam Sofer*'s ruling that one may not put oneself in a position where one will be the resident on call on *Shabbat*, given that *Shabbat* is *dechuyah* and not *hutrah*, if other competent residents are available to perform the necessary duties.[60]

- One may boil water or turn on a light for a sick patient, rather than wake a neighbor who has already prepared boiled water or has a lit lamp.
- One may fix downed power lines on *Shabbat*, rather than stationing someone next to the power lines over *Shabbat* to ensure safety.

These examples demonstrate that though *Shabbat* may be *dechuyah* in *pikuach nefesh* situations, one may use the dispensation of *pikuach nefesh* to perform *melakhah* even if there is an alternative, if the alternative is inconvenient. This may also be relevant with regard to a physician who knows he or she will need to return to the hospital on *Shabbat* morning but wants to go home before *Shabbat*, despite the inevitability of having to violate *Shabbat* to return to the hospital.

57 *Be-Ikvei Ha-Tzon* ch. 9.

58 Responsa *Yoreh De'ah* 338.

59 *Chatam Sofer* in fact permits a *kohen* to train to become a physician in the first place, since this training itself is permitted, and if later the *kohen* finds himself in a position where he must risk contact with the dead, this will then be permitted at that time. The question of whether contemporary *kohanim* may train to become doctors is more complex than *Chatam Sofer*'s case, since today medical students participate in an anatomy course where they must inevitably come in contact with cadavers for no immediate medical purpose.

60 R. Schachter notes a possible objection to *Chatam Sofer*'s ruling from *Pitchei Teshuvah* (*Yoreh De'ah* 370:1) who argues that perhaps, even if there are other equally competent physicians available, the *kohen* should still accept the responsibility of treating dying patients because of the principle "*lo mi-kol adam zokheh adam lehitrape'ot*," "a person might not be healed by every other person." This principle suggests that the *kohen* should accept the responsibility of treating dying patients because, ultimately, it might be the case that only this *kohen* proves capable of successfully healing a given

Violating a Positive Commandment

R. Schachter also raises the concern that working in a hospital on *Shabbat* for *pikuach nefesh* might be the violation of a positive commandment, *"u-vayom ha-shevi'i tishbot,"* "On the seventh day you shall rest."[61] In addition to all the *melakhot* which one is forbidden to perform on *Shabbat*, there is an additional obligation, *shabbaton*, dictating that one is to rest on *Shabbat* by abstaining from *melakhah*. He cites Ramban[62] who writes that fulfillment of the *mitzvah* of *shabbaton* requires that one not even work on *Shabbat* in ways that are not specifically *melakhot*. Ramban notes that one could easily work as usual on *Shabbat* without ever violating a *melakhah*, carrying produce from one area to another in a walled city, selling wares or exchanging money. This would be completely antithetical to the spirit of *Shabbat*, which is intended as a day of rest. Therefore, the Torah states that, as part of the *mitzvah* of *shabbaton*, one must refrain from doing one's normal work on *Shabbat*. *Chatam Sofer*[63] echoes Ramban and states emphatically that one may not keep one's shop open on *Shabbat*. R. Schachter argues that this law would apply to a physician as well, even if he or she does not violate any Torah or rabbinic law on *Shabbat*. However, he notes that because the issue at hand is a positive commandment, this might allow for some leniency. For a negative commandment, one is required to forfeit all of one's assets to avoid violating the commandment,[64] whereas one is not required to spend as much in order to fulfill a positive commandment.[65] He notes that R. Moshe Feinstein[66] allows one to forgo a positive commandment if this is required in order to earn a living. Therefore, it would appear that if one is required to forgo the *mitzvah* of *shabbaton* in order to complete residency and become licensed as a physician, one would be permitted to do so.

Aside from the general concern of not fulfilling the *mitzvah* of *shabbaton* due to working on *Shabbat*, R. Yitzchak Zilberstein[67] raises an additional specific concern relating to acts of *pikuach nefesh*. R.

---

patient. (See discussion of this principle later in this chapter.) R. Schachter disputes *Pitchei Teshuvah*'s assertion, arguing that this principle applies only in the realm of vows, where we allow one who vowed not to benefit from a certain person to receive medical treatment from that person, since that individual might be uniquely capable of healing him or her, and it is assumed that the vow was not intended to include this type of benefit.

61 Exodus 34:21.
62 Leviticus 23:24.
63 *Choshen Mishpat*, 195.
64 Rama, *Yoreh De'ah*, 157:1.
65 Rama, *Orach Chayyim*, 656:1.
66 *Iggerot Moshe, Choshen Mishpat*, 1:93; *Even Ha-Ezer* 1:97.
67 *Torat Ha-Yoledet*, ch. 59, pp. 399–401.

Zilberstein raises the possibility that a doctor who violates *Shabbat*, even if his or her *melakhot* for the sake of *pikuach nefesh* would be permitted, would not be fulfilling the obligation of *shabbaton*.[68] However,

68 The basis for this suggestion is a comment by R. Shimon Shkop to explain a difficulty that arises in understanding a discussion in the Gemara. The Gemara (*Ketuvot* 3b) notes that the original custom was for a bride and groom to get married on Wednesday, but this eventually posed a "danger," and the custom changed so that they would get married on Tuesday instead. To explain what this "danger" might have been, Rabbah notes that the local ruler made an edict that a woman who got married on Wednesday would be forced to first cohabit with the ruler. The Gemara challenges this explanation, stating that this would not be considered a "danger," since the cohabitation with the ruler was not prohibited since it was forced upon the woman and is categorized as *ones*, an act committed under duress. (It appears, based on his discussion, that R. Shimon Shkop translates *ones* as "an act committed under duress," but it could be alternatively translated as referring specifically to rape.) The Gemara concludes that perhaps some young women would be especially modest and would rather give up their lives than submit to this forced cohabitation, and thus the custom of getting married on Wednesday would become dangerous.
    R. Shimon Shkop (cited in R. Shmuel Rozovsky's *Chiddushei Rabbi Shmuel, Ketuvot, siman* 4) explains that this could not be merely a case of duress, since one is not permitted to willingly create a situation where one will be forced to violate a prohibition due to duress, and it must be a situation of *pikuach nefesh*, which one is permitted to create. However, he still questions this resolution, since, as noted earlier, Ba'al Ha-Ma'or prohibits intentionally creating a situation of *pikuach nefesh* on *Shabbat*. He therefore explains that Ba'al Ha-Ma'or does not believe that one is prohibited from creating a situation where one will violate a negative commandment because of *pikuach nefesh*. Indeed, in such a situation, one has actually not violated the negative commandment at all, since one may violate almost any negative commandment to avoid danger to life. Rather, Ba'al Ha-Ma'or's ruling is based on the fact that one who violates *Shabbat* due to *pikuach nefesh* is also failing to fulfill the positive commandment of *shabbaton*, and one is prohibited from intentionally creating a situation whereby one is unable to fulfill a specific positive commandment. (As another example of this, R. Shimon Shkop notes that the Gemara in *Yevamot* 26a states that one is not allowed to intentionally circumvent the *mitzvah* of *yibum*.) This concern would not apply in the case of a woman being taken by the local ruler, since there is no positive commandment in that case.
    Based on this comment of R. Shimon Shkop, R. Zilberstein suggests that a doctor might be required to avoid working in the hospital on *Shabbat* since otherwise one is entering a situation in which one will not be able to fulfill the *mitzvah* of *shabbaton*. However, he cites both R. Yosef Shalom Elyashiv and R. Chaim Pinchas Scheinberg who explain that this is not the case. R. Elyashiv notes that just as one who violates *Shabbat* to perform a circumcision or to serve in the *Beit Ha-Mikdash* does not fail to fulfill the obligation of *shabbaton*, one who violates *Shabbat* for *pikuach nefesh*, which is also

he cites R. Yosef Shalom Elyashiv and R. Chaim Pinchas Scheinberg who both rule that this is not a concern (see earlier footnote).

Becoming Accustomed to Violating *Shabbat*

A concern that a medical student must consider when applying for a spot at a residency program that does not accommodate *Shabbat* is that he or she will constantly have to violate *Shabbat*, though in permitted ways, and that this might make an indelible imprint on his or her habits. Certainly, as explained earlier, not all *melakhot* may be performed on *Shabbat* for an ill person, and one must be careful to ensure that one does not, out of habit, perform *melakhot* which are not permitted on behalf of a patient on *Shabbat*. Even more disconcerting is that one might become so accustomed to violating *Shabbat* in the hospital that one might forget it is *Shabbat* and perform *melakhot* that are completely

---

an obligatory *mitzvah*, does not fail to fulfill the obligation of *shabbaton*. Instead, R. Elyashiv suggests that Ba'al Ha-Ma'or only believes that one fails to fulfill the obligation of *shabbaton* when the need to violate *Shabbat* is incidental to the *mitzvah*, such as in a case where the hot water needed for the circumcised infant spills. Since it is possible to circumcise an infant on *Shabbat* without heating up water, one who does heat up water for this purpose on *Shabbat* fails to fulfill the obligation of *shabbaton*. However, the *mitzvah* of *pikuach nefesh* for a patient on *Shabbat*, by definition, requires the performance of *melakhah* on behalf of the patient. Therefore, just as circumcision and service in the *Beit Ha-Mikdash* do not cause one to fail to fulfill the obligation of *shabbaton*, similarly, one still fulfills the *mitzvah* of *shabbaton* if one performs *melakhah* for *pikuach nefesh*. For this reason, R. Elyashiv rules that a physician (in a Jewish hospital in Israel) should not specifically avoid working in the hospital on *Shabbat* if another religious physician would be required to take his or her place.

R. Scheinberg disagrees with R. Elyashiv's reasoning but comes to the same conclusion. He argues that in contrast to circumcision or service in the *Beit Ha-Mikdash*, the *mitzvah* of *pikuach nefesh* is a general one, and does not instruct that a particular medical procedure is warranted on *Shabbat*. Thus, one might conclude that if one violates *Shabbat* to perform a lifesaving act, one has indeed failed to fulfill one's obligation of *shabbaton*, and should avoid doing so unless no one else is available. R. Scheinberg also notes that both circumcision and service in the *Beit Ha-Mikdash* must necessarily be performed on *Shabbat*. Some infants will necessarily reach the eighth day of life on *Shabbat* and require circumcision, and service in the *Beit Ha-Mikdash* must be performed every day, including *Shabbat*. However, there may never be a need for a Jewish physician to violate *Shabbat* for *pikuach nefesh*, since other options might be available, including asking a non-Jewish physician to perform *melakhah*. Thus, violating *Shabbat* for *pikuach nefesh* is not comparable to circumcision and service in the *Beit Ha-Mikdash*, and might cause one to fail to fulfill the obligation of *shabbaton*.

unrelated to patient care, for example, turning on the light in the resident call room.[69]

R. Hershel Schachter[70] suggests that this concern itself may be a reason to prohibit regularly violating *Shabbat* due to *pikuach nefesh*. He points to the Gemara[71] which discusses the possibility of reciting *kiddush* on *Yom Kippur*. Though one would be prohibited from drinking the wine oneself, the Gemara suggests the option of giving the wine to a child to drink. However, the Gemara rejects this possibility, since there is a concern that the child, who has become accustomed to drinking wine on *Yom Kippur*, may become habituated (*"atei lemisrach"*) to drinking wine on *Yom Kippur* and may continue to do so after he or she has reached adulthood when drinking wine is prohibited. This, argues R. Schachter, is evidence that one is discouraged from adopting practices which are permitted in the current situation but may lead to habits which will cause one to violate a prohibition.[72]

69 R. Yitzchak Zilberstein (*Torat Ha-Yoledet*, pp. 9–11) uses this observation to explain why *Sefer Chasidim* (*siman* 793) advises praying on behalf of a pregnant woman that she not go into labor on *Shabbat*. R. Zilberstein notes that there is obviously no prohibition of violating *Shabbat* on behalf of a woman in labor to ensure that she delivers safely. Therefore, he suggests that the prayer is due to the concern that one might violate *Shabbat* in a way which is not permitted on *Shabbat* since, in one's anxious haste, one is liable to violate *Shabbat* in a way which is not permitted according to *halakhah*.
70 *Be-Ikvei Ha-Tzon*, ch. 9.
71 *Eruvin* 40b.
72 It appears that this problem is not mentioned by other authorities in referencing the issue of working in a hospital on *Shabbat*. These authorities might believe that the concern of *"atei lemisrach"* is not applicable to this case. Indeed, it appears that when this concept is invoked in the Gemara, it is generally in reference to prohibiting children from performing actions which are prohibited to adults:
    • The Mishnah in *Bekhorot* (35a) relates a case in which children tied the tails of firstborn animals in a way which caused them to become blemished, and thus invalidated as firstborn sacrifices. Generally, when a firstborn animal becomes blemished accidentally, one is permitted to eat the animal. On the other hand, if the animal is blemished intentionally, one is not permitted to eat it, since such a dispensation would encourage one to continue causing animal blemishes, as it benefits the animal's owner who may eat the animal without bringing it as a sacrifice. The Gemara explains that though the children's actions are not considered intentional, Chazal still prohibited eating the animal in this case, since we wish to discourage children from causing blemishes to a firstborn animal. As this activity will eventually be prohibited when the children reach the age of *mitzvot*, we do not want children to be habituated to this activity, and so it is still prohibited to eat the animal in this case.

In addition to the more practical concern that one will become habituated to violating prohibitions, such that there may be a halakhic concern with encouraging such habituation, R. Schachter notes that there may be an even more fundamental halakhic problem with becoming accustomed to violating *Shabbat*. He notes that R. Avraham Yeshayahu Karelitz, author of *Chazon Ish*, distinguishes between *chillul Shabbat*, desecration of *Shabbat*, and *bittul Shabbat*, nullification of *Shabbat*. R. Karelitz argues that while it is permitted and mandated to violate *Shabbat* (*chillul Shabbat*) in a case of *pikuach nefesh*, *bittul Shabbat*, acting in a way that shows indifference to *Shabbat*, is still prohibited even for *pikuach nefesh*. It is recounted[73] that in the years after the Holocaust, Jewish groups were flown out from Palestine, under the auspices of the United Nations, to rescue Jews who had remained in hiding places during the war. A situation arose in which the plane was required to take off on *Shabbat*, and R. Karelitz ruled that it was permitted to do so because

---

- The Gemara in *Shabbat* (139a) discusses whether one is permitted to plant hops in a vineyard, or if this is considered *kilayim*, the prohibited planting of grain crops in a vineyard. The Gemara suggests that many rabbis prohibited planting hops in a vineyard, but adds that R. Mesharshaya would give hops to a non-Jewish child to plant in a vineyard. The Gemara explains that he did not allow a Jewish child to do this, lest the child become habituated to planting *kilayim*.
- The Gemara in Bava *Metzia* (75a) cites an opinion that one may lend money with interest to one's children in order that they understand the concept of interest and will be discouraged from wanting to lend with interest in the future (see Rashi ad loc). This opinion is rejected, since we do not want the children to become habituated to lending with interest, which will be forbidden to them once they reach the age of *mitzvot*.

Each of these cases appears to be based fundamentally on the concern that we must not educate children to perform actions which are prohibited, since they may not understand that the actions which they will come to perform habitually are actually prohibited. This would appear different from the case of the resident, who understands that the action is normally prohibited on *Shabbat* and is only permitted due to *pikuach nefesh*.

One case that appears in the Gemara which does not involve children regards a person who cannot find an *etrog* on *Sukkot*. The Gemara (*Sukkah* 31b) states that one should not use another fruit instead of an *etrog*, even though this could potentially remind the person that an *etrog* should be sought in the future when possible, because we are afraid that one will become habituated to bringing the alternate fruit. Even though this case does appear to be more similar to the case of violating *Shabbat* for an ill patient, those authorities who do not cite habituation as a concern may believe that the case of violating *Shabbat* is different, since the action one is doing is fundamentally permitted and even mandated, whereas using a different fruit instead of an *etrog* fulfills no *mitzvah* at all and has no purpose.

73 See *Pe'er Ha-Dor*, vol. 2, pp. 92–93.

of *pikuach nefesh*. However, when a second identical situation arose, he strongly prohibited leaving on *Shabbat*. He explained that he had originally permitted flying on *Shabbat* due to *pikuach nefesh*, but it now surfaced that those who were planning the missions no longer took *Shabbat* into consideration when making their plans. Therefore, flying on *Shabbat* would amount to *bittul Shabbat*, wherein *Shabbat* is no longer part of one's considerations, and this is prohibited even for *pikuach nefesh*.

R. Karelitz's explanation for this distinction[74] is that while most Torah prohibitions may be violated to save a life, this is not true of the prohibition of desecrating God's name, *chillul Hashem,* for which one must give up one's life to avoid violating. The complete uprooting of a *mitzvah*, argues R. Karelitz, is a form of *chillul Hashem.* As an example, R. Karelitz notes that *Noda Be-Yehudah* and *Chatam Sofer* prohibited autopsies, even though the knowledge gained from autopsies might save a future patient, because one may only violate prohibitions to save the life of someone who is currently in danger, not a hypothetical future patient. However, one might argue that autopsies frequently result in saving lives, and we should still violate several prohibitions in performing an autopsy in order to save those lives. R. Karelitz concludes that the authorities who prohibited this felt that a permissive ruling would completely negate the prohibition of performing an autopsy, such that it would be completely unobserved, given that every autopsy could provide medical information which could be useful in some hypothetical situation. The complete uprooting of the prohibition would be a form of *chillul Hashem.* Therefore, these authorities felt that one may not perform an autopsy, even if it means saving lives, unless there is a definite patient whose life might be saved by the autopsy.[75]

R. Schachter explains that a resident who works consistently on *Shabbat* is likely to perform his or her duties the same way he or she does during the week. This typically includes performing *melakhot* on the basis of unlikely concerns of *pikuach nefesh*, in an attempt to avoid any possible life-threatening situations. However, many of these scenarios are very unlikely, and would not independently warrant violating *Shabbat* were it not for the fact that the patient is already categorized as dangerously ill.[76] Therefore, tending to these concerns on *Shabbat* on

74 See *Pe'er Ha-Dor*, vol. 3, pp. 185–186.
75 The distinction between a definite patient and a future, hypothetical one is explained by R. Karelitz in *Chazon Ish* (*Ohalot* 22:32) to be a matter of probability: the likelihood that a future patient will benefit from the information gained by this autopsy is very remote, and therefore does not warrant violation of the prohibition.
76 R. Schachter notes that the dispensation to tend to even unlikely concerns of *pikuach nefesh* on *Shabbat* stems from the dispensation to heal the patient of mortal illnesses that are already known. By analogy, he notes that when checking a recently slaughtered animal for lung adhesions, one

a regular basis, without concern for whether it is *Shabbat* or a weekday, may also be a concern of *bittul Shabbat*, and would be prohibited.

Other authorities appear not to share R. Schachter's concern. They may not adopt R. Karelitz's *bittul Shabbat* framework, or they may not believe that consistently working on *Shabbat* to prevent even unlikely concerns of *pikuach nefesh* is a problem of *bittul Shabbat*. For example, *Nishmat Avraham* advises that in deciding whether to perform a *melakhah* on *Shabbat*, one should assess whether it would be medically advisable to perform this *melakhah* in treating the patient during the weekday. This suggests that one should treat a patient on *Shabbat* the same way one would during the week, even including unlikely concerns of *pikuach nefesh*.

Regardless, R. Schachter's concern that one not become accustomed to violating *Shabbat*, for practical or fundamental concerns, underscores the necessity of being very careful when performing *melakhah* on *Shabbat* to ensure that it does not become part of one's routine.

Residency, *Shabbat*, and Jewish Values

In addition to halakhic concerns raised above, it is important to consider what Jewish non-legal sources might say about whether a Jewish medical student should apply for a residency which will not accommodate *Shabbat*. To be clear, if *halakhah* forbids working in a hospital on *Shabbat*, as is suggested by several sources discussed above, then regardless of whether there might be other Jewish values which support working in the hospital on *Shabbat*, it would be unequivocally prohibited to do so. However, if there is no fundamental prohibition of working in a hospital on *Shabbat*, and there would be no concern that one will violate *halakhah* while working in a hospital, one could then consider whether working in a hospital on *Shabbat* would be viewed positively or negatively in Jewish thought. We will examine a number of issues which might be related to working in a hospital on *Shabbat*, both those advocating for and against this practice, and examine how traditional Jewish sources might relate to these issues.

---

also checks for other *tereifot*, defects which render the animal non-kosher, even though one is normally not required to check for such defects. Once one is already checking for lung adhesions, which are more common and thus require checking, one is also required to check for other defects. Similarly, when treating a patient for a mortal illness which the physician already knows about, he or she is also permitted to tend to other unlikely concerns of *pikuach nefesh*.

Jewish Values Promoted by *Shabbat*-Accommodating Programs

The Spirit of *Shabbat*

As mentioned earlier, Ramban[77] writes that the Torah commands us to rest on *Shabbat*, refraining even from activities which are technically not *melakhot* but which contravene the spirit of the day. Ramban argues that refraining from such activities is included under the *mitzvah* of *shabbaton*, resting on *Shabbat*. Ramban notes that, according to Torah law only, it would be theoretically possible to run one's business on *Shabbat* by performing only actions which are not *melakhot* and asking non-Jews to do actions which are *melakhot*. Therefore, the Torah added that one must rest on *Shabbat*, reserving it for resting and cessation of work. *Chatam Sofer*,[78] citing this statement of Ramban, writes that keeping one's shop open on *Shabbat* is a violation of *Shabbat*. He notes that Nechemiah, leader of the Jewish people during the rebuilding of Jerusalem after the first exile, made great efforts to dissuade the Jews from keeping their shops open on *Shabbat*.[79]

It is apparent from Ramban's commentary that working on *Shabbat*, even without performing *melakhah*, is to be viewed negatively, and as a violation of a positive commandment in the Torah. However, it is equally apparent that treating ill patients would be an exception to this category; indeed, entire works have been written about how a physician should treat patients in the hospital on *Shabbat*. Still, it might be argued that if one can avoid working in the hospital on *Shabbat*, one should do so, as the spirit of the laws of *Shabbat* suggests that one should spend *Shabbat* resting and engaging in spiritual endeavors.

Shabbat is, without question, a pillar of Jewish observance. Jews throughout history have made numerous sacrifices to observe *Shabbat*. While the nature of the resident's duties in the hospital may allow for an exception to the requirement to abstain from work on *Shabbat*, the place of *Shabbat* in Jewish history and Jewish thought should certainly give the medical student pause as he or she makes a decision regarding residency.

Effect on Family

Medical students with families must be especially careful if they are considering accepting a residency position which does not accommodate *Shabbat*. *Shabbat* is traditionally a time to spend with family, and one who regularly works in the hospital on *Shabbat* may lose valuable

---

77 Leviticus 23:24.
78 Responsa, *Choshen Mishpat* 195.
79 Nechemiah 13:14–22.

family time. In Jewish sources, *Shabbat* is noted as a special time for married couples to spend time with each other. [80]

Furthermore, a resident with children must be very careful to ensure that the children understand the value of *Shabbat* and realize that their parents also value *Shabbat*. A child who knows that his or her parent always works on *Shabbat* may not internalize the importance of *Shabbat*, and the parents must therefore make sure that their children know that *Shabbat* observance is important to them.

Jewish Values Which May Favor Choosing a Residency Program Which Does Not Accommodate *Shabbat*

Choosing One's Preferred Medical Specialty

For many medical students, the reason for choosing a residency program that does not accommodate *Shabbat* observance is that the student is interested in a medical specialty for which no such programs exist, such as surgery, ophthalmology, or obstetrics/gynecology. If one is interested in such a field, and can choose a residency program which does not accommodate *Shabbat* but in which one will be able to observe *Shabbat* as we have outlined above, is there some Jewish value to choosing the field which appeals to one's interests?

One Gemara[81] suggests that indeed, God designed the world so that different people would have different career interests, making each person find a particular career appealing. Rashi[82] adds that God did this so as to ensure that the world would not be lacking in people with a given career ability. Along similar lines, R. Bahya ibn Pakuda[83] writes that God creates each person with unique abilities that suit a given career path, just like He creates animals with features that enable them to survive in their natural habitat. Therefore, R. Bahya writes, one should choose the career which appears to naturally suit him or her, based on one's interests, abilities and temperament, trusting that God will arrange that this career will allow him or her to be successful. It would seem that there is a Jewish value to choose a career which appeals to one's interests, and that one who is passionate about a field with no *Shabbat*-accommodating residency programs might be justified in

---

80 *Shulchan Arukh* (*Orach Chayyim* 280:1) writes that marital intimacy is a fulfillment of the *mitzvah* of *oneg Shabbat*. He also adds that Torah scholars were accustomed to fulfilling their requirement of marital intimacy, as dictated by the *ketuvah*, on *Shabbat* (see *Ketuvot* 62b). *Bach* (*Orach Chayyim* 280) adds that one must be especially careful not to upset one's spouse on Friday night for this reason.

81 *Berakhot* 43b.

82 Ad loc, s.v. *yippah lo umanuto*.

83 *Hovot Ha-Levavot, Sha'ar Ha-Bitachon*, ch. 3.

choosing such a field, assuming that one is permitted to enter such a program, as discussed above.

Ensuring Observant Jewish Physicians in Each Medical Specialty

An additional value which might be gained by one working in a residency program which does not accommodate *Shabbat* is that entering a field without *Shabbat*-accommodating residencies might enable one to make a unique contribution to the Jewish community. One specific example is an infertility specialist who can appreciate the halakhic issues involved with *niddah* and how they affect fertility. Not only in this specific case, but in every specialty, unique contributions could be made by an observant Jewish physician, who might be able to tend to other Jews in need of medical services related to that specialty, with extra care and sensitivity for fellow Jews. This might be an additional reason to consider entering a specialty which does not have any *Shabbat*-accommodating residency programs.

Superior Medical Training

Many observant medical students wish to train in residency programs which do not accommodate *Shabbat* because these programs are perceived to provide better training for their residents. Medical students hope that their superior training will translate into their being more competent physicians. Does obtaining superior medical training possess value in Jewish thought?

One might suggest that this is related to the question of whether there is a *mitzvah* to learn medicine. There is a *mitzvah* for a physician to treat patients, based on the verse, "*ve-rappo yerappe*,"[84] but this does not necessarily mean that there is a *mitzvah* to *learn* medicine. However, one statement in the Gemara[85] suggests that this, too, may be a *mitzvah*. The Gemara recounts that R. Huna asked his son why he did not go to study with R. Chisda. His son explained that R. Chisda was teaching mundane matters regarding how one should act while relieving oneself to avoid health complications. R. Huna exclaimed that these were not mundane matters, but matters important to human life, which are of significant importance. Indeed, R. Yitzchak Herzog[86] writes that learning medicine is a *mitzvah* based on this Gemara, and *Levushei Mordekhai*[87] also appears to allude to this Gemara when writing that learning medicine is a *mitzvah*. R. Yaakov Breisch[88] also notes that learning medicine is a

---

84 Exodus 21:19.
85 *Shabbat* 82a.
86 Responsa, *Yoreh De'ah* (vol. 5), *siman* 145, p. 557.
87 Third edition, 29:2.
88 *Chelkat Ya'akov*, *Yoreh De'ah* 190.

mitzvah, and links this *mitzvah* to the *mitzvah* to heal the sick.[89] Aside from these authorities that argue that learning medicine is a *mitzvah*, many Jewish authorities throughout the ages have advocated for the study of medicine and assigned it positive value.[90] Another source, *Sefer Chasidim*,[91] radically suggests that one who can learn medicine and does not is held liable for the deaths of those whom one could have saved.

In contrast to these authorities, R. Moshe Feinstein[92] writes in two responsa that the study of medicine is not a *mitzvah*. He argues that although saving a life or healing a patient is a *mitzvah*, there is no *mitzvah* to become a doctor so that one will be equipped to then perform this *mitzvah*. As an analogy, he notes that while there is a *mitzvah* to give charity, there is no *mitzvah* to become wealthy so that one is able to give charity. Based on this argument, R. Feinstein prohibits a *kohen* to come in contact with cadavers in order to study medicine, and prohibits autopsies that will yield information important in future medical discoveries. It is not clear how R. Feinstein would relate to other sources we have discussed that appear to support the study of medicine.[93] Although R. Feinstein rejects the notion that studying medicine *per se* is a *mitzvah*, he nevertheless states that one should accept a position at a residency program which does not accommodate *Shabbat*, as long as one is certain that one will not violate *Shabbat* when this is not permitted by Jewish law, because one should attempt to train in the hospital where one will be best trained.[94] He is also cited as ruling that one may attend a lecture or medical conference on *Shabbat* if he or she will not violate *Shabbat* in doing so and the lecture or conference will significantly impact his or her mastery of medicine.[95] Thus, R. Feinstein clearly maintains that there is positive value to becoming the most competent physician possible even though one does not technically fulfill a *mitzvah* through the training process.

---

89 *Levushei Mordekhai* and R. Breisch also both write that learning medicine may also be a *mitzvah* because medicine is a profession, and study of any profession is considered a *mitzvah*.

90 See Dr. Avraham Steinberg, "*Be-din mitzvat limmud refuah*," *Assia* vol. 2, pp. 16–20.

91 1469.

92 *Iggerot Moshe, Yoreh De'ah* 2:151; 3:155.

93 Dr. Avraham Steinberg (*Encyclopedia Hilkhatit Refu'it*, vol. 4, entry *limmud refuah*, p. 340, footnote 41) suggests that R. Feinstein may believe that there is a *mitzvah* to study medicine, but not such that it would override another prohibition (such as a *kohen* coming in contact with cadavers, or performing an autopsy).

94 Fred Rosner and Rabbi Moses D. Tendler, *Practical Medical Halacha*, New York: Feldheim, 1980, p. 116.

95 Ibid., pp. 114–115.

Although many sources ascribe positive value to the study of medicine, perhaps even suggesting that it is a *mitzvah*, it is evident that the *poskim* only marshal this as an important value to be given weight when there is no opposing halakhic concern. That is, studying medicine is *not* considered an act of *pikuach nefesh*, such that one can violate *Shabbat* in order to study medicine in case the acquired knowledge saves the life of a future patient. This is based on the principle introduced by *Noda Be-Yehudah*,[96] namely, that the principles of *pikuach nefesh* only apply when there is a *choleh lefaneinu*, an ill person present. For this reason, he prohibits performing an autopsy on the grounds that the medical information gleaned may help a future patient; an autopsy may only be performed, *Noda Be-Yehudah* asserts, if there is a patient present whose life will be saved by this information. Similarly, in our case, it is clear that the ability to save a future patient's life based on superior training one obtains in one's residency program does *not*, by itself, justify working in the hospital on *Shabbat*.[97] The only justification for working in a hospital on *Shabbat* is that one is saving patients *now*, not in the future.

In addition, although it would appear that there is positive value in obtaining the best clinical training possible, one should be sure that one is indeed sacrificing the spirit of *Shabbat* observance because one will be training in a program which will make him or her a more competent physician, rather than because one will be training in a prestigious program. Though it is possible that the program's prestige reflects its quality resident training, it is also possible that the prestige reflects the standard of care given to patients, or the prestige of the hospital's associated university. Prestige alone certainly does not justify working on *Shabbat*. Even if the training is indeed superior, one should carefully and honestly assess whether the improved training in the hospital which does not accommodate *Shabbat* is worth the loss of the spirit of *Shabbat* observance. As each situation is different, the medical student is advised to consult with a competent halakhic advisor who can guide him or her through this difficult decision.

Unique Ability in *Pikuach Nefesh*
From the foregoing discussion, it is quite clear that the only dispensation to work in a hospital on *Shabbat* is based on the fact that one's activities (the ones that may be performed on *Shabbat*) are classified as *pikuach nefesh*, saving a life. However, it would appear that if another person is available to cover one's shift on *Shabbat*, then the fact that one would be performing *pikuach nefesh* activities does

---

96   *Mahadura tinyana, Yoreh De'ah, siman* 210.
97   See *Be-Ikvei Ha-Tzon* 9:6, where R. Hershel Schachter makes this argument in regard to why one may not accept a spot in a residency program which does not accommodate *Shabbat*.

not mean that one should *prefer* to be involved in *pikuach nefesh* on *Shabbat*. The dispensation to perform *pikuach nefesh* on *Shabbat* only appears to permit and mandate such actions when warranted, not to encourage one to pursue being personally involved in *pikuach nefesh* activity on *Shabbat*. Thus, as discussed earlier, many authorities believe that *pikuach nefesh* is only *dechuyah* on *Shabbat*, and one should try to lessen the severity of the prohibition which one is transgressing on behalf of the patient, if this does not impact patient care.

However, some have suggested[98] that another principle related to *pikuach nefesh* might be operative in this case which would perhaps encourage one to pursue *pikuach nefesh* activities on *Shabbat*. The Yerushalmi[99] introduces an intriguing principle, "*lo mi-kol adam zokheh lehitrape'ot*," "One does not merit to be healed by every person." The context of this principle is a discussion of one who vows not to receive any benefit from a particular physician, and then falls ill. The Yerushalmi rules that even if other physicians are available to treat him, this specific physician may come to heal him, due to the principle of *lo mi-kol adam zokheh lehitrape'ot*. This principle is cited in many later works, and several *rishonim*[100] suggest that the Talmud Bavli also regards it to be true. Later, *Tur*[101] and *Shulchan Arukh*[102] cite this principle in order to demonstrate that a Jewish physician is required to treat a patient who comes to him or her for medical treatment.

The precise meaning of this principle, however, is debated. There are several explanations that are suggested (or assumed) by later authorities:

1. *Korban Ha-Edah*[103] suggests that the Yerushalmi's intent is that in a *pikuach nefesh* situation, we are sensitive to any possibility of threat to life, even a remote one. As such, each physician must be involved in treating the patient, in case other physicians are ultimately unable to find the cure for this patient.

2. R. Yaakov Breisch,[104] R. Moshe Feinstein,[105] and R. Eliezer Waldenberg[106] all write that one may violate *Shabbat* to bring a

---

98 See Rabbi Dr. Raymond Sultan and Dr. Sammy Sultan, "*Shomer-Shabbat Residency*," *The Journal of Halacha and Contemporary Society*, vol. LVIII (Spring 2009), pp. 45–59.

99 *Nedarim* 4:2.

100 Rosh, *Nedarim* 4:8; Ran, *Nedarim* 41b s.v. *ela refuat nefesh gufo*. *Ma'aseh Roke'ach* (*Nedarim* 6:8) argues that Rambam (ad loc) also maintains this principle.

101 *Yoreh De'ah* 336.

102 *Yoreh De'ah* 336:1.

103 *Nedarim* 4:2, s.v. *u-meshani*.

104 *Chelkat Ya'akov, Yoreh De'ah* 131.

105 *Iggerot Moshe, Orach Chayyim* 1:131.

106 *Tzitz Eliezer* 13:55.

patient's preferred physician to the hospital to treat the patient, based on *lo mi-kol adam zokheh lehitrape'ot*. Similarly, R. Shmuel Wosner[107] and R. Hershel Schachter[108] write that one may violate *Shabbat* to bring a more qualified physician. However, if the physicians are equal, there is no reason that both must be involved, and therefore, no prohibition may be violated to bring the second physician. According to these authorities, the Yerushalmi is teaching that one may violate *Shabbat* to bring another physician only if doing so would be of value to the patient. With regard to residents, therefore, it appears that there would be no advantage for an observant Jewish resident to work in the hospital on *Shabbat* if other residents can cover the shift since it is generally assumed that all residents are of equal ability with regard to medical treatment.

3.   Another explanation, mentioned by *Shevut Ya'akov*[109] and others, is that the Yerushalmi's principle is related to a statement in the Gemara[110] that when one becomes ill, it is predestined exactly how the illness will be cured and by whom it will be cured. Therefore, the Yerushalmi is suggesting that since a particular physician may be the one who is predestined to cure a given patient's illness, this physician must be involved in the patient's care, even in the case of a prohibition. However, even according to this explanation, it would appear that there may be no preference for the observant Jewish resident to work in the hospital on *Shabbat*. Since there is no way of knowing the predestined outcome of the patient's illness and which resident is destined to properly treat it, it is difficult to say that one should try to work in the hospital on *Shabbat* in case he or she is the correct physician, since it is equally possible that another resident who can cover the shift is the predestined physician. Indeed, *Alei Tamar*[111] writes that since there is no way of knowing who is the predestined healer, the patient should choose the physician with whom he or she feels most comfortable or who has successfully treated him or her before, as that is a sign which suggests that this will be the physician who will successfully treat him or her. There is thus no suggestion that an observant Jewish resident should attempt to shoulder the responsibility of treating patients on *Shabbat* if another resident is available.

It seems that according to many of the above authorities, the principle of *lo mi-kol adam zokheh lehitrape'ot* does not ultimately bear on the

---

107 *Shevet Ha-Levi*, 3:164.
108 *Be-Ikvei Ha-Tzon* 9:2.
109 1:86.
110 *Avodah Zarah* 55a.
111 On Yerushalmi, *Nedarim* 4:2, s.v. *lo mi-kol adam zokheh lehitrape'ot*.

question of whether there is a positive value associated with the observant Jewish physician being involved in *pikuach nefesh* on *Shabbat*.

Choosing Where One Will Live

A final factor which may motivate a medical student to choose residency programs that do not accommodate *Shabbat* is the geographic location of the residency programs which accommodate *Shabbat*. In some fields, there are residency programs that accommodate *Shabbat*, but they might be few in number and located in areas where the medical student may not want to live for several years. This may be because of proximity to family, a spouse's job, the presence of an observant Jewish community, or wanting to be near other similar Jews whom one might potentially date. These all are Jewish values – the *mitzvah* of honoring one's parents attests to the importance of family in Jewish law and thought; proximity to a Jewish community enables one to perform many *mitzvot*, such as *tefillah be-tzibbur*; and finding a person to marry is certainly an important value in Judaism. As mentioned earlier, each individual should discuss these factors with a competent halakhic advisor to determine the correct solution for himself or herself.

Working in a Non-*Shabbat*-Accommodating Program

If one does accept a position in a residency program that does not accommodate *Shabbat*, the issues we have discussed thus far will influence how one should conduct oneself with regard to being on call on *Shabbat*. Here, we will discuss the ramifications of the halakhic attitude toward *pikuach nefesh* with regard to how one should act when one is assigned call on *Shabbat*.

Switching Call

As discussed earlier, it is clear that a Jewish resident in a program which does not accommodate *Shabbat* must do his or her best to avoid working on *Shabbat* in the hospital. This is for several reasons:

1. According to most contemporary authorities, we consider *Shabbat* to be *dechuyah*, not *hutrah*, when it comes to *pikuach nefesh*. Thus, one must do one's utmost to avoid violating *Shabbat* in cases of *pikuach nefesh*, or to minimize the level of prohibition violated in treating the patient, as long as this does not risk endangering the patient in any way. R. Hershel Schachter, as discussed above, argues that this principle indicates that a Jewish medical student is not allowed to accept a residency program which does not accommodate *Shabbat*. This does not seem to be the opinion of other *poskim*, including R. Moshe Feinstein, who is cited as allowing a medical student to accept a residency program that does not accommodate

Shabbat. However, R. Feinstein writes clearly that because *Shabbat* is *dechuyah*, a Jewish resident should try to switch call so that he or she is not on call on *Shabbat*.

2. As discussed above, many contemporary authorities understand that the dispensation to violate *Shabbat* to save the life of a non-Jewish patient is based on the concern that if Jewish physicians did not do this, non-Jewish physicians would not properly treat Jewish patients, thus endangering Jewish lives. However, one could easily avoid this concern by not working in the hospital at all on *Shabbat*, thus not creating a situation where one would be required to violate *Shabbat* for the non-Jewish patient to avoid a potential future *pikuach nefesh* situation. For this reason, R. Yehoshua Neuwirth writes that a Jewish resident must offer to take extra shifts or pay a co-resident to switch call with him or her.[112]

112 R. Neuwirth does not indicate the extent of this ruling, that is, how many extra shifts would a Jewish resident be required to offer in order to convince the co-resident to work on *Shabbat*, or how much money would the Jewish resident have to offer the co-resident? With regard to extra shifts, it would seem that the Jewish resident should make a somewhat more-than-reasonable offer, i.e., switching two calls for one. If the resident offers to perform more extra shifts, it is likely that he or she will always have to make such an offer, given that word will travel that this resident is willing to offer this many shifts in order to avoid working on *Shabbat*. These extra shifts are likely to add up and become so overwhelming as to make the resident less capable of effectively managing patients, perhaps even endangering patients. It should be noted that the Accreditation Council for Graduate Medical Education (ACGME) policy (Common Program Requirements, VI.G.1; see https://www.acgme.org/acgmeweb/Portals/0/PFAssets/ProgramRequirements/CPRs2013.pdf) indicates that residents may not work for more than 80 hours per week, likely because working for more hours per week endangers the resident and his or her patients.

Regarding paying a co-resident to convince him or her to agree to a switch, it is hard to set a clear limit on how much must be paid. Although Rama (*Orach Chayyim*, 656:1) rules that one must spend one's entire fortune to avoid violating a negative commandment, that is not exactly the situation here, since when one violates *Shabbat* to treat a hospital patient, this action is permitted. We are merely discussing how much one should spend to avoid entering a situation where one will be permitted to violate *Shabbat*. This also does not seem to be similar to a positive commandment, for which *Mishnah Berurah* (656:8) cites Rabbeinu Yerucham (*Toledot Adam Ve-Chavvah*, *netiv* 13, *chelek* 3) who writes that one *must* spend up to one-tenth of one's assets if necessary, just like for *tzedakah*. Therefore, there may not be a prescribed amount that one must pay. Just as with offering to perform extra calls, offering any significant amount of money will likely cause other residents to expect that amount of money, so one should probably not offer more than a small amount of money.

3. As discussed above, there is a very real concern that working in the hospital on *Shabbat*, for permitted reasons, will lead one to become accustomed to violating *Shabbat* and perhaps even violating *Shabbat* when it is not permitted at all, such as at home. Each *Shabbat* which one does not work in the hospital reduces the likelihood of this outcome, both by reducing the total number of *Shabbatot* during which one works in the hospital as well as creating intervening "free" *Shabbatot* between those during which one is working so as to prevent habituation.

Because one is required to switch call to avoid working on *Shabbat* if one can, one should attempt to select a residency program in which the Friday night and Saturday calls are not the least desired calls in the schedule. If, for example, a given program's schedule makes Saturday night or Sunday calls less desirable than Friday night or Saturday calls, it will be significantly easier to switch calls with other residents without having to offer any other incentives. It is easy to find out which calls are considered better or worse by asking current residents in the program; one may need to contact the residents privately, rather than during the residency visit day, in order to obtain an honest answer.

Moreover, one must be extremely careful to show proper gratitude toward a co-resident who has offered to switch call so the Jewish resident can avoid working on *Shabbat*, even if, objectively, the trade favors the co-resident. One is absolutely not entitled to have one's religious needs accommodated, and it is extremely important to make a *kiddush Hashem* by showing gratitude toward a co-resident who does accommodate one's request. One should strongly consider giving a token of gratitude (e.g., baked goods, candy, a small gift certificate for a coffee shop, a nicely written thank-you card) to show appreciation. This will likely benefit not only the Jewish resident, but other future Jewish residents who work in the program.

Intent in Treating Patients

Jewish Patients

When violating *Shabbat* to treat Jewish patients in the hospital, one should do so with the intent that this *melakhah* is being performed for *pikuach nefesh*. If one forgets to have this intent, however, it appears that one has still not violated *Shabbat*. The basis for the question of whether one has violated *Shabbat* is the Gemara[113] which discusses a fisherman who casts a net on *Shabbat*, at a time when a child has fallen into the water, without the knowledge that the child is in danger. If the fisherman catches both fish and the child in his net, the Gemara cites a debate as to whether he has violated *Shabbat*. According to the

---

113 *Menachot* 64a.

Gemara, the basis of the debate is whether we focus on the fisherman's actions or his intent. Based on his intent only, one would say that the fisherman intended to violate *Shabbat*, and although his actions led to *pikuach nefesh*, he has still violated *Shabbat*. Focusing on the fisherman's actions, however, one would conclude that the fisherman has not violated *Shabbat*, since his action of using a net led to *pikuach nefesh*, and therefore it is permitted on *Shabbat*. It appears from this Gemara that when performing a *melakhah* for *pikuach nefesh*, one is required to have intent to perform an act of *pikuach nefesh*, or the action will still be considered a violation of *Shabbat*. Despite this, Rambam[114] rules that one's actions, rather than one's intentions, determine whether one has violated *Shabbat*, though Ra'avad[115] disagrees. R. Yitzchak Zilberstein[116] and R. Zalman Nechemiah Goldberg[117] appear to rule like the opinion that we focus on one's actions, and thus one would not be required to have explicit intent.

Regardless, in the case of a physician working in a hospital, the discussion in the Gemara may not be a concern. When a physician performs a *melakhah* to save the life of a Jewish patient, it is obvious that the *melakhah* is being performed for *pikuach nefesh*, even if the physician does not specifically concentrate on this intention. This is similar to the ruling of *Chayyei Adam*[118] cited by *Mishnah Berurah*[119] in reference to the requirement of intent in order to fulfill a *mitzvah*. Although *Shulchan Aruch*[120] rules that one must have intent to fulfill a *mitzvah* when performing the *mitzvah*, *Chayyei Adam* qualifies this ruling and states that if it is obvious from one's actions that the purpose of the actions is to fulfill the *mitzvah*, one fulfills the *mitzvah* even without intent. Similarly, it would appear that a physician in a hospital is clearly violating *Shabbat* for the purpose of *pikuach nefesh*, and thus specific intent would not be required. Indeed, R. Hershel Schachter[121] writes that this reasoning applies to a physician treating Jewish patients in a hospital, and explicit intent is not needed.

Non-Jewish Patients

The question of intent is more complicated for a physician treating a non-Jewish patient. As we have seen, while modern-day authorities permit a Jewish physician to violate *Shabbat* to save the life of a non-Jewish patient, most authorities understand that the basis of this

114 *Shegagot* 2:15; *Shabbat* 2:16.
115 *Shabbat* 2:16.
116 *Torat Ha-Yoledet* 13:10.
117 *Halakhah U-Refuah*, vol. 4, pp. 181–191.
118 68:9.
119 60:10.
120 *Orach Chayyim* 60:4.
121 *Be-Ikvei Ha-Tzon* 9:3.

dispensation is that refraining from saving the patient's life could endanger future Jewish patients, since non-Jewish physicians will be less willing to save their lives. Thus, according to this reasoning, it would not be implicitly obvious that the Jewish physician is saving the non-Jewish patient in order to save Jewish patients' lives, and it would appear that the physician might be required to explicitly intend to save Jewish patients' lives while violating *melakhah*. Indeed, R. Schachter[122] rules that this is the case. Furthermore, R. Schachter notes that the Jewish physician must not only have this intention the first time he or she violates *Shabbat* to save a non-Jewish patient's life, but during every subsequent instance.[123] However, it could be that this concern would not be applicable, if it were determined that the *halakhah* is in accordance with the view in the aforementioned Gemara that one's actions, and not one's intention, is relevant when assessing situations of *pikuach nefesh*.[124]

122 Ibid.
123 Although there are situations in Jewish law when explicit intention during the first time an action is performed allows one to forgo explicit intention during subsequent actions, R. Schachter notes that this is only true when the multiple actions are steps in one long process, such as the writing of a *get* or performing services related to one sacrifice in the *Beit Ha-Mikdash*, but not in the case of treating multiple non-Jewish patients on *Shabbat*.
124 R. Yitzchak Zilberstein (*Torat Ha-Yoledet* 13:10) suggests that there might be a distinction between different situations. He cites the ruling of *Biur Halakhah* (316:7, s.v. *ha-tzad*), who discusses the case of one who traps a dangerous animal for the purpose of using the animal's carcass for medicinal purposes. Normally, though trapping an animal is prohibited on Shabbat, trapping a dangerous animal is permitted in order to prevent lethal injury to humans. *Biur Halakhah* writes that if one traps a dangerous animal for the purpose of using the animal carcass for medicinal purposes, one has still violated *Shabbat*, even though the same action also eliminates the threat to human life. R. Zilberstein asks why *Biur Halakhah* does not consider this case comparable to catching fish while simultaneously saving a child, or, if he rules like the opinion that this case is also prohibited since we focus on one's intent, why he does not cite the Gemara and state that he rules in accordance with this opinion. R. Zilberstein therefore suggests two possible resolutions:
1.　The case of trapping the animal is different, since no one is yet endangered by the animal, and trapping the animal merely prevents a future situation of *pikuach nefesh*. In such a situation, one must specifically intend to perform *melakhah* for the purpose of *pikuach nefesh*, or one will be considered to have violated *Shabbat*, whereas if the *pikuach nefesh* situation exists already, such as in the case of a child drowning, one need not have explicit intent. Based on this distinction, it would appear that in our case of a Jewish physician treating non-Jewish patients, one would need to have explicit intent to save future Jewish patients, since the *melakhah* is being performed to avoid a future situation of *pikuach nefesh*.

Even if one is not absolutely required to have the correct intent, it is obviously preferable to have the correct intent when performing *melakhah*. Moreover, according to R. Ovadia Yosef[125] and R. Eliezer Waldenberg,[126] intending to perform *melakhah* only to save future patients' lives transforms the *melakhah* into a *melakhah she-einah tzerichah le-gufah*, a *melakhah* performed to produce an outcome which is not typically the goal of the *melakhah*. This is generally assumed to be only a rabbinic prohibition, which then might be completely permitted on *Shabbat* in order to save a non-Jew's life, due to the possible dispensation for violating rabbinic prohibitions to avoid ill will between Jews and non-Jews.[127]

However, in addition to the halakhic aspects of the discussion, there is an ethical factor to consider. A Jewish physician who, before violating *Shabbat* to save the life of a non-Jew, thinks to himself or herself that this is permitted only to save future Jewish patients, risks becoming less concerned for his or her non-Jewish patients. As noted in the previous chapter, the dispensation to violate *Shabbat* even to save a Jewish patient's life is only because the patient may observe *Shabbat*

---

2.   Alternatively, the Gemara may be discussing a case of *shogeg*, unintentional violation of *Shabbat*, in which the person fishing did not intend to violate *Shabbat* (thinking it was not *Shabbat* or that fishing is not prohibited on *Shabbat*). This is indeed how Rambam reads the Gemara. R. Zilberstein explains that it may be that only in the case of unintentional violation of *Shabbat*, we focus on one's actions. However, with regard to deliberate violation of *Shabbat*, we focus on one's intent, because the dispensation to violate *Shabbat* for *pikuach nefesh* is based on the principle of *ones*, that one has been forced to violate *Shabbat* against one's will. Thus, without intent for *pikuach nefesh*, one's action cannot be considered "against one's will." According to this distinction of R. Zilberstein, in *any* situation of *pikuach nefesh*, one is required to have the proper intent to avoid violationg *Shabbat*. However, one might suggest that when a Jewish physician is treating a non-Jewish patient on *Shabbat*, he or she clearly believes that this action is permitted on *Shabbat*, though the physician may not have explicit intent that the action is being performed to save future Jewish patients. It seems that having an *incorrect* intention regarding why this *melakhah* is permitted on *Shabbat* (thinking that one's actions are directly permitted because of the non-Jewish patient's life at stake) should be no worse than not being aware that one is performing *melakhah* on *Shabbat* (*shogeg*). It is likely better, since one realizes that the act is for *pikuach nefesh*, just that one is not explicitly thinking about the correct reason for why the situation is one of *pikuach nefesh*.

125 *Halakhah U-Refuah* vol. 1, pp. 147–150; *Yabbia Omer, Orach Chayyim* 8:38.

126 *Tzitz Eliezer*, 8:15, ch. 6.

127 See the previous chapter for a more extended discussion of this issue.

and other *mitzvot* in the future, and thus *Shabbat* can be violated to preserve future *Shabbatot*. Thus, the physician must remember that the dispensation to save Jewish lives on *Shabbat* does not mean that non-Jewish patients' lives are unimportant; rather, the dispensation exists only in order to honor *Shabbat* itself.

Furthermore, as discussed in the previous chapter, several contemporary authorities believe that Jewish physicians are required to save non-Jewish patients' lives for fundamental reasons that are unrelated to future Jewish patients. Most prominently, R. Ahron Soloveichik[128] has been frequently cited as advocating for this approach, and it is also noted by R. Nachum Rabinovitch[129] and R. Aharon Lichtenstein.[130] In particular relevance to this issue, R. Lichtenstein is cited as stating that if he were in a situation which required performance of a *melakhah* to save the life of a non-Jew, he would violate *Shabbat* on principle, for fundamental reasons, and rely on the views that permit this. It would appear that even if one chooses to follow those authorities who allow *Shabbat* violation to avoid future danger to Jewish patients, one could also keep in mind while violating *Shabbat* that one is also doing so for fundamental reasons, even if one feels more comfortable with the halakhic support offered by the more limited dispensation. Such an approach has the advantage of ensuring that one does not become inured to the plight of one's non-Jewish patients while treating them on *Shabbat*.

Conclusions

In this chapter, we have discussed numerous issues which are related to the question of whether one should accept a position in a residency program that does not accommodate *Shabbat*. We have seen three types of concerns in this regard:

1. Practical halakhic constraints that arise when one works in the hospital on *Shabbat*, including the requirement to limit one's *melakhah* activity to those actions which are specifically necessary for the patient's recovery, and the difficulty of mastering the relevant laws of *Shabbat*;
2. Fundamental halakhic objections to working in a hospital on *Shabbat*, including the treatment of patients on *Shabbat* when someone else is available to treat them, and the possible halakhic problem involved with entering a situation where one will be required to violate *Shabbat* due to *pikuach nefesh*;

---

128 "*Be-inyan mevakrin cholei akum mipenei darkei shalom*," *Od Yisra'el Yosef Beni Chai*.

129 *Melumedei Milchamah*, pp. 146–148; "A Halakhic View of the Non-Jew," *Tradition*, 8:2 (1966), pp. 27–39.

130 See R. Dov Karoll, "Laws of Medical Treatment on Shabbat," *Verapo Yerape* vol. 1, p. 219.

3. Jewish values which may oppose working in a hospital on *Shabbat*, or may advocate for accepting a residency position which does not accommodate *Shabbat* in some situations.

It is abundantly clear from our discussion that each individual's situation is unique, and one should not attempt to make this decision, with far-reaching consequences, himself or herself. Rather, one should discuss one's circumstances with a trusted and competent halakhic advisor who can help guide him or her in making this important choice. The importance of being in touch with a halakhic advisor is compounded by the fact that if one does work in the hospital on *Shabbat*, one will certainly have many halakhic questions which arise, and one will benefit significantly from having someone to whom one can ask these questions.

Shabbat is the Jewish people's God-given gift, and Jews have observed and treasured *Shabbat* for millennia. Regardless of the decision one makes with regard to a residency program, it is most important that one continue to value *Shabbat* and commit to observing it, both in its intricate halakhic details and its spirit.

Afterword

In recent years, the number of available *Shabbat*-accommodating programs has dwindled, due to a number of factors. This unfortunate reality makes it incumbent on all observant Jews to make an effort to conserve the number of these programs that remain and motivate the creation of new *Shabbat*-accommodating programs, especially in fields which do not have any.

This charge can apply both to those who accept positions in *Shabbat*-accommodating programs and those who accept positions in other programs. For those who accept positions in *Shabbat*-accommodating programs, it is crucial that they make every effort to create a *kiddush Hashem*, reflecting well on observant Jews and observant Jewish residents. An observant Jewish resident who does not go out of his or her way to help other residents in the program or who unfairly or unnecessarily exploits his or her accommodations motivates the program to eliminate the *Shabbat*-accommodating program. If one benefits from a *Shabbat*-accommodating program but then ruins the opportunity for future observant Jewish medical students, this is tragic and a *chillul Hashem*. Less extreme but also crucial, one must make an effort to be an excellent resident and make a good impression on supervisors, convincing them that one is competent and deserves to have a spot in the program. This will certainly motivate the program directors to continue offering the *Shabbat*-accommodating program.

For those who enter fields in which there are no *Shabbat*-accommodating residency programs, it is worthwhile considering the effect one can have in this field with regard to *Shabbat*-accommodating programs. While one did not have the opportunity to benefit from such a program, one should consider the possibility of pursuing a professional position wherein one would be able to make such a program available. There exist several specialties in which no *Shabbat*-accommodating program is available, but there is no reason why such a program could not exist. In these specialties, an observant Jewish physician who wished for such a program as a medical student but could not find one, could truly impact *Shabbat* observance for future Jewish physicians in that field. One who enters such a field should certainly consider this as an option as one plans one's future career.

Chapter 22

Writing Medical Notes on *Shabbat*: Theory and Practice*

Rabbi Raphael Hulkower, MD

A contemporary Rosh Yeshiva once remarked that in current times the two biggest problems for medical practice on *Shabbat* are "writing and riding." This chapter will attempt to address the former of the two. Although writing is not an intrinsic part of medical therapy, in the advent of the modern hospital system, with large volumes of patients, writing has become an essential part of medical care. Medical note writing allows physicians to communicate orders or discuss plan of care with other physicians, nurses and ancillary staff in an efficient manner. Documentation also enables physicians to record and recall vast amounts of information which would otherwise inevitably be lost or irretrievable given the volume of patients requiring care in the average hospital system. In some but certainly not all cases, such writing is vital for patient safety and care and may qualify as *pikuach nefesh*, saving a life, for which one is allowed to violate *Shabbat*. As with all aspects of medical care on *Shabbat*, whether one is allowed to violate *Shabbat* depends upon the severity of illness and the severity of the *Shabbat* desecration. Thus, knowledge of the laws of writing on *Shabbat* is an important area of concern for those physicians who may find themselves in a situation where their expertise is needed on *Shabbat*. Although this area of *halakhah* does not pertain to medical student training *per se*, the discussion is relevant for those contemplating residencies or future career positions which may involve medical care on *Shabbat*.

---

*   This chapter has been reviewed and edited by Rabbi Mordechai Willig, *shlita*. Many parts of this chapter have been adapted from Raphael Hulkower, "Pens, Pads, and PCs – Writing on Shabbat for Medical Care," *The Journal of Halacha and Contemporary Society*, Spring 2013.

This chapter will begin with a brief discussion regarding the prohibition of writing on *Shabbat* followed by an analysis of technological solutions to this prohibition, which are applicable in certain situations. Readers interested in a more in-depth discussion of these topics are referred to an article by the same author.[1] Finally, we will attempt to begin the discussion of what type of information is considered permissible for medical writing on *Shabbat*. This is meant to be a general discussion, especially the final section, and readers are encouraged to avail themselves of their local halakhic authorities to ultimately guide them on specific applications of these *halakhot* should they be necessary.

The Prohibition of Writing on *Shabbat*

As with all *melakhot*, writing is prohibited on *Shabbat* since it was one of the actions involved in constructing the *Mishkan*.[2] Letters or symbols were written on the beams in the *Mishkan* to assist in its reassembly.[3] In order to violate this prohibition on a Biblical level, one must write in a manner similar in quality and quantity to the writing in the *Mishkan*. As *Shulchan Arukh* is brief on this topic, *Mishnah Berurah* delineates the requirements for writing to be a Biblical violation. Writing must meet the following criteria to be considered a Biblical violation:

- *Quantity*: Writing must contain at least two letters or symbols to be a Biblical violation. This is true even if the letters do not form a word.[4] According to *Mishnah Berurah*,[5] writing one letter still involves a Torah violation based upon the concept of *chatzi shiur*.
- *Language*: According to Rama[6] and *Or Zarua*,[7] only writing in Hebrew is a Biblical violation of *Shabbat*. However, *Mishnah Berurah*[8] remarks that this is the minority opinion and common practice is to treat writing in any language as a Biblical prohibition.

---

1   Ibid.
2   *Shabbat* 49b.
3   *Shabbat* 103b.
4   *Shabbat* 103a.
5   *Shulchan Arukh, Orach Chayyim* 340; *Mishnah Berurah* 3 and 22. *Chatzi shiur* is the idea that the size limits listed in the Torah are provided to determine when one is obligated to offer a sacrifice; however, one may still be violating a Torah prohibition with even a smaller quantity.
6   *Shulchan Arukh, Orach Chayyim* 306:11. See also *Nishmat Avraham, Orach Chayyim* 340, section 4 who lists others who agree with Rama and *Or Zarua*.
7   2:84.
8   *Shulchan Arukh, Orach Chayyim* 306; *Mishnah Berurah* 47, and *Biur Halakhah* ad loc. *Shulchan Arukh, Orach Chayyim* 340, *Mishnah Berurah* 22.

- *Symbols*: Rambam[9] equates writing two meaningful symbols with writing two letters as a prohibition of writing. *Mishnah Berurah*,[10] based upon the Rambam in *Peirush Ha-Mishnayot*,[11] understands symbols to be limited to the use of letters which represent numbers. However, *Maggid Mishneh*[12] understands that the Rambam's ruling includes any meaningful symbol.
- *Performance*: Only writing with one's dominant hand is a Biblical violation of writing – a unique concept which does not apply to other *melakhot*. Writing with one's weaker hand is not considered normal writing and only involves a rabbinic violation of *Shabbat*. Similarly, writing in a back-handed manner (*shinui*), such as holding a pen upside down and flipping over one's hand, is not a Biblical violation of writing.[13] *Nishmat Avraham*[14] suggests that writing using fingers without involving the thumb may also be considered a *shinui*.
- *Permanence*: Just as the writing involved in the construction of the *Mishkan* was meant to last, only permanent writing is a Biblical violation of *Shabbat*. Therefore, writing with either non-permanent ink or on a non-permanent surface will only involve a rabbinic violation.[15]

Writing that does not meet any of these criteria is still a rabbinic violation of writing on *Shabbat*, which must be avoided. However, the distinction between rabbinic and Biblical violation is extremely important in navigating medical practice on *Shabbat*, as rabbinic violations are sometimes permitted for non-critically ill patients even when Biblical prohibitions are not allowed.

Categories of Sick Patients in *Halakhah*

The topic of providing medical care on *Shabbat* has been addressed elsewhere in this volume,[16] but a few points will be highlighted that are relevant for the topic of writing on *Shabbat* for medical purposes. As writing which lacks the aforementioned qualities still constitutes a rabbinic violation of *Shabbat*, writing on *Shabbat* is never permitted for those people who are only mildly sick. Writing on *Shabbat*, therefore, is most relevant for *choleh she-ein bo sakkanah* (non-critically ill patients)

---

9   *Mishneh Torah, Hilkhot Shabbat* 11:10.
10 *Shulchan Arukh, Orach Chayyim* 340, *Mishnah Berurah* 22.
11 *Shabbat* 12:3.
12 *Maggid Mishneh* on Rambam *Hilkhot Shabbat* 11:10.
13 *Shulchan Arukh, Orach Chayyim* 340, *Mishnah Berurah* 22.
14 *Orach Chayyim* 340, section 2.
15 *Shulchan Arukh, Orach Chayyim* 340, *Mishnah Berurah* 22. Writing in pencil is considered permanent according to *Mishnah Berurah*.
16 See Chapter 20.

and *choleh she-yesh bo sakkanah* (critically ill patients). Essentially, this means that writing on *Shabbat* may not be permitted for those patients who are stable enough to be treated as outpatients, but is permitted for all inpatients, as nowadays, most patients admitted to the hospital are clearly sick enough to at least be considered a *choleh she-ein bo sakkanah.*

Choleh She-Ein Bo Sakkanah

For the medical needs of patients who are literally bedridden or otherwise incapacitated from illness that is not life-threatening, one is permitted to ask a non-Jew to violate even a Torah prohibition.[17] Furthermore, according to the most accepted opinion in *Shulchan Arukh*, a Jew may violate a rabbinic prohibition for these patients, provided it is performed in an unconventional manner (*shinui*).[18] According to *Mishnah Berurah*, one may rely on this ruling even if a non-Jew is available.[19] *Mishnah Berurah* also cites *Chayyei Adam*, who permits one to perform a rabbinic prohibition **without** a *shinui* when it is not possible to perform the action with a *shinui*.[20] Other authorities allow a Jew to perform even a Torah prohibition with a *shinui*[21] and R. Shlomo Zalman Auerbach permitted one to be lenient in this matter if a non-Jew is not available.[22] Practically, if one determines that writing is necessary for the care of a non-critically ill patient, a Jew himself or herself may perform the writing provided that: 1) the writing itself is done in a way that only involves a rabbinic prohibition and 2) a *shinui* is also incorporated. When this is not possible, many authorities would still allow one to perform the act provided that one of the two above stipulations is still met. Where a limb is endangered, there is even less debate that a Jew himself or herself should be able to perform an act of writing that is only a rabbinic violation, even without a *shinui*.[23]

17 *Shulchan Arukh, Orach Chayyim* 328:17 and *Mishnah Berurah* 47 ad loc.
18 *Shulchan Arukh, Orach Chayyim* 328:17. This is based upon the opinion of the Ramban in *Torat Ha-Adam, Sha'ar Ha-Meichush*. See also *Chidushei Ramban* on *Beitzah* 22a and *Tur, Orach Chayyim* 328:17.
19 328:54. See also *Chayyei Adam* 69:12.
20 *Shulchan Arukh, Orach Chayyim* 328; *Mishnah Berurah* 102. See also *Iggerot Moshe, Orach Chayyim* 3:53.
21 *Shulchan Arukh Ha-Rav, Orach Chayyim* 328:19; *Eglei Tal*, "Melekhet Tochen" 17:38 part 10; *Tehillah Le-David, Orach Chayyim* 328 note 22; *Ketzot Ha-Shulchan* 134:4.
22 *Nishmat Avraham, Orach Chayyim*, introduction to *siman* 328, p. 389.
23 *Shulchan Arukh, Orach Chayyim* 328:17.

Choleh She-Yesh Bo Sakkanah

Although one is permitted and obligated to violate even Torah prohibitions to treat a critically ill patient, Ramban rules that one should still try to minimize the *Shabbat* violations provided that doing so will not delay the treatment.[24] Although Rambam seems to disagree, Rama rules that the custom is to try to follow this opinion of Ramban.[25] Therefore, even when treating critically ill patients, one should try to minimize the violations involved in any necessary medical writing on *Shabbat* by utilizing writing methods that only involve rabbinic prohibitions provided that this will not delay care.

Downgrading Writing to a Rabbinic Prohibition

In order to attempt to attenuate the prohibition of writing on *Shabbat* from a Torah prohibition to a rabbinic prohibition, one must remove any of the five characteristics previously mentioned. Practically, writing fewer than two letters or symbols is inconceivable in medical documents, although it raises the point that one should try to minimize one's words/letters even when writing is permitted. The fact that one most likely is not writing in Hebrew (except, of course, in Israel) is helpful according to Rama and *Or Zarua*, but, as mentioned, this is the less accepted view. Therefore, the most effective means to downgrade writing to a rabbinic violation is by changing the performance of the actions through a *shinui*, or by making the writing non-permanent.

Writing in an unconventional manner can easily make writing a rabbinic act, but has many obvious drawbacks. Writing with one's weaker hand or flipping over one's dominant hand (or writing without the thumb according to some) is a simple act but is often limited by the fact that this process makes writing extremely time-consuming or less legible – both of which may delay care to some or all of one's patients. Therefore, technological solutions to create non-permanent writing are often more ideal options. Of course, whenever a *shinui* can still be used, this is always preferred in order to further downgrade the severity of the *Shabbat* violation.

---

24 Ramban's *Torat Ha-Adam, Sha'ar Sakkanah*, cited in *Maggid Mishneh* on Rambam *Hilkhot Shabbat* 2:11.
25 Rama on *Shulchan Arukh, Orach Chayyim* 328:12. See however *Shulchan Arukh, Orach Chayyim* 328, *Mishnah Berurah* 37 who states that this is NOT a longstanding custom.

Ideal Writing Method 1: Disappearing Ink

Rashi vs. Rambam

Zomet, a *halakhah* and technology institute in Israel which produces solutions to practical halakhic issues, markets a disappearing ink pen, known as the "Shabbat Pen" (*Shabbat Eit*), for use in situations where one may violate a rabbinic violation for medical purposes. The permissibility of using disappearing ink pens is based upon a Mishnah:

> If one wrote with liquids, with fruit juices, in the dirt of the roads, or with scribes' dust, or with any other matter that is not lasting, he is exempt (from bringing a *chatat* offering).[26]

Although the Mishnah rules that one is not liable for writing with non-permanent ink, a *davar she-eino mitkayyem, Shulchan Arukh*[27] and *Or Zarua*[28] rule that such writing still involves a rabbinic prohibition. The Tosefta[29] adds that one is exempt from a Biblical violation, not only when writing with non-permanent ink, but also when the surface onto which one writes is non-permanent. Rambam[30] follows both the Mishnah and Tosefta, ruling that one must write both with a permanent ink and on a permanent surface in order to be liable for writing on *Shabbat.*

The length of time that defines writing as temporary or permanent is disputed among medieval and modern halakhic authorities. The Mishnah addresses this issue somewhat ambiguously:

> This is the rule: Whoever performs work, and his work endures "*be-Shabbat,*" is liable (to bring a *chatat* offering).[31]

The word "*be-Shabbat*" may be interpreted in differing ways in this context. According to the majority of *rishonim*, including Rashi,[32] Ran,[33] Me'iri,[34] and *Tosafot Yom Tov,*[35] the word "*be-Shabbat*" is detailing *when* the work is being performed – "on *Shabbat.*"[36] According to this

---

26 *Shabbat* 104b.
27 *Orach Chayyim* 340:4 and *Mishnah Berurah* 18.
28 2:76.
29 Tosefta *Shabbat* 11:8 (Lieberman Edition).
30 Rambam *Hilkhot Shabbat* 11:15.
31 *Shabbat* 102b. The word "*be-Shabbat*" is deliberately not translated as its meaning is the cause of debate.
32 Ad loc, s.v. *be-Shabbat.*
33 In *dappei ha-Rif* 37a, s.v. *be-Shabbat.*
34 Ad loc, s.v., *zeh ha-kelal.*
35 *Shabbat* 12:1, s.v., *be-Shabbat.*
36 This mainstream interpretation is not without obvious difficulties. For example, *Peri Chadash* asks why the Mishnah needs to state that the work

view, the Mishnah has not clearly defined a time limit besides using the word "endure." This is in contrast to the opinion of Rambam. Rambam[37] records this Mishnah in the context of the *melakhah* of dyeing. Rambam again includes the word "*Shabbat*" in his concise code, implying that the term is necessary to define temporary vs. permanent for all *melakhot*. Thus, for Rambam, the Mishnah reads, "Whoever performs work and his word endures *for the duration of Shabbat*, he is liable."[38] This interpretation of "*be-Shabbat*" is simpler in language, but it brings up a conceptual difficulty which Rashi avoids. According to Rambam, whenever any work or writing lasts until the end of *Shabbat*, that act is a violation of *Shabbat*. This would mean that whether the work was done one minute after *Shabbat* starts, and lasts nearly 24 hours, or was done at the end of *Shabbat,* and lasts only a few minutes, the act would be viewed as a violation of *Shabbat*.

R. Shlomo Zalman Auerbach vs. R. Yitzchak Yaakov Weiss

This dispute between Rambam and Rashi (and others) lies at the heart of the debate over disappearing ink pens. R. Shlomo Zalman Auerbach[39] permitted the use of such pens, even when the ink lasts beyond the end of *Shabbat* – even for many days in some cases. In following the majority opinion, against Rambam, R. Auerbach's view is based upon four major points: 1) In order to violate a Torah prohibition, the writing must be similar to that performed in the *Mishkan*. Such writing was meant to endure significantly longer than even a few days. 2) Rashba[40] and other authorities explain that "permanent" must last some "significant" period of time, and no one would ever write anything significant with ink that will disappear in a few days. 3) There are examples in *halakhah* where both *Shulchan Arukh* and Rambam permit writing which lasts longer than one day.[41] 4) R. Auerbach adds that he is comfortable ruling leniently on this matter, as most people will not be writing in Hebrew

---

is being done on *Shabbat*. This is obvious, as the entire Tractate *Shabbat* is dealing with *Shabbat*! See R. Mordechai Eliyahu's *"Ketivah chiyunit be-Shabbat be-deyo mitnaddef"* in *Techumin* 11 pp. 107–112 for a discussion of possible answers to *Peri Chadash*.

37   *Hilkhot Shabbat* 9:13.
38   The understanding of Rambam is also stated by *Maggid Mishneh* ad loc.
39   *Minchat Shlomo*, 91:11. Also previously published in *Halakhah U-Refuah* vol. 1, pp. 235–236.
40   *Shabbat* 115b s.v. *ha de-amrinan.*
41   *Shulchan Arukh* (*Orach Chayyim* 340:5) permits one to scratch a mark on parchment even though such marks last at least a day. Rambam (*Hilkhot Shabbat* 11:16) himself rules that one is liable for writing on one's skin since the fading is due to the body's warmth. R. Auerbach argues that the body's heat should be irrelevant, since writing on one's skin lasts longer than a day anyways, and should be considered permanent according to Rambam's understanding of the Mishnah.

(or at least are writing in modern Hebrew script, a font not used in the Torah), and thus this writing is only a rabbinic violation according to *Or Zarua.*

In contrast to R. Auerbach's position, R. Yitzchak Yaakov Weiss[42] rules that disappearing ink pens whose writing lasts longer than a day violate a Biblical prohibition. R. Weiss believes that we should follow Rambam's opinion for multiple reasons: 1) Rambam provides the clearest understanding of the Mishnah. 2) R. Weiss contends that other authorities only argue with Rambam in how to interpret the Mishnah; however, they may still agree with Rambam regarding the final *halakhah*. 3) R. Weiss references the same comment of Rashba mentioned above by R. Auerbach, but believes that it supports his view. Rashba's point, according to R. Weiss, is simply that writing need not be everlasting to be "permanent." Rather, it must remain long enough to be useful in record keeping. R. Weiss explains that if a doctor is writing with a disappearing ink pen in order to last long enough to re-copy the information later, then that time frame is considered useful or "permanent." These points taken together, R. Weiss concludes by stating that writing "which lasts at least **one day** and is done with full intention (*melekhet machshevet*) to remember the information, involves a Biblical violation." However, R. Weiss does acknowledge a weakness in his "one day" position, since the language of Rambam implies that the definition of "permanence" is lasting until the end of *Shabbat*, regardless of when the writing was performed.

R. Mordechai Eliyahu[43] also adopts the approach of R. Shlomo Zalman Auerbach. R. Eliyahu addresses R. Weiss's argument by mentioning that, normally, when doctors write down information they do not intend to copy the information at a later point. Therefore, this system of writing with disappearing ink and then copying the information after *Shabbat* is certainly not considered the normal manner of writing, and the original document is considered "non-permanent." R. Eliyahu concludes that it is preferable for physicians to use such ink for essential writing on *Shabbat*, and he recommends they also try to use their weaker hand, when possible, to further minimize the *Shabbat* violation.

42 *Minchat Yitzchak,* 7:13. Also previously published in *Halakhah U-Refuah,* vol. 1, pp. 233–235.
43 R. Mordechai Eliyahu, *Techumin* volume 11, pp. 107–112. For additional support for R. Auerbach's view see also R. Levi Yitzchak Halperin, *Halakhah U-Refuah* vol. 1, pp. 237–249. He notes that *Ketzot Ha-Shulchan* (in footnote to *Baddei Ha-Shulchan* 146:20) also followed Rashi's interpretation of the Mishnah in practice.

Problems with Using Disappearing Ink

While disappearing ink remains an important tool to consider for use in writing essential medical notes on *Shabbat*, such pens also pose a number of important practical problems that should be considered.

1) *Disappearing ink pens are not easily attainable*: One cannot simply buy a disappearing ink pen in a regular store, and if the pen runs out, they are not available at most hospitals. While Zomet markets the official pen with R. Auerbach's approval, such pens are hard to obtain in the United States. Otherwise, such pens are often sold as novelty items which may not be reliable to use from either a halakhic or professional standpoint.

2) *Varying time to disappearance*: Many who have used such pens have noted that the length of time the ink endures depends upon conditions in which the writing is stored. Writing left out in the open air will disappear at a much faster rate than when stored in a chart or cabinet. Temperature and humidity may also affect the time to disappearance. This poses problems at both extremes: the ink may disappear too quickly, before one may have a chance to re-read or copy the note after *Shabbat*. Alternatively, the ink may last long enough that it may no longer be considered halakhically temporary.[44] Disappearing ink pens, therefore, may pose significant threats to patient safety and halakhic observance. These dangers should not be minimized.

3) *Concern for medical errors*: In addition to the above point, such pens always need to be used with great care as the physician writing with them must be responsible enough to copy the notes after *Shabbat* before they disappear. Laxity in such matters may cause harm to patients or lead to *chillul Hashem* when such acts are seen as unprofessional.

4) *Obsolete*: As electronic medical records become more universal, handwritten notes will likely soon become obsolete, making such pens of limited use for official medical charts.

5) *Odd writing*: As such pens use special chemical compounds, the writing produced may look noticeably different from the average pen marks. For example, Zomet's pens write like a felt-tipped marker with a purple colored ink. From a halakhic point of view, this is advantageous because it may ensure that users realize they are writing with a special *Shabbat* ink. However, the writing may appear unprofessional from the hospital administration's perspective. This means that if one does intend to use such pens for official chart documentation, their use will be obvious to most readers.

---

44 For more discussion on the halakhic ramifications of various storing methods of disappearing ink, see R. Levi Yitzchak Halperin, *Ma'aseh Choshev,* vol. 2, ch. 15 and vol. 3, pp. 233–239.

Thus, if one intends to use such pens, one should inform one's colleagues and superiors.

Due to these concerns, among others, such pens are probably not the first choice in dealing with medical note writing on *Shabbat*. Moreover, as will be discussed, computer writing is a more preferable method. However, such pens still may have an important use if one needs to write brief notes on *Shabbat* for personal use that will not be placed in the official medical chart. For example, a physician, who may need to write notes to organize his or her thoughts about a case, or a resident or fellow, who may be caring for many patients and needs to write down brief pieces of information when a computer is unavailable, might be able to utilize the disappearing ink pen. Such writing is quick and easily transportable without the halakhic concerns of printing (to be discussed). It should be noted that when writing only brief personal notes, one may find it feasible to write with the weaker hand with such a pen, which is perhaps halakhically preferable to writing via computer, as one is now incorporating two methods of downgrading the act to a rabbinic level – temporary ink and *shinui*.

Ideal Writing Method 2: Writing on a Computer

While writing via computer has been readily available for decades, the growth of electronic medical records in recent years has brought this method of medical note-taking to the forefront of our halakhic discussion. If writing notes via computer provides another, or preferable, option to essential medical note-taking on *Shabbat*, this would be a tremendous benefit to Sabbath-observant physicians and their patients. As electronic medical records are the "standard of care" in many, if not most, hospitals, being able to write an electronic note would allow physicians to safely and efficiently document notes or orders for their patients without many of the concerns created by disappearing ink or writing with one's weaker hand.

In order to discuss the permissibility of electronic note writing on *Shabbat*, one must address a few areas of concern. Is writing on a computer screen a violation of writing on *Shabbat*? May one operate a computer in the first place? May one save information onto a computer's memory? May one print from a computer on *Shabbat*?

1) Is writing on a computer screen a violation of writing on *Shabbat*?

Whether one is using an older cathode ray screen, or a newer LCD or plasma monitor, all screen writing operates in a conceptually similar manner.[45] The letters produced on screen are composed of tiny discrete

---

45 R. Dr. Zev Lev and Zomet recommend the newer LCD and plasma screens over the older cathode ray monitors, since cathode ray monitors often use

dots or pixels of light which are being emitted constantly at high speed. The pixels are too small for the naked eye to appreciate that they are not a single image, and the light flashes at speeds too fast to discern that that the image is in fact "flickering" as opposed to constantly present. The former point is not raised by most *poskim*; however, R. Dr. Zev Lev notes that this may be a reason for leniency since such writing is not considered valid "writing" in other areas of *halakhah* such as divorce bills or a *Sefer Torah*.[46] Most authorities are more concerned about the latter point, whether writing on a computer screen is considered *temporary* writing by nature of its ethereal existence. The writing only exists as long as the electric current is running, and the image itself is produced through the emissions of light which continuously shine and fade away, rather than via a constant image.

Based upon this temporary quality of computer screen writing, many halakhic authorities rule that such writing is not a Biblical violation of writing on *Shabbat*. R. Ovadia Yosef[47] discusses whether one is allowed to write on *chol ha-mo'ed* using a computer. After ruling leniently in that matter, he concludes:

> In my opinion, typing on a computer definitely has no concern at all of being a violation [of writing] since the letters are not printed onto a permanent material; rather they simply *appear* on the screen of the computer alone.

Similarly, *Nishmat Avraham*[48] cites R. Shlomo Zalman Auerbach's opinion that screen writing is not a Torah violation of *Shabbat* since the writing is simply produced by the firing of electrons; however he implies that screen writing may still involve a rabbinic violation. *Nishmat Avraham* himself explains that the firing of electrons merely causes the *form* of letters to appear on the screen.

Expanding upon this topic, R. Gedalya Aharon Rabinowitz[49] reasons that writing on a screen is not considered permanent writing on *Shabbat* based upon four salient arguments. 1) The writing only exists

---

a heated incandescent filament as the source of electrons, which may violate a Biblical prohibition of *mavir* (lighting a flame) or *bishul* (cooking).

46 R. Zev Lev, *Ma'archei Lev*. (Jerusalem: Mossad Harav Kook, 1995), chapter 8, section 7–8. The idea that writing formed by combining small dots is not considered normal writing is based upon the Talmud Yerushalmi *Shabbat* 12:4 and *Gittin* 2:3 and the commentary of the *Korban Ha-Edah*.

47 *Yabbia Omer, Orach Chayyim* 8:48. Italics added by author.

48 *Nishmat Avraham, Orach Chayyim* 340:6(11).

49 R. Gedalya Aharon Rabinowitz, "The use of a computer for medical purposes in the hospital on *Shabbat*," (Hebrew) *Halakhah U-Refuah* vol. 5, pp. 134–138.
     Thus based on the third and fourth arguments, both the text and the intention can be viewed as temporary.

while the computer is operating. If the computer is turned off, the letters disappear, demonstrating their transient nature. 2) Writing on a screen is not comparable to the paradigmatic writing performed in the Mishkan. When the letters were written on the Mishkan's pillars, this writing was set in place and immobile; however, letters written on a computer screen are able to be moved around on the screen. 3) People do not intend for the writing on a screen to remain there permanently. The sole purpose of displaying the writing on a screen is to ensure the information is correct until it is eventually stored in memory or printed.[50] 4) R. Rabinowitz's final argument is similar to the arguments established by R. Ovadia Yosef and R. Auerbach: the writing is considered non-permanent because the letters are not constantly illuminated but rather glowing and fading at speeds too fast to perceive with the eye.

This final argument, used by R. Ovadia Yosef, R. Auerbach and R. Rabinowitz is disputed by R. Yisrael Dovid Harfenes in *Nishmat Shabbat*.[51] R. Harfenes argues that *halakhah* should only take into account what is visible to the eye. If humans cannot discern that screen writing is "flickering," the image should be considered a permanent image. In spite of this objection, R. Harfenes writes that the use of "screen savers" should resolve all concerns about screen writing, since the image will inevitably disappear without any human intervention.

In contrast to these opinions, R. Shmuel Wosner[52] rules that writing on a computer screen is a Biblical violation of *Shabbat*. R. Wosner argues that this act is not temporary since the writing "endures for an amount of time long enough to perform the complete required activity as desired. This meets the definition of permanent." R. Wosner strengthens his assertion with an interesting comparison to a ruling of Rambam. Rambam rules that writing on one's skin is a Torah violation even though it fades, since the writing itself is enduring while an outside factor (body heat) "erases" the original writing. Similarly, when one performs a new task on the computer screen, this "erases" the previous writing, but the writing itself could have endured much longer if

---

50 This third argument, R. Rabinowitz says, depends upon a dispute between Rama and *Levush*. In Responsa 119, Rama rules that if one writes in a manner that could be enduring but one's intention is that it not be enduring, one is not violating a Torah prohibition. *Levush* (*Orach Chayyim* 340:4) disagrees. As our practice is to follow Rama, one can extrapolate that screen writing should be permissible since one does not intend for the writing to endure.

51 7:137.

52 *Shevet Ha-Levi* 6:37. One can distinguish between writing on human skin and on a monitor. Writing on skin could endure if not for the fact that an outside process, body heat, erases it. Computer writing is the opposite – the writing itself can only be sustained by the outside process, the flow of the electricity.

one had not used the computer. R. Harfenes agrees with R. Wosner in theory but also presents a rebuttal. Granted, the writing would remain on the screen if one does not "erase" it by performing another task. Nevertheless, some *poskim*, such as Rama,[53] permit the use of writing *designed* to be constantly written and erased, such as the words written on the sides of the pages of a library book. Since the book is designed to be opened and closed, the words on the sides of the pages will be formed and erased over and over and should not be considered permanent. Similarly, although letters on a screen could be sustained if another task was not performed, the intended design of a computer is for writing to be displayed and then erased to display new information. According to these authorities, suggests R. Harfenes, writing on a monitor would still be considered temporary writing.

SUMMARY: The majority of halakhic authorities consider writing on a computer screen to only be a rabbinic violation on *Shabbat*. Using a monitor with a screen saver installed would likely make the violation only rabbinic in nature according to all opinions.

2) May one operate a computer in the first place?

Whether one may operate a computer on *Shabbat* for the purpose of writing medical notes is an application of the topic of using electrical appliances on *Shabbat*. This important topic is discussed in Chapter 25, but will be briefly reviewed here. As modern computers do not use incandescent lights, the only issue to address is the use of electricity itself. A wide variety of halakhic arguments have been advanced to explain why the use of electricity is prohibited on *Shabbat*, ranging from a Biblical prohibition (*boneh*, "building" or *makeh be-pattish*, "completing a product") to a rabbinic prohibition (*molid*, "creating a new item") to a tradition without an exact basis in the laws of *Shabbat*. The vast majority of halakhic authorities rule that the prohibition is only rabbinic. However, since *Chazon Ish* famously ruled that completing an electrical circuit (even without lights) involves a Torah prohibition of *boneh* or *tikkun mana*, halakhic authorities commonly take his view into account.[54] According to *Chazon Ish*, turning on a computer, or any electrical appliance, is a Biblical prohibition. As such, if one is attempting to only consider rabbinically prohibited ways to record information on *Shabbat*, the computer must be turned on before *Shabbat*, or at least by a non-Jew on *Shabbat*.

---

53 Responsa 119. This is the same responsum cited by R. Rabinowitz. See footnote 50.
54 Rabbis Michael Broyde and Howard Jachter, "The Use of Electricity on Shabbat and Yom Tov," *The Journal of Contemporary Halacha and Society*, vol. 21 (Spring 1991). pp. 4–47.

Assuming that one is working with a computer that has been turned on prior to *Shabbat*, what are the halakhic concerns in operating the computer – such as pressing keyboard buttons or clicking the mouse? Clicking a mouse or key button closes an electrical circuit for an extremely short period of time. R. Dr. Zev Lev explains that according to *Beit Yitzchak*, who holds that completing electrical circuits violates the rabbinic prohibition of *molid*, one is certainly violating a rabbinic prohibition when pressing a key, as this *creates* an electrical pulsation. Although the circuit is only closed for a millisecond, the action of creating something new is considered enduring since a command is followed by the computer as a result.

R. Rabinowitz[55] argues that even *Chazon Ish* would agree that one is not violating *boneh* or *tikkun mana* with a keystroke. Turning on electricity is considered turning an unusable object into a usable device according to *Chazon Ish*. However, pressing a key is simply *using* an already functional computer, not creating it.[56] In addition, states R. Rabinowitz, the small circuits closed by pressing a key are only closed for a moment and then reopened to allow other keys to operate. Even if *Chazon Ish* would consider pressing a key to be *boneh*, this split-second act of "building" is not long enough to be considered permanent. R. Rabinowitz states that R. Shlomo Zalman Auerbach also understood *Chazon Ish* in this manner.[57]

R. Yisrael Rosen, Dean of Zomet, explains[58] that his institution follows the approach that pressing keys is only a rabbinic violation. However, he cites R. Shaul Yisraeli's recommendation that one also try to operate the computer with a *shinui*. He suggests using a plastic thimble placed on one's finger that extends beyond the finger's length, with a knob on the end to allow one to press buttons. Alternatively, one can use a stylus, stick or even a spoon handle.

---

55 Rabbi Gedalya Aharon Rabinowitz, "The Use of a Computer for Medical Purposes in the Hospital on *Shabbat*," (Hebrew) *Halakhah U-Refuah* vol. 5, 134–138.

56 R. Rabinowitz believes that when *Chazon Ish* said that completing an electrical circuit violates *boneh*, this refers to constructing the appliance, not the electrical circuit, as it is inconceivable to consider the circuit itself a device. Thus, pressing a key is simply using the constructed computer, even if a new circuit is closed as a result.

57 See *Minchat Shlomo* 10:6. Although R. Rabinowitz's position is strengthened based upon the agreement of R. Auerbach, R. Rabinowitz also states that this argument can be made regarding saving information to a disk or hard drive – a matter in which R. Auerbach clearly disagrees, as will be discussed.

58 R. Yisrael Rosen, in "Halachico-Technical Solutions to Using a Computer on *Shabbat* designated for Input and Receiving Patients," (Hebrew) *Assia* vol. 4, pp. 135–138 and note 2.

The use of a mouse is similar to pressing keyboard buttons, as its operation may also close electrical circuits. As such, according to most opinions its use would only involve a rabbinic violation. R. Yisraeli's suggestion to use a *shinui* would still be ideal where possible. Also, Zomet recommends one use an optical mouse instead of the older ball mouse, since an optical mouse is essentially a camera, whereas the ball mechanism involves a series of circuits. Touch-sensitive surfaces (common to laptops) are less ideal, as they use numerous circuits in series.

Touchscreens, such as those utilized by iPads or other tablets, present a more complex question. In some respects they are equally or more problematic for *Shabbat* usage. They still make use of numerous circuits, since the signals travel from the touchscreen to the processor as electrical impulses. Also, some types of touchscreen are harder to operate using a *shinui*. Older "resistive" touchscreens operate on a mechanism responsive to pressure, which allows the user to activate the screen commands with either a finger (even gloved) or a stylus. Such models enable one to use a *shinui* as recommended by Zomet and Rav Yisraeli. However, newer "capacitive" touchscreens require minimal pressure, but may only be operated by touch with a material that can conduct electrical current, such as an ungloved finger but not with an ordinary stylus. As such, some *shinui* methods are not compatible with capacitive touchscreens.[59] In other respects, touchscreen use may be preferable. Sophisticated touch operations may allow one touch to replace numerous key strokes, minimizing the number of *Shabbat* violations one has to perform to write medication orders or notes.

In an attempt to make computer operations on *Shabbat* less problematic, Zomet sells a "*Shabbat* mouse" and "*Shabbat* keyboard," both of which operate on the principle of indirect action (*gerama*).[60] These products make computer use even more ideal, since operating a computer is now two rabbinical steps removed: closing electrical circuits without lights is only a rabbinic violation, and using *gerama* is only a rabbinic violation (permitted in cases of need). These products may be even superior to regular *gerama*, since they only modulate existing currents. The current is always present, but the frequency or voltage is changed. In this way, no new circuit is created, potentially avoiding a problem of *boneh* or *molid*.[61]

---

59 http://electronics.howstuffworks.com/iphone2.htm. Downloaded 2012-8-16.
60 http://www.zomet.org.il/Eng/?CategoryID=253&ArticleID=318. Downloaded 2012-05-01.
61 See R. Yisrael Rosen, "Changing Electrical Current on Shabbat – Halachico-Technical Principles and Applications (Hebrew)," *Techumin* vol. 26, pp. 83–100. As R. Rosen points out, this technology could revolutionize what people traditionally consider "*Shabbat*" activities, raising concerns of *marit ayin* (people *appear* to do *melakhah*) or *uvdin de-chol* (regular weekday behavior), but seems to avoid classic concerns about electricity on *Shabbat*.

SUMMARY: While the use of electricity only involves a rabbinic violation according to most authorities, turning on a computer would violate a Biblical prohibition according to *Chazon Ish*. However, most authorities rule that operating a computer which is already on would only involve rabbinical violations even according to *Chazon Ish*. Operating a computer using a *shinui* or *gerama* is still recommended and ideal in most situations.

3) May one save information onto a computer's memory?

Writing electronic medical notes is only useful if one is able to store the information for future reference via digital memory or by printing a hard copy. Such actions raise additional halakhic concerns.

R. Shlomo Zalman Auerbach held that saving information onto a hard drive or diskette on *Shabbat* may be a violation of *boneh*. *Nishmat Avraham* explains that saving information may be viewed as turning the hard drive or disk into a new object. Using materials to create an object of greater value is conceptually similar to building a house.[62] Or, as R. Yehoshua Neuwirth explains, an empty disk has no value. By adding information to it, you *create or build* something of value.[63] Retrieving previously saved information, such as lab values or a prior note, however, would not be a problem, as this is simply using the existing object.

Other halakhic authorities argue with this approach. Instead, they view the act of saving data as a repeatable, reversible process akin to *using an object* rather than creating a new one. R. Dr. Zev Lev[64] makes this argument explicitly regarding saving information onto a diskette and R. Harfenes[65] makes the argument regarding a hard drive. R. Harfenes adds that one could even argue that saving data *decreases* the value of the memory device due to limited data capacity. Presumably these arguments could be applied to CDs, DVDs, and USB flash drives as well.

R. Rabinowitz concurs, but suggests that one could distinguish between different situations of data storage. Saving information on a disk or hard drive is not considered fixing an object but rather *using* an existing object. As such, it may not violate *boneh* even according to *Chazon Ish*.[66] However, according to *Chazon Ish*, entering a diskette into the disk drive (presumably a CD, DVD, or USB drive is comparable) may violate *tikkun mana* as one prepares the object for use in its originally intended manner. Similarly, preparing the disk to receive information (e.g., "formatting" a disk, or erasing data to create new space) is

---

62 *Nishmat Avraham, Orach Chayyim* 340:6(11), p. 569.
63 *Shemirat Shabbat Ke-Hilkhatah* ch. 66, note 211.
64 R. Zev Lev, *Ma'archei Lev*, 8:3.
65 R. Harfenes, *Nishmat Shabbat* 7:139.
66 R. Rabinowitz, *Halakhah U-Refuah* vol. 5, p. 136.

also considered "preparing the object for use."[67] Therefore, using a hard drive or a removable memory device inserted before *Shabbat* with adequate memory for all of *Shabbat*, would avoid any problems of *tikkun mana* or *boneh*.

R. Rabinowitz and R. Harfenes also argue that saving data does not violate the prohibition of writing on *Shabbat* by writing new code within a memory device. As the data code is not made of discernible letters and the code markings are not "detectable by the senses," creating such invisible magnetic markings does not violate the Biblical prohibition of writing or *roshem* (making a mark).[68]

R. Yisrael Rosen[69] explains that Zomet's position is to view data storage on a computer as only a rabbinic violation. However, to account for those who view the matter more stringently, they recommend the action be performed with, at least, a *shinui* (as with other computer operations) or, ideally, through *gerama* using their "*Shabbat* mouse."[70]

SUMMARY: There is a dispute between modern halakhic authorities as to whether saving information to digital memory constitutes a Biblical or rabbinic violation of *Shabbat*. While some rely on the lenient approach, it is ideal to perform the act of saving with a *shinui* or through *gerama* when possible. One should try to use a hard drive or other internal memory as opposed to inserting a portable memory device.

4) May one print from a computer on *Shabbat*?

While many authorities view typing on a screen, operating a computer and even saving to a hard drive as only a rabbinic violation of *Shabbat*, printing is viewed as a more serious violation. *Nishmat Avraham*[71] quotes R. Yehoshua Neuwirth's opinion that printing is a Biblical violation of *Shabbat*. If one must print, he suggests asking a non-Jew to perform the action. If this is not possible and one is dealing with a critically ill patient, he suggests pressing the print key with the knuckle

---

67 R. Dr. Zev Lev states this concern about formatting as well. See *Ma'archei Lev*, chapter 8, section 3.

68 R. Rabinowitz, *Halakhah U-Refuah* vol. 5. p. 136. R. Rabinowitz supports the idea that undetectable markings are not *roshem* based on Rama (*Orach Chayyim* 340:4) who rules that writing letters in the air is permitted. *Taz* (ad loc note 3) explains that this is because "the marking is not detectable." R. Harfenes agrees with R. Rabinowitz in *Nishmat Shabbat* 7:139. R. Rabinowitz's opinion is also based upon the halakhic analysis of R. Levi Yitzchak Halperin who argued that saving information onto tapes is not a violation of writing or *roshem*. See Halperin, *Ma'aseh Choshev*, vol. 2, chapter 10.

69 *Techumin* vol. 26, p. 93.

70 http://www.zomet.org.il/Eng/?CategoryID=253&ArticleID=318. Downloaded 2012-05-01.

71 *Nishmat Avraham, Orach Chayyim* 340:6(11), p. 571.

of a finger instead of using the finger itself in order to minimize the violation by using a *shinui*. Furthermore, R. Neuwirth and R. Harfenes both write that one should *not* view operating a printer in a normal manner as an indirect act since the writing is not created by one's hand directly. Rather, pressing the button is considered the act which causes the printer to function.[72] This approach is supported by R. Halperin[73] who explains that using a machine to print information is considered an act of "writing" by enabling its production. The effect of connecting two objects together is directly ascribed to a person, as seen by the *melakhah* of *havarah* (lighting a flame) where one is liable not only for directly creating fire but also for bringing straw close to an existing fire. R. Rabinowitz[74] and R. Dovid Ribiat[75] concur as well.

R. Moshe Feinstein appears to disagree with the concept that one is fully responsible for the *melakhah* of writing caused by pressing a button. In the context of printing labels for the care of critically ill patients, R. Feinstein was asked whether is it preferable to write the label by hand, so that one will only write the minimum information required and possibly use one's opposite hand, or to use an electric stamping machine which will print additional non-vital information. R. Feinstein ruled that using the electric stamping machine was preferable because "no Biblical prohibition is performed by the person." The use of electricity did not violate any Biblical prohibition, nor did the mechanical writing involve a Biblical violation because:

> Only [a person's] initial force is viewed as a person's action, such that the writing is considered writing performed by a person... but not that which is written by a second force, which is the electrical writing. Even though the person caused this [machine] to write, this is definitely not considered a true act of the person.[76]

Although R. Feinstein was not writing in the context of printing from a computer, pressing a button to cause an electrical stamping machine

---

72 *Shmirat Shabbat Ke-Hilkhatah* ch. 66, note 211; *Nishmat Shabbat* 7:140. This view is supported by *Chazon Ish*'s ruling (*Orach Chayyim* 36) that one violates the *melakhah* of plowing on *Shabbat* even when using a mechanical plow, since pressing the button is considered causing the activity. *Beit Yitzchak* (*Orach Chayyim* 57) and R. Tzvi Pesach Frank (*Har Tzvi* 185:3) also hold that one is responsible for actions caused by machines when a human action starts the chain of events.

73 *Ma'aseh Choshev* vol. 2, p. 194.

74 *Halakhah U-Refuah* vol. 5, ibid.

75 *The 39 Melochos*, p. 953. R. Ribiat also considers printing to be *ketivah*.

76 R. Moshe Feinstein, "Writing on *Shabbat* in the Hospital." (Hebrew) *Techumin* vol. 4 pp. 423–425.

to print out letters is a very close parallel, and he considered this preferable even to writing by hand with a *shinui*, which is only a rabbinic violation.

As the majority of opinions rule that printing is a Biblical prohibition on *Shabbat*, R. Rosen of Zomet suggests modifying the printer to operate indirectly, using *gerama*. This solution was endorsed by R. Dov Lior and R. Shaul Yisraeli, although R. Yisraeli adds that one should press the print key using a *shinui*, such as wearing a plastic thimble. R. Ovadia Yosef also endorsed the *gerama* printer, even for use with non-critically ill patients.[77]

SUMMARY: The majority of halakhic authorities rule that printing involves a Biblical violation of writing on *Shabbat* and should be avoided. When absolutely necessary, printing should ideally be performed via assistance from a non-Jew, or by using *gerama*, or a *shinui*.

What is *Necessary* Writing on *Shabbat*? Beginning the Discussion

While medical note writing has become an essential part of modern medical care, it is certainly not an actual medical treatment. Although this chapter has presented a modern halakhic discussion on some permissible ways to record vital medical information on *Shabbat*, no opinion quoted above addresses the toughest question of all: What information is considered "essential" or "necessary" to be written on *Shabbat*? To some extent, this topic is better left as a personal or private matter, as no one rule or guideline can predict every medical situation. Individual clinical judgment is often required to determine what is needed for patient care. Nevertheless, bringing this topic to a public forum for discussion may aid current or future physicians in formulating plans for their clinical behavior on *Shabbat*.

Avoiding Writing

Even if one has a disappearing ink pen or a computer at his or her disposable, one should always consider whether there is a viable way to write one's notes either before or after *Shabbat*, even if this requires extra time and effort (provided this will not significantly impact patient safety). For example, if one must care for patients on a Saturday, it is often possible to write some or all notes after *Shabbat* has ended. If one is worried about forgetting information, one can write briefer notes for one's own records to minimize the amount of writing. If one is caring for patients on a Friday that will extend beyond the start of *Shabbat*, it may be possible to

---

77 R. Rosen, *Assia* vol. 4, pp. 135–138 and note 2.

write the template or general details of one's notes and only change or add what is essential on *Shabbat* itself. Furthermore, many hospitals allow physicians to addend their notes. This would enable physicians to write only the information which is necessary in their notes on *Shabbat*, but to add additional information after *Shabbat* which may be less essential and required merely for formality, financial or educational purposes.

Is a "SOAP" note essential?

The use of daily progress notes in a "SOAP" note format (Subjective, Objective, Assessment, Plan) is nearly ubiquitous in American teaching hospitals. This format serves the dual purpose of conveying patient information and providing a standard writing format for residents. Although fellows and attendings will often follow a similar outline, in my own experience physicians at higher levels of training are often given "license" to write more summative notes – briefer and treatment directed. Such freestyle notes are more halakhically ideal for multiple reasons. Their content is care-oriented and less likely to include information simply written for educational or legal formality. In addition, due to their clinical experience, fellows and attendings usually have the acumen and confidence to know with more certainty what information is essential versus nonessential.[78] For those faced with the challenge of writing SOAP notes on *Shabbat*, a few points are worth discussing:

- *Subjective, Assessment, and Plan*: Although one should try to be brief in wording, a patient's subjective complaints would appear to be easy to justify including in a note. While minor complaints can often be omitted safely, knowing whether a patient's headache, chest pain, or diarrhea is old or new is important and essential for ongoing inpatient care. For patients who are stable, simply writing "no overnight events" may still be a useful way to fulfill one's duties. While Assessment and Plan is obviously essential, one should strive to be as brief as possible and consider using a template or modifying a previous note if this will minimize the quantity of writing.
- *Objective*: In our age of computerized hospital records, the objective section is probably the most dispensable part of a SOAP note, as vital signs and lab results are already recorded for others to observe. In many situations one can safely omit this data from one's notes (assuming one has reviewed the information personally) as other providers will often review the results themselves. If this option will make the note appear unfinished, perhaps one can simply write "reviewed" as part of their template written before *Shabbat* as

---

78 Both reasons often make non-*Shabbat*-accommodating fellowships and attending positions halakhically more feasible than non-*Shabbat*-accommodating residencies.

mentioned above. Alternatively, if one simply lists the significant or abnormal findings, perhaps this can be justified as another physician covering overnight may not have the time to review all the data personally and a summary of the important values would be "essential." Including a brief physical exam, even with normal findings, is also clinically important so that other providers will know the patient's baseline exam should his or her status decline rapidly. Again, having a template that one can simply copy and modify may be ideal.

Discharge Summaries and Death Certificates

Discharge papers and especially death certificates pose the greatest problem of medical writing on *Shabbat* as they are ostensibly not serving a *pikuach nefesh* purpose. The best solution is to be proactive and have a good relationship with one's colleagues. Most discharges are planned and the majority of the paperwork can be written ahead of time. Asking a non-Jewish colleague to make a small adjustment to one's paperwork is a small favor of time that can easily be repaid. *Nishmat Avraham*[79] writes that one is allowed to ask a non-Jew to write emergency room discharge papers even for a healthy patient if doing so will make more beds available for other sick patients to receive treatment, since this is a *tza'ar le-rabbim*. Presumably, in most busy hospitals, the same can be said for inpatient hospital beds, where discharging a patient will open up a bed for a patient waiting in the ER to receive better care. Similarly many physicians involved in the care of a deceased patient can sign a death certificate, although one should, perhaps, avoid asking directly.

79 *Nishmat Avraham, Orach Chayyim* 340:6(7,26).

Chapter 23

Observing Positive *Mitzvot* of *Shabbat* in the Hospital

Jerry Karp, MD, PhD

Much attention is given to avoiding the violation of *Shabbat* prohibitions when on call in the hospital over *Shabbat*. However, equally important is making sure to fulfill the positive commandments associated with *Shabbat*. In addition to being obligated in fulfilling these *mitzvot*, the observance of these *mitzvot* is essential in remembering the spirit of the *Shabbat* day even while working in the hospital, and as such these obligations deserve special attention.[1]

Showering before *Shabbat*

As part of *kavod Shabbat*, honoring *Shabbat*, *Shulchan Arukh*[2] writes that one is obligated to wash one's face, hands, and feet before *Shabbat* in hot water. Rama adds that one is obligated to wash one's entire body before *Shabbat*. One who is working in the hospital on Friday afternoon and whose shift will not end until after *Shabbat* will obviously be unable to shower before *Shabbat*. However, Rama cites *Tur*[3] who writes, based on the Gemara,[4] that if one is unable to wash one's entire body before *Shabbat*, one should at least wash one's face, hands, and feet. *Mishnah Berurah*[5] notes that nowadays, one need only wash one's face and hands, since the contemporary practice is not to walk around

---

1   Many of these topics are discussed at length in various works, including *Shemirat Shabbat Ke-Hilkhatah* vol. 2; R. Simcha Bunim Cohen's *The Radiance of Shabbos*, Artscroll/Mesorah Publications, 1986; *Shiurei Hilkhot Shabbat* by R. Yosef Zvi Rimon, *Tevunot*, 2003.
2   *Orach Chayyim* 260:1.
3   *Orach Chayyim* 260.
4   *Shabbat* 25b.
5   260:4.

barefoot. Thus, one who is working in the hospital as *Shabbat* begins should make an effort to wash one's face and hands with hot water soon before *Shabbat* starts.[6] This will suffice to fulfill the *mitzvah* of *kavod Shabbat*, and will also help the physician appreciate the impending arrival of *Shabbat*. *Mishnah Berurah*[7] also notes that if one will be unable to shower immediately before *Shabbat*, one may shower earlier (even Thursday) with the intent that this is in preparation for *Shabbat*. R. Yehoshua Neuwirth[8] cites this opinion, writing that one should also, preferably, wash one's hands and face immediately before *Shabbat*, since this is the main time for the *mitzvah*.

Wearing *Shabbat* Clothing

The Gemara[9] derives from the Biblical phrase, *"ve-kibadto,"*[10] "you shall honor it," that one's *Shabbat* clothing should be different from one's weekday clothing. This is indeed the ruling of *Shulchan Arukh*,[11] who writes that one must attempt to have nicer clothing designated for *Shabbat*. *Mishnah Berurah*[12] cites *Chayyei Adam*[13] who adds that this is the case even if one is alone for *Shabbat*, since the clothes are intended to honor *Shabbat*. A resident working in the hospital can indeed wear nicer *Shabbat* clothing while still maintaining the requisite hospital dress code. A man can wear a white dress shirt, if he normally wears colored dress shirts during the week. He can also wear a nicer tie, belt, watch, and/or cufflinks. A woman can designate a special outfit, nicer than her weekday outfits, that she wears only on *Shabbat*. In addition to fulfilling an obligatory *mitzvah* of *kavod Shabbat*, wearing special *Shabbat* clothing will remind the resident that it is *Shabbat*, and may be a vital method of reminding oneself not to perform *melakhot* that are not necessary for patient care, as discussed in Chapter 21.

Wearing *Shabbat* clothing may not be possible for a resident in a surgical specialty who is required to wear scrubs in the hospital for infection control purposes. However, even such a resident should try to find some accessory that he or she can wear that can be special for *Shabbat*, and perhaps he or she should even designate a special set of

---

6   *Biur Halakhah* writes that one does not discharge one's obligation by washing with cold water (he is ambivalent regarding lukewarm water). However, he proposes that perhaps one might discharge one's obligation even with cold water if one sweats after washing in cold water.

7   260:5.

8   *Shemirat Shabbat Ke-Hilkhatah*, 42:47, footnote 170–171.

9   *Shabbat* 113a.

10   Isaiah 58:13.

11   *Orach Chayyim* 262:2.

12   262:6.

13   5:7.

scrubs (even a different color, if this is permitted by the hospital). At the very least, this will fulfill the Gemara's requirement that one's *Shabbat* clothing be different from one's weekday clothing,[14] as well as help to remind the resident that it is *Shabbat*. If one has the option of wearing scrubs, but this is not required, it would appear that the resident should wear special *Shabbat* clothes that are not scrubs.

Lighting Candles for *Shabbat*

Must a Resident Light *Shabbat* Candles?

An integral part of the *Shabbat* experience is lighting *Shabbat* candles. The Gemara[15] emphasizes that beyond the distinctive atmosphere created by the presence of the candles, lighting the candles is a requirement. However, there is some debate as to the purpose of lighting *Shabbat* candles, which will have ramifications with regard to whether the resident on call must light the candles. According to Rashi,[16] lighting candles is required because of *kavod Shabbat*: when one lights candles for *Shabbat*, this indicates that one is honoring *Shabbat* by creating a festive and dignified atmosphere. *Tosafot*[17] suggest an alternative reason, that lighting candles is required for *oneg Shabbat*, enjoyment of *Shabbat*, since one's *Shabbat* meal will be more enjoyable with the presence of candlelight. Rambam[18] appears to record both the reasons of *kavod Shabbat* and *oneg Shabbat*, and several later authorities[19] explain that Rambam believes both reasons are operative in lighting candles. A third reason for lighting *Shabbat* candles may appear in the Gemara[20] which states that if one can only purchase candles for *Shabbat* or for *Chanukah*, one should purchase *Shabbat* candles since they are intended to promote *shalom bayit*, domestic peace. As Rashi explains, candles promote peace, since when the room is dark, one cannot see where one is going and might trip and fall. Though in *Hilkhot Shabbat*, Rambam does not mention *shalom bayit* as a reason for lighting candles on *Shabbat*,

---

14 The Gemara specifically notes that one's *Shabbat* clothing should be *different* from one's weekday clothing, while *Tur* and *Shulchan Arukh* specifically rule that one should prepare *nice* clothing for *Shabbat*. It is unclear whether clothing that is different but not specifically nicer than one's weekday clothing fulfills the obligation, at least to a minimal degree.
15 *Shabbat* 25b.
16 *Shabbat* 25b, s.v. *chovah*.
17 *Shabbat* 25b, s.v. *hadlakat*.
18 *Shabbat* 5:1 and 30:5.
19 See *Arukh Ha-Shulchan, Orach Chayyim* 263:2; R. Yitzchak Ze'ev Soloveichik (cited in *Chiddushei Ha-Grach al Ha-Shas* [stencils], *siman* 11 on *Hilkhot Shabbat* 5:1).
20 *Shabbat* 23b.

he does mention this reason elsewhere[21] when discussing why *Shabbat* candles are prioritized over *Chanukah* candles. *Arukh Ha-Shulchan*[22] suggests that Rambam does not mention this reason in *Hilkhot Shabbat* since he merely subsumes the *shalom bayit* reason under *oneg Shabbat*.

In the context of a resident working in a hospital on Friday night, both *kavod Shabbat* and *oneg Shabbat* are factors that could necessitate lighting *Shabbat* candles.[23] If the resident is single, and there is thus no one in his or her home lighting on the resident's behalf, then it is clear that the resident must light *Shabbat* candles. On the other hand, if the resident is married, the resident's spouse is home to light *Shabbat* candles,[24] so the resident has already fulfilled the *mitzvah* of *kavod Shabbat*.[25] However, there is still the requirement of *oneg Shabbat*, which mandates that there be light wherever the resident is eating, working and sleeping.[26] Indeed, *Shulchan Arukh*[27] rules that one who is a guest at another's home must participate in lighting *Shabbat* candles, either by paying money to the host to own a part of the candles or by asking the host to give a part of the candle to him or her as a gift,[28] even if one's spouse is lighting *Shabbat* candles at home. Thus, although the resident's spouse is lighting *Shabbat* candles at home, the resident must still make sure there is light where he or she will be staying. In the hospital wing, there is already electric lighting, and therefore there would be no need to light *Shabbat* candles. However, since the resident will likely eat or sleep in the on-call room, this room is designated for the use of the resident only, and the resident is then required to ensure that there

21 4:14.
22 *Orach Chayyim*, 263:2.
23 For an introduction to how the factors of *kavod Shabbat* and *oneg Shabbat* apply in special scenarios, see *Piskei Teshuvot* 263:23, and R. Yosef Zvi Rimon's *Shiurei Hilkhot Shabbat*, pp. 53–58.
24 R. Simcha Bunim Cohen (*The Radiance of Shabbos*, p. 10, footnote 18) notes that according to R. Moshe Feinstein, there is no difference between a husband lighting and a wife lighting, so a married female resident can rely on her husband's lighting at home.
25 It should be noted that this principle does not extend to one's parents or roommates, and their lighting cannot work to exempt the resident, unless the resident will be returning home that night to eat and/or sleep. With regard to roommates, it seems that one would have to arrange with the roommate to light on his or her behalf in the shared dining room (either paying the roommate for a share of the candles' value, or having the roommate bestow that value to him or her as a gift – see *Mishnah Berurah* 263:34), then make sure to return and eat in that shared room to benefit from the light. In addition, the resident would then need to ensure that there is some light in his or her private room, to fulfill *oneg Shabbat*.
26 See *Biur Halakhah* 263:6, s.v. *bachurim*.
27 *Orach Chayyim* 263:7; see *Mishnah Berurah* 263:32.
28 See *Mishnah Berurah* 263:34.

is light in this room by lighting *Shabbat* candles. Lighting candles in the on-call room could then be accompanied by the recitation of a *berakhah* as well.[29] If the resident will be returning home to eat on Friday night, and someone will be lighting on his or her behalf at home, then he or she need not light *Shabbat* candles as long as the rooms where the resident will be working are well-lit.[30]

Using Electric Lights

Since in many cases, the resident will be required to light *Shabbat* candles, this will pose a problem in the hospital, as the hospital will generally not permit lighting candles due to the fire hazard this poses. For that reason, we must discuss an alternative option: using electric lights. Whether electric lights are considered akin to candles in *halakhah* is a complicated topic and we will only address it briefly here.[31] In a responsum, R. Ovadia Yosef[32] discusses the question of whether electric lights can be used for *Shabbat* candles. He rules that electric lights do indeed fulfill the *mitzvah* of lighting *Shabbat* candles. As part of his discussion, he rebuts several arguments by earlier authorities regarding why electric lights should not count:

1. *Levushei Mordekhai*[33] argues that *Shabbat* candles must have both oil and a wick in order to fulfill the *mitzvah*. R. Yosef refutes this argument based on the Gemara[34] which recounts the story of R. Chanina ben Dosa's daughter who was distraught since she had accidentally lit *Shabbat* candles with vinegar instead of oil. R. Chanina replied that God would ensure that just as oil burns, the vinegar

---

29 See *Shemirat Shabbat Ke-Hilkhatah* 45:3; *Nishmat Avraham* 263:2 (p. 199).

30 It is generally accepted that with the advent of electricity, one must only formally light *Shabbat* candles where one is eating, though there must be electric light in other places where one will be, due to the requirement of *oneg Shabbat*. Still, as long as there is electric light in these places, one need not light designated *Shabbat* candles and a *berakhah* is not recited. See *Shemirat Shabbat Ke-Hilkhatah* (45:3).

31 Extensive discussion of this far-reaching topic can be found in R. Michael Broyde and R. Howard Jachter, "The Use of Electricity on *Shabbat* and *Yom Tov*," *Journal of Halacha and Contemporary Society*, vol. xxı (Spring 1991); *idem.*, "Electrically Produced Fire or Light in Positive Commandments," *Journal of Halacha and Contemporary Society*, vol. xxv (Spring 1993). For a review of sources regarding using electric lights for *Shabbat* candles, see *Encyclopedia Talmudit* vol. 18, s.v. *chashmal*, section 4 (pp. 181–184); see the Appendix in that volume, section 16, for a bibliography of sources on the topic of electricity and *Shabbat*.

32 *Yechavveh Da'at* 5:24.

33 *Mahadura telita'ah*, *Orach Chayyim* 59.

34 *Ta'anit* 25a.

would burn, and her *Shabbat* candles would remain lit; indeed, miraculously, the candles lasted until after *Shabbat* was over. R. Yosef points out that if *Shabbat* candles may only be lit with oil, R. Chanina's daughter would also have been distraught over having recited a *berakhah le-vatalah*, a blessing in vain, even if the candles miraculously remained lit, since at the time she recited the blessing, the candles were filled with vinegar, which would not fulfill the *mitzvah*. Therefore, R. Yosef concludes, there is no requirement for oil or a wick in *Shabbat* candles, and electric lights fulfill the *mitzvah* as well.

2. R. Shimon Greenfeld[35] writes that while he is not well-versed in the science of electricity, he surmises that the electric lights could not be used for *Shabbat* candles because they do not contain a flame, and they cannot be used to light other flames. R. Greenfeld notes that the presence of light alone does not fulfill the *mitzvah* of lighting *Shabbat* candles, since precious stones can reflect light but obviously cannot be used as *Shabbat* candles. R. Yosef disagrees and argues that electric lights are indeed considered flames, noting that previous generations of rabbinic authorities believed this as well,[36] and thus prohibited one from turning on an incandescent light on *Shabbat*.

3. *Mishpetei Uziel* argues that electric lights do not fulfill the *mitzvah* of *Shabbat* candles because the light might suddenly turn off if there is a power outage, and then one will not be able to experience *oneg Shabbat*. R. Yosef disagrees, noting that power outages are extremely rare, and if it were necessary to be concerned for unlikely scenarios, one would also have to be concerned that a regular *Shabbat* candle might be accidentally extinguished by wind or water, such that no candle could fulfill the *mitzvah*. Thus, R. Yosef concludes, there is certainly no reason to be concerned that the power will be interrupted and the electric light will go out.

R. Yosef concludes that if at all possible, one should use regular candles, since all agree that these fulfill the *mitzvah*, and it is clearer that the intent in lighting the candles is for *kavod Shabbat*; however, in a situation where this is not possible, such as a resident on call in a hospital, one may certainly use electric lights and recite the blessing as well. R. Shlomo Zalman Auerbach[37] also allows one to use electric lights for *Shabbat* candles. However, he adds that if possible, one should light a flashlight rather than using an electric light connected to an external power source,

35 Responsa of Maharshag, 2:107.
36 Among others, R. Yosef cites R. Chaim Ozer Grodzinsky (*Achiezer* 3:60); *Chazon Ish* (50:9); the Rogatchover Gaon (cited by R. Shlomo Yosef Zevin, *Soferim U-Sefarim*, responsa, p. 316); and R. David Tzvi Hoffman (*Melammed Le-Ho'il*, 49).
37 *Shemirat Shabbat Ke-Hilkhatah*, ch. 43, footnote 22.

since the flashlight operates based on its own battery, and the presence of the light is not dependent on the operation of the electric company. This obviates a concern raised by R. Chaim Halberstam[38] that if one's light is dependent on an external source, one could not recite a *berakhah* on lighting. In addition to R. Auerbach, R. Yosef Eliyahu Henkin[39] and R. Eliezer Waldenberg[40] permit reciting a *berakhah* over electric lights, while R. Moshe Feinstein[41] and R. Yaakov Kamenetsky[42] are cited as ruling that one should *not* recite a *berakhah* over electric lights.

Importantly, we must note that the entire preceding discussion is only in reference to incandescent lights. This is because in incandescent lights, the metal filament inside the bulb is heated until it glows, producing light. According to Rambam,[43] heating metal until it glows is a violation of the Biblical prohibition of lighting a flame, and thus we can extrapolate that an incandescent bulb is akin to a flame which is required for *Shabbat* candles. Fluorescent light is certainly not considered a flame, since the light is produced by excitation of a gas inside the bulb and subsequent photon emission from that gas, and this is not considered a flame in *halakhah*. Similarly, LED lights produce light when electrons in a semiconductor reach a low-energy state and can release the extra energy as light; this, too, is not considered a halakhic flame. Indeed, R. Shmuel Yudelevitz[44] notes clearly that fluorescent lights do not qualify for *Shabbat* candles because there is no flame. Given the relative novelty of fluorescent lighting, this distinction is not discussed explicitly by many of the above *poskim*, though it is difficult to ascertain whether this is because they did not intend to address fluorescent lighting, and they would only permit using incandescent lights, or because they believe there is no halakhic distinction. Indeed, R. Howard Jachter and R. Michael Broyde[45] argue that R. Yehoshua Neuwirth[46] and R. Ovadia Yosef[47] might believe that fluorescent and LED lights can be used for *Shabbat* candles, as they do not mention any distinction in this context, yet they do specify that only incandescent lights can be used for

---

38 *Yerushat Peleitah*, 7.
39 *Edut Le-Yisra'el*, p. 123.
40 *Tzitz Eliezer*, 1:20, ch. 11.
41 Cited in R. Simcha Bunim Cohen's *The Radiance of Shabbos*, p. 12, footnote 26.
42 Cited in R. Dovid Ribiat's *The 39 Melochos*, vol. 1, introduction to *melekhet Shabbat*, footnote 697.
43 *Shabbat* 12:1.
44 *Ha-Chashmal Le-Or Ha-Halakhah*, 3:6.
45 "Electrically Produced Fire or Light in Positive Commandments," *Journal of Halacha and Contemporary Society*, vol. xxv, Spring 1993, p. 98 and footnote 26.
46 *Shemirat Shabbat Ke-Hilkhatah* 43:4.
47 *Yalkut Yosef* 264:62.

havdalah.[48] A more explicit stance on this issue is cited from R. Yosef Shalom Elyashiv,[49] who is noted to have permitted the use of fluorescent lights for *Shabbat* candles because the requirement is that one produce illumination for *Shabbat*, and there is no requirement for a flame.[50] R. Eliezer Melamed[51] recommends using incandescent lights only; if one only has a fluorescent light, he recommends lighting it without a *berakhah*, but suggests that one who relies on the lenient view and recites a *berakhah* is on solid ground.

Thus, in situations where a resident must light *Shabbat* candles, as outlined above, the resident should prepare by bringing a flashlight containing (preferably) an incandescent bulb to the hospital (ensuring in advance that the battery is still functional) and lighting it in the room where he or she will eat. If the resident did not bring a flashlight, he or she can use any incandescent light in that room, or according to some views, even a fluorescent or LED light.

Kiddush

The resident on call Friday night is required to recite *kiddush*. While we will not discuss all the laws of *kiddush* here, we will discuss three issues that are specifically relevant to the resident:

1. While *kiddush* is traditionally recited on wine, one who does not have wine[52] may recite *kiddush* on bread instead during the evening *kiddush*, although not for the daytime *kiddush*.[53] For the daytime *kiddush*, one could use *chamar medinah*, generally

48 *Shemirat Shabbat Ke-Hilkhatah* 61:32; *Yalkut Yosef* 298:5.
49 Cited in *Shevut Yitzchak*, vol. 8, chapter 3.
50 The authors of *Encyclopedia Talmudit* (s.v. *chashmal*, footnote 308) suggest that a precedent for this position can be found in *Moshav Zekeinim* (Leviticus 24:2), which cites the view of Rabbeinu Meshulam who states that a luminescent precious stone can be used for *Shabbat* candles. Even Rabbeinu Tam, cited there as disagreeing, argues only that an act of lighting is required, disqualifying the use of the stone; however, he might agree that if one is turning on a fluorescent light, this would suffice for the *mitzvah* of lighting *Shabbat* candles, as he appears not to dispute the assumption that no flame is needed.
51 *Peninei Halakhah, Shabbat* 4:5, footnote 2.
52 Although most *rishonim* understand the Gemara (*Pesachim* 106b) to suggest that there is no preference for wine over bread, Rabbeinu Tam (*Tosafot* ad loc, s.v. *mekadesh a-rifta*) understands the Gemara differently, arguing that one may not recite *kiddush* on bread, and therefore Rama (*Orach Chayyim* 272:9) rules that one should not recite *kiddush* on bread if wine is available.
53 *Maggid Mishneh* (*Hilkhot Shabbat* 29:10) explains that *kiddush* is not recited on bread during the day because there is no special *berakhah* for *kiddush* during the day, and so if one simply recited *ha-motzi* as *kiddush*,

understood as another alcoholic beverage such as beer or liquor, for the recitation of *kiddush*.[54] There is some debate about whether non-alcoholic beverages are included in *chamar medinah*. While R. Ovadia Yosef[55] does not permit using non-alcoholic beverages, *Arukh Ha-Shulchan* cites lenient opinions regarding tea or milk, and R. Moshe Feinstein[56] writes that in a dire situation one may recite *kiddush* on tea, milk, or any beverage that is consumed not for the express purpose of quenching thirst (thus, R. Feinstein excludes soda from the category of *chamar medinah*). R. Eliezer Waldenberg[57] and R. Yehoshua Neuwirth[58] also permit these beverages for use during the daytime *kiddush* when there are no others available. Only if wine and *chamar medinah* are not available, one may use bread for the daytime *kiddush*.[59] Similarly, only if wine and bread are not available during the evening, several authorities allow one to use *chamar medinah* for the evening *kiddush*.[60] Thus, a resident on call during *Shabbat* should make sure to bring a small bottle of grape juice to the hospital for the recitation of *kiddush*. If one forgot or was unable to do so, then at night one should recite *kiddush* on bread (which one should have anyway for the purpose of the *Shabbat* meal), while in the daytime one should recite *kiddush* on *chamar medinah* including tea, coffee,[61] or milk. Alcoholic beverages should be avoided as these can impair physician judgment.

2. There is some discussion among contemporary *poskim* regarding the type of cup one may use for *kiddush*. R. Moshe Feinstein[62]

---

there would be no way to know that this *berakhah* is intended for *kiddush*, in order to fulfill *kavod Shabbat*.

54 *Shulchan Arukh* and Rama, *Orach Chayyim* 272:9.
55 *Yabbia Omer, Orach Chayyim* 3:19, *Yechavveh Da'at* 2:38.
56 *Iggerot Moshe, Orach Chayyim* 2:75.
57 *Tzitz Eliezer* 8:16.
58 *Shemirat Shabbat Ke-Hilkhatah,* 50:9-11.
59 *Shulchan Arukh, Orach Chayyim* 289:2; *Mishnah Berurah* 289:10; *Arukh Ha-Shulchan, Orach Chayyim* 289:5.
60 These include R. Shlomo Zalman Auerbach (*Shemirat Shabbat Ke-Hilkhatah* ch. 53, footnote 7) and R. Ovadia Yosef (*Yabbia Omer* vol. 3 19:10).
61 Regarding instant coffee, which may be more easily available to residents than other beverages, R. Shlomo Zalman Auerbach (*Shemirat Shabbat Ke-Hilkhatah,* ch. 60, footnote 18) permits its use for *kiddush* and *havdalah*. R. Yehoshua Neuwirth (ibid.) notes, however, that based on a ruling of *Arukh ha-Shulkhan* (*Orach Chayyim* 296:13), it might appear that instant coffee could not be used, as it is simply water with an added solute.
62 *Iggerot Moshe* 3:39.

writes that one should not use a disposable paper cup for *kiddush*.[63] He explains that the Gemara[64] requires that a cup of wine used for *kiddush* must be "*chai*," which *Tosafot*[65] explain to mean that the cup must be whole; this is indeed the ruling of *Shulchan Arukh*.[66] R. Feinstein extrapolates that the requirement of "*chai*" indicates that the cup must be beautiful, and since a paper cup is disposable and insignificant, it does not meet this requirement and may not be used for *kiddush*. However, he suggests that there may be some room for leniency if no other options are available. R. Eliezer Waldenberg[67] disagrees with R. Feinstein, arguing that a broken cup is disqualified for use in *kiddush* since it was once whole, and its breakage invalidates it, whereas a disposable paper cup is just as it was when it was created, and it is thus fit for *kiddush*.[68] R. Yosef Eliyahu Henkin[69] and R. Ovadia Yosef[70] both rule that while a more beautiful cup is preferred for *kiddush*, if one is not available, one may certainly use a disposable cup. R. Shlomo Zalman Auerbach[71] also rules that a disposable cup is not preferable, but may be used; he notes that especially in the case of a beautiful disposable cup which is intended for this purpose, and which could be used at a distinguished meal, one may certainly use such a cup for *kiddush*. In the case of a resident working at a hospital, when no other cup is available, most authorities would permit using

63 R. Simcha Bunim Cohen (*The Radiance of Shabbos*, p. 43, footnote 5) adds that he asked R. Feinstein about using a sturdier disposable plastic cup, and that R. Feinstein did not distinguish between paper and plastic cups.

64 *Berakhot* 51a.

65 *Berakhot* 50b s.v. *modim*; *Shabbat* 76b s.v. *kedei*.

66 *Orach Chayyim* 183:3. While this ruling is with respect to the cup used for *birkat ha-mazon*, *Mishnah Berurah* (271:44) notes that elsewhere *Shulchan Arukh* (*Orach Chayyim* 271:10) explains that the requirements for the cup for *kiddush* and for *birkat ha-mazon* are identical.

67 *Tzitz Eliezer*, 12:23.

68 R. Waldenberg also refutes an argument of the Satmar Rebbe (cited in *Sheraga Ha-Me'ir* 55:2), who suggests that according to Rambam (*Keilim* 5:7), disposable vessels are not considered vessels (and thus, in that context, cannot become ritually impure). R. Waldenberg explains that in the case discussed by Rambam there, the vessel in question was one which no one may ever have intended to use as a vessel, and thus can only become ritually impure if one had intended to use it as a vessel. In contrast, a disposable paper cup was manufactured in order to be used as a cup, and so it is fit for *kiddush*. R. Waldenberg also notes that Rambam elsewhere (*Keilim* 2:1) explicitly rules that a vessel made out of flimsy paper can still become ritually impure.

69 Responsum published in *Am Ha-Torah* vol. 10 (5739), p. 6.

70 *Yalkut Yosef*, *Shabbat* vol. 1, 271:41 and footnote 53 (pp. 277–278).

71 *Shemirat Shabbat Ke-Hilkhatah* 47:11 footnote 51.

a disposable *kiddush* cup. However, if possible, the resident should consider bringing a beautiful *kiddush* cup to the hospital, which is not only preferred for *kiddush*, but which will also enhance one's *Shabbat* observance in the less festive atmosphere found in the hospital where the resident is spending *Shabbat*.

3. The Gemara[72] establishes that *kiddush* must be recited in a place where one is eating (*kiddush be-makom seudah*). As part of this requirement, Rama[73] stipulates that immediately after reciting *kiddush*, one must eat a *Shabbat* meal in that location.[74] This might be a problem for a resident on *Shabbat*, who might recite *kiddush* but be called to attend to a patient before being able to eat. *Nishmat Avraham*, however, cites R. Yehoshua Neuwirth who rules that as long as one remained in the same hospital building, one need not recite *kiddush* again. He argues that since the entire hospital building is owned by one proprietor, and the resident reciting *kiddush* knew that it was possible that he or she might get called away to take care of a patient, there is no need to recite *kiddush* again. With regard to what must be eaten following *kiddush*, one may eat either a *kezayit* of bread or other food which requires a *mezonot*,[75] or may drink an extra *revi'it* of wine in addition to the cheekful (*melo lugmav*) which one drank to fulfill the *mitzvah* of *kiddush*.[76]

Shabbat Meals

The Gemara[77] states that one is required to eat three meals over the course of *Shabbat*, and promises that one who fulfills this *mitzvah* will be saved from future calamities that will precede the Messianic era. For a hospital resident, it may be difficult to eat these three meals in the way that one would normally eat them at home, but the resident must do his or her utmost to perform this *mitzvah*.

If a resident was on call Friday night, and had no time to eat a *Shabbat* meal, Rama[78] rules that he or she is then required to eat three meals on *Shabbat* day, one before midday and two after midday. On the other hand, if a resident finds only a very short time to eat on Friday night, but is worried that if he or she recites *kiddush*, there will not be enough time to eat the requisite-sized meal, *Nishmat Avraham*[79] cites

72 *Pesachim* 101a.
73 *Orach Chayyim*, 273:3.
74 *Mishnah Berurah* (273:14) notes that one may interrupt between recitation of *kiddush* and eating a meal in order to prepare for the meal.
75 See *Magen Avraham* 273:11 and *Mishnah Berurah* 273:25.
76 *Shulchan Arukh, Orach Chayyim* 273:5; *Mishnah Berurah* 273:21–22.
77 *Shabbat* 117b–118a.
78 Commentary to *Shulchan Arukh, Orach Chayyim* 291:1.
79 *Orach Chayyim*, 271:2(4), p. 211.

R. Yehoshua Neuwirth who rules that one may eat the meal without reciting *kiddush*, especially if one was able to recite *ma'ariv* so that he or she already recited *kiddush* as part of *shemoneh esrei*. In either case, since one did not recite *kiddush* at night, one should recite the nighttime *kiddush* before one's first meal of the day,[80] omitting only "*vayekhulu*," since this prayer refers to God's completion of creation which occurred on Friday evening.[81]

As part of the requirement of eating *Shabbat* meals, one must recite *ha-motzi* on two whole loaves or rolls of bread (*lechem mishneh*).[82] With regard to the third meal (*se'udah shelishit*) on *Shabbat* afternoon, Rama[83] cites differing opinions about whether *lechem mishneh* is required, though he advises that one should try to procure *lechem mishneh* for this meal too, and *Mishnah Berurah*[84] concurs. *Shulchan Arukh* also cites some opinions that allow for eating *mezonot*, or meat or fish, or even fruit, for *seudah shlishit*, though he recommends that one should eat bread if possible. For the first two meals, however, it is clear that one must have *lechem mishneh* at each of these meals. *Shulchan Arukh*[85] rules that one should eat an egg-sized amount (*ke-beitzah*) of bread at each meal, and *Mishnah Berurah*[86] adds that one should eat slightly more than this amount so that one's eating is considered an established meal (*se'udat keva*), though if this is not possible, one may eat even an olive-sized amount (*ke-zayit*) of bread.

---

80   *Shulchan Arukh, Orach Chayyim* 271:8.
81   Rama, commentary to *Shulchan Arukh*, ibid, and *Mishnah Berurah* 271:40. *Mishnah Berurah* (271:39; see also *Sha'ar Ha-Tziyyun* 47) adds that one may recite *kiddush* until sunset on Saturday night. If one did not recite *kiddush* until that point, one may still recite *kiddush* until nightfall (during the *bein ha-shemashot* period, when it is uncertain whether it is *Shabbat*). However, as *Peri Megadim* (*Mishbetzot Zahav* 271:11) advises, if one was able to recite any *shemoneh esrei* over the course of *Shabbat*, one should omit God's name from the *kiddush* when reciting it after sunset. This is because according to *Magen Avraham* (271:1), the recitation of *shemoneh esrei* may fulfill one's Biblical requirement of *kiddush*, such that recitation of *kiddush* over wine is only a rabbinic requirement, and in cases of uncertainty regarding rabbinic requirements, we are more lenient, such that it is advised not to recite God's name. However, if one did not recite *shemonei esrei* over the course of *Shabbat*, one should still recite God's name in *kiddush*, since one's *kiddush* fulfills a Biblical requirement, and we are stricter regarding uncertainty in Biblical requirements.
82   *Shabbat* 117b; *Shulchan Arukh, Orach Chayyim* 274:1.
83   Commentary to *Shulchan Arukh, Orach Chayyim* 291:4.
84   291:20.
85   *Orach Chayyim* 291:1.
86   291:2.

Havdalah

At the conclusion of *Shabbat*, one is required to recite *havdalah* in order to signal the end of *Shabbat*. Without recitation of *havdalah*, one is still bound by the prohibition of performing *melakhah* on *Shabbat*. Therefore, for a resident on duty, it is imperative that one formally end *Shabbat* as soon as nightfall comes so that one may perform *melakhah* on behalf of one's patients without any violation of *Shabbat*. If the resident cannot recite *havdalah* immediately after the end of *Shabbat*, he or she should instead recite the phrase *"barukh ha-mavdil bein kodesh le-chol,"* which allows one to perform *melakhah*, though one must still recite *havdalah* later.[87]

In order to recite *havdalah*, one must procure wine, *besamim* (spices) and a flame. Each of these may present some difficulty for a resident on duty:

1. Although one should ideally recite *havdalah* with wine (or for a resident on call, grape juice), if this is not available, one may use *chamar medinah*, such as beer; as noted above, a resident on call could use milk, coffee or tea.[88] One may not use bread for *havdalah*.[89]

2. The *berakhah* of *borei minei besamim* may be recited on any spice.[90] If one does not have *besamim*, one may still recite *havdalah* without reciting this *berakhah*,[91] and if one procures the *besamim* later, he or she may recite the *berakhah* then. Conversely, if one knows one will be unable to recite *havdalah* later that night, but one does have access to *besamim*, one may recite that *berakhah* alone.[92]

3. The *berakhah* of *borei me'orei ha-esh* should ideally be recited over the flame of a "torch," that is, a flame emanating from two separate wicks.[93] However, if one is only able to procure a flame emanating from a single wick, one may still recite *borei me'orei ha-esh* on this flame.[94] The question of whether the resident may use an electric

---

87 *Shulchan Arukh, Orach Chayyim* 299:10.

88 See the above discussion regarding *kiddush* for a full discussion of what is included within the category of *chamar medinah*.

89 *Shulchan Arukh*, ibid.

90 Some plausible options that one might find in the hospital include coffee, aromatic fruit, cinnamon, and lemon juice.

91 *Shulchan Arukh, Orach Chayyim* 298:1.

92 Rama, *Orach Chayyim* 298:1.

93 *Shulchan Arukh* and Rama, *Orach Chayyim* 299:2.

94 *Shulchan Arukh* ibid. and Mishnah *Berurah* 299:7. *Mishnah Berurah* (299:6) explains that a torch is preferable so that it is recognizable that the light is being used for a *mitzvah*. R. Yehoshua Neuwirth (*Shemirat Shabbat Ke-Hilkhatah* ch. 61, footnote 76) notes that nowadays, since we have electric lighting, this requirement is less essential since it is clear that when one lights a candle, there is a special significance of the candle which indicates that it is being used for a *mitzvah*.

flame for *havdalah* is similar to the question discussed earlier of using an electric light for *Shabbat* candles. As in that case, a fluorescent or LED light is not considered a flame for this purpose and may not be used. Even with regard to an incandescent light, there is a unique concern with using the light for *havdalah*, in that the light is inside the bulb. This creates a problem, since Rashi[95] writes, based on his interpretation of the Gemara, that one may not use a light for *havdalah* that is obscured by glass. This is also the ruling of *Shulchan Arukh*,[96] who writes in *Beit Yosef*[97] that the Yerushalmi[98] also appears to rule this way. However, *Magen Avraham*,[99] based on the objection of Rashba,[100] argues that the Gemara is not discussing glass. Rashba contends that the Gemara cannot be discussing glass, since the Gemara elsewhere[101] writes that one may not recite *keriat shema* in the presence of an immodestly dressed person who can be seen through glass, indicating that if one can see something through glass, this is indeed significant. However, *Biur Halakhah*[102] argues that one should follow the ruling of *Shulchan Arukh*, since it is ostensibly followed by Rama[103] and the Vilna Gaon.[104] This is also the ruling of R. Ovadia Yosef.[105] R. Tzvi Pesach Frank[106] argues that one may not use electric light for *havdalah* since it is not considered fire and therefore one may not recite the blessing *borei me'orei ha-esh*. Other *acharonim* permitted the use of electric lights for *havdalah*, including R. Chaim Soloveichik[107] and R. Chaim Ozer Grodzinski,[108] and this is also the opinion of several contemporary authorities

---

95 *Berakhot* 53b, s.v. *pannas*.
96 *Orach Chayyim* 298:15.
97 *Orach Chayyim* 298:15.
98 *Berakhot* 8:6.
99 298:20.
100 *Berakhot* 53b, s.v. *haytah*.
101 *Berakhot* 25b.
102 298 s.v. *o be-tokh aspaklaria*.
103 *Darkhei Mosheh Ha-Arokh* 298 s.v. *ve-suma*. Rama does not disagree with *Shulchan Arukh*, leading *Biur Halakhah* to argue that he agrees with *Shulchan Arukh*'s ruling.
104 *Biur Ha-Gra, Orach Chayyim* 298:15 s.v. *aspaklaria*.
105 *Yabbia Omer* 1:17–18, 6:48:12, 4:40:5; *Yechavveh Da'at* 2:39; *Yalkut Yosef* 298:5 (*Shabbat* vol. 1, p. 473).
106 *Har Tzvi, Orach Chayyim* 2:114. He also rules that one may not use electric lights for *Shabbat* candles.
107 Cited in *Nachalat Shimon* 15.
108 Cited in *Kokhevei Yitzchak*, 1:11.

including R. Eliezer Waldenberg[109] and R. Aharon Lichtenstein.[110] As is his view for *Shabbat* candles, R. Moshe Feinstein rules that if one uses electric lights for *havdalah*, one should not recite a *berakhah*.[111] As with *besamim*, one may recite *Havdalah* without reciting the *berakhah* of *borei me'orei ha-esh*, and then recite that *berakhah* later in the evening if one procures an appropriate flame.[112]

There is a debate as to whether women are required to recite *havdalah*. *Shulchan Arukh*[113] cites a view that women are required to recite *havdalah* just as they are required to recite *kiddush*. Although women are generally exempt from time-bound positive *mitzvot*, they are obligated in positive *mitzvot* related to *Shabbat*, since they are already obligated in the negative commandments related to *Shabbat*.[114] However, *Shulchan Arukh* cites an opposing view that women are not required to recite *havdalah*, and on this basis, Rama recommends that a woman hear *havdalah* from a man who is required to recite it. *Bach*[115] questions the Rama's logic: generally, women are permitted and encouraged to perform positive commandments from which they are exempt, and are even permitted (according to Ashkenazim) to recite the accompanying blessing. *Magen Avraham*[116] offers a resolution: perhaps women are permitted to perform time-bound *mitzvot* with a *berakhah* when the *mitzvah* is performing some action, but if the *mitzvah* is *only* the *berakhah*, women would not be permitted to recite the *berakhah* unless they are obligated to do so. Despite this explanation, *Magen Avraham* rules against Rama and permits women to recite *havdalah* for themselves. On the other hand, *Taz*[117] rules that *havdalah* is different from other time-bound positive *mitzvot* which women may perform themselves since it is only a rabbinic obligation,[118] and therefore women

---

109 *Tzitz Eliezer* 1:20, ch. 13. He posits that there is no concern due to the fire being inside glass, since that is the nature of electric light. Moreover, he argues that earlier sources cite *Pirkei De-Rabi Eliezer* (ch. 20) which permits using starlight for *havdalah*, which would suggest that one may certainly use electric light.
110 Cited by R. Yosef Zvi Rimon in *Shiurei Hilkhot Shabbat*, p. 135.
111 Cited by R. Simcha Bunim Cohen in *The Radiance of Shabbos*, pp. 19, 137.
112 *Shulchan Arukh, Orach Chayyim* 298:1.
113 *Orach Chayyim*, 296:8
114 See *Berakhot* 20b.
115 *Orach Chayyim* 296.
116 296:11.
117 *Orach Chayyim* 296:7.
118 The assertion that *havdalah* is only a rabbinic requirement is subject to debate. Rambam (*Sefer Ha-Mitzvot, aseh* 155) and *Semag* (*aseh* 29) believe that *havdalah* is required by the Torah as part of *zakhor et yom ha-Shabbat le-kadesho*, remembering *Shabbat*. Another possible source is the verse, "*u-lehavdil bein ha-kodesh...*," which appears in the Torah (in a different context) immediately before the laws of childbirth, which the Gemara

should not recite *havdalah* themselves. *Mishnah Berurah*[119] and *Arukh Ha-Shulchan*[120] rule that a woman should preferably hear *havdalah* from a man, but if this is not possible, she may recite it herself. Thus, it would appear that a female resident on call in the hospital at the end of *Shabbat* who has the necessary items for *havdalah* may recite it for herself.

Shabbat Checklist

The resident who is on call over part of *Shabbat* should plan ahead and remember to bring the following items:

- *Shabbat*-appropriate outfit
- Electric lights for *Shabbat* candles (have extra batteries just in case)
- Wine or grape juice (Friday night, *Shabbat* morning, *havdalah*)
- *Kiddush* cup
- Two rolls for *lechem mishneh* for each *Shabbat* meal
- Special food for *Shabbat* meals
- Fragrance for *havdalah*
- Candle to light for *havdalah*, if possible

(*Shevuot* 18b) uses as a basis for a homiletical note that reciting *havdalah* after *Shabbat* will cause one to merit male children. However, *Maggid Mishneh* (*Shabbat* 29:1) cites an opinion that *havdalah* is only a rabbinic requirement. In any case, all opinions agree that the requirement to recite *havdalah* on a cup of wine is only a rabbinic requirement, and according to the Torah, one would suffice by saying *barukh ha-mavdil bein kodesh le-chol*.

119 298:36.
120 *Orach Chayyim*, 298:5.

Chapter 24

Phlebotomy and Related Procedures on *Shabbat*

Jerry Karp, MD, PhD

Many of the most halakhically complex and problematic duties of a resident (or any clinician) on *Shabbat* involve procedures that puncture the patient's skin, such as drawing blood, administering injections, and aspirating fluid. In this chapter, we will discuss whether these procedures may be performed on *Shabbat*. Recall[1] that for any given procedure, if the procedure is necessary to prevent possible danger to the patient, then performing the procedure is certainly allowed. However, even in this case, if a procedure is generally prohibited on *Shabbat*, then it would be preferable to perform it in an irregular manner (using a *shinui*) if possible. Additionally, if one is performing a procedure for a patient who is not dangerously ill, then only rabbinic prohibitions may be violated, and only with a *shinui*. Thus, it is important to ascertain whether a given procedure is permitted, and if not, we must ascertain what level of prohibition it violates.

Tearing Open Equipment Packaging

Many of the items used in drawing blood or in similar procedures must first be removed from their packaging. Therefore, we begin with a discussion regarding whether it is permitted on *Shabbat* to tear open packaging.

Although most authorities assume that tearing paper violates the *melakhah* of *kore'a*, tearing,[2] one may argue that this action is more

---

1   See Chapter 20.
2   There is a debate among *acharonim* regarding whether tearing paper is a violation of *kore'a* on *Shabbat*, or whether this *melakhah* only applies to fabric or other materials which are made of individual components which

IV. Residency and Shabbat

consistent with destruction, since it results in functional loss to the packaging, and destructive actions (*mekalkel*) are not Biblically prohibited on *Shabbat*, though they are still rabbinically prohibited. Indeed, the Mishnah[3] already notes that tearing for a destructive purpose is not a Biblical prohibition. However, we must inquire as to whether tearing open a package is indeed destructive, since one has achieved a constructive purpose by gaining access to what is inside the package. This question is debated by *acharonim* with regard to tearing open the seal on a letter on *Shabbat*. *Peri Chadash*[4] rules that tearing open a seal on *Shabbat* is a Biblical prohibition, while *Chakham Tzvi*[5] argues that one may ask a non-Jew to tear open the seal, suggesting that the prohibition is only rabbinic. *Biur Halakhah*[6] suggests that *Chakham Tzvi's* rationale is that tearing the seal on the letter is considered a *melakhah she-einah tzerikhah le-gufah*, a *melakhah* performed for an alternate purpose from the conventional one associated with the *melakhah*, since one's tearing does not accomplish any purpose with respect to the letter itself, but simply allows one to gain access to the letter. However, *Biur Halakhah* argues against this logic, stating that this case is one in which the tearing indeed accomplishes a constructive purpose with regard to the letter itself, and therefore tearing the seal on the letter should be prohibited by the Torah. He notes, though, that tearing is only considered a

---

one separates by tearing. Rambam (*Shabbat* 10:11, 23:6) and *Shulchan Arukh* (*Orach Chayyim* 340:17) write that one who tears a paper violates *Shabbat* because in doing so, a functional item is created, namely, a piece of paper that is of the desired size. They only mention that one has violated the *melakhah* of *kore'a* in a case where two pieces of paper were fastened to one another and were separated. *Shulchan Arukh Ha-Rav* (*Orach Chayyim* 340:17) concludes from this that the prohibition of *kore'a* applies only when one is separating two materials from one another, like when one is tearing fabric (since one is separating the threads from one another), but not in a case where one is tearing a whole entity, such as paper or leather. *Nishmat Adam* (*Hilkhot Shabbat* 29:2) proposes this distinction as well, but rejects it, noting that the Yerushalmi (*Shabbat* 7:2) already discusses the *melakhah* of *kore'a* with regard to leather. Similarly, *Biur Halakhah* (340 s.v. *ein shovrin*) completely rejects the distinction of *Shulchan Arukh Ha-Rav*. He proposes a novel explanation of Rambam and *Shulchan Arukh*, arguing that *kore'a* applies only when one intends to use both sides of the material being torn, on both sides of the tear. Thus, one who tears paper and intends to use only the torn piece of paper that results, and not the piece of paper from which it is torn, does not violate *kore'a*. However, when one separates two fastened pieces of paper, one intends to use both, and therefore one does violate *kore'a*. Indeed, most *acharonim* generally assume that *kore'a* does apply to paper.

3   *Shabbat* 105b.
4   *Yoreh De'ah* 118:1.
5   *Siman* 39.
6   340 s.v. *ha-neyar*.

constructive act with regard to a seal on a folded letter (e.g., a wax seal). This excludes tearing an envelope open to retrieve the letter inside as one does not need the envelope afterward, and thus tearing the envelope is a destructive act.[7] R. Moshe Feinstein[8] also concludes that tearing open the seal on an envelope is only a rabbinic prohibition.

In any case, even if destructive tearing is a rabbinic prohibition, this will pose a problem for a resident performing a procedure on a patient who is not dangerously ill, since then one may only perform rabbinic prohibitions with a *shinui*. However, many *poskim* permit tearing open packaging on *Shabbat*, as long as no useful container is created in the process. This dispensation is based on the Tosefta[9] which permits tearing open the leather covering of a wine barrel on *Shabbat*, as long as one does not intend to create a spout. Indeed, *Beit Yosef*,[10] *Magen Avraham*[11] and *Mishnah Berurah*[12] cite this Tosefta and rule in accordance with it. However, the rationale for this dispensation is unclear, and several explanations are offered by contemporary *poskim*:[13]

1. One explanation offered is that there is indeed a rabbinic prohibition in this act of tearing, as destructive tearing is still rabbinically prohibited, but the rabbinic prohibition of performing destructive *melakhah* is suspended in cases of *Shabbat*-related need. This explanation is similar to that offered by Rashi[14] in explaining why one is permitted, according to the Mishnah,[15] to break open a barrel containing dried figs on *Shabbat*. He notes that this is a destructive act which is permitted on *Shabbat*. Other *rishonim* clarify that while destructive acts are generally rabbinically prohibited on *Shabbat*, Rashi is arguing that they are permitted when there is a *Shabbat*-related need. It should be noted that other *rishonim* do

---

7   He ultimately argues that one should ideally not rely on this explanation and should not ask a non-Jew to open the envelope, since he believes that R. Yehudah's opinion in the Gemara is that even when one performs a destructive *melakhah* that causes a constructive outcome in another context, this is still a Biblical prohibition on *Shabbat*.
8   *Iggerot Moshe, Orach Chayyim* 1:122 *anaf* 8.
9   *Shabbat* 16:13 and *Beitzah* 3:13 (Lieberman edition).
10 *Orach Chayyim* 314.
11 *Orach Chayyim* 314:14.
12 314:25.
13 According to *Shulchan Arukh Ha-Rav*, discussed in footnote 2, the explanation of the Tosefta is that one may tear the leather covering a barrel on *Shabbat* because tearing leather is never considered a violation of the *melakhah* of kore'a. Another explanation of the Tosefta, offered by *Chazon Yechezkel* (*Beitzah* 3:9) is that the leather covering is treated like the barrel itself, and since there cannot be "tearing" of the barrel, there is also no *melakhah* of kore'a with respect to the leather covering.
14 *Shabbat* 146a s.v. *shover*.
15 *Shabbat* 146a.

not cite Rashi's principle, and explain the Mishnah differently; in particular, *Tosafot*[16] and Rosh[17] argue that breaking a barrel would violate the prohibition of *soter*, destroying a structure, on *Shabbat*, were it not for the fact that the barrel in this case is a *mosteki*, an unstable structure formed by gluing together broken pieces. This is also the ruling of *Shulchan Arukh*.[18] Still, R. Ovadia Yosef[19] and R. Moshe Feinstein[20] argue that this is the basis for the Tosefta's dispensation. According to this reasoning, the resident can tear open the packaging even without a *shinui* since the medical supplies are certainly considered a *Shabbat*-related need.

2. *Shevitat Shabbat*[21] argues that when a wrapper envelops food which is needed on *Shabbat*, the wrapper is considered secondary to the food, just like the shell of a nut, and may thus be torn open on *Shabbat*. This is similar to the ruling of *Shulchan Arukh*,[22] based on *Kol Bo*'s understanding of the Gemara,[23] that one may cut open a basket of dried figs on *Shabbat* to access the dried figs because it is considered similar to the shell of a nut that one may cut open to access the nut. R. Shlomo Zalman Auerbach[24] also subscribes to this explanation and permits tearing open food packages on *Shabbat* for this reason. He further extends this dispensation to opening packages that contain non-food items.[25] Similar to *Shevitat Shabbat*'s explanation, *Chazon Ish*[26] proposes that when one is tearing destructively to access the item inside, this is not considered the *melakhah* of *kore'a* at all.

Thus, according to most *poskim*, the resident would be permitted to tear open the packaging to access the medical supplies necessary for the procedure, and a *shinui* would not be necessary.

However, the resident must still be concerned with tearing the packaging across letters. Indeed, *Mishnah Berurah*,[27] in writing about tearing a seal on a letter, notes that in addition to the concern of tearing

16 *Eruvin* 34b s.v. *ve-amai.*
17 *Eruvin* 3:5.
18 *Orach Chayyim* 314:1.
19 *Yalkut Yosef, Shabbat* vol. 2, 314 footnote 22 (p. 520).
20 *Iggerot Moshe, Orach Chayyim* 1:122, *anaf* 8.
21 *Ma'aseh Choshev* ch. 3.
22 *Orach Chayyim* 314:8.
23 *Shabbat* 146a.
24 Cited in *Shemirat Shabbat Ke-Hilkhatah* 9:3, footnote 11.
25 R. Yehoshua Neuwirth, in *Shemirat Shabbat Ke-Hilkhatah*, does not mention any distinction between food and non-food items, and the dispensation to open packages for non-food items is implied in several rulings in *Shemirat Shabbat Ke-Hilkhatah*, e.g., 16:18.
26 *Orach Chayyim* 51:13.
27 340:41.

on *Shabbat*, there is a separate concern of tearing through writing. Similarly, R. Shlomo Zalman Auerbach[28] rules that it is prohibited to tear open a package when this will involve tearing through letters, since this violates the *melakhah* of *mochek*, erasing. It should be noted that the prohibition in question is only rabbinic, since one is not erasing for the purpose of writing in the same space, and the action one is performing is entirely destructive (*mekalkel*) – there is no utility to the erasing itself.[29]

There may be some room for leniency in this situation. R. Yechezkel Landau[30] discusses a similar case, that of cutting a cake which has writing on it. Although Rama,[31] based on the ruling of Mordekhai,[32] prohibits cutting the cake on *Shabbat*, R. Landau argues that it should be permitted, since one does not want the writing on the cake to be erased, making this situation a *pesik reisha de-lo nicha lei*, an unavoidable but undesirable ancillary outcome of an action. Although this is generally not sufficient to permit an action, in this case there are two factors which make the action only rabbinically prohibited, namely, that the action has no constructive purpose and is thus *mekalkel*, and also that one is erasing in an indirect manner (*ke-le'achar yad*). Therefore, R. Landau argues, this case is permitted, since it is a *pesik reisha de-lo nicha lei* in a situation with two factors which downgrade the *melakhah* to a rabbinic prohibition.[33] The case of opening a wrapper with writing on it is similar, in that destroying the text is a *pesik reisha de-lo nicha lei*, and involves the same two rabbinic factors, and thus it would appear that R. Landau would permit this case as well. R. Ovadia Yosef[34] permits this for similar reasons.

Another possible reason for leniency might be the position of Rama[35] and *Taz*[36] that separating letters, or even parts of a letter, from one another on *Shabbat* is permitted. The basis for their ruling is the Gemara[37] which states that one violates the *melakhah* of *kotev*, writing, which requires that one write two letters on *Shabbat*, even if one writes

28 Cited in *Shemirat Shabbat Ke-Hilkhatah*, 9:12 and footnote 47.
29 R. Auerbach adds that while he considers tearing a wrapper itself to be permissible when the item inside is needed for *Shabbat*, since it is like opening a nut, such logic is not applicable to permit erasing.
30 *Dagul Me-Revavah, Orach Chayyim*, 340.
31 *Orach Chayyim*, 340:3.
32 *Shabbat* 369.
33 R. Landau argues that the case that Mordekhai was discussing was that of a *children's* cake which had letters written on it for the purpose of the children eating the letters as a positive omen.
34 *Yalkut Yosef, Shabbat* vol. 2, 314:19 and footnote 21. R. Yosef rules that this case would be permitted as a *pesik reisha de-lo nicha lei* even with only one factor downgrading the prohibition to a rabbinic one.
35 Responsa 119.
36 *Orach Chayyim* 340:2.
37 *Shabbat* 104a.

two letters in two separate places. This indicates that the letters constitute writing even if they are separated, and therefore, just as one violates a *melakhah* by writing two letters separately, one does not violate a *melakhah* when the letters are separated, since they are still considered writing, and one has not erased the writing.[38] This would suggest that tearing open a wrapper, thereby separating parts of the letters on the wrapper from one another, does not violate *mochek*. However, *Magen Avraham*[39] and *Levush*[40] disagree with this reasoning and prohibit separating parts of a letter from one another. R. Shlomo Zalman Auerbach does cite the aforementioned Gemara to permit separating two full letters from one another on *Shabbat*, so that one is permitted to tear between letters, but does not permit separating parts of a letter from one another.

Though R. Auerbach is generally strict about this issue, he still notes[41] that for the purpose of treating an ill patient on *Shabbat*, one can be lenient if necessary. He explains that fundamentally, this should be permitted the same way that tearing in order to open a package is permitted in order to reach *Shabbat* necessities; moreover, this is an entirely destructive act. Therefore, he recommends making an effort to avoid tearing through letters, but permits this if there is no other option.

It should be noted that generally, the prohibition of *mochek* on *Shabbat* applies not only to words, but to pictures, and therefore one should not tear through pictures on a wrapper on *Shabbat*. However, R. Auerbach[42] notes that we are lenient with regard to tearing through simple designs such as gridlines on a package; similarly, the authors of *Orechot Shabbat*[43] argue that it is not prohibited to tear through lines or simple shapes on *Shabbat*.

Sterilizing Skin with an Alcohol Wipe

Before puncturing the patient's skin, it is necessary to sterilize the skin with an alcohol wipe. Performing this action may be problematic on *Shabbat*, since one may be squeezing the wipe to extract the alcohol onto the patient's skin. Squeezing cloth on *Shabbat* may fall under one of two *melakhot*: *melabbein* (laundering), or *dash* (threshing).

38 *Taz* argues that separating parts of a letter from one another is no more problematic than separating two whole letters from one another since one never violates the *melakhah* until two letters are written, such that half a letter has the same status as one full letter.
39 *Orach Chayyim* 340:7.
40 *Orach Chayyim* 340:4.
41 *Shemirat Shabbat Ke-Hilkhatah* 33:4 and footnote 29; also cited in *Nishmat Avraham* 313:1, summary part 1.
42 *Shulchan Shlomo*, 340:8(2).
43 Vol. 1, ch. 15, footnote 28.

With respect to *melabbein*, the Gemara[44] writes that it is prohibited to stop a barrel of wine with a cloth on *yom tov*. As Rashi[45] explains, the prohibition is due to the concern that one will squeeze the cloth which has absorbed the wine. Rabbeinu Tam, commenting on this Gemara, notes that the prohibition of squeezing in this case could not be due to *melabbein*, since this prohibition only applies when one squeezes water out of the cloth, not other liquids. This would suggest that an alcohol wipe would not present a concern of *melabbein*, since the absorbed liquid is not water. Furthermore, R. Moshe Feinstein[46] argues that the prohibition of *melabbein* does not apply when one is squeezing liquid out of a disposable cloth that one intends to throw away. Thus, there would be no concern of *melabbein* for disposable alcohol wipes.

The remaining *melakhah* to be considered is *dash*. Many *rishonim* assume that the prohibition of squeezing is related to the prohibition of *mefarek*, extracting, which is a *toladah* of *dash*. Just as one is not allowed on *Shabbat* to extract wheat from chaff, the act of threshing, one is not permitted to extract any material from another source, including the act of squeezing liquid out of a material. It is possible, though, that if the use of an alcohol pad on *Shabbat* violates the prohibition of squeezing, the prohibition violated might only be a rabbinic one. This is because it is generally accepted that the Torah prohibition of *dash* applies only to materials that grow from the ground.[47] If an alcohol pad is manufactured from a synthetic material, the prohibition of *dash* would only be rabbinic.[48]

The question of whether one may use an alcohol pad on *Shabbat* appears to be similar to a more commonly discussed question of whether

---

44 *Ketuvot* 6a.

45 Ad loc, s.v. *asur lehadukah*.

46 *Iggerot Moshe, Orach Chayyim* 2:70.

47 See the Gemara in *Shabbat* 75a; rulings of Rambam *Shabbat* 8:7, *Eglei Tal, Dash* 4; *Shevitat Shabbat, Dash* 3. However, R. Avraham ben ha-Rambam (cited in *Eliyah Rabbah* 320:3, *Yabbia Omer* 5:31) rules that the *toladot* of *dash* do apply even to materials that do not grow from the ground, and thus the prohibition in this case would be a Torah prohibition as well. However, this does not appear to be the view of the majority of halakhic authorities.

48 Research by this author suggests that leading medical supply manufacturers produce the cloths for alcohol wipes from a combination of a synthetic polymer and rayon. Rayon is a "regenerated" fiber, in that it is produced by harvesting cellulose from plant sources, liquefying it, squeezing it through small holes, and then allowing it to solidify in the shape of fibers (see *Encyclopedia Britannica*, 13th edition, s.v. "rayon"). The question remains whether such a cloth is considered to be *gedulei karka*, grown from the ground, given that it is partially formed from synthetic material, and the remainder is a material which originated from a natural product but was chemically reconstituted to form a modified fiber.

one may use baby wipes on *Shabbat*. This latter question is discussed at length by contemporary *poskim*.[49] Several factors are discussed by these *poskim* as important in resolving the question. First, it is debated whether the liquid is absorbed into the wipe, in which case use of the wipe is prohibited since it causes the liquid to be extracted, or remains primarily on the surface of the wipe, in which case one may use the wipe since no liquid is squeezed out during use. R. Moshe Feinstein[50] is cited as permitting use of baby wipes if it can be determined that the liquid is present mostly on the surface of the wipe. Other authorities, including Dayan Yitzchak Weiss,[51] prohibit using baby wipes on *Shabbat*, assuming that the liquid is mostly present inside the wipe and is being squeezed out during use. Another factor is whether use of the wipe on *Shabbat* will lead to extraction of the liquid from it. R. Shmuel Wosner[52] prohibits use of baby wipes on *Shabbat* since liquid will certainly be squeezed out, while others including R. Shlomo Aviner,[53] assume that liquid will not be extracted from the wipe since the wipe is only slightly damp. Other *poskim* who have ruled leniently on this issue include R. Ovadia Yosef[54] and R. Shlomo Zalman Auerbach.[55]

According to those *poskim* who permit use of baby wipes, it would appear that use of an alcohol pad on *Shabbat* to sterilize skin before drawing blood would be permitted for the same reasons.[56] If one does not wish to rely on the view of these *poskim*, one might be able to use the alcohol pad with a *shinui*, such as wiping it on the patient's skin

---

49 Excellent summaries of this topic are available. See R. Aryeh Leibowitz, "Using Baby Wipes on Shabbat," http://www.bknw.org/uploads/5/9/9/5/5995719/ using_baby_wipes_on_shabbos.pdf, and R. Gil Student, "Babywipes on Shabbos," http://www.torahmusings.com/2012/11/babywipes-on-shabbos.

50 Cited in R. Dovid Ribiat, *The 39 Melochos*, vol. 2 pp. 352–353 and footnote 137.

51 *Minchat Yitzchak* 10:25.

52 *Shevet Ha-Levi* 8:59. R. Wosner notes that he initially assumed it was possible to use the wipe without any liquid being extracted from it, but was later informed that this was impossible, such that he ruled that use of the wipes is prohibited on *Shabbat*.

53 *She'eilat Shlomo* 3:114.

54 *Yalkut Yosef, Shabbat* vol. 2, 302:31.

55 Cited in *Shemirat Shabbat Ke-Hilkhatah* ch. 14, footnote 94. Note that there is some controversy about R. Auerbach's opinion on this matter; see R. Gil Student's article, cited in footnote 49.

56 R. Shlomo Zalman Auerbach (cited in *Shemirat Shabbat Ke-Hilkhatah* 33:10 and footnote 46) makes this connection explicitly, and permits both use of baby wipes and use of alcohol pads on *Shabbat*. A more categorically lenient view is presented by R. Eliezer Waldenberg (*Tzitz Eliezer* vol. 8 *siman* 15 14:11; and vol. 9 *siman* 17 2:33), who argues that even wetting a cotton cloth with alcohol and using it to wipe the area of the skin is permitted, since both the cloth and the liquid will be discarded immediately, such

with one's little finger. If, as discussed earlier, use of an alcohol pad is only a rabbinic prohibition, use of the pad with a *shinui* (itself a rabbinic violation) constitutes a *shevut de-shevut*, a double-rabbinic violation, which is generally permitted for the sake of an ill person (even not dangerously ill) on *Shabbat*.[57]

Assembling an Apparatus

For many procedures involving needles, the needle must be connected to some other apparatus, such as a syringe or a plastic needle holder which is connected to a Vacutainer tube. We must therefore discuss if assembling an apparatus for use in injection or blood drawing is permitted on *Shabbat*.

The Gemara[58] notes that there is a debate between Beit Shammai and Beit Hillel as to whether the *melakhah* of *boneh*, building, applies only to objects attached to the ground, or also to movable objects (*keilim*). Since Beit Hillel is lenient and rules that *ein binyan be-keilim*, the *melakhah* of *boneh* does not apply to *keilim*, one would expect that there would be no prohibition of *boneh* in assembling an apparatus for injection or blood drawing, since such an apparatus is a *keli* and not attached to the ground. However, several discussions in the Gemara appear to suggest that there is a prohibition of *boneh* with respect to the assembly of *keilim*. For example, the Gemara prohibits on *Shabbat* the assembly of a lamp made of links,[59] the insertion of a handle into an ax,[60] building a barrel,[61] and the assembly of a bed made of separate parts.[62] The

---

that the action performed is not similar to the typical form of prohibited squeezing on *Shabbat*. He notes that one should also use a large piece of cotton cloth so that the part held by the physician remains dry, such that it is no longer certain that any liquid will be squeezed from the cloth anyway: the liquid that is deposited on the skin may be that which had not been absorbed in the cloth, and one's fingers are not actively squeezing the damp part of the cloth.

57 Another option might be to procure alcohol and use a dropper to sterilize the skin with it, then wipe with a synthetic cloth, which would certainly be permitted. However, this option is not easily available in most situations. R. Shlomo Zalman Auerbach (cited in *Shemirat Shabbat Ke-Hilkhatah* 33:10) also recommends the use of a nylon pad, since it is synthetic and non-absorbent, and there is no *sechitah* from a non-absorbent cloth; however, the synthetic materials used in manufacturing alcohol pads found in hospitals are significantly more absorbent, so it would appear that this leniency would not apply to those alcohol pads.
58 *Beitzah* 22a.
59 *Shabbat* 46a.
60 *Shabbat* 102b.
61 *Shabbat* 74b.
62 *Shabbat* 47a.

rishonim propose several resolutions to this issue. According to Rashi,[63] *boneh* indeed does not apply to *keilim*, and in all of these cases, the actions are prohibited due to the performance of some other *melakhah*, such as *makkeh be-pattish*, completing a process. This appears to be the opinion of Rif as well, according to Ran[64] and Rashba.[65] However, *Tosafot* in several places propose alternate, related distinctions: *boneh* applies to *keilim* when one is assembling parts that were not previously assembled together (as opposed to modifying an existing structure),[66] or when one is building a new implement for the first time,[67] or when one is performing an action that requires strength or expertise.[68] Other *rishonim*, including Ramban,[69] Rashba,[70] Ritva[71] and Ran[72] explain that *boneh* applies when assembling a *keli* for the first time, or if re-assembling a *keli* in a manner which requires strength or expertise, such that its previous disassembly is considered to have revoked its status as a *keli* and its subsequent reassembly is considered to be as if one is assembling the *keli* for the first time.

Shulchan Arukh appears to adopt these distinctions proposed by the *rishonim*, writing that it is prohibited to assemble a lamp made of separate parts on *Shabbat* since one is fashioning a new implement.[73] Similarly, it is prohibited to assemble a bed made of separate parts on *Shabbat* if the assembly is done forcefully. If one assembles the bed without force, but the assembly is sturdy, this violates a rabbinic prohibition, since we are concerned that one might assemble the bed forcefully. However, if one assembles the bed in a manner such that the parts are only weakly connected, this is completely permitted.[74]

This ruling would suggest that it is prohibited to attach a needle to a syringe, or to a needle holder for connection to a Vacutainer tube, on *Shabbat*. However, many *poskim* believe that this ruling does not apply in our case. In general, two cases are addressed by *poskim*: a case in which one of the parts of the apparatus is not disposable while the other is, and a case in which both parts are disposable. In the first case, the physician will have to detach the disposable part from the apparatus after use to throw it away. Therefore, the results of one's

---

63 *Shabbat* 47a s.v. *chayav chatat*; 74b s.v. *ve-i chaytei le-fumei.*
64 *Chidushei Ha-Ran (Meyuchasim) Shabbat* 102b, s.v. *hai.*
65 *Shabbat* 102b, s.v. *hai.*
66 *Beitzah* 22a s.v. *u-Beit Hillel*; *Shabbat* 46a s.v. *de-chulyot.*
67 *Shabbat* 74b s.v. *chavita.*
68 *Shabbat* 102b s.v. *hai.*
69 *Shabbat* 102b, s.v. *Rav amar.*
70 *Shabbat* 102b, s.v. *hai.*
71 *Shabbat* 102b, s.v. *ayil.*
72 *Shabbat* 102b s.v. *Rav amar*; *dappei ha-Rif* on *Shabbat* 37a.
73 *Shulchan Arukh, Orach Chayyim* 279:7.
74 *Shulchan Arukh, Orach Chayyim* 313:6.

boneh action are only temporary. The Yerushalmi[75] discusses temporary *boneh*, noting that the Tabernacle, whose assembly is the basis for determining which actions are prohibited on *Shabbat*, was frequently assembled and disassembled. This generates a debate in the Yerushalmi about the assembly of the Tabernacle. According to one opinion, even though the assembly might have remained for some time, the fact that the Israelites knew that they were bound for the land of Israel meant that the assembly was considered only temporary, and thus we may derive that temporary assembly is still prohibited on *Shabbat*. According to a second opinion, the fact that God ordained when to travel dictates that the assembly was considered permanent, and so we cannot assume that temporary assembly is prohibited on *Shabbat*. The Gemara[76] also appears to assume that assembly of the Tabernacle was considered permanent assembly. The question of the practical *halakhah* has been debated by *acharonim*: *Chatam Sofer*[77] rules that temporary assembly is permitted on *Shabbat*, and *Shulchan Arukh Ha-Rav*[78] rules that assembly that will be undone is rabbinically prohibited, whereas if it is undone within the same *Shabbat*, it is permitted entirely. On the other hand, *Or Same'ach*,[79] *Yeshuot Ya'akov*,[80] *Shevitat Shabbat*,[81] and *Machaneh Chayyim*[82] prohibit temporary assembly on *Shabbat*. Many *poskim*, including R. Ovadia Yosef[83] and R. Eliezer Waldenberg,[84] permit assembling an apparatus in which one part is disposable, since they rule in accordance with the first group of *acharonim* who permit temporary assembly on *Shabbat*, especially if it is to be undone within the same *Shabbat*.

The second case, however, in which both parts of the apparatus are disposable, presents greater difficulty. This is because the physician is accustomed to disposing of the entire apparatus after it is used, without disassembling it, and thus the assembly is not temporary. Even if the physician intends to disassemble it after use, R. Shlomo Zalman Auerbach[85] notes that his or her intention is considered insignificant, because the typical manner of using the apparatus is to dispose of it before disassembly. *Nishmat Avraham* adds that one might compare

---

75 *Shabbat* 7:2.
76 *Shabbat* 31b.
77 Responsa 1:72.
78 *Orach Chayyim* 313:21.
79 *Shabbat* 10:12.
80 314:1.
81 *Ma'aseh Choshev* 1 (p. 8).
82 *Orach Chayyim* 23.
83 *Yechavveh Da'at* 2:56.
84 *Tzitz Eliezer* 13:46.
85 Cited in *Nishmat Avraham, Orach Chayyim* 313:1, footnote 13.

this case to that of binding a *lulav* on *yom tov*, which Rashi[86] prohibits since one will dispose of the *lulav* after *yom tov* while it is still tied, and so the tie is considered permanent.

Despite this concern, many *poskim* still permit assembling the apparatus on *Shabbat*. R. Shlomo Zalman Auerbach[87] explains that tying a *lulav* may be different since one specifically desires the tie, as tying the *lulav* is considered fundamental to the *mitzvah* or at least an ideal way of performing the *mitzvah*. R. Auerbach also argues[88] that assembling such an apparatus is permitted because one does so immediately before use, and thus the assembly should not be construed as creating a *keli* but instead as part of the use of the apparatus. This explanation is based on a fundamental debate between *Shulchan Arukh Ha-Rav*[89] and *Chazon Ish*,[90] predicated on the ruling of *Magen Avraham*[91] and *Taz*[92] who permit screwing lids onto their respective containers. *Shulchan Arukh Ha-Rav* explains that this is permitted because the lids are frequently screwed on and off, and an object that is frequently attached and detached is not subject to *boneh*. *Chazon Ish*, however, explains that this case is permitted because the lid is already considered a functional item before it is screwed onto the container, but if an object is not considered functional until it is attached to another object, even if it is frequently assembled and disassembled, the object is still subject to *boneh*. R. Auerbach explains that according to *Chazon Ish*, since the apparatus does not function until it is assembled, it will be prohibited to assemble the apparatus on *Shabbat*, but he argues that other authorities will permit assembling the apparatus since they do not believe that making an object functional *per se* violates *boneh*. R. Yosef Shalom Elyashiv[93] also permits assembling the apparatus, explaining that since the two parts are manufactured with the intent that they will be assembled together, one can view the act of *boneh* as having already occurred with the manufacture of each part separately, such that their subsequent assembly does not violate *boneh*. R. Eliezer Waldenberg[94] permits assembling the apparatus, even if each part is disposable, because the fact that the apparatus remains assembled does not indicate that the assembly step was meant to be permanent, as the only reason the physician did not disassemble the apparatus was because he or she did not care whether it remained assembled or not. Additionally, R. Waldenberg recommends that the physician could

86 *Sukkah* 33b s.v. *hutar ogdo.*
87 *Shemirat Shabbat Ke-Hilkhatah* vol. 3, ch. 35 footnote 63.
88 *Minchat Shlomo* 2:13; also cited in *Nishmat Avraham* 313.
89 *Orach Chayyim* 313:21.
90 *Orach Chayyim, Shabbat* 50:9.
91 313:12.
92 *Orach Chayyim* 313:7.
93 Cited in *Orechot Shabbat* vol. 1, 8:72, footnote 105.
94 *Tzitz Eliezer* 15:17.

assemble the apparatus with the intent to disassemble it after use, as he argues that many *acharonim* disagree with *Biur Halakhah*'s conclusion that one's intent is insignificant compared to the typical intent, and he suggests that even *Biur Halakhah* would agree that if the typical intent is to allow the apparatus to remain assembled only due to apathy, one's intent to disassemble the apparatus after use becomes significant. Dayan Yitzchak Weiss[95] permits assembling the apparatus; among other reasons, he argues that the apparatus *cannot* be assembled forcefully (such that there is no Torah prohibition), and so there is not even a rabbinic prohibition to assemble the apparatus.[96]

Extracting Blood

The Gemara[97] teaches that wounding a living creature such that a collection of blood forms under the skin, even if the blood remains confined by intact skin, thereby never actually exiting the body, is prohibited on *Shabbat*. The *melakhah* from which the prohibition derives is a point of debate among the *rishonim*. According to Rambam,[98] wounding is a form of *mefarek*, extracting, which is a *toladah* of the *melakhah* of *dash*, threshing, therefore amounting to a Torah prohibition on *Shabbat*. Other *rishonim*, including Rashi,[99] *Tosafot*,[100] Ramban,[101] Rashba,[102] Ritva,[103] and Me'iri,[104] argue that the prohibition is due to *netilat neshamah*,

---

95 *Minchat Yitzchak* 8:27; also cited in *Nishmat Avraham* 313.
96 This assertion is debated by *acharonim*, specifically with regard to a debate between *Tur* (*Orach Chayyim* 313) and Maharam mi-Rotenburg (cited in *Tur* ibid.) whether one may assemble a cup made of separate parts on *Shabbat*. According to *Taz*, the debate is about whether a *keli* which is normally assembled securely may be assembled weakly on *Shabbat*. However, according to *Shulchan Arukh Ha-Rav* (*Orach Chayyim* 313:21) and *Chazon Ish* (*Orach Chayyim, Shabbat,* 50:10 s.v. *u-be-Beit Yosef* and s.v. *ve-ha-Mechaber*), the debate is whether a *keli* which cannot be assembled forcefully may be assembled securely on *Shabbat*, since there is now no Torah prohibition that can be violated and so perhaps there is also no rabbinic prohibition. Since *Mishnah Berurah* (*Orach Chayyim* 313:46) is lenient with regard to the case of the cup in a situation of *Shabbat*-related need, we would conclude that according to *Shulchan Arukh Ha-Rav* and *Chazon Ish*, it is permitted to assemble an object securely on *Shabbat* if it cannot be assembled forcefully.
97 *Shabbat* 107a–107b.
98 *Shabbat* 8:7–8.
99 *Shabbat* 107a s.v. *ve-hachovel.*
100 *Shabbat* 107a s.v. *shemoneh sheratzim.*
101 *Shabbat* 107a s.v. *shemoneh sheratzim.*
102 *Shabbat* 107a s.v. *ha-tzadan.*
103 *Shabbat* 107a s.v. *shemoneh sheratzim.*
104 *Shabbat* 107a s.v. *chovel.*

"extracting life," which is a *toladah* of the *melakhah* of *shochet*, slaughtering. Since blood represents life,[105] creating a wound that results in blood loss is akin to a partial slaughtering, therefore amounting to a Torah prohibition on *Shabbat*. Both, however, agree that the prohibition against extracting blood derives directly from Biblical, rather than rabbinic law, and, as such, is only permitted for the sake of a patient who is dangerously ill.

Placing a Bandage

Shulchan Arukh[106] rules that it is permitted to bandage a wound on *Shabbat*, even if the patient is not at all ill, because bandaging a wound is not a form of medicine, but simply protects the wound. Therefore, after drawing blood, a physician may place a bandage on the puncture site on *Shabbat*.

Ideally, one should use an adhesive bandage for this purpose, since it need not be cut on *Shabbat*. As discussed earlier, the package may be torn on *Shabbat*, though the lettering should be avoided if possible. One concern is removing the paper tabs that protect the adhesive surfaces on *Shabbat*. Dayan Yitzchak Weiss[107] prohibits removing these tabs on *Shabbat*, because one is thus making the bandage a functional item, and thereby performing the *melakhah* of *makkeh be-pattish*. Another concern he raises is that one is separating glued items, which *Shulchan Arukh*[108] writes is prohibited on *Shabbat* because one is performing *kore'a*, tearing.[109] R. Yosef Shalom Elyashiv[110] is also stringent in this case. However, R. Moshe Feinstein[111] is cited as ruling that one may

---

105 This assertion is based on the verse (Deuteronomy 12:25), "*ki ha-dam hu ha-nefesh*," "Since the blood is the soul."

106 *Orach Chayyim* 328:23–24.

107 *Minchat Yitzchak* 5:39, 9:41.

108 *Orach Chayyim* 340:14.

109 R. Yaakov Warhaftig, who wrote a letter to Dayan Weiss asking this question, suggested that this case should be similar to the case of papers which became stuck together on *Shabbat*, which *Magen Avraham* (*Orach Chayyim* 340:18) permits. Dayan Weiss responds that in this case, the tabs were intentionally pasted to the bandage to be removed only upon use, and so one must be stringent.

110 Cited in R. Pesach Eliyahu Falk's *Machazeh Eliyahu* 70.

111 Cited in R. Yaakov Posen's *Kitzur Hilkhot Shabbat* (p. 155; ch. 44, footnote 117). R. Simcha Bunim Cohen (*The Shabbos Home*, vol. 1, p. 94 and footnote 19) suggests that R. Feinstein's position is based upon his general ruling (*Iggerot Moshe, Orach Chayyim* 2:84) that *kore'a* only applies to two attached objects that must be torn to separate them, but since separating the tab from the bandage does not require tearing, it is not prohibited to remove the tab on *Shabbat*.

remove these tabs on *Shabbat*. R. Chaim Pinchas Scheinberg[112] also permits this, arguing that the tabs are not intended to remain fastened for a specific length of time, only until the customer uses the bandage, and so this is to be considered a temporary fastening, which may be undone on *Shabbat*. R. Shlomo Zalman Auerbach[113] also permits this because the tab is only attached for the purpose of removal immediately before use, and so the attachment is not considered permanent.

R. Shlomo Zalman Auerbach[114] notes that using gauze and adhering it to the skin with an adhesive tape is more problematic on *Shabbat*, since one is attaching the tape to the gauze on *Shabbat*, which violates the *melakhah* of *tofer*, sewing. R. Eliezer Waldenberg[115] also advises against attaching a gauze bandage to the skin with an adhesive tape, but writes that if necessary, one may attach the gauze with adhesive tape if the tape is also placed on the patient's skin, since this is not the typical form of *tofer*. Another halakhic concern with using gauze and tape is that it is prohibited to tear off a piece of tape on *Shabbat* to place on the gauze, since this is a violation of *kore'a*, tearing, or *mechatekh*, measured cutting. Therefore, it is strongly preferable to use an adhesive bandage on *Shabbat*.

Specific Procedures

Drawing Blood

The act of drawing blood requires the violation of a Torah prohibition on *Shabbat*, and therefore would only be permitted for a dangerously ill patient, and only when there is no other option. Fortunately, this procedure is usually under the purview of the nurse's or phlebotomist's duties, and therefore the resident should not need to perform blood drawing on *Shabbat*, avoiding several halakhic problems. However, in a case where the resident must draw blood on *Shabbat* for a dangerously

---

112 In *Sefer Ha-Zikaron* for R. Aryeh Zev Gurvitz, p. 210.

113 *Shulchan Shlomo* 328:45. In *Shemirat Shabbat Ke-Hilkhatah* 35:26 and footnote 66, R. Auerbach is cited as being stringent, but he is cited as reversing his position in vol. 3, ch. 35 footnote 63. Still, R. Auerbach, as well as R. Eliezer Waldenberg (*Tzitz Eliezer* 16:6), advise removing the tabs on the bandage before *Shabbat* if possible and replacing them with sterile tabs, which can then be removed on *Shabbat* since their presence on the bandage would certainly be temporary. R. Auerbach also notes (*Shulchan Shlomo*, 328 footnote 96) that removing the tabs is certainly not *makkeh be-pattish* since the tabs are only an external cover and the bandage is already considered complete.

114 Cited in *Shemirat Shabbat Ke-Hilkhatah* 35:25.

115 *Tzitz Eliezer* 8:15 14:6; 12:41.

ill patient, he or she may do so. *Nishmat Avraham*[116] notes that it is also permitted to draw blood to run tests on behalf of a dangerously ill patient, even if the results will not be available until the next day, but the blood must be obtained that day so that test results can be returned as soon as possible. R. Yehoshua Neuwirth[117] advises that one attempt to obtain all the necessary blood in one draw so as to reduce the number of *melakhot* violated.

Subdermal and Intramuscular Injections

It is completely permitted to perform a subdermal or intramuscular injection on *Shabbat*, even for a patient who is not dangerously ill.[118] This is because one does not draw blood in performing this type of injection; even if some blood is accidentally removed, this is not definitely bound to occur, so the extraction of blood is a *davar she-eino mitkavven*, an unintended outcome of an action which was not inevitable, which is permitted on *Shabbat*.

Some *poskim*[119] consider the possibility that these injections might violate *boneh* on *Shabbat*, because one is making a *petach yafeh*, a well-fashioned hole in the skin. The Gemara[120] notes that making a *petach yafeh* in a barrel is prohibited on *Shabbat*. However, these authorities explain that performing an injection is not a violation of *boneh*, since the hole exists only for a short period of time, and disappears after the syringe is removed. Indeed, Rashi[121] already notes that fashioning a *petach yafeh* only violates *Shabbat* if it lasts for a day.

Intravenous Injection and Line Placement

In contrast to subdermal and intramuscular injection, intravenous injection and line placement may be prohibited on *Shabbat*. This is because blood is extracted when the needle is inserted into the vein, which the resident wants to see in order to know that the needle has been properly placed. For this reason, R. Yechezkel Abramsky and *Chazon Ish* are cited[122] as prohibiting intravenous injection and line placement on *Shabbat*. Later, R. Shlomo Zalman Auerbach and R. Eliezer Waldenberg

---

116 *Orach Chayyim*, 316:2(2), p. 343.
117 *Shemirat Shabbat Ke-Hilkhatah* 40:27.
118 See *Nishmat Avraham* 316:2(4), citing *Shemirat Shabbat Ke-Hilkhatah* 32:58.
119 *Shevet Ha-Levi* 1:61(1), 8:79(1).
120 *Shabbat* 146a.
121 *Ketuvot* 6b s.v. *im la'asot lah peh*.
122 See *Shemirat Shabbat Ke-Hilkhatah* 32, footnote 151. Note that R. Eliezer Waldenberg (*Tzitz Eliezer* 9:17 2:20) argues that the citation of *Chazon Ish*'s view is mistaken.

debated this case as well. R. Waldenberg[123] argues that this case is in fact a *melakhah she-einah tzerikhah le-gufah*, a *melakhah* performed for a different outcome from the typical outcome of the *melakhah*, since one does not actually want the blood itself, but really wants to perform an injection.[124] R. Auerbach[125] initially agreed with R. Waldenberg, but later reconsidered this position, pointing out that there are several instances where one causes bleeding but does not desire the blood itself, and yet this is still prohibited on *Shabbat*.[126] Most authorities generally agree with R. Auerbach's position, and thus intravenous injection and line placement are prohibited on *Shabbat* except for a dangerously ill patient. *Nishmat Avraham* adds that intravenous line placement for the purpose of having an open line in the future is prohibited unless one is concerned that this might be necessary for saving the patient's life in the future.[127]

123 *Tzitz Eliezer* 8:15 14:12; 9:17 2:36; 10:25 ch. 1; 13:45.
124 R. Waldenberg also adduces support from the position of Maharam ibn Chabib (*Kol Gadol* 1:43), who argues that the blood in veins near the skin where one is injecting is *mifkad pakid*, stationary and isolated from the circulation, such that extraction of this blood is not prohibited on *Shabbat*. See the discussion of fluid aspiration below.
125 *Shemirat Shabbat Ke-Hilkhatah* 32:58 and footnote 151; *Shulchan Shlomo* 320:2(4).
126 For example, the Gemara (*Ketuvot* 5b) discusses whether there is a prohibition for a newly married couple to consummate the marriage on Friday night, since the woman will exhibit hymenal bleeding. There, the Gemara does not assume that the bleeding is a *melakhah she-einah tzerikhah le-gufah*, even though one does not want the blood, since the bleeding itself proves that the woman is a virgin.
127 Another concern with line placement is that of *boneh*, since in this case, the *petach yafeh* that one has made remains open. However, R. Yitzchak Zilberstein notes that based on the Gemara (*Shabbat* 146a), a hole is only considered a *petach yafeh* according to Torah law if it is designed to allow fluid to pass through it in both directions, and generally intravenous lines are placed for fluid to enter but not exit. But if one intends to use the same site for intravenous infusion and for blood drawing, this would still pose the problem of a Torah prohibition of *boneh*. R. Zilberstein explains that there are several reasons to permit this anyway. First, he cites R. Chaim Pinchas Scheinberg who notes that *Mishnah Berurah* (303:82) rules that *boneh* does not apply to the human body, and argues that this position can be relied upon in cases of need. Additionally, he notes that the line may not be open for an entire day, which is Rashi's criterion for the hole to be considered a *petach yafeh*. Therefore, intravenous line placement would not pose a concern of *boneh*.

Fluid Aspiration and Lumbar Puncture

R. Yehoshua Neuwirth[128] rules that aspirating fluid from body cavities is not a violation of *Shabbat* because the fluid is considered *mifkad pakid*, stationary and isolated from circulation. There is no prohibition on *Shabbat* to extract stationary, non-circulating fluids from the body. This is apparent from the Gemara,[129] which presents the view that the first marital relations between husband and wife are permitted on Friday night, despite the resultant hymenal bleeding, because this blood is isolated from circulation; likewise, aspirating other fluids isolated from circulation is not subject to any prohibition on *Shabbat*. R. Neuwirth also rules that lumbar puncture is permitted on *Shabbat*, as cerebrospinal fluid extracted from the spinal canal is considered *mifkad pakid* since it does not circulate in the cardiovascular system.

128 Cited in *Nishmat Avraham, Orach Chayyim* 316:2(6).
129 *Ketuvot* 5b.

Chapter 25

Using Electricity in the Hospital on *Shabbat*

Jerry Karp, MD, PhD

Working in a hospital on *Shabbat* is complicated not only by what must be done directly for patient care, but also by other ancillary actions that the resident may need to perform. In many cases, the chief concern is the use of an electronic device on *Shabbat*. In this chapter, we discuss the use of electricity on *Shabbat*, and discuss its applications to lights, telephones, security cards, electronic doors, elevators and escalators. At the outset, it should be noted that technology is ever-changing, and so it is important to be in contact with a halakhic advisor with whom one can discuss specifics of one's situation.

Introduction to Electricity on *Shabbat*

Perhaps the most exciting and difficult halakhic issue tackled by *poskim* in the last two hundred years is the question of electricity on *Shabbat*. In approaching this topic, it is crucial to understand the exact parameters of the question. In particular, some electric devices function to perform a *melakhah* which is prohibited on *Shabbat*. As one overt example, consider a tractor being used to plow a field. In this case, it is obvious that use of the tractor is prohibited, independent of its electric nature, because it functions to perform the *melakhah* of plowing. On the other hand, some electric devices are not used to perform any *melakhah*. As an example, an electric fan is not violating any *melakhah*, as blowing air is not *per se* a *melakhah*. The question is whether operating an electric device is itself prohibited on *Shabbat*, regardless of whether it performs any prohibited action.

Closing an Electric Circuit on *Shabbat*

The question of whether it is prohibited to close an electric circuit on *Shabbat*, even if it does not lead to the performance of another *melakhah*, is the subject of significant debate among nineteenth- and twentieth-century *poskim*.[1] While many *poskim* believe that it is indeed prohibited, there are many proposed explanations for why this is so. We will discuss three of the most commonly discussed concerns,[2] as well as the opinion of R. Shlomo Zalman Auerbach who critically analyzes all of the proposed rulings.

The View of *Chazon Ish*: *Boneh* or *Makkeh be-Patish*

R. Avraham Yeshayahu Karelitz (*Chazon Ish*) proposes that use of an electric device on *Shabbat* violates the prohibition of *boneh*, building.

---

1   There are several excellent overviews of this topic. Among others, see R. Michael Broyde and R. Howard Jachter, "The Use of Electricity on Shabbat and Yom Tov," *Journal of Halacha and Contemporary Society*, vol. xxi (Spring 1991), pp. 4–47; *Encylopedia Talmudit* vol. 18, s.v. *chashmal*, section 2, and associated appendix; and *Ha-Chashmal Be-Halakhah*, ch. 2 and 9, which present an annotated bibliography summarizing the major positions regarding electricity on *Shabbat*. These works have significantly influenced the presentation of this summary.

2   Two other concerns are raised, albeit less often, among *poskim*:
    1. R. Shmuel Aharon Yudelewitz (*Chashmal Le-Or Ha-Halakhah*, 2:6, pp. 111–112) suggests that use of electricity on *Shabbat* creates a concern that increased fuel will be consumed at the power station in order to accommodate one's electrical usage. He writes that this is not a *davar she-eino mitkavven*, an uncertain and unwanted ancillary outcome of one's actions, because one prefers the increased fuel consumption to losing power. R. Shlomo Zalman Auerbach (*Shemirat Shabbat Ke-Hilkhatah* ch. 23, footnote 137) rejects this argument since the additional fuel consumption is unlikely to occur (especially as others might be reducing their power consumption at the same time, and in any case it is unlikely that one person's action will affect the fuel consumption). He also notes that even if this were to occur, it would be merely *gerama*.
    2. *Chazon Ish* (*Orach Chayyim* 50:9) suggests the possibility that when the electric circuit is closed, the wire will be heated to the degree of *yad soledet bo*, untouchably hot, such that one has violated the prohibition of cooking on *Shabbat*. R. Auerbach (*Minchat Shlomo* 1:12, p. 107) rejects this, since one does not intend to heat up the wire, and heating up the wire actually damages it; additionally, since the wire returns to its normal state immediately after the circuit is opened, and no one can recognize the change, R. Auerbach suggests that no prohibition is violated.

In a letter to R. Shlomo Zalman Auerbach defending his position,[3] he offers two reasons to consider completing an electric circuit to be *boneh*. First, he argues that completing the circuit is a way of physically assembling an object, which is prohibited on *Shabbat*. *Chazon Ish* prohibits this even though one will often open and close the circuit, so that the circuit's closure is seemingly temporary. It should be noted that this is consistent with his general opinion about assembling objects on *Shabbat*: as an example, he notes that screwing the cover onto a container is permitted on *Shabbat* not because one commonly opens and closes the container, but because the cover and container are individually to be considered complete objects even before they are attached, and thus *boneh* does not apply because the objects are already complete.[4] Secondly, *Chazon Ish* argues that completing a circuit turns the circuit into a functional object, comparable to a change from death to life; this action, in itself, violates *boneh*. He similarly argues that turning the circuit into a functional object might be a violation of *makkeh be-pattish*, the final hammer blow, an action that completes the process of making an object. This latter possibility is also suggested by R. Ben-Tzion Uziel[5] and R. Eliezer Waldenberg.[6]

R. Shlomo Zalman Auerbach[7] argues that *boneh* is not applicable to closing an electric circuit. Since the circuit is frequently opened and closed, he suggests that closing a circuit is not to be considered building, but use of the object. This suggestion is in line with *acharonim*, such as *Shulchan Arukh Ha-Rav*,[8] who understood that screwing a cover onto a container is not prohibited on *Shabbat* because the cover is frequently placed on the container and taken off, so it cannot be considered *boneh*. R. Auerbach similarly argues[9] that *makkeh be-pattish* can only apply if the final action is forceful and permanent, whereas it is easy to close a circuit, and one often intends to open the circuit soon afterward.

Most notable about *Chazon Ish*'s position is that according to him, use of an electric device is a Torah prohibition and not merely a rabbinic prohibition. This is of great consequence to residents in the hospital, since most *poskim* rule that Torah prohibitions may never be violated for a patient who is not dangerously ill.[10] Additionally, since even with

3 *Minchat Shlomo* 1:11, pp. 92–93; for the original statement of his position, see *Chazon Ish, Orach Chayyim, Shabbat* 50:9.
4 See further discussion of this topic in Chapter 24, in the section entitled "Assembling an Apparatus."
5 *Mishpetei Uziel* 1:13.
6 *Tzitz Eliezer* 1:6. R. Waldenberg also agrees with *Chazon Ish* that *boneh* is violated.
7 *Minchat Shlomo* 1:9, section 3(2), p. 81.
8 *Orach Chayyim* 313:21.
9 *Minchat Shlomo* 1:9, section 3(5), pp. 82–83.
10 See Chapter 20.

regard to treating patients who are dangerously ill, it is better to violate only rabbinic prohibitions and not Torah prohibitions, this position would suggest that use of an electric device might not be better than an alternative option, and in some cases might be worse.

The View of R. Yitzchak Shmelkes: *Molid*

An alternative approach is postulated by R. Yitzchak Shmelkes, author of *Beit Yitzchak*. He argues[11] that using electric devices is prohibited because enabling the current to flow through the wires is a violation of the rabbinic prohibition of *molid*, creating something new on *Shabbat*. The prototypical example of this prohibition appears in the Gemara[12] with reference to adding a fragrance to a garment, which is prohibited due to *molid*. Similarly, closing an electric circuit violates a rabbinic prohibition by creating new current which was not present before.

One of the earliest authors who disagreed with R. Shmelkes was in fact R. Shmelkes's own son-in-law, R. Alter Steiglitz.[13] R. Steiglitz argues that *molid* only applies when one creates a new entity which is apparent to one of the five senses, whereas electricity is not apparent to the senses. This argument was also advanced later by R. Eliezer Waldenberg.[14] R. Shlomo Zalman Auerbach[15] adds three other reasons why *molid* should not apply. First, he notes, since the circuit is designed to carry electric current, such that the addition of current is part of the circuit's intended function, there is no prohibition of *molid*. Second, the current is not permanent, since one will also turn off the electric device, opening the circuit and causing the cessation of current flow; R. Auerbach contends that *molid* does not apply when the entity is repeatedly created and removed. Third, he argues that we cannot innovate new applications of the prohibition of *molid*; as proof, he notes that although creating heat is described by the Gemara[16] with the verb *molid*, nowhere does the Gemara suggest that cooking a food is not only prohibited because of *bishul*, cooking, but also because of *molid*. This leads to the conclusion that *molid* only applies in the select instances where Chazal explicitly noted that the prohibition applies.

Creating Sparks on *Shabbat*

Several authorities argued that opening or closing an electric circuit is prohibited because sparks are inevitably created when the circuit is opened or closed. Among the earliest authorities espousing this view

---

11   *Beit Yitzchak*, notes to *Yoreh De'ah* 31 (p. 158).
12   *Beitzah* 23a.
13   *Tzelach Ha-Chadash, Kuntres Acharon*, 1.
14   *Tzitz Eliezer* 1:20, ch. 10.
15   *Minchat Shlomo* 1:9, section 3(6), pp. 83–84.
16   *Shabbat* 48a.

is R. David Zvi Hoffmann.[17] He notes that although the sparks are unwanted, they are an inevitable consequence of opening a circuit, and so opening a circuit is a *pesik reisha de-lo nicha lei*, an action that leads to an inevitable albeit unwanted prohibited consequence, which is still rabbinically prohibited according to most views[18] except *Arukh*.[19] R. Hoffmann's view is also espoused by R. Yaakov Breisch[20] and Dayan Yitzchak Weiss.[21] R. Shlomo Zalman Auerbach[22] rejects this view, arguing that creating the spark by closing the circuit is a backhanded manner of performing the action (*ke-le'achar yad*). Moreover, the spark incrementally damages the wire, so the action is destructive (*mekalkel*). Based on the view of R. Yechezkel Landau[23] that a *pesik reisha de-lo nicha lei* is permitted for a rabbinic prohibition, R. Auerbach is not concerned about the possibility of creating a spark.

R. Shlomo Zalman Auerbach's View

Although R. Auerbach argues against all the views cited thus far with regard to the prohibition of electricity, he notes[24] that since R. Yitzchak Shmelkes has already ruled that closing a circuit violates the prohibition of *molid*, he is unable to argue against this position. Additionally, he writes that he is concerned that many people will be unable to understand the distinction between turning on an electric device that causes a *melakhah* to be performed and turning on an electric device that performs no *melakhah*. For this reason, he writes that we should be stringent with regard to electricity and not use electric devices, even when they do not perform a *melakhah*. He notes that perhaps there is room to be lenient if there is a "great need." In any case, it is important to note that at most, according to R. Auerbach, use of an electric device that does not perform a *melakhah* is a rabbinic prohibition, and it is therefore always preferable to choose this option over a Torah prohibition, when one must violate a prohibition to save a life.

R. Asher Weiss's View

In a recent responsum, R. Asher Weiss,[25] agreeing that previous suggestions for which *melakhah* is violated by closing an electric circuit are

---

17 *Melammed Le-Ho'il, Orach Chayyim* 49.
18 *Tosafot, Shabbat* 103a s.v. *lo tzerikha, Yoma* 34b s.v. *hani mili, Ketuvot* 6a s.v. *hai*; Ramban, *Shabbat* 111a s.v. *hai*; Rosh, *Shabbat* 12:1. This view is codified in *Shulchan Arukh, Orach Chayyim* 320:18.
19 In entries *pesak* and *sevar* (5); also cited in *Tosafot* ibid.
20 *Chelkat Ya'akov, Orach Chayyim* 75 and 76.
21 *Minchat Yitzchak* 3:38.
22 *Minchat Shlomo* 1:10, section 2(4), pp. 97–98.
23 *Dagul Me-Revavah* 340:3.
24 *Minchat Shlomo* 1:9, section 3(7), p. 84.
25 Responsa *Minchat Asher, Orach Chayyim* 30.

questionable, proposes an alternative explanation for why using electrical devices is prohibited on *Shabbat*. According to R. Weiss, use of such devices constitutes a Torah prohibition, namely violation of the *melakhah* of *makkeh be-pattish*. R. Weiss does not argue, as *Chazon Ish* does, that use of an electrical device constitutes completion of an object. Rather, he notes that the Yerushalmi[26] relates that R. Yochanan and Reish Lakish spent three and a half years categorizing each prohibited action on *Shabbat*, assigning them to one of the thirty-nine *melakhot* if possible, or otherwise, relegating them to the category of *makkeh be-pattish*. In other words, R. Weiss concludes, any significant creative action on *Shabbat* that cannot be categorized into one of the primary thirty-nine categories is still prohibited under *makkeh be-pattish*. Use of an electrical device, R. Weiss argues, is the quintessential creative action on *Shabbat*, and is thus prohibited as *makkeh be-pattish*, a Torah prohibition. Although this is a novel interpretation, it is an important dissenting approach from the majority view that use of an electrical device that does not perform *melakhah* violates only a rabbinic prohibition.

Modulating the Current in an Electric Circuit on *Shabbat*

Our discussion thus far has been with regard to closing an electric circuit on *Shabbat*, thus creating current where none existed before. However, the situation might be different if the circuit is already closed, but one is modifying the amount of current in the circuit.

According to *Chazon Ish*, who prohibits closing a circuit due to a concern of *boneh*, modifying the current in the circuit involves neither the physical assembly of the circuit, as it is already closed, nor the creation of a functional object, since the circuit was previously functional. Therefore, R. Auerbach[27] suggests that modifying the current in a circuit should not be prohibited even according to *Chazon Ish*.

According to R. Yitzchak Shmelkes, modifying the current in a circuit would be prohibited if the prohibition of *molid* applies even when one is augmenting a newly created entity. This appears to be subject to a dispute among *acharonim*. According to *Shulchan Arukh Ha-Rav*,[28] there is no prohibition to augment a fragrance already present in a garment, only to add a new fragrance not previously there. This position is also espoused by *Chayyei Adam*,[29] and may be the position of *Magen Avraham*.[30] The opposing position, that one may also not augment a

26 *Shabbat* 7:2.
27 *Minchat Shlomo* 1:12, section 3(4), p. 126.
28 *Orach Chayyim* 511:7.
29 93:14.
30 511:11. See Prof. Ze'ev Lev, "*Molid zerem chashmali be-Shabbat*," *Techumin* 2, p. 41; R. Levi Yitzchak Halperin, *Ma'aliot Be-Shabbat*, ch. 13, pp. 166–167.

fragrance that is already present in a garment, may be the intention of *Magen Avraham*,[31] and is also the position of *Mishnah Berurah*[32] and *Arukh Ha-Shulchan*.[33] R. Shlomo Zalman Auerbach rules that the prohibition of *molid* does not apply when increasing or decreasing current in a circuit; this position is echoed by R. Ovadia Yosef.[34] However, Dayan Yitzchak Weiss[35] and R. Yaakov Breisch[36] disagree and prohibit this as well. R. Moshe Feinstein appears to prohibit this barring exceptional circumstances, as he prohibits use of a microphone on *Shabbat* since one is modifying the current,[37] though he permits speaking to a person using a hearing aid which would appear to be a very similar case.[38]

Opening a Circuit

Whether opening a circuit is permitted is dependent on the prohibition involved in closing a circuit. If closing a circuit is prohibited due to *boneh*, as suggested by *Chazon Ish*, then opening a circuit is *soter*, destroying; indeed, this is *Chazon Ish*'s position.[39] If closing a circuit is prohibited due to *molid*, then no prohibition can be violated by opening the circuit. Although it is common practice not to turn off electrical appliances on *Shabbat*, R. Michael Broyde and R. Howard Jachter[40] note that this is likely a function of tradition rather than a specific prohibition. While maintaining traditional practice is of great import generally, in a situation of *pikuach nefesh*, it is obvious that one may turn off an electrical appliance if this is necessary, and that if one is faced with a choice between turning off an appliance and performing some other *melakhah*, the former option is greatly preferable.

Turning on Lights

As a first application of the prohibition of using electrical devices on *Shabbat*, we consider turning on lights, which may be necessary in some cases as part of emergent patient care.

31 See ibid.
32 511:26.
33 *Orach Chayyim* 511:12.
34 *Yabbia Omer* 1:19.
35 *Minchat Yitzchak* 3:60.
36 *Chelkat Ya'akov* 3:137 (*Orach Chayyim* 144).
37 *Iggerot Moshe, Orach Chayyim* 4:84.
38 *Iggerot Moshe, Orach Chayyim* 4:85. A brief discussion of this disparity can be found in R. Shlomo Brody, *A Guide to the Complex*, ch. 24, pp. 74–76.
39 *Shabbat* 50:9.
40 "The Use of Electricity on Shabbat and Yom Tov," *Journal of Halacha and Contemporary Society*, vol. xxi (Spring 1991), pp. 21–23.

Incandescent Lights

When one flips a switch to turn on an incandescent light, this causes current to flow through the metal filament in the light bulb. The resistance in the filament generates significant heat, which eventually causes the filament to glow, producing light. This process, according to almost all opinions, leads to the violation of a Torah prohibition. There is some debate as to exactly which prohibition: Rambam[41] rules that heating a metal until it glows violates the prohibition of *mavir*, lighting a fire, while Ra'avad[42] argues that the prohibition violated is *mevashel*, cooking, or *makkeh be-pattish*, completing the final step of a process. Numerous *acharonim*[43] follow Rambam and therefore prohibit turning on an incandescent light as a prohibition of *mavir*.

Fluorescent Lights and LEDs

In contrast to incandescent lights, turning on other types of lights may not violate a Torah prohibition. In a fluorescent light bulb, when the current is turned on, this causes the emission of electrons which collide with gas particles, which in turn emit light. No metal filament is involved, and therefore, there is no Torah prohibition of *mavir* upon turning on a fluorescent light.[44] In LED lights, light is emitted when current causes electrons to cross a diode and become reduced in energy, emitting the excess energy as light; in these lights, as well, no prohibition of *mavir* is involved.

According to most *poskim*, turning on these types of lights is only a rabbinic prohibition, that of using electricity on *Shabbat*, as discussed earlier. Therefore, if one must turn on a light on *Shabbat*, one should preferably turn on a fluorescent or LED light rather than an incandescent light.

41 *Shabbat* 12:1.
42 Commentary to Rambam, ibid.
43 These authorities include R. Yitzchak Shmelkes (*Beit Yitzchak, Yoreh De'ah* 1:120, section 4), R. David Zvi Hoffmann (*Melammed Le-Ho'il, Orach Chayyim* 49), R. Chaim Ozer Grodzinski (*Achiezer* 3:60), *Chazon Ish* (*Orach Chayyim* 50:9; he primarily assumes that one violates *mevashel* but also raises the possibility that *mavir* is violated) R. Shlomo Zalman Auerbach (*Minchat Shlomo* 1:12, section 1–2), Dayan Yitzchak Weiss (*Minchat Yitzchak* 3:60), R. Eliezer Waldenberg (*Tzitz Eliezer* 3:17), and many others.
44 Earlier fluorescent lights involved "starters," which produced sparks to begin the process of generating light, and thus it would be a Torah prohibition to turn on these fluorescent lights. R. Broyde and R. Jachter (ibid., footnote 15) note that this is the reason earlier works recorded that turning on fluorescent lights was a Torah prohibition, but this is no longer a concern.

Using a Telephone on *Shabbat*

Over the course of *Shabbat*, the resident will likely be required to place telephone calls in order to take care of his or her patients. Though using a telephone on *Shabbat* is commonly prohibited, for many reasons, it is useful to the resident to know which actions involved in use of a telephone are prohibited, as well as the severity of the prohibition associated with each action. Knowledge of these *halakhot* will help the resident to determine which methods of using a telephone are optimal on *Shabbat* when one must use the telephone for patient care. Obviously, in an emergent situation, one should use the telephone normally, in the most efficient way possible. While the basics of the issue are discussed here, this is a complicated area in *halakhah*, in which changes in technology are frequent, and thus it is prudent to consult with a halakhic advisor to determine a practical plan for *Shabbat*.

Opening and Closing Circuits

Upon lifting a telephone receiver, one closes an electric circuit, thus violating any prohibitions involved therein, as discussed earlier. Similarly, when one replaces the receiver, one opens a circuit, which may violate a prohibition as discussed earlier. For these reasons, if one must use a telephone, it would be best to lift the telephone receiver with a *shinui*, such as with one's elbow. Alternatively, one could use the speakerphone by pressing the speaker button (using a *shinui*, such as with one's knuckle), obviating the need to pick up the receiver.[45] Pressing a button on the telephone also causes a circuit to close. This behooves the resident to do two things: to press any necessary buttons with a *shinui*, such as with one's knuckle, and to minimize the number of buttons pressed.

The question of pressing buttons on *Shabbat* is also applicable to cell phones. Many cell phones have capacitive touch screens, in which pressing a button causes a change in capacitance of a circuit, thereby instructing the cell phone's computer to perform an action. It would appear, then, that pressing buttons on a cell phone causes a change in current, rather than closing a circuit; as noted earlier, there are more significant grounds for leniency in such a case, meaning that using a cell

---

45 This action will cause the dial tone to begin, which may be prohibited because of the production of sound, as discussed later. As noted later, R. Broyde and R. Jachter suggest that many authorities may not consider producing a dial tone to be a violation of this prohibition since the dial tone is not audible to anyone but the person placing the call; if one places a call on speakerphone, this may reintroduce a concern of this prohibition, though it would seem that R. Shlomo Zalman Auerbach might be lenient, as he is with regard to causing the telephone to ring.

phone on *Shabbat* might be preferable to using a regular phone.[46] One may also be able to program frequently used numbers into one's cell phone memory before *Shabbat*, allowing one to minimize the number of buttons pressed. It may also be prudent to plan in advance of *Shabbat* and to deactivate any security mechanisms on the phone which require one to press extra buttons on *Shabbat*. One might alternatively be able to minimize prohibited actions by using the voice control feature on one's phone, such that one must perform only two prohibited actions: pressing the button that activates this feature (with a *shinui*, preferably), and telling the phone to call the number.[47]

If one is using a cell phone, it would be best to let the person on the other end hang up, which will cause the cell phone to automatically hang up without the need to perform any *melakhah*.

Producing Sound on *Shabbat*

The act of placing a telephone call causes the generation of sound in multiple ways. This effect must be considered when placing a telephone call on *Shabbat*, as producing sound is generally a rabbinic prohibition.

The prohibition of making sound on *Shabbat* is based on the Mishnah[48] which prohibits clapping or dancing on *Shabbat*. The Gemara explains that Chazal prohibited these actions because they were concerned that involvement with any kind of music might cause one to fix a musical instrument, which would violate a Torah prohibition.

---

46 One problem of using a cell phone is that pressing a button also causes writing to appear on the screen. The concern of writing on a computer screen has already been discussed in Chapter 22. However, many hospital phones also have LCD screens which feature writing upon dialing, and so cell phones are no worse in this regard. Another concern is that the cell phone has a backlight which is illuminated when the phone is used; turning on this light is a rabbinic prohibition, as discussed earlier. However, hospital phones likely have small LED lights which will illuminate when buttons are pressed, so the cell phone may again be no worse. It is advisable to speak with a halakhic advisor to determine which telephone is preferable on *Shabbat*, given one's specific options.

47 Causing a *melakhah* to be performed through one's voice is generally assumed to be prohibited just like performing the *melakhah* in any other way. R. Yisrael Rosen ("*Mikrofon ve-ramkol be-Shabbat*," *Techumin* 15, pp. 371–392; also available in English translation online at www.zomet. org.il/eng/?CategoryID=198&ArticleID=283) summarizes the halakhic literature surrounding this question, and proposes an alternative possibility, that causing a *melakhah* to be performed with one's voice is only prohibited if one holds the electrical device in one's hand at the time or performs some other action. In the case of a cell phone, this is true anyway, and therefore all will agree that one violates the prohibition.

48 *Beitzah* 36b.

Though implied in this prohibition, the Gemara[49] elsewhere explicitly extends this to making any kind of musical noise with an object. There, the Gemara recounts that Ula was dismayed that someone knocked on a door on *Shabbat*, producing sound and violating the aforementioned rabbinic prohibition, while Rabbah was not concerned, explaining that the prohibition applies only when making musical noise. Although Rabbeinu Chananel[50] rules in accordance with the stringent view of Ula, Rif[51] and Rambam[52] rule in accordance with Rabbah, and *Beit Yosef*[53] argues that this is the ruling of Rosh[54] as well. Therefore, *Shulchan Arukh*[55] rules that one may not produce musical sounds on *Shabbat*, but does not extend this prohibition to making any form of sound. However, Rama,[56] expressing the view of Maharil,[57] adds that one is also prohibited from making non-musical noise if one does so using an object whose primary function is to make noise; thus, he prohibits using a door-knocker on *Shabbat*, since its function is to produce noise, but one is permitted to knock with one's fist on the door.

Based on Rama's extension of the prohibition, many *poskim* argue that using an appliance which works by making a sound is prohibited on *Shabbat*, even if the sound is non-musical. This would suggest that use of a telephone might violate the rabbinic prohibition of making sound on *Shabbat*, at several stages of its use:

- When picking up the receiver, the telephone produces a dial tone to indicate that a call can be placed. R. Levi Yitzchak Halperin[58] argues that this violates the prohibition of producing sound on *Shabbat*. However, other authorities do not mention that this is prohibited, and R. Michael Broyde and R. Howard Jachter[59] argue that this is because the dial tone is inaudible to anyone else not holding the receiver, and so its production does not violate the prohibition on *Shabbat*.

- R. Yitzchak Shmelkes,[60] in an early responsum about using a telephone often cited by later authorities, argues that since when the call is placed, the telephone on the other end begins to ring, use of

49 *Eruvin* 104a.
50 *Eruvin* 104b s.v. *u-parik*.
51 *Eruvin* 35a in *dappei ha-Rif*.
52 *Shabbat* 23:4.
53 *Orach Chayyim* 338.
54 *Eruvin* 10:20.
55 *Orach Chayyim* 338:1.
56 Ibid.
57 Responsa (*chadashot*) 38:4.
58 *Ma'aseh Choshev* vol. 1, ch. 2, p. 60.
59 "The Use of Electricity on Shabbat and Yom Tov," *Journal of Halacha and Contemporary Society*, vol. xxi (Spring 1991), p. 32.
60 *Beit Yitzchak*, notes to *Yoreh De'ah* 31 (p. 158).

a telephone is prohibited because it produces a sound on *Shabbat*. This position is echoed by R. Chaim Ozer Grodzinski.[61] R. Ben-Tzion Uziel[62] rules that causing a telephone to ring violates the prohibition, arguing that the telephone ringing *is* a musical sound, and is thus prohibited (presumably, even according to *Shulchan Arukh*'s position). As one would expect, R. Levi Yitzchak Halperin, who prohibited even producing a dial tone, also prohibits using a telephone due to its ringing on the receiving end. On the other hand, R. Shlomo Zalman Auerbach[63] argues that there may be room for leniency with regard to causing the telephone to ring. He notes that *Tosafot*[64] were already lenient regarding producing noise, particularly with regard to clapping and dancing on *Shabbat*, since most people today are not proficient in fixing musical instruments; although *Eliyah Rabbah*[65] notes that this leniency is generally employed only for clapping and dancing, and not for producing sound through objects, R. Auerbach argues that there is additional room for leniency in this case, since the telephone ring is not musical.[66] While, as noted earlier, Rama prohibits producing even non-musical sound, *Biur Halakhah* explains that this prohibition is based primarily on the prohibition of *uvda de-chol*, performing mundane actions which are in the spirit of a weekday, and perhaps such prohibitions could be more easily suspended in situations of great need.[67]

- R. Schmelkes[68] also argues that speaking on the telephone violates the prohibition of creating a sound. However, R. Auerbach[69] argues that the prohibition of producing a sound does not apply to sound being produced by one's mouth, even if the sound is being transmitted by another entity (the phone). R. Eliezer Waldenberg[70] also writes that

---

61 *Achiezer* 4:6; also published in *Ha-Darom*, vol. 32 (*Tishrei* 5731), pp. 42–43.

62 *Mishpetei Uziel* vol. 1, *Orach Chayyim* 13.

63 *Minchat Shlomo*, 1:9, section 3(9), pp. 85–86.

64 *Beitzah* 30a s.v. *tenan*.

65 *Orach Chayyim* 339:1.

66 This may no longer be the case today, as many individuals have cell phones with musical rings. However, hospital phones will have non-musical rings, and even when calling another healthcare worker's cell phone, it is likely that the call recipient's phone, especially in a professional setting, will be set to "vibrate," or will have a non-musical ringtone.

67 R. Auerbach also argues, with regard to the rotary telephones of his day, that causing a telephone to ring could be *gerama*, a *melakhah* performed indirectly, since the telephone only rings when one releases one's finger from the rotary dial and the dial moves itself due to release of the spring.

68 *Beit Yitzchak*, notes to *Yoreh De'ah* 31 (p. 158).

69 *Minchat Shlomo*, vol. 1, 9:2, section 3 (pp. 75–76).

70 *Tzitz Eliezer* 1:20:10, section 1.

since Rama[71] permitted producing sound by one's mouth, without performing any action, talking on a telephone does not violate this prohibition.

Speaking on the Telephone

In addition to the concern of producing sound on *Shabbat* raised by speaking on the telephone, an additional concern is that when one speaks on the telephone, the current in the wire is modulated. As noted earlier, whether this is prohibited is subject to debate. Those who permit modulating current on *Shabbat* also permit speaking on a telephone. Specifically, R. Shlomo Zalman Auerbach[72] rules that once the telephone connection has been made, there is no need to concern oneself with limiting the words that one says during the conversation, since no prohibition is violated in speaking, and one can freely say "hello," "thank you," or similar phrases. R. Auerbach notes that one should not speak about matters that are unrelated to the emergency necessitating speaking on the phone, since one should only be lenient when there is a need.

Automatic Doors on *Shabbat*

Many hospitals have automatic doors at the front of the hospital that are attached to sensors which detect whether someone is in the vicinity of the doors, automatically opening to allow entry. Is a hospital resident permitted to walk through these doors on *Shabbat*? We will discuss whether one's effect on the sensors which causes a *melakhah* is prohibited on *Shabbat*, and what options are practically available for the resident faced with this situation on *Shabbat*. To begin this discussion, we will explain the various electronic systems in place to control automatic doors and their associated halakhic problems.

Radar Sensors

Radar systems transmit electromagnetic waves in the area surrounding the door. If all objects in this area are stationary, then they will reflect the waves back to the transmitter, and the reflected waves will have the same frequency as the transmitted waves. However, if a person is moving in the door area, this will cause the frequency of the reflected waves to change, based on the Doppler effect. The system will detect the change in frequency and interpret this as motion near the door area, causing the door to open.

71 *Orach Chayyim* 338:1.
72 Cited in *Shemirat Shabbat Ke-Hilkhatah*, 32:41 and footnote 111*.

The consensus of almost all *poskim* is that activating such a sensor on *Shabbat* is prohibited.[73] R. Yisrael Rosen explains that one who effects a *melakhah* is considered to be responsible for the effect regardless of how it is accomplished, whether with one's hands or through one's presence or motion, given that one intended the effect.[74] R. Yehoshua Neuwirth[75] similarly notes that walking through the area and thus opening the door is not considered a *pesik reisha*, an inadvertent prohibited effect of one's otherwise permitted action, but a *ma'aseh*, a direct performance of *melakhah* prohibited on *Shabbat*.[76]

73 One notable exception is the opinion of R. Nachum Rabinovitch (*"Nispach: be-din chayshanim,"* Emunat Ittekha 104, pp. 66–68) and his students R. Eli Reif and R. Dr. Dror Fixler (*"Hafalat chayshanim be-Shabbat,"* Emunat Ittekha 104, pp. 54–65), who argue that use of electronic sensors is actually completely permitted on *Shabbat*. The basis for this assertion is a ruling by R. Shmuel Wosner (*Shevet Ha-Levi* 9:69) that one is permitted to walk past a sensor on *Shabbat* that will cause a light to turn on. R. Rabinovitch, R. Reif and R. Dr. Fixler suggest that this is generally applicable to any sensor, and one is permitted to activate any sensor on *Shabbat* as long as one does not do any action whose sole purpose to activate the sensor; on the other hand, if one walks normally in a certain area, which also causes the activation of a sensor, this is permitted. This position is not widely adopted. Among those who strongly disavow this position in writing is R. Eitam Henkin, *Hashem yikkom damo*, who was murdered by a terrorist in October 2015. R. Henkin (*"Gidrei ha-isur be-delet chashmalit u-she'ar chayshanim be-Shabbat: teguvah,"* Emunat Ittekha 105, pp. 81–85) notes that causing a *melakhah* to be performed through a sensor is prohibited because one intends to cause the *melakhah* by activating the sensor, even if one's actions do not visibly demonstrate this intent. One summary of this debate, written in English, is recorded by R. Gil Student, http://www.torahmusings.com/2014/12/electronic-sensors-on-shabbos/.

74 It is true that if a *melakhah* is performed through *gerama*, it is not a Torah prohibition (see later discussion regarding photoelectric sensors). However, R. Rosen notes that performing a *melakhah* through a complex mechanism is not *gerama*, and actions can only be considered *gerama* if there is a time delay between the performance of the action and the effect, and in addition, there is some other force which causes the effect which retroactively causes one's actions to share responsibility for the effect.

75 Letter printed in *Ve-Shav Ve-Rafa*, 1:16, p. 62.

76 R. Moshe Harari (*Kedushat Ha-Shabbat* vol. 1, pp. 77–85) notes that there are varying opinions regarding how an action performed by an electronic sensor on *Shabbat* is classified. He notes that R. Yosef Shalom Elyashiv informed him that such an action is to be classified as irregular performance of the *melakhah*, which would downgrade its severity to that of a rabbinic prohibition. However, the context of his remark is the case of a light which is turned on by one's walking in the area, which might differ from the case of an automatic sliding door, since the typical manner of opening an automatic door is by walking in front of it, whereas lights are usually turned on by flicking a light switch and not by walking. R. Harari also cites

Passive Infrared Sensors

Another type of sensor detects infrared waves being emitted in the area surrounding the door. The amount of infrared radiation emitted from an area is a function of the temperature in that area. Therefore, when the sensor detects an increase in infrared radiation from an area near the door, it interprets this as the presence of a person near the door (whose body temperature is higher than the normal surroundings) and opens the door.

In this case, the person's presence near the door is clearly activating the door-opening mechanism. R. Levi Yitzchak Halperin[77] notes that such a mechanism is clearly considered one's direct *melakhah* on *Shabbat*, and is prohibited, just as in the case of the door controlled by a radar sensor.

Photoelectric Sensors

In a third type of sensor, a photoelectric cell produces a continuous infrared light beam in the area in front of the door, which is then received by a detector. When a passenger walks in front of the door, he or she interrupts the light beam. When the detector senses that the light was not received, it disables the electronic mechanism which closes the doors, thus causing the doors to open. R. Levi Yitzchak Halperin[78] notes that when a passenger "blocks the light beam" by entering, in reality, he or she has not yet performed a *melakhah*. The light beam is not continuous; rather, there are extremely frequent emissions of photons, such that when a person steps in front of the beam, he or she is essentially interrupting all *future* photons from crossing. The *melakhah* is only performed when that next photon fails to reach the photoelectric sensor. The question, then, is whether one's standing in the doorway, which indirectly causes the deactivation of the closing mechanism, is prohibited on *Shabbat*.

Gerama

Generally, the indirect causation of the performance of a *melakhah*, termed *gerama*, does not violate *Shabbat* as does the direct performance

---

several *poskim* (*Cheshev Ha-Efod* 3:83; R. Dov Lior, letter published in *Kedushat Ha-Shabbat* vol. 1, appendix C, pp. 302–303) who rule that an action performed by an electronic sensor on *Shabbat* is considered a *pesik reisha*; however, again, this might be true only with regard to turning on a light using an electronic sensor, which might be considered an ancillary goal of walking in an area with a sensor, and not with regard to opening an automatic door which is the direct purpose of walking in the area.

77 *Ma'aseh Choshev* 1:12, p. 171 (conclusion 5).
78 *Ma'aseh Choshev* 1:12, section 17; *Ma'aliot Be-Shabbat*, ch. 14, p. 179.

of a *melakhah*. The Gemara[79] explains that since the Torah commands
"lo ta'aseh kol melakhah," "do not perform any *melakhah*,"[80] the active
voice (*"ta'aseh"*) teaches that only active performance of *melakhah* is
prohibited on *Shabbat*, but not indirect performance (*gerama*). The context of this statement in the Gemara is a discussion of using *gerama*
to put out a destructive fire by surrounding the fire with earthenware
jugs of water which will eventually catch fire and burst, releasing water
which will extinguish the fire. Because this Gemara is discussing a case
in which *gerama* is needed to prevent a significant loss, Rabbeinu Yoel[81]
concludes that *gerama* is only permitted in case of potential loss, but not
otherwise. Rama[82] codifies this limitation to when *gerama* is permitted,
and thus it is generally accepted that *gerama* is rabbinically prohibited
except in cases of loss. There is some discussion[83] about whether *gerama*
might also be permitted for the sake of an ill person.[84] *Chazon Ish*[85] permits *gerama* in this case also, as do R. Shlomo Zalman Auerbach,[86] R.
Yehoshua Neuwirth,[87] R. Ovadia Yosef,[88] and R. Shaul Yisraeli.[89]

Although *gerama* is permitted in a limited number of situations, it
is questionable whether walking in front of an automatic door is considered a situation of *gerama*. Blocking a light beam, which causes the
door's closing mechanism to be disabled due to the detector not receiving the light signal, is categorized as a situation in which one is removing a preventative mechanism (the light beam which prevents the door
from opening). This is most similar to a case which halakhic literature

---

79   *Shabbat* 120b.
80   Exodus 20:9.
81   Cited in Mordekhai, *Shabbat* 399.
82   *Orach Chayyim* 334:22.
83   Many of the prevailing opinions about *gerama* for the sake of an ill
     person are discussed by R. Yisrael Rosen, *"Gerama be-Shabbat: ha-musag
     ve-shimushav,"* Techumin 34, pp. 19–30.
84   The authors of *Orechot Shabbat* (ch. 29, footnote 46) note that *Magen
     Avraham* (328:53) appears to permit *gerama* on behalf of an ill person, but
     add that he justifies this based on an earlier comment of *Shulchan Arukh*
     (*Orach Chayyim* 328:17), which permits violation of a rabbinic prohibi-
     tion for an ill person. However, this is not *Shulchan Arukh*'s final ruling, as
     he concludes there that one may only violate a rabbinic prohibition with a
     shinui on behalf of an ill person (see Chapter 20). Therefore, the authors of
     Orechot Shabbat conclude that *Magen Avraham*'s comment must only be
     within the approach that violating any rabbinic prohibition is permitted for
     an ill person on *Shabbat*.
85   *Shabbat* 38:9.
86   *Minchat Shlomo* 1:13, p. 127.
87   *Shemirat Shabbat Ke-Hilkhatah* 13:25 and footnote 93.
88   *Techumin* 1, p. 518.
89   *Techumin* 31, p. 73.

terms *bidka de-maya*, a "blast of water." The Gemara[90] describes a case in which a person tied up another person and placed him or her next to a body of water which was blocked by a barrier, then removed the barrier, causing the tied up person to drown. Is the person who removed the barrier liable for murder, given that removal of the barrier was an indirect method of killing the other person? The Gemara distinguishes between cases of *ko'ach rishon*, primary causation, and *ko'ach sheini*, secondary causation, concluding that in the former case, the person is liable for murder, whereas the latter case is considered only *gerama*. The meaning of this distinction, however, is debated. Rashi[91] explains that *ko'ach rishon* is a case in which the person was tied up in proximity to the barrier, such that when the barrier was removed, the water immediately drowned him or her, whereas *ko'ach sheini* is a case in which the person was tied up farther away, so that time elapsed between removal of the barrier and when the water drowned the person. *Yad Ramah*[92] suggests two alternative distinctions: either *ko'ach rishon* refers to drowning caused by the water immediately next to the barrier, whereas *ko'ach sheini* refers to drowning caused by water farther away from the barrier which was not released immediately upon the removal of the barrier; or *ko'ach rishon* refers to water that was only restrained by the barrier which the person removed, while *ko'ach sheini* refers to water that was restrained by an additional barrier, such that the person who removed the first barrier assumes reduced responsibility for the drowning. According to Rashi, removing a preventative mechanism is only considered *gerama* if the effect is time-delayed. *Yad Ramah* might consider removing a preventative mechanism *gerama* if the ensuing effect is somehow otherwise restrained. If the rules of *gerama* delineated by the Gemara in this case were applied to *Shabbat*, it would mean that removing a preventative mechanism is generally not *gerama*, and would be completely prohibited on *Shabbat*, unless the effect of removing the preventative mechanism were considered *ko'ach sheini*.

Blocking a Light Beam

R. Yehoshua Neuwirth[93] raises the possibility that standing in front of the automatic door and blocking the light beam would be considered *ko'ach sheini*, such that it would only be *gerama* on *Shabbat* and might be permitted in limited situations. However, he appears to rule that blocking a light beam which causes the door to open is not considered *ko'ach sheini* and is prohibited on *Shabbat*. Additionally, several

---

90   *Sanhedrin* 77b.
91   Ad loc, s.v. *be-ko'ach rishon* and *aval be-ko'ach sheini*.
92   Ad loc, s.v. *amar*.
93   *Shemirat Shabbat Ke-Hilkhatah* 23:53 and footnote 146.

authorities, including *Chazon Ish*[94] and *Or Same'ach*,[95] rule that even *ko'ach sheini* is completely prohibited on *Shabbat*.

R. Levi Yitzchak Halperin proposes an alternative reason for permitting blocking the light beam and thus causing the door to open. He suggests that while removing a preventative mechanism is subject to the rules discussed above, preventing a preventative mechanism from occurring in the future is completely permitted. His basis for this dispensation is the Gemara[96] which permits closing the door to a room with a lit candle in it, even though this prevents the wind from passing through and extinguishing the candle. R. Halperin concludes that this means one is preventing the preventative mechanism (the wind) from entering, and thus is causing the candle to burn longer, which the Gemara permits because one is accomplishing this only by preventing a preventative mechanism that will occur in the future. Therefore, one may walk in front of the automatic door since one is preventing a future mechanism (the light beam) from preventing the doors' opening. However, R. Yisrael Rosen[97] completely rejects this distinction. He notes that the candle in the room is already lit, and one does not light the candle by preventing the wind from blowing, but simply allows the candle to continue burning; this is different from preventing a preventative mechanism from causing a new *melakhah* to happen. He reports that R. Shlomo Zalman Auerbach[98] was asked this question, and replied that there is no distinction between removing a currently-active preventative mechanism and preventing a future preventative mechanism: removal of a preventative mechanism is only considered *gerama* if there is a time delay.

Entering After a Non-Jew

To summarize, we have seen that according to most *poskim*, all types of automatic doors present halakhic problems for an observant Jew who needs to pass through them on *Shabbat*. Several *poskim*[99] advise that one could pass through automatic doors on *Shabbat* by waiting for a non-Jew to enter, then passing through immediately afterward. In this way, one does not cause any *melakhah* to occur oneself – the door opening mechanism is triggered by the non-Jew.[100]

94 *Bava Kamma* 14:12.
95 *Shabbat* 9:2.
96 *Shabbat* 120b.
97 "*Gerama be-Shabbat: musag ve-shimushav,*" *Techumin* 34, pp. 19–30.
98 Cited in *Chashmal Be-Shabbat*, p. 70.
99 See *Yalkut Yosef, Shabbat* vol. 5, "*Inyanei chashmal be-Shabbat,*" 32 (p. 207); *Orechot Shabbat* 26:26 and footnote 39.
100 It is questionable whether one is permitted to enter immediately after a Jew who does not keep *Shabbat*. The authors of *Orechot Shabbat* (25:29 and footnotes 61–62) note that this appears to be similar to the question

Some *poskim* question how one is subsequently permitted to leave the door area, even after entering in a permitted fashion. Indeed, once one leaves the door area, the doors will close, and one will then be responsible for the *melakhah* involved in the doors' closing. For this reason, R. Simcha Bunim Cohen[101] advises that one should ideally enter *between* two non-Jews, such that the first non-Jew's entrance causes the doors to open, while the last non-Jew's entrance and subsequent leaving of the door area causes the doors to close, and the Jew is not responsible for the performance of any *melakhah*. Others do not specify this requirement, suggesting that such actions are not necessary.[102] The authors of *Orechot Shabbat*[103] cite R. Moshe Yadler who permits walking through the opened automatic doors, if it is not possible to walk through before another non-Jew. The basis of this dispensation is that one has no interest in the doors' closing and one does not intend to effect the doors' closing. In situations such as these, the authors of *Orechot Shabbat*[104] cite R. Yosef Shalom Elyashiv, R. Shmuel Wosner[105] and R. Nissim Karelitz who permit such actions on *Shabbat*.

Opening Secure Doors on *Shabbat*

In many hospitals, certain rooms or areas are restricted for security purposes. Hospital wings designated for pediatric patients or obstetric care often have numerous locked doors, which can be opened only by an ID card, in order to prevent child abduction. Similarly, the resident break

---

of whether one may enter a room on *Shabbat* that was unlocked through the violation of a prohibition. This is subject to a dispute between R. Yosef Shalom Elyashiv (cited in R. Yitzchak Zilberstein's *Melakhim Umnayikh*, 48, p. 525) who is lenient, and R. Moshe Feinstein (*Iggerot Moshe, Orach Chayyim* 2:71) and R. Shlomo Zalman Auerbach (cited in *Shemirat Shabbat Ke-Hilkhatah* 10 footnote 44) who are stringent. However, the authors of *Orechot Shabbat* (26:4) and R. Eliezer Melamed (*Peninei Halakhah, Shabbat* 17:11) note that it is permitted to enter a hospital through automatic doors if following medical personnel, since their violation of *Shabbat* is permitted in order to save lives.

101 *The Shabbos Home* vol. 2, p. 486.

102 R. Cohen himself does not mention this requirement in his newer volume, *The Aura of Shabbos*, p. 171.

103 26:26, footnote 39, citing *Beirurei Halakhah: Me'or Ha-Shabbat* 4:14 footnote 130*.

104 26:31, footnote 44. The context of the discussion in this footnote is walking on the street past a sensor which will turn on a light in front of a house. These *poskim* rule that if one needs to walk in that area, one need not be concerned that the light will turn on, since the light is not turning on for one's benefit, and one's actions are sufficiently distant from the light, such that one has not violated a *Shabbat* prohibition.

105 *Shevet Ha-Levi* 9:69.

room, call room, supply room, or other rooms might require punching in a code or use of an ID card to allow entry.

Gaining entry to these areas will thus necessitate the violation of at least a rabbinic prohibition by closing an electric circuit. Obviously, if patient care is needed emergently, one must violate this rabbinic prohibition and act quickly to care for the patient. If care is needed less emergently, it would be preferable to ask a non-Jew to use his or her card or code to open the door. Alternatively, one could open the door using a *shinui*: for example, one could punch in a code using one's knuckles, or one could flash an ID card in front of the sensor by holding it with one's teeth or elbow. In the case of a patient who is not dangerously ill, one may still ask a non-Jew to open the door, since one is permitted to ask a non-Jew to violate any prohibition on behalf of a patient, even one who is classified as a *choleh she-ein bo sakkanah*.

Riding Elevators on *Shabbat*

A resident on call on *Shabbat* may need to move from one floor in the hospital to another distant floor. In some cases, this may be extremely difficult without the use of an elevator, particularly in a large hospital, but even in a hospital with fewer floors, if the resident has to frequently switch between floors, using the stairs may become very exhausting. In some hospitals, stairs are not accessible at all floors, necessitating the use of the elevator. Therefore, we will discuss whether riding in an elevator is permitted on *Shabbat*, and if so, under what circumstances is it permitted. We will first discuss the various technical halakhic issues involved in riding an elevator on *Shabbat*, and will later discuss how they might apply to a resident physician.

Pressing Elevator Buttons

It is obvious to the passenger that pressing the elevator buttons illuminates them, and for this reason alone, pressing the buttons will be at least a rabbinic prohibition due to closing the circuit controlling the light. In addition, if the lights which are illuminated by pressing the buttons are incandescent lights, one will be violating a Torah prohibition. These prohibitions are in addition to any prohibitions violated due to any circuits that may be closed in the elevator due to pressing the button. For these reasons, it is clearly prohibited to press an elevator button on *Shabbat*, and this may be even a Torah prohibition.

If the Jewish passenger enters the elevator and simply intends to ride until the elevator stops at a floor of another passenger's choosing, or at a floor requested by someone waiting at another floor, R. Yehoshua

Neuwirth[106] rules that there would not be a prohibition of benefiting from another passenger pressing an elevator button. In this case, the other passenger pressed the button for his or her own benefit, and it is permitted to benefit from *melakhah* performed by a non-Jew for his or her own benefit.[107]

The ideal situation is a "*Shabbat* elevator" which automatically stops on every floor, obviating the need to press elevator buttons. For physicians, though, this might not be a viable option if the elevator is very slow, especially when emergent care is needed on another floor. Obviously, one should not hesitate to press buttons or ride the elevator if the time gained by doing so could save a patient's life.

Automatic Elevator Doors

Most modern elevator doors work automatically, opening and closing on their own at predefined times. In order to prevent the doors from closing while a passenger is standing in the threshold, most elevators have a photoelectric sensor, in which a continuous infrared light beam is transmitted, and if a passenger blocks transmission of the beam, the door does not close. This mechanism is identical to that used in some automatic door systems, which were discussed above. As noted there, most *poskim* prohibit causing the automatic doors to open by blocking the light beam.[108] A common suggestion to avoid this, as discussed earlier, is to enter immediately after a non-Jew, such that the non-Jew triggers the mechanism and the Jew does not cause the performance of any *melakhah*. This suggestion would certainly be applicable to elevator doors as well.

106 *Shemirat Shabbat Ke-Hilkhatah*, 30:54; see also updated edition of *Shemirat Shabbat Ke-Hilkhatah* 23:59*.
107 R. Broyde and R. Jachter (ibid., pp. 83–84) discuss whether it would be permitted to implement this plan when the other passenger pressing the button is a non-observant Jew. They note that this question revolves around whether the non-observant Jew's action is tantamount to an intentional violation, in which case it might be prohibited, or an unintentional violation, in which case it might be permitted. Even if the violation is intentional, it might be permitted anyway, since there is no permanent change in the elevator as a result of the non-observant Jew's actions; however, R. Yehoshua Neuwirth (*Shemirat Shabbat Ke-Hilkhatah* 23:51) still prohibits this.
108 There may be another concern, which is that when the light beam is broken, a buzzer sounds to indicate that something is blocking the doorway. This means that the passenger is responsible for causing the buzzer to sound, which involves violating the prohibition of creating electric current on *Shabbat* and possibly a concern of making sound on *Shabbat* which may also be a rabbinic prohibition (see earlier discussion in the section entitled "Producing Sound on *Shabbat*").

Note that in any situation in which one intends not to press any elevator buttons, since as noted earlier, this is generally prohibited absent urgent medical need, one will be entering the elevator at the same time as a non-Jewish passenger is entering or exiting. This is because one will be unable to enter the elevator on a given floor without a non-Jew pressing the call button at that floor and then entering or a non-Jewish elevator passenger coincidentally exiting at that floor; similarly, one will only be able to exit on a floor in which another elevator passenger has requested to exit. For this reason, one can make sure to enter or exit the elevator at the same time as a non-Jew so that he or she will not cause the performance of any *melakhah*.[109]

Ascending in the Elevator

When an elevator ascends with more passengers riding in it, this necessitates an increase in electric current in the circuit connected to the elevator's motor, since more power is needed to lift the increased weight in the elevator. Therefore, whether one may ride in an ascending elevator would appear to depend on whether one is permitted to cause an increase in the current in an electrical circuit on *Shabbat*, which was discussed earlier.[110]

---

109 If one enters or exits the elevator before it is set to close, when it is set to be open anyway, it would appear that this is permitted on *Shabbat*. This assumes, though, that the elevator dwell time (the elapsed time before the elevator doors are programmed to close) is not affected by passengers entering or exiting. If the elevator is programmed to attempt to close the doors after a predetermined time interval, regardless of whether passengers entered or exited during the elevator car's stay at the floor, then entering the elevator has no effect, and it would be permitted on Shabbat. However, if by entering the elevator, the photoelectric detector senses the passenger's presence and extends the dwell time, then the passenger's entering the elevator has caused an effect in the elevator's circuitry. If this effect is produced only by modifying the current in a circuit which is already closed, perhaps some *poskim* would permit this, as we will discuss later with regard to elevator weighing mechanisms. R. Simcha Bunim Cohen (*The Aura of Shabbos*, p. 169 in footnote) cites R. Yechezkel Feldberger who permits entering an elevator since one does not know if the elevator will close earlier because one entered it, and many elevators close automatically after a specified amount of time regardless of whether an individual entered. With regard to the effect of the entering passenger on the door that closes later, perhaps R. Auerbach would classify this as *ko'ach sheini*, due to the delay between the passenger's action and the door closing, and so it would be permitted in situations when *gerama* is permitted.

110 See *Ma'aliot Be-Shabbat* ch. 13; R. Michael Broyde and Rabbi Howard Jachter, "The Use of Elevators and Escalators on Shabbat and Yom Tov,"

Several *poskim* prohibit riding in an ascending elevator on *Shabbat*. Dayan Yitzchak Weiss[111] argues that it is prohibited to cause the increase in electric current in the circuit on *Shabbat*. Similarly, R. Yaakov Breisch[112] argues that there is no fundamental difference between riding in an elevator and riding on a train, which R. Yitzchak Shmelkes[113] prohibited on *Shabbat* because the train needs additional electric power with the addition of passengers. R. Shmelkes also prohibited riding on a train because it is *uvda de-chol*, a weekday-specific activity.[114] On the other hand, several *poskim* clearly permit riding in an ascending elevator, including R. Isser Yehuda Unterman[115] and R. Yosef Eliyahu Henkin.[116] R. Shlomo Zalman Auerbach[117] also permits riding in an ascending elevator. R. Hershel Schachter[118] is cited as agreeing that it is fundamentally permitted, though he advises that one should avoid riding in an ascending elevator whenever possible.

Journal of Halacha and Contemporary Society, vol. xxix (Spring 1995), pp. 66–67; and R. Jachter's *Gray Matter* vol. 4, p. 114.

111 *Minchat Yitzchak* 3:60.

112 *Chelkat Ya'akov* 3:137 (*Orach Chayyim* 144).

113 *Beit Yitzchak*, notes to *Yoreh De'ah* 31 (p. 158).

114 R. Moshe Feinstein (*Iggerot Moshe, Orach Chayyim* 2:95) appears to agree with this position. While he initially writes that riding in an elevator which is already being operated by a non-Jew for his or her own purposes is permitted on *Shabbat*, he then writes that since the electric power supplied to the elevator increases when there are additional passengers, it may be prohibited for that reason. However, in another responsum (*Iggerot Moshe, Orach Chayyim* 2:80), R. Feinstein discusses the concern of a landlord who wishes to allow the elevator in his building to be operated by the tenants rather than by his employee, even though non-religious Jews in his building might then use the elevator on *Shabbat*. In that responsum, R. Feinstein implies that if the Jew does not press the elevator button, and a non-Jew does not press the button on the Jew's behalf, there is no other prohibition inherent in riding the elevator on *Shabbat*. See R. Michael Broyde and R. Howard Jachter, "The Use of Elevators and Escalators on Shabbat and Yom Tov," *Journal of Halacha and Contemporary Society*, vol. xxix (Spring 1995), footnote 16.

115 *Shevet Yehudah, Orach Chayyim* 32 and *mahadura batra* pp. 315–317; *Torah She-be'al Peh* vol. 9, pp. 13–15. R. Michael Broyde and R. Howard Jachter (ibid.) cite R. Unterman as relating that R. Yisrael Meir Kagan, author of *Mishnah Berurah*, did not object to riding in an ascending elevator on *Shabbat*, since he reportedly witnessed someone riding in an elevator on *Shabbat* and did not object.

116 *Am Ha-Torah*, vol. 13 (5740), pp. 10–11; *Edut Le-Yisra'el*, 20; *Kol Kitvei Ha-Gaon Ha-Rav Henkin* 2:19(2).

117 Cited in *Shemirat Shabbat Ke-Hilkhatah* 23:49 and footnote 138.

118 Cited in R. Jachter's *Gray Matter*, vol. 4, p. 115.

Descending in the Elevator

One might assume that if riding an ascending elevator is permitted, riding a descending elevator is certainly permitted, as no additional current is generated to accommodate the passenger's increased weight. In fact, since the passenger's weight would help the elevator descend, the elevator's motor must perform less work in order to function properly. Indeed, R. Shlomo Zalman Auerbach[119] permits riding a descending elevator on *Shabbat*, and all the aforementioned authorities who permit riding an elevator do not distinguish between an ascending elevator and a descending elevator.

However, R. Levi Yitzchak Halperin, head of the Institute for Science and Halacha in Jerusalem, argues that while riding in an ascending elevator is permitted on *Shabbat*, riding in a descending elevator is prohibited. In *Ma'aliot Be-Shabbat*, his seminal work on the subject of riding elevators on *Shabbat*, he explains at length the reasoning behind his conclusion, developed through years of research on the technological underpinnings of elevator function. His halakhic concerns with riding a descending elevator are based on three technical points:[120]

1. When a passenger rides in an elevator, his or her weight assists the elevator in descending. Because of the passenger's weight, the elevator's motor needs to do less work in lowering the elevator, and thus less power is supplied to the motor. As the elevator descends, it operates electrical switches and lights which are necessary in the elevator's function. By assisting in the elevator's descent, the passenger becomes responsible for the operation of these switches and lights. Therefore, the passenger riding a descending elevator violates *Shabbat* by his or her participation in the *melakhot* violated by the elevator.[121]

---

119 Cited in *Shemirat Shabbat Ke-Hilkhatah* 23:49 and footnote 138.

120 See *Ma'aliot Be-Shabbat*, ch. 1.

121 It should be noted that the weight of the passenger causes a significant change in the work that the elevator performs. This is because most elevators are designed such that the motor does not usually work to raise the entire weight of the elevator car and its passengers. Instead, the cable holding the elevator car is passed over a pulley and is attached to a counterweight on the other end whose weight is approximately that of the elevator car plus half of the elevator's capacity. Supposing the counterweight weighs exactly the weight of the elevator car plus half the elevator's capacity, if the passenger weight in the elevator car is exactly half the elevator's capacity, the elevator motor now needs to do no work to move the elevator up or down, since any work done to raise the elevator car is exactly balanced by the work done by the counterweight as it descends. If the elevator is 60% full, the elevator's motor does not have to work to raise the entire elevator car and its passengers, but only has to do enough work to lift 10% of the elevator's capacity, as the elevator car's weight and 50% of its capacity is

2. In order for the elevator to slow down when it is descending, the elevator may employ a braking system which may generate opposing electric current to slow down the elevator.[122]
3. When the elevator is at full capacity, it must dissipate some of its energy in order not to move too quickly. It accomplishes this by allowing the motor to be converted into a generator, which then returns energy to the power supply. This electrical energy is used to power surrounding electrical devices, many of which may perform *melakhot* which are prohibited on *Shabbat*. The passenger in a descending elevator is thus responsible for *melakhot* which may be completely unrelated to descending in an elevator.[123]

Before discussing halakhic issues which relate to R. Halperin's argument, it should be noted that there is some disagreement regarding the second and third technical issues that R. Halperin raises. Prof. Ze'ev Lev,[124] founder of the Jerusalem College of Technology, argues that no "new" current is created by the elevator as it brakes; the elevator simply generates an electromotive force in the opposite direction of the power supply, thus decreasing the voltage and subsequently the current in the circuit. Thus, the question is reduced to that of whether it is permitted to modulate current in a circuit on *Shabbat*. Additionally, Prof. Lev argues, it is unlikely that when the motor is converted to a generator, the electrical energy generated powers surrounding electrical devices. This is because if the generator produces AC voltage, it must be at the same frequency and phase as needed by a nearby electrical device to successfully power it.

R. Halperin's arguments, which lead to the conclusion that it is prohibited for a Jewish passenger to ride a descending elevator on *Shabbat*, are predicated on several general assumptions about the nature of *melakhah* on *Shabbat*. R. Halperin assumes that the actions of the passenger are halakhically meaningful, even though (1) the work appears to be attributable to the elevator motor, and (2) the passenger performs no active *melakhah*. If one were to argue that either of these factors is significant, one might conclude that it is permitted to ride in a descending

---

balanced by the counterweight. Thus, the weight of the passenger makes a much more significant change in the elevator's function.
122 *Ma'aliot Be-Shabbat*, pp. 63–64.
123 R. Halperin argues that these *melakhot* are not to be considered in the category of *melakhah she-einah tzerikhah le-gufah*, *melakhah* performed for a purpose other than its typical purpose, given that the passenger does not have any interest in these *melakhot* and is generally unaware of their performance. He argues that the passenger is interested in the performance of these *melakhot*, since otherwise no energy would be dissipated and the elevator would move too quickly. See *Ma'aliot Be-Shabbat* pp. 65–69 for detailed discussion.
124 "*Shimush be-Ma'alit otomatit be-Shabbat*," *Techumin* 5, p. 66.

elevator on *Shabbat*. Indeed, as we will see, several *poskim* argue with R. Halperin, arguing that one (or both) of the above factors is significant, such that riding in a descending elevator is permitted. We will examine each of the above factors and see how R. Halperin and others understand its effect on the halakhic status of riding in a descending elevator.

1. The Work is Attributed to the Elevator Motor

R. Shlomo Zalman Auerbach[125] argues that one is permitted to ride a descending elevator on *Shabbat*. His primary argument for leniency is that the *melakhah* is performed by the elevator motor – and would be performed regardless of the presence of the passenger. Although it is true that the passenger's weight contributes energy toward the descent process, this process would have occurred regardless of any passengers. R. Auerbach argues that if a person performs a *melakhah* which would have occurred in an identical fashion without his or her participation, this cannot be categorized as *melekhet machshevet*, "thoughtful work," which is a necessary criterion for the *melakhah* to be prohibited on *Shabbat*.[126] R. Halperin[127] argues that this is not the case. In addition to refuting R. Auerbach's examples of this principle, he notes that there are several instances in which the Gemara describes a case of prohibited

125 Cited in *Shemirat Shabbat Ke-Hilkhatah*, ch. 23, footnote 140.
126 R. Auerbach notes numerous manifestations of this principle. The following are some notable examples:
  • R. Akiva Eiger (*Orach Chayyim* 318:1) writes, based on Ritva (*Shevuot* 17b s.v. *ve-ha*), that if a pot was on the fire on *Shabbat* and one moved the coals, causing the pot to cook more quickly, one violates *Shabbat*. R. Auerbach notes that the implication is that one's action is only a violation of *Shabbat* if the pot cooks more quickly. However, if one were to move the pot from one fire to an adjacent fire, where it would cook identically, one does not violate *Shabbat*. Even though one has performed an action which causes the pot to cook, since it would have cooked the same way without the action, one has not performed a *melakhah* on *Shabbat*.
  • R. Meir Arik (*Minchat Pittim, Orach Chayyim* 336:8) and *Tehillah Le-David* (*Orach Chayyim* 336:8) rule that it is permitted to drag a flowerpot with a hole in it along the ground. R. Auerbach explains that this is because the plant inside will grow just as it would before, even though the person has caused it to derive sustenance from different earth.
  • Ramban and Ritva (*Gittin* 19a s.v. *deyo*) suggest that if one wrote on *Shabbat* on top of identical writing, one does not violate *Shabbat* because one's writing has not had any additional effect and thus it is not considered *melekhet machshevet*. R. Auerbach argues that this case establishes his principle: since the person's action does not accomplish anything different from the status quo, one does not violate *Shabbat*.
127 *Ma'aliot Be-Shabbat*, ch. 9.

melakhah in which the result of the *melakhah* does not differ from the status before the action.[128]

Even if one were to reject R. Auerbach's principle, one might still permit riding in a descending elevator based on the principle that the passenger is not performing *melakhah* alone, but in concert with the elevator motor, and thus this is to be treated as a case of *shenayim she-asa'uhu*, two people performing a *melakhah* together.[129] The Gemara[130] notes that if two people perform a *melakhah* together, there is debate regarding whether they are liable in a case where both people are capable of performing the *melakhah* individually, as well as in a case in which neither is capable of performing the *melakhah* individually. The *halakhah* is in accordance with R. Yehudah, that if both are individually capable, both violate only a rabbinic prohibition, while if neither is individually capable, both violate a Torah prohibition. The Gemara notes, however, that all agree that if one person is individually capable and the other is not, the individually capable person is liable. While the Gemara does not address whether the other person is liable as well, many later authorities believe that the other person is not liable at all,

128 Among others, he notes the following examples:
- Both the Gemara (*Keritot* 20a) and Yerushalmi (*Shabbat* 2:5) rule that one is liable for blowing on two candles, one which is lit and one which is not lit, in such a way that the lit candle is extinguished and the unlit candle is lit. There is some debate as to why one might have thought one is not liable (see Rashi ad loc s.v. *im be-neshimah achat*; Rabbeinu Gershom ad loc s.v. *de-tanya*; *Or Same'ach, Shabbat* 9:2), but no one claims that this is a case in which there is no *melekhet machshevet*.
- The Gemara (*Chullin* 15b) rules that if one slaughtered an animal on behalf of an ill person on *Shabbat*, a healthy person may not eat the meat. This is because the animal was considered *muktzeh* at the start of *Shabbat* since it had no permissible use, as animal slaughter is normally prohibited on *Shabbat*. However, R. Halperin contends, if R. Auerbach's principle were correct, it would be possible to permissibly slaughter an animal on *Shabbat*: one could set up a machine to slaughter the animal, or have a non-Jew slaughter an animal, but then hold the slaughtering knife as the animal is being slaughtered. In this way, the slaughter is valid, since it was performed by a Jew, but it does not violate *Shabbat*, since the slaughter would have occurred without the Jew's participation. In that case, the animal should not be *muktzeh* as it had a permissible use on *Shabbat*.

129 One might have argued that this construct does not apply in the case of a person acting in concert with a machine, rather it applies only to two people acting in concert. However, R. Yisrael Rosen ("*Ma'alit otomatit be-Shabbat,*" *Techumin* 5, pp. 89–93) argues that the construct does apply here, bringing numerous examples from the Gemara and later authorities in which the construct is used to describe similar cases.

130 *Shabbat* 92b.

and does not even violate a rabbinic prohibition.[131] The question, in applying this construct to our case, is whether this is a case in which the elevator motor is considered capable of causing the elevator to descend and the passenger is incapable, such that the passenger violates no prohibition, or if both parties are considered incapable, such that the passenger could violate a Torah prohibition by riding in the elevator.[132] R.

131 See *Ma'aliot Be-Shabbat*, pp. 106–115, for a complete discussion.
132 Another manifestation of this construct, in this same case of riding a descending elevator, is whether an observant Jew riding a descending elevator with many other passengers can claim that he or she is considered "incapable" while the remaining group of passengers is considered "capable," such that he or she is then permitted to ride. This question is discussed at length by R. Halperin (*Ma'aliot Be-Shabbat*, ch. 11). He suggests that the principal source for examining this question is the Gemara (*Shabbat* 93a) which discusses the case of a *zav*, one who has had an impure emission, and who generally renders impure anything that he sits upon, sitting on an animal when there are garments under each of the animal's legs. The Gemara rules that each garment remains pure, since the animal could stand on only three legs, and so the fourth leg is considered to be providing only auxiliary strength. The assumption is that just as when two people perform an action together, and one provides only auxiliary support (since he or she cannot perform the *melakhah* individually, whereas the other person is capable), his or her action is not halakhically significant, the same is true for the fourth leg which is providing only auxiliary support, as it cannot support the animal alone while the other three legs can. The question regarding the group of passengers in the elevator appears to depend on how the Gemara here is interpreted:

- Rashi (ad loc s.v. *mipenei*) writes that each leg of the animal is considered the "fourth" leg, and all legs are considered "capable"; he would thus assume that each passenger in the elevator is considered "capable," and violates a rabbinic prohibition.
- *Tosafot* (ad loc s.v. *mipenei*) write that each leg is considered the "fourth" leg, and each leg is considered "incapable" with respect to the other "capable" legs; thus, each passenger in the elevator is considered "incapable" with respect to the remainder of the group which is considered capable, and each passenger violates no prohibition. This also appears to be the ruling of *Avnei Nezer* (*Orach Chayyim* 45) and R. Shlomo Zalman Auerbach (cited in *Shemirat Shabbat Ke-Hilkhatah* ch. 23, footnote 140).
- Rambam (*Hilkhot Metamei Mishkav U-Moshav* 7:6) and Me'iri (*Shabbat* ad loc s.v. *zav*) write that we cannot determine which leg is the "fourth" leg, providing only auxiliary strength, and so we cannot determine that any of the garments are impure; thus they all remain pure. R. Halperin argues that since Rambam and Me'iri did not believe that each leg could be distinguished from the rest of the legs (declaring it either "capable" or "incapable"), they must believe that one cannot separate an individual from a group in that manner, and so all passengers in the elevator are to be considered "incapable," such that they

Halperin[133] argues that the elevator motor is to be considered incapable of causing the elevator to descend, since when the passenger is in the elevator, the elevator motor receives a diminished current due to the decrease in the amount of work it must perform, and with that amount of current, the motor is incapable of causing the elevator to descend. R. Halperin's argument is that although the elevator motor is sometimes capable on its own of causing the elevator to descend, its *present* physical state does not permit it to do so.[134] On the other hand, R. Shlomo Zalman Auerbach,[135] R. Yisrael Rosen[136] and Prof. Ze'ev Lev[137] argue that the motor's present physical state does not determine whether it is considered capable; rather its potential capability determines its status.[138]

---

all violate Torah prohibitions. (See, however, *Chazon Ish, Zavim* 3:12 who interprets Rambam in accordance with Rashi's position.)

R. Halperin believes one should be stringent in accordance with his interpretation of Rambam's opinion.

133 *Ma'aliot Be-Shabbat*, pp. 115–124.

134 R. Halperin (*Ma'aliot Be-Shabbat* pp. 124–129) also discusses the question of whether the fact that the elevator is capable of moving the elevator down at the beginning of the ride (when the current reaching the motor has not yet diminished) means that it is still categorized as "capable," thus permitting the passenger to ride in the elevator; he concludes that the motor must be capable of moving the elevator to its destination, without assistance from the passenger's weight, in order for it to be classified as "capable."

135 Cited in *Shemirat Shabbat Ke-Hilkhatah* ch. 23, footnote 140.

136 "*Ma'alit otomatit be-Shabbat*," *Techumin* 5, pp. 86–89.

137 "*Shimush be-ma'alit otomatit be-Shabbat*," *Techumin* 5, pp. 70–72.

138 This debate between R. Halperin and other authorities hinges on how they interpret several statements in the Gemara and later authorities regarding cases of two parties performing a *melakhah* in concert. One source that both sides bring is *Tosafot* (*Shabbat* 93a s.v. *amar mar*), who write that one is considered "incapable" if one performs a *melakhah* using a finger, when one could have performed the *melakhah* by using a stronger part of the body. R. Halperin interprets this to mean that if one performs the *melakhah* with another person, in a physical position that precludes one from performing the *melakhah* individually, one is considered "incapable." R. Rosen argues that *Tosafot* would distinguish between assuming a physical position in which one could not perform the *melakhah* individually, which would render one "incapable," and assuming a physical position in which one could perform the *melakhah* but one is not contributing one's normal strength, in which case one is considered "capable." As R. Rosen notes, this is certainly the case in the Gemara's example of two people carrying an object on *Shabbat* when each could carry it alone: neither person is contributing his or her full strength because each is relying on the other's support, and yet each is considered "capable."

2. The Passenger Performs No Active *Melakhah*

A second argument to permit riding a descending elevator is that the passenger appears not to be performing any *melakhah* actively. R. Halperin[139] argues that since one's weight is assisting in the elevator's descent, it is as if one is actively performing *melakhah*. On the other hand, R. Auerbach,[140] R. Rosen[141] and Prof. Lev[142] argue that the effect of one's weight is not considered responsible for performing a *melakhah*. R. Halperin brings several proofs for this argument from other areas of *halakhah* where the effects of a person's weight are likened to one's actions, particularly in the area of *nezikin* (property damage).[143] Prof. Lev argues that it is inappropriate to compare *Shabbat* law to property damage laws, as the latter are based on personal responsibility (such that one must accept responsibility for the effects of one's weight in causing damages), whereas on *Shabbat* one is only responsible for *melekhet machshevet*, which should not apply when the *melakhah* is performed solely by one's weight.[144]

In addition, R. Rosen[145] argues that even if it were true that the effects of a person's weight are likened to his or her actions, this might

---

139 *Ma'aliot Be-Shabbat* ch. 7.

140 Cited in *Shemirat Shabbat Ke-Hilkhatah*, ch. 23 footnote 140.

141 "*Maalit otomatit be-Shabbat*," *Techumin* 5, pp. 79–83.

142 "*Shimush be-ma'alit otomatit be-Shabbat*," *Techumin* 5, pp. 59–65.

143 R. Halperin notes three cases of property damage due to a person's weight, in which the person is responsible as if he or she actively caused damage:

    1. The Gemara (*Bava Kamma* 27a) notes that if one falls off a roof due to a wind which could have been anticipated, causing damage, one is responsible to pay for damages as if one actively caused damage oneself; thus, one is not only responsible for the principal of the damage, but other obligations such as reimbursement for the damaged person's embarrassment and lost wages.

    2. The Gemara (*Bava Kamma* 10b) rules that if five people sat on a bench and it remained sturdy, but then broke when a sixth person sat down, only the sixth person is liable for damages. However, if the first five people could have risen after the sixth person sat down, but did not, they too are liable for damages. Here, the first five people's responsibility for damages is solely due to their continued sitting and subsequent effects of their weight on the bench.

    3. The Gemara (*Bava Kamma* 31b) discusses how to assign financial culpability in cases in which two people, carrying their belongings, bump into each other and cause damage to the belongings. If one of the people stopped walking prematurely, the Gemara rules that he or she alone is liable for damages. In this case, the damage was caused because the other person bumped into him or her, while he or she failed to change position, so his or her standing weight has actually caused the damage.

144 He notes that *Chazon Ish* (*Bava Kamma* 2:2) alludes to this distinction.

145 "*Ma'alit otomatit be-Shabbat*," *Techumin* 5, pp. 83–86.

not be true if the person is completely passive and another force is using one's weight for a constructive purpose. As proof, R. Rosen notes that *Tosafot*[146] rule that although one is normally required to give up one's life rather than murder another person, this rule does not apply if one's role in the murder is completely passive. For example, if the murder is to be committed by criminals who intend to throw one's body on top of another person, killing that person, one is not required to refuse to participate and thereby give up one's life. Similarly, argues R. Rosen, although one's weight is performing a *melakhah*, it is only doing so because it is being utilized by the elevator motor to accomplish its task, and therefore this *melakhah* is not attributed to the elevator passenger.

Elevator Weighing Mechanisms

In many modern elevators, when a passenger enters the elevator, a computerized weighing mechanism detects the current weight of the elevator load to determine the speed of ascent or descent. Therefore, we must ask if a passenger entering an elevator violates *Shabbat* due to his or her effects on the weighing mechanism.

R. Halperin[147] argues that if an elevator has a weighing mechanism, it is prohibited to ride in the elevator regardless of whether it is ascending or descending. He argues that the weighing mechanism in the elevator may operate by closing a circuit, or by modulating the current in the circuit. In the former case, one is responsible for closing the circuit, which is prohibited. In the latter case, R. Halperin argues that modulating current in this situation is still prohibited since its effects create a discernible change in the elevator's motion.

R. Michael Broyde and R. Howard Jachter[148] argue that these weighing mechanisms may not pose a halakhic concern on *Shabbat*. They note that no other halakhic works which discuss elevators on *Shabbat* discuss this question, even though they are familiar with R. Halperin's written work discussing it. They suggest, therefore, that there are several factors permitting riding in the elevator despite the presence of the weighing mechanism. First, they note that the passenger is likely to be unaware of whether there is a weighing mechanism in the elevator, and it is generally difficult to gather technical information about the elevator in a given building.[149] Thus, riding the elevator becomes a situation of *safek pesik reisha*, a case in which one is uncertain if one's actions are

146 *Sanhedrin* 72b s.v. *ve-ha Ester.*
147 *Ma'aliot Be-Shabbat*, ch. 15.
148 "The Use of Elevators and Escalators on Shabbat and Yom Tov," *Journal of Halacha and Contemporary Society*, vol. XXIX (Spring 1995), pp. 77–79.
149 Although one is often required to gather information in order to know whether one is violating a prohibition (see *Shakh, Yoreh De'ah* 98:9), R.

leading to a secondary, certain outcome, for which several *poskim*[150] tend toward leniency. Second, even if the elevator contains a weighing mechanism which causes a circuit to close, most authorities rule that this is, at most, a rabbinic prohibition. Third, if the weighing mechanism causes modulation of the current in a circuit, R. Broyde and R. Jachter argue that many *poskim* would likely be lenient, in contrast to R. Halperin's position. In sum, the case is one of a *safek pesik reisha* for a rabbinic prohibition (or possibly no prohibition at all), suggesting that one can be lenient.[151] R. Eliezer Melamed[152] argues that activation of the weighing mechanism is a *pesik reisha de-lo nicha lei*, a *pesik reisha* which one does not want, activated itself through *gerama*, an indirect mechanism, and so it is permitted.[153] Alternatively, R. Shaul Yisraeli[154] notes that one may enter the elevator immediately after a non-Jew, since then the non-Jew triggers the elevator weighing mechanism, and the subsequently entering Jewish passenger merely modifies the current in the mechanism, which is permitted.

For Whom Is Riding in an Elevator Permitted?

Although we have noted that many *poskim* view riding elevators as a technically permitted activity on *Shabbat*, these *poskim* generally show ambivalence toward riding elevators on *Shabbat*. R. Yehoshua Neuwirth notes that because of the more stringent opinion held by R. Halperin, one who is able should be strict and not ride in an ascending elevator on *Shabbat*. He more generally notes that one should avoid riding elevators on *Shabbat* if possible. R. Yosef Eliyahu Henkin,[155] while also permitting riding in an elevator, advises that this leniency be followed only by the ill or infirm in cases where riding the elevator is necessary to perform a *mitzvah* such as attending synagogue services. Similar ambivalence is expressed by R. Hershel Schachter and R. Mordechai Willig, both of

---

Broyde and R. Jachter argue that this is not the case when gathering such information is very difficult or impossible.

150 *Biur Halakhah* 316:3 s.v. *ein mino nitzod*; *Melammed Le-Ho'il* 3:102.

151 Additionally, they add, one is not aware of the actions of the weighing mechanism; even if one is aware that weighing mechanisms exist, one does not know whether the elevator which one is riding contains such a weighing mechanism, and if the weighing mechanism operates through prohibited means. Therefore, riding the elevator would be *mitasek*, performance of a *melakhah* without one's awareness, for which one is not liable.

152 *Peninei Halakhah*, *Shabbat* 17:4.

153 This is based on the ruling of R. Shlomo Zalman Auerbach (*Minchat Shlomo, mahadura kamma*, 10:6) who permits a *pesik reisha* on *Shabbat* if it is effected through *gerama*.

154 *Be-Mareh Ha-Bazak*, 2:23.

155 *Edut Le-Yisra'el*, 20.

whom are cited[156] as advising that one avoid relying on the leniency of using elevators on *Shabbat* if possible.

Obviously, a resident physician is performing many *mitzvot* in taking care of patients on *Shabbat*, so one might argue that this justifies his or her use of the elevator on *Shabbat*. Needless to say, if there is concern that not using the elevator might endanger a patient in any way, one *must* take the elevator on *Shabbat*. If the situation is even more emergent, one may obviously press buttons and use the elevator as one would on a weekday. R. Moshe Feinstein[157] is cited as ruling that a resident should use the elevator if his or her services are needed emergently, but also if one is concerned that if one uses the stairs, one will become exhausted and unable to care for patients properly.

Even if one is taking the elevator on *Shabbat*, one should ideally minimize the degree of *Shabbat* violation. Therefore, one should try to press elevator buttons with a *shinui*, such as with one's elbow or the back of one's hand. Given the concern of activating the automatic door sensor, one could also enter the elevator with a *shinui*, such as by entering backwards;[158] if one is entering the elevator simultaneously with a non-Jew, such a *shinui* is unnecessary, as noted earlier.

If the patient being seen is not dangerously ill, it would appear that one is permitted to ask a non-Jew to press the button,[159] since one is

156 See R. Jachter's *Gray Matter*, vol. 4, pp. 115, 123.
157 R. Moshe D. Tendler and Fred Rosner, *Practical Medical Halacha*, p. 105; Fred Rosner, "Rabbi Moshe Feinstein's Influence on Medical Halacha," *The Journal of Halacha and Contemporary Society*, vol. xx (Fall 1990), pp. 49, 51.
158 See R. Simcha Bunim Cohen's *The Shabbos Home* vol. 2, p. 486, footnote 40, who cites R. Pesach Falk as permitting this if no other option is available.
159 If one is not taking the elevator in order to provide care to a patient on *Shabbat*, asking a non-Jew might not be permitted. As a general rule, one may not ask a non-Jew to perform *melakhah* on one's behalf on *Shabbat*. Thus one may not ask a non-Jew to press the button, or even to benefit from the actions of a non-Jew who pressed the button specifically on behalf of the Jewish passenger, even without being asked. However, R. Michael Broyde and R. Howard Jachter ("The Use of Elevators and Escalators on Shabbat and Yom Tov," Journal of Halacha and Contemporary Society, vol. xxix (Spring 1995), p. 85 and footnote 86) note that the case of a non-Jew pressing elevator buttons is definitely one of asking a non-Jew to violate only a rabbinic prohibition. Although a Torah prohibition could be violated by illuminating incandescent lights in the elevator buttons, if these are present, such a violation would be a *pesik reisha*, an inevitable ancillary outcome of pressing the button, and one is permitted to ask a non-Jew to perform an action which has only a prohibited ancillary outcome (*Mishnah Berurah* 253:99). Thus, the only prohibition with which one must be concerned is that caused by closing electric circuits through pressing the elevator button, which is a rabbinic prohibition according to most authorities.

permitted to ask a non-Jew to perform even a Torah prohibition on behalf of an ill patient, even one who is classified as a *choleh she-ein bo sakkanah*. This ruling is explicitly cited from R. Yehoshua Neuwirth.[160]

Escalators

R. Yehoshua Neuwirth[161] notes that if an escalator works continuously and is not affected by a passenger stepping on or off of it, then there is no prohibition of using an escalator on *Shabbat*, since one has not caused the performance of any *melakhah*. R. Ovadia Yosef[162] also rules that this is permitted though he advises that one avoid using the escalator if possible, just as an automatic elevator. R. Broyde and R. Jachter[163] note that an escalator should pose no problem at all on *Shabbat*, unlike an automatic elevator, since there is no change in current when the passenger steps on the escalator. They suggest that the increased hesitancy of permitting escalator use on *Shabbat* is limited only to Israel, where the cost of electricity may have resulted in escalator systems that conserve power based on whether passengers are using the escalator. In any case, it is clear that given the choice between using an elevator or an escalator to move between floors in the hospital, the latter is undoubtedly preferable.

Though it is still generally prohibited to ask a non-Jew to perform even a rabbinic prohibition on *Shabbat*, this is sometimes permitted, as in the case of performing a *mitzvah*. One should ask a competent halakhic advisor which situations might qualify for such a leniency.

160 *Nishmat Avraham*, vol. 1, introduction to *siman* 328, 6(9), p. 399.
161 *Shemirat Shabbat Ke-Hilkhatah* 23:52.
162 *Yalkut Yosef, Shabbat* vol. 5, p. 195.
163 "The Use of Elevators and Escalators on Shabbat and Yom Tov," *Journal of Halacha and Contemporary Society*, vol. xxix (Spring 1995), pp. 86–87.

Chapter 26

Traveling to the Hospital on *Shabbat*

Jerry Karp, MD, PhD

Among the more significant halakhic impediments to being a resident on call on *Shabbat* is traveling to the hospital. In this chapter, we will discuss whether one is required to stay in the hospital from the start of *Shabbat*, in order to avoid any prohibitions that might be violated while traveling, as well as which halakhic concerns are to be considered if one is permitted to travel to the hospital on *Shabbat*. For a discussion regarding whether one may travel home from the hospital after one's duties at the hospital have ended, see Chapter 27.

Must One Remain in the Hospital at the Start of *Shabbat*?

If a resident is assigned call starting in the middle of *Shabbat*, such that he or she must be present in the hospital during *Shabbat*, or may be called to the hospital on *Shabbat* to tend to lifesaving needs, may the resident be home at the beginning of *Shabbat*, knowing that he or she will need to violate *Shabbat* to return to the hospital? At stake is the comfort of the resident who wants to eat and sleep on Friday night at home, as well as the family life of the resident which may suffer if the resident is not at home for at least some of *Shabbat*. This is especially important to residents who are on call every *Shabbat* or almost every *Shabbat*. If such residents must stay in the hospital on Friday night so as not to violate *Shabbat* by traveling back to the hospital, they will likely miss almost all *Shabbat* meals with their families.

R. Moshe Feinstein[1] answers this question sharply in the negative, arguing that the resident must stay in the hospital or at a local site within walking distance of the hospital on *Shabbat*. He argues that the resident is required to do this even if it means he or she will be unable to fulfill the positive *mitzvot* of *Shabbat* such as *kiddush* and eating the *Shabbat* meals.[2] In contrast, R. Shlomo Zalman Auerbach[3] argues that there is room to be lenient in this case and allow the resident to stay home on Friday night, especially when the resident is on call every *Shabbat*. He notes that the resident is not required to perform *melakhah* or other actions before *Shabbat* in order to avoid needing to perform *melakhah* on *Shabbat* for *pikuach nefesh*.[4] R. Auerbach notes that while *Sefer Chasidim*[5] instructs that a woman in her ninth month of pregnancy plan ahead of *Shabbat* to avoid *Shabbat* violation, following this stipulation is merely meritorious conduct, rather than required. Indeed, *Mishnah Berurah*,[6] in citing *Sefer Chasidim*, writes that such conduct is "*ra'ui*," preferable rather than obligatory. R. Auerbach does take note of *Sefer Chasidim*'s recommendation, though, suggesting that if a resident is only on call very occasionally, it would be preferable for the resident to stay in the hospital on Friday night; he advises that one be lenient in a case where the resident is on call frequently, such that his or her family life and enjoyment of *Shabbat* will suffer by not being home on Friday night. He adds that there is even more room for leniency if one will return to the hospital by employing a non-Jewish driver, since one is certainly not required to plan ahead to avoid asking a non-Jew to violate *Shabbat* to save a life. Indeed, one is even allowed to ask a non-Jew to violate *Shabbat* for a patient who is not dangerously ill.

1   *Iggerot Moshe, Orach Chayyim* 1:131.
2   He notes an exception to this ruling: if there is nowhere that the resident is able to stay overnight within walking distance to the hospital, the resident may travel to the hospital on *Shabbat*, and is not required to stay outside overnight. If there is a place nearby where the resident can pay to stay, the resident is required to spend his or her money to stay in this local place rather than travel on *Shabbat*.
3   Cited in *Shemirat Shabbat Ke-Hilkhatah* ch. 32, footnote 104; *Shulchan Shlomo, Orach Chayyim* 248:7.
4   This contrasts with our discussion in Chapter 21 regarding choosing a residency program. There, it was noted that one is required to avoid putting oneself in a situation on *Shabbat* wherein one will be required to violate *Shabbat* in order to save a life. The difference between these two scenarios is that in the scenario discussed there, one has generated the *pikuach nefesh* situation oneself on *Shabbat*, which is prohibited, whereas here, the *pikuach nefesh* situation is generated automatically without one's actions. In the latter situation, one does not have to try to prevent the *pikuach nefesh* situation from occurring, if one is not creating it oneself.
5   *Siman* 845.
6   330:1.

A more restrained degree of leniency is offered by R. Yehoshua Neuwirth, who distinguishes between a resident who is assigned in-house call on *Shabbat* and a resident who is assigned home call and may be contacted on *Shabbat* to travel to the hospital. In the former case, since the resident must be in the hospital on *Shabbat*, he or she must stay in the hospital when *Shabbat* starts. R. Neuwirth notes several cases discussed by the Gemara and *rishonim* in which one is required to perform *melakhot* before *Shabbat* to avoid performing them on *Shabbat* for *pikuach nefesh*.[7] However, in the latter case, R. Neuwirth rules that the resident may travel home before the start of *Shabbat* since there is no guarantee that the resident will be required to return to the hospital on *Shabbat*. He also references the stipulation of *Sefer Chasidim* who requires a pregnant woman to prepare in advance of *Shabbat*, but notes that giving birth is a one-time occurrence, while the resident is on call every week, and so he or she need not abide by *Sefer Chasidim*'s stringency. R. Neuwirth still notes that even in such a case, staying over *Shabbat* in proximity to the hospital is meritorious conduct. *Nishmat*

---

7   He notes three cases:
1.   The Gemara (*Shabbat* 69b; cited in *Shulchan Arukh* 344:1–2) discusses a case in which one is walking in the desert and does not remember which day is *Shabbat*. This individual should begin his or her own count and should designate the seventh day as *Shabbat*, during which he or she recites *kiddush* and *havdalah*. This individual must avoid performing *melakhah* on all days, unless he or she must do so in order to live, in which case he or she may perform the minimum *melakhah* necessary on all seven days. If this individual knows that a particular day is definitely not *Shabbat* (e.g., he or she knows that *Shabbat* is one of two adjacent days, but does not know which one), he or she is permitted to perform *melakhah* on all other days that are definitely not *Shabbat*. Because of this, *Olat Shabbat* (344:2) reasons that one may only do work on these days, and not those which might be *Shabbat*; *Mishnah Berurah* (344:11) rules in accordance with this opinion. This line of reasoning suggests that one must perform *melakhah* before *Shabbat* in order to avoid performing *melakhah* on *Shabbat* for *pikuach nefesh*.
2.   *Shulchan Arukh* (*Orach Chayyim* 331:6–7) rules that one is required to perform ancillary needs of a circumcision (that require performance of *melakhah*) before *Shabbat*, and *Mishnah Berurah* (331:24) adds that if one did not do so, one may not perform the *berit milah* until after *Shabbat* when these ancillary needs may be performed.
3.   *Shulchan Arukh* (*Orach Chayyim* 248:4) rules, based on the responsum of Rivash (1:17–18), that one may not begin a journey into the desert before *Shabbat* knowing that one will be required to violate *Shabbat* for *pikuach nefesh*.
     The last two cases are discussed in more detail in Chapter 21. R. Neuwirth's position appears to reject the distinction proposed by R. Auerbach discussed in footnote 4.

Avraham[8] reports that even R. Neuwirth agrees that if one can travel back to the hospital with a non-Jew, one is permitted to stay at home for *Shabbat*.[9]

Means of Travel on *Shabbat*

If one is permitted to travel to the hospital on *Shabbat*, one must still evaluate which method of traveling on *Shabbat* is most halakhically ideal. Here, we will discuss the various halakhic concerns involved in traveling on *Shabbat* in order to determine which means of travel might be chosen. The reader is encouraged to discuss the particulars of one's situation with a halakhic advisor who can help to decide what method is best for a given individual.

Driving a Car

The most halakhically problematic means of traveling to the hospital is driving a car. As one is driving, one is constantly causing additional fuel combustion, which violates a Torah prohibition. Additionally, car lights are frequently illuminated, including brake lights and turn signals; causing illumination of these lights is likely to be a rabbinic prohibition, according to those authorities who consider closing an electric circuit a rabbinic prohibition.[10] Furthermore, when one arrives at the hospital, one will face several halakhic difficulties with regard to turning off the car, since doing so is not of any benefit to any patient in the hospital. For these reasons, one should avoid driving a car oneself as a method of traveling to the hospital, if other options are available. If there are no other options, one should speak with a halakhic advisor regarding the permissibility of driving a car to the hospital and how one should navigate these concerns.

Riding in a Car Driven by a Non-Jew

A more halakhically preferable solution is to be driven to the hospital by a non-Jewish driver, such as a taxi driver. In this case, the resident who asks the driver to transport him or her to the hospital violates only the prohibition of *amirah le-akum*, asking a non-Jew to perform a *melakhah* on *Shabbat*, which is permitted even for a patient who is

8 *Orach Chayyim* 329:7(2), pp. 505–506.
9 Dr. Avraham Steinberg (*Encyclopedia Hilkhatit Refuit*, s.v. *Shabbat*, p. 462) appears to suggest that this view is universal. However, R. Moshe Feinstein does not mention any dispensation to travel with a non-Jew, though it is possible that he would permit it, as his responsum relates only to driving oneself to the hospital.
10 See the introduction to Chapter 25 for a more comprehensive discussion.

not dangerously ill.[11] Ideally, one should call the driver before *Shabbat* to arrange transportation on *Shabbat*,[12] but if this is not possible, calling on *Shabbat* would violate a rabbinic prohibition of using a phone (according to most authorities[13]), and thus one should ideally pick up the telephone and dial the number with a *shinui*. Alternatively, one could ask a non-Jew to dial the phone, or to call a taxi using a smartphone app. Paying a taxi driver involves the exchange of money, which is *muktzeh*.[14] Therefore, if possible, one should try to create an account with the taxi company before *Shabbat* such that one need not pay money on *Shabbat*; many newer taxi companies with smartphone apps also automatically make deductions from one's credit card account, and so this may be the most preferable option.

Public Transportation

Taking public transportation on *Shabbat* would appear to pose fewer halakhic challenges than hiring a taxi driver, particularly if the driver would be making the same stops anyway regardless of whether the Jewish passenger was present. However, there are still several halakhic concerns with riding public transportation on *Shabbat*. Many 19th and 20th century *poskim*, in addressing the question of whether Jews could ride trains on *Shabbat*, noted that riding a train or other vehicle is not in the spirit of *Shabbat*, and thus must be avoided on *Shabbat*. Most notably, *Chatam Sofer*[15] suggested that due to the inherent turbulence of riding a train, which would interfere with one's enjoyment of *Shabbat*, riding trains is prohibited on *Shabbat*. He attributes the underlying principle to Ramban,[16] who suggests that the Torah's instruction to rest on *Shabbat* (*shabbaton*) indicates that one may not perform actions that are not strictly in the category of *melakhah* but still interfere with one's ability to properly observe the spirit of *Shabbat*. A similar concern was noted by R. Yitzchak Shmelkes.[17] Many contemporary authorities cite a concern for violating the spirit of *Shabbat* (using the terms "*ziluta de-Shabbat*" or "*uvda de-chol*") as the main halakhic reason not to ride

---

11 *Shulchan Arukh* 328:17.
12 This does not obviate the prohibition of *amirah le-akum*, as one is still prohibited to ask a non-Jew before *Shabbat* to perform *melakhah* on *Shabbat* (*Shulchan Arukh, Orach Chayyim* 307:2–3); however, contacting the taxi company before *Shabbat* relieves one of the need to place a telephone call on *Shabbat*.
13 See Chapter 25 for a discussion of using a telephone on *Shabbat*.
14 *Shulchan Arukh, Orach Chayyim* 310:7.
15 *Yoreh De'ah* 6:97.
16 Leviticus 23:24.
17 *Beit Yitzchak*, notes to *Yoreh De'ah* 31 (p. 158).

public transportation on *Shabbat.*[18] These authorities include R. Moshe Feinstein,[19] R. Ovadia Yosef,[20] and R. Eliezer Waldenberg.[21] However, it would appear that these authorities do not consider riding public transportation to be any worse than riding with a non-Jewish taxi driver in this regard, as both methods of travel presumably create the same concerns. Rather, riding public transportation would seem to obviate many of the halakhic concerns involved in riding with a non-Jewish driver, as noted.[22]

However, riding public transportation on *Shabbat* generates other technical halakhic problems. Most prominently, one must still pay the driver with money or give the driver a bus ticket, and money or its substitute are both *muktzeh* on *Shabbat.*[23] For this reason, *Nishmat Avraham*[24] advises (citing support from R. Yehoshua Neuwirth) that riding with a non-Jewish taxi driver whom one contacted in advance of *Shabbat* would be preferable to riding public transportation to the hospital.

---

18 See *Piskei Teshuvot* 248:2 (footnote 21), p. 56, for a complete listing of authorities who discuss this question.

19 *Iggerot Moshe, Yoreh De'ah* 1:44.

20 *Yechavveh Da'at* 6:16.

21 *Tzitz Eliezer* 1:21.

22 Another halakhic concern noted by *poskim* that might apply to public transportation is that of concern for leaving the *techum Shabbat*, though this concern applies equally to public transportation and a private cab. One should speak with a halakhic advisor regarding one's specific geographic location to determine whether the *techum Shabbat* is violated by traveling from one's home to the hospital where one works, and if this changes the permissibility of traveling on *Shabbat.*

23 *Shulchan Arukh, Orach Chayyim* 310:7.

24 *Orach Chayyim* 308:1, p. 312.

Chapter 27

Driving Home from the Hospital on *Shabbat*

Jenny Apsan, MD

J udaism's utmost regard for the sanctity and saving of lives and sub-sequent halakhic principle of *pikuach nefesh* (saving a life), superseding the laws of *Shabbat*, is well-known. Thus, in any life-threatening situation, a physician is permitted to do whatever measures are necessary to treat a patient. Once the doctor has entered the hospital under such pretenses and the lifesaving procedure is over, what is he or she allowed to do? This question is critically important for paramedics, doctors, and even family members accompanying a loved one to the hospital on *Shabbat*. This topic may also weigh heavily on a medical student's decision to pursue a *Shabbat*-accommodating or non-*Shabbat*-accommodating residency program. Even if one elects to work in a *Shabbat*-observant resident program, one might be caught in an emergent scenario warranting one to stay past sunset on Friday evening, especially on the earliest *Shabbatot* in the middle of the winter. Thus, the question of whether one may return home is especially relevant to medical students, residents, and attending physicians alike. In this chapter, we will present an analysis of the early halakhic sources which may relate to this modern issue, and then discuss practical ramifications of these sources.[1]

---

1   A more extensive discussion of this topic can be found in R. J. David Bleich, "Returning from Mission of Mercy on the Sabbath," *Tradition* 2 (4), Winter 1987, pp. 102–112; Dr. Fred Rosner and Rabbi Wilfred Wolfson, "Returning on the Sabbath from a Lifesaving Mission," Journal of Halacha and Comtemporary Society, vol. IX, Spring 1985; Jonathan Wiesen, "Driving Home on Friday for the Observant Physician: Toward a New Mindset" *Verapo Yerape* vol. 2, pp. 123–145; *Nishmat Avraham* vol. 1 p. 220. Two recorded lectures delivered by R. Jeremy Wieder (http://www.yutorah.org/lectures/lecture.cfm/703781) and R. Howard Apfel (http://

Early Talmudic Sources

Hittiru sofan mishum techillatan

An important Talmudic principle which serves as a launch point for our discussion is the dictum of *"hittiru sofan mishum techillatan,"* "They permitted the end for the sake of the beginning." This principle states that Chazal occasionally lifted a *Shabbat* prohibition in order to prevent people from not performing some other action which Chazal viewed as positive. The concept is initially encountered in the Gemara[2] where Ula enumerates four particular examples which rely on this logic. For example, Chazal permitted spreading out animal hides on a *yom tov* after slaughtering an animal (which would ordinarily be prohibited, as it is part of the process of tanning) so that people would not hesitate to slaughter the animal to use for *yom tov* fearing that by doing so the animal hides would go to waste because they could not be tanned. The Gemara here notes no association between this principle and the

---

www.yutorah.org/lectures/lecture.cfm/796406 and http://www.yutorah.org/lectures/lecture.cfm/796520) are also useful.

2   In addition to the example mentioned in the main text, *Beitzah* 11b lists several cases in which the principle is to be employed:
   - According to Beit Hillel, one may remove and then replace shutters (*terisin*) on portable public shops on *yom tov*. The dispensation to remove the shutters from the shops on *yom tov* was to enable people to obtain goods necessary for *yom tov*. However, replacing the shutters would not be necessary for this purpose. But if replacing the shutters were not permitted, shop owners would not open their shops, thus preventing people from obtaining *yom tov* needs. Therefore, Beit Hillel permitted not only removing the shutters, but replacing them as well.
   - A *kohen* may replace a bandage on his hand in the *Beit ha-Mikdash* on *yom tov*. Since he would need to remove the bandage before performing service in the *Beit ha-Mikdash*, so as not to have any object separating between his hand and the object he was holding, he was permitted to replace the bandage afterward so as to encourage him to remove the bandage and participate in service in the *Beit ha-Mikdash*.
   - Normally, food touched by one who is not knowledgeable about Torah law is assumed to have become *tamei*, ritually impure, since we are concerned that this person is not sufficiently knowledgeable about Torah law to have prevented himself or herself from becoming *tamei*. However, a general exception is during *yom tov*, when Chazal decreed that wine and dough sold to such a person does not become *tamei*, so as not to embarrass people who are not knowledgeable. R. Yehudah notes that even after *yom tov*, the barrel of dough or wine from which one is selling to people remains pure, and one can sell the dough or wine as pure after *yom tov*. This dispensation is to encourage people to sell dough and wine on *yom tov* so that people will be able to celebrate *yom tov*.

concept of *pikuach nefesh*. It is also unclear if the list in the Gemara is comprehensive, and the principle is restricted to Ula's four examples, or if the Gemara is demonstrating a principle that can be more broadly applied. Ultimately, as we will see, many *rishonim* use this dictum as a foundational principle by which to understand other Talmudic passages.

The Dispensation for Rescuers

A related principle is based on a Talmudic passage which explicitly discusses cases of returning from lifesaving missions on *Shabbat*. The Gemara is commenting on an apparent contradiction between two Mishnayot. One Mishnah[3] establishes the numerical boundaries of what constitutes *techum Shabbat*, the extent of the city limits. If a person travels past this boundary on *Shabbat*, he or she may then not move more than four *ammot* (about seven feet) in any direction. However, for witnesses coming to testify about a new moon, Rabban Gamliel gives a dispensation of 2,000 *ammot* for a person who left the *techum* to serve as a witness. The Gemara adds that this dispensation is not limited to witnesses but also applies to "one who comes to assist for birthing, [or] one who comes to rescue others from fire, from soldiers, and from a river."

A second Mishnah[4] records the dispensation of 2,000 *ammot* for one who left the *techum Shabbat* permissibly but was then informed that the need was already fulfilled. However, the end of the Mishnah recounts that anyone who goes out to save someone can, in fact, "return to one's [original] place" following a mission. This Mishnah appears to contradict the first Mishnah which grants only 2,000 *ammot* to those who have completed a lifesaving mission, as this one implies that one can travel even beyond this distance.

Importantly, two *rishonim*, *Tosafot*[5] and Rashba,[6] invoke the principle of *hittiru sofan mishum techillatan* as the justifications for both of these dispensations, to travel 2,000 *ammot* or even to "return to one's original place."[3] In other words, if rescuers were not permitted to return home following a lifesaving mission, they might be less inclined to set out on the mission in the first place.[7]

---

3   *Rosh Hashanah* 23b.
4   *Eruvin* 4:3.
5   *Eruvin* 44b s.v. *kol.*
6   *Beitzah* 11b s.v. *be-pelugta.*
7   Both *Tosafot* and Rashba are pressed to explain why the Gemara which introduces the principle of *hittiru sofan mishum techillatan* does not mention this example. They both explain that the Gemara there only listed examples in which one might have thought that the dispensation stemmed from a different principle, and the Gemara explains that the guiding

These two Mishnayot present several questions. First, does the dispensation to travel more than 2,000 *ammot* apply to anyone who saves a life on *Shabbat*, or only to the specific situations listed in the Mishnah (fire, enemy soldiers, or a person drowning in a river)? More importantly, what exactly is the dispensation: May one return to one's home, as is implied by one Mishnah, or may one only travel up to 2,000 *ammot*, as is implied by the other Mishnah?

The ambiguity between the dispensation of 2,000 *ammot* and "returning to one's original place" forces the Gemara[8] to give two resolutions:

1. The first resolution, attributed to R. Yehudah, is that when the Mishnah stated that the rescuers could "return to their [original] place," this was not meant to suggest that they could travel more than 2,000 *ammot*. Instead, this statement was only intended to convey an additional dispensation that the rescuers may, in addition to traveling home up to 2,000 *ammot*, carry their weapons with them, in order to prevent a possible subsequent attack by the enemy.

2. The second resolution, suggested by R. Nachman bar Yitzchak, is that rescuers may indeed travel home more than 2,000 *ammot*, but only in cases when "the enemy's hand is winning." In other words, imminent danger due to the enemy allows for one to travel more than 2,000 *ammot*. On the other hand, if the rescuers were victorious, they may travel only 2,000 *ammot* following the lifesaving mission.

According to both answers, it seems on the surface that the dispensation to travel after the lifesaving mission is based on safety, and that this dispensation is limited to a case in which the rescuers are in further imminent danger.

The noted ambiguities of the dispensations to travel 2,000 *ammot* or to "return to one's original place" are discussed by Rambam[9] and *Shulchan Arukh*,[10] who imply that both the answers of R. Yehudah and of R. Nachman bar Yitzchak influence the *halakhah*. Thus, both Rambam and *Shulchan Arukh* note that if "the hand of the non-Jews is dominant," one is permitted to go home with weapons. It remains unclear whether one may violate other prohibitions besides that of *techum Shabbat*. Furthermore, in contrast to this apparently limited dispensation, Rambam seemingly provides a more expansive dispensation elsewhere,[11] stating "when they come to capture their enemies, they are

---

principle behind the dispensation is in fact *hittiru sofan mishum techillatan*. In contrast, in the case of the rescuers' return, the guiding principle of *hittiru sofan mishum techillatan* is "obvious," as Rashba states.

8   *Eruvin* 45a.
9   *Shabbat* 27:17.
10   *Orach Chayyim* 407.
11   *Shabbat* 2:23.

permitted to return to their homes with weapons so that they do not hesitate to come in the future [*she-lo lehakhshilan le-atid la-vo*]," perhaps giving a blanket permission to return regardless of the safety of the scenario or the circumstance of war. Rambam's position thus remains unclear.

Biblical vs. Rabbinic Prohibitions

Our readings of the above sources open a wide range of opinions regarding what the principle of *hittiru sofan* allows one to do following a lifesaving incident. The complexity of the sources leads to a gamut of opinions from allowing strictly what the Gemara allowed, walking 2,000 *ammot*, to allowing the violation of any Biblical prohibition on *Shabbat* to fully return home. Even a close read of our original Talmudic sources leads to ambiguity regarding this question. For example, the first three cases listed in the Gemara that establishes the principle of *hittiru sofan mishum techillatan* are all cases of rabbinic prohibitions. Similarly, the prohibition of *techumin*, discussed in the case of witnesses for the new moon, is generally understood to be a rabbinic prohibition. On the other hand, the dispensation for rescuers to travel with weapons, discussed in the Gemara with regard to rescuers, and the dispensation for witnesses for the new moon to travel with food and walking sticks[12] can certainly be considered as permitting the violation of Biblical prohibitions of carrying in the public domain.

On one end of the spectrum lies R. Tzvi Pesach Frank,[13] who disregards the notion that *Tosafot* or Rashba imply anything about transgressing Biblical or even rabbinic law and maintains that the dispensation of the Gemara to "return to one's original place" in a lifesaving mission is solely limited to one defending an attack, who can then bring weapons home. In other words, the soldiers are only permitted to return home with their weapons in order to protect themselves from danger. This limited interpretation leaves little room for expansion of the general principles to our discussion of physicians. R. Frank posits that the intention of the principle of *hittiru sofan mishum techillatan*, according to Rashba and *Tosafot*, is that rescuers are permitted to travel home after the rescue mission on *Shabbat* even though they are placing themselves in danger, thus necessitating the violation of Biblical prohibitions, i.e., carrying weapons home. Entering such a situation is itself a rabbinic prohibition, which is suspended in this situation due to *hittiru sofan mishum techillatan*. Thus, the application of this principle in

---

12 See *Chatam Sofer* (*Orach Chayyim* 203) where he implies that witnesses must have engaged in Biblical prohibitions when going to testify and returning from testifying about the new moon.
13 *Har Tzvi, Orach Chayyim* 2:10.

this situation is not at all related to concern regarding future situations of endangered lives, but is simply intended to allow one to return home and thereby enter a situation wherein one will be required to violate a Biblical prohibition.[14] In the case of no danger, he posits, one has only the Talmudic dispensation of 2,000 *ammot* and no more. He or she may not, therefore, violate rabbinic or Biblical prohibitions to return home.

Magen Avraham,[15] and later R. Shlomo Zalman Auerbach,[16] argue that there is wider room for dispensations following a lifesaving mission, yet they do not go beyond allowing the violation of rabbinic regulations as seen by the dispensation of traveling more than 2,000 *ammot*, which violates only a rabbinic decree.[17] It should also be noted that beyond the halakhic details of what is permitted, R. Auerbach emphatically states that physicians ultimately would never hesitate if a patient was in danger, and thus extra measures of permitting the violation of Biblical law are completely unnecessary; this contrasts with a fundamental premise of R. Moshe Feinstein, discussed below, who states one can violate Biblical prohibitions so as to ensure people will go out next time. In reality, R. Auerbach agrees with R. Frank's reading of the Gemara, but he differs in permitting rabbinic violations because he notes that some doctors might be swayed not to return to the hospital were rabbinic violations not permitted upon their return.

R. Auerbach also notes that one can also be lenient with regard to rabbinic prohibitions, especially given the more lenient ruling of *Chatam Sofer* in this context. In a responsum to a physician who was called to save lives on *Shabbat*, *Chatam Sofer*[18] implies that a doctor

14   R. J. David Bleich (*Contemporary Halakhic Problems* vol. 4, p. 131) argues that R. Frank's explanation is contradicted by Rashba's own writing, since Rashba himself applied *hittiru sofan mishum techillatan* in the case of a midwife, whom he ruled was permitted to return home. R. Bleich notes that Rashba's ruling itself is difficult due to the Mishnah which appears to limit the dispensation to return home to soldiers returning from a rescue mission and not to a midwife, who appears to be limited to 2,000 *ammot*. However, with regard to Rashba's opinion, it appears that he certainly does not limit the application of *hittiru sofan mishum techillatan* to soldiers.

15   497:18.

16   *Minchat Shlomo* 1:8.

17   Since traveling more than 2,000 *ammot* on *Shabbat* is a violation of a rabbinic decree (see *Beit Yosef, Orach Chayyim* 397), some conclude that the Gemara is stipulating that any rabbinic decree can be violated when returning home, under the principle of *hem ameru ve-hem ameru*, the Sages who enacted the decree also provided the exception to their decree. Indeed, R. Shlomo Kluger (*U-Bacharta Ba-Chayyim,* 99) and *Minchat Chinukh* (*mitzvah* 24, p. 115) rule that one who travels on *Shabbat* to call for medical assistance may not travel back more than twelve *mil* (24,000 *ammot*), as traveling this distance is considered to be a Biblical prohibition.

18   *Choshen Mishpat* 194.

may disregard Biblical law after tending to a dangerously ill patient in order to return home. In this responsum, he also cites the opinion of R. Yaakov Emden[19] who permits this as well. Elsewhere,[20] *Chatam Sofer* suggests that the rabbinic dispensation of *hittiru sofan mishum techillatan* is based on one of the original sources for permitting *Shabbat* violation in the case of danger to life, "*ve-shameru benei yisra'el et ha-Shabbat,*" "and the children of Israel will observe the *Shabbat,*"[21] from which the Gemara[22] derives the principle, "Violate one *Shabbat* in order that one may guard many future *Shabbatot.*" *Chatam Sofer* explains that Chazal were empowered to permit violations of Biblical prohibitions on *Shabbat* in order to encourage people to save lives on *Shabbat,* so that those who are saved would be able to then observe many future *Shabbatot.* Thus, he brings the dispensation out of the precise realm of *hittiru sofan* and into the realm of *pikuach nefesh* itself, explaining that the rabbis expanded the parameters of *pikuach nefesh.*[23]

R. Moshe Feinstein[24] suggests a novel alternative interpretation of the first Gemara regarding a midwife or rescuer, adding a unique nuance. He explains that the dispensation for a midwife to travel 2,000 *ammot* following the birth refers to a case of one who is aware that his or her lifesaving mission will last the entire day. Therefore, by beginning the journey, the rescuer indicates that he or she is willing to go even without the ability to return home. Thus, the dispensation following the lifesaving mission is limited only to traveling 2,000 *ammot.* However, for other rescuers whose mission lasts a total of a few hours, it is apparent that the rescuer might hesitate to go on a lifesaving mission in the future, and the principle of "*hittiru sofan mishum techillatan*" allows transgression of even Biblically prohibited actions to return home. R. Feinstein explains R. Nachman's stance in the Gemara completely differently from earlier commentators. According to R. Feinstein, R. Nachman's distinction between a case when "Israel's hand is winning" and a case when "the enemy's hand is winning" is not that the rescuers may return home when the enemy was victorious in order to protect themselves from further danger. There is, for R. Feinstein, no danger component at all. Instead, the rescuers may return home only in a case when "Israel's hand is winning," that is, in situations when Jews are living in peace and not under dictatorship, such that enemies would never dare to attack for a long time, and thus the lifesaving mission would be quicker, allowing the rescuers to return home. In such a situation, the rescuer is permitted

19 *She'eilat Yaavetz,* 1:132.
20 6:99 s.v. *de-ika.*
21 Exodus 31:16.
22 *Yoma* 85b.
23 For more extensive discussion on this, see Jonathan Weisen, *Verapo Yerape* vol. 2, pp. 123–145.
24 *Iggerot Moshe, Orach Chayyim* 4:40.

to return home because if the rescuer were required to remain at the scene until after *Shabbat*, he or she might not be willing to come next time. However, in a situation where Jews are living under dictatorial rule and cannot rely upon the government's protection, rescuers know when leaving for a lifesaving mission that they may have to remain for a long time, and so they will leave regardless of whether they are permitted to return. Thus, there is no dispensation to travel more than 2,000 *ammot* following the rescue mission. R. Feinstein also explains the ambiguity in Rambam's rulings to fit this distinction, stating that the broader dispensation is for a short rescue mission while the narrower dispensation is for a lengthy rescue mission. In summary, the Mishnah's limited dispensation of 2,000 *ammot* applies to a midwife, firefighter or any rescuer who intends to stay for a prolonged time, who has shown by his or her willingness to leave on the mission that he or she does not need an external incentive to ensure future willingness to embark on such a mission.

Other Considerations: The Modern-Day Doctor

In identifying the parameters of extrapolation from the Gemara to our current case, we must analyze the similarities and differences between the cases. In applying the Gemara's rule to a resident physician, one must consider the following details which might limit the ability to be lenient:

1. In contrast to the rescuers discussed in the Gemara, and even the Hatzolah members discussed primarily in R. Feinstein's responsum, residents and physicians are paid for their services. Since the dispensation is intended to prevent hesitation on the next call, one might argue that the leniency does not apply to those who paid for their services, since this payment might encourage them to come to the hospital on *Shabbat*, even if they may be required to stay afterward. R. Hershel Schachter[25] argues that indeed paid physicians are not entitled to the leniency of *hittiru sofan mishum techillatan* in this case. On the other hand, one could argue that a paid physician might still hesitate to come to the hospital. As an example, R. Howard Apfel[26] proposes that in a medically complicated situation, a physician might reason that the patient does not need immediate attention on *Shabbat*, when a more objective calculation, without the consideration of the physician being required to stay in the hospital for the remainder of *Shabbat*, would determine that the physician should come to the hospital. Furthermore, perhaps the salary plan is relevant. An attending physician might be paid per patient while a resident may have a per annum salary, so the resident might be less inclined to travel to the hospital for the patient.

25 *Be-Ikvei Ha-Tzon*, 9:7, p. 52.
26 In the recorded lecture cited in footnote 1.

2. Similarly, one might argue that the dispensation does not apply to one who works a shift-based job. Since the resident has no choice but to travel to the hospital for his or her shift, he or she is likely to come next time, even if he or she cannot travel home at the end of this shift. Therefore, it might be difficult to argue that the resident is permitted to travel home in order to avoid the possibility that he or she may hesitate to come to the hospital for the shift.[27]

Thus, the dispensation provided by *hittiru sofan mishum techillatan* might not apply to a resident physician. One case in which it might still apply is a resident who stays late on Friday afternoon in order to take care of an emergent situation. Since the resident might rationalize that he or she may leave without staying late, and the patient will not need his or her attention, it is reasonable to argue that the resident should be permitted to travel home on Friday night so as not to dissuade the resident from staying in this situation.[28] Yet, the dispensation might still not apply in this situation. R. Hershel Schachter[29] notes that the mechanism of the dispensation might require that the initial lifesaving action took place on *Shabbat*, and so a resident who stayed in the hospital to take care of a patient on Friday afternoon might not be permitted to take advantage of the dispensation.

Even if one were permitted to travel home, one would still be required to minimize the prohibitions violated, as in any case where one is permitted to violate *Shabbat*. For example, shuttle services that require no payment and will run regardless of whether one is taking the shuttle may be an optimal way to travel home. If this is not possible, driving with a non-Jew may be an alternative practical solution. Setting up a preexisting system before *Shabbat* will help to minimize prohibitions. Thus, ideally, the non-Jew should be aware of one's situation and should carry and open car doors for the person returning home. If the driver is not familiar in advance, one should still ask the driver to perform these actions, rather than performing them oneself, as asking a non-Jew to perform a *melakhah* is only a rabbinic prohibition. If this is not possible, one can use a *shinui* to open the door and to carry. The transportation should ideally be pre-paid before *Shabbat* to avoid performing transactions on *Shabbat*. An alternative possibility is to order a car service using one's smartphone (or ask a non-Jew to order the car service on the phone) with a company where one has an account, so that one need not make a transaction on *Shabbat*.

27 With regard to students, one might still argue that the student is less obligated to come, and so the dispensation applies to him or her; however, one also would have to assess whether the student is typically involved in lifesaving care of the patient.
28 For a more robust discussion of this logic, see Jonathan Weisen, *Verapo Yerape*, vol. 2, pp. 123–145.
29 *Be-Ikvei Ha-Tzon*, 9:7, p. 52.

Chapter 28

Switching *Shabbat* Call with Colleagues

Jerry Karp, MD, PhD

Given the halakhic complexities of working in a hospital on *Shabbat*, combined with the student's or resident's interest in being home for *Shabbat*, a student or resident may be motivated to switch *Shabbat* call with a colleague. In this chapter, we discuss whether implementing such a swap is permitted in *halakhah*.

Switching with a Non-Jew

The ideal option for the observant student or resident is to switch with a non-Jewish colleague. R. Moshe Feinstein[1] recommends that ideally this practice should be followed every time an observant Jew is on call for *Shabbat*, since *Shabbat* is *dechuyah*, suggesting that one should try to avoid violating *Shabbat* prohibitions to save a patient's life whenever possible. Going further, R. Yehoshua Neuwirth[2] writes that switching call is *mandated* whenever an observant student or resident is placed on call on *Shabbat*.[3]

---

1   *Iggerot Moshe, Orach Chayyim* 4:79.
2   *Shemirat Shabbat Ke-Hilkhatah* 40:65**.
3   One might ask how it is permitted to switch call with a non-Jew since *Shulchan Arukh* (*Orach Chayyim* 328:12) rules that one should avoid asking a non-Jew to save lives on *Shabbat*, instead encouraging prominent Jews to violate *Shabbat* for this mandated case. Although Rama (ad loc) suggests that the custom is to ask a non-Jew to violate *Shabbat* when time is not of the essence, *Taz* (*Orach Chayyim* 328:5) vociferously disagrees, arguing that one should not ask a non-Jew to violate *Shabbat* for the Jewish patient when a Jew can perform the *melakhah*. However, R. Zalman Nechemiah Goldberg (*Halakhah U-Refuah*, p. 189) suggests that even *Taz*'s assertion is only true when one finds oneself in a lifesaving situation, but not when

417

Switching with a Non-Observant Jew

In contrast to switching call with a non-Jewish student or resident, switching call with a non-observant Jewish student or resident creates a host of halakhic concerns. The major concern is that one is causing that student or resident to violate *Shabbat*, thereby potentially violating the Torah prohibition of *lifnei ivver*, causing another to violate the Torah.

This issue has been discussed among contemporary *poskim*, in the context of switching hospital call but also in the similar context of an observant soldier in the Israeli army switching army duty with a non-observant soldier. In both of these contexts, the person newly assigned to work on *Shabbat* is likely to violate *Shabbat*, though in a permitted context (saving patients' lives or protecting Jewish lives from enemy harm). We will see that there are widely divergent opinions as to whether the switch is mandated, permitted, or prohibited.

The Switch Benefits the Non-Observant Jew

One possible argument is that by switching, the observant student or resident has conferred halakhic benefit toward his or her non-observant colleague. Specifically, the non-observant colleague is likely to violate *Shabbat* anyway, even if he or she is not working and is relaxing at home. Thus, working in the hospital should be no worse, from a halakhic standpoint, for this colleague. Moreover, when this colleague is working in the hospital to save lives, the *melakhot* he or she performs are permitted, and so rather than violate *Shabbat*, the colleague is now observing *Shabbat*, and actually violates fewer prohibitions than if he or she were not on call. For this reason, R. Moshe Feinstein[4] argues that the observant student or resident is mandated to switch call with his or her non-observant colleague so as to lessen the colleague's violation of *Shabbat*. This ruling is echoed by R. Yitzchak Zilberstein,[5] though he

---

there is a potential lifesaving situation in the future which one is avoiding by appointing a non-Jew to take care of it.

4   *Iggerot Moshe, Orach Chayyim* 4:79.

5   *Shiurei Torah Le-Rofe'im*, vol. 2, pp. 286–287. This ruling appears to contradict R. Zilberstein's ruling in *Torat Ha-Yoledet* (13:6 and footnote 8), where he cites the ruling of *Beit Ha-Levi* (discussed later) that one who violates *Shabbat* but would have done so anyway is still considered to have violated *Shabbat*; for this reason, R. Zilberstein recommends employing an observant Jewish taxi driver rather than a non-observant driver to drive a woman in labor to the hospital. One possible distinction between these cases is that the taxi driver is likely to perform the same action (driving the taxi) regardless of whether it is in order to save the patient's life; additionally, the taxi driver may not know that he or she is saving a patient's life. On the other hand, the doctor is only performing the lifesaving *melakhah*

recommends avoiding this switch if possible for other reasons discussed below, but permits making the switch if working on *Shabbat* will be difficult.

R. Shlomo Min-Hahar,[6] discussing switching duty in the Israeli army, suggests an alternative benefit accrued by making the switch. He notes that if the non-observant colleague works on *Shabbat*, all violations will be considered unintentional, since nowadays non-observant Jews are generally considered to be in the category of *tinok she-nishbah*, "captive children," and their Torah violations are not presumed to be intentional.[7] Therefore, it is better that the non-observant colleague work on *Shabbat*, since then any *Shabbat* violation is unintentional, which is better than if the observant Jew works on *Shabbat*, such that all *Shabbat* violations (though permitted) would be intentional.

The Switch Adversely Affects the Non-Observant Jew

Several *poskim*, chief among them R. Shlomo Zalman Auerbach,[8] suggest that the observant student or resident should *not* switch with his or her colleague. R. Auerbach's ruling is based on two concerns. First, R. Auerbach notes that the non-observant colleague will not be intending to perform a *mitzvah*, but rather believes he or she is performing a prohibited action on *Shabbat*, without concern for the prohibition. Although the colleague is ultimately performing what should be a permitted act, R. Auerbach notes that the Gemara[9] states that one who performs an action which he or she believes to be prohibited, but in fact turns out to be permitted, is still in need of atonement. One example is a person who eats meat which he or she believes to be non-kosher, but discovers later that the meat was kosher, must still atone for performing an action which he or she thought was prohibited. Another example cited by the Gemara is a woman who takes a vow which is later annulled by her husband, but she violates the vow without knowing that her husband annulled it; she still requires atonement for performing an action she thought was prohibited. R. Auerbach adds that *Tosafot*[10] rule that the prohibition of *lifnei ivver*, causing another to violate the Torah, also applies to this situation. Thus, the observant student or resident would still be violating a prohibition by causing his or her colleague to perform

---

because there is a life in danger, and would otherwise be performing other *melakhot*; additionally, the doctor is certainly aware that a life is in danger. See R. Hershel Schachter's distinction discussed below.

6   *Techumin* vol. 22, p. 85.
7   See Chapter 20 for further discussion of this principle.
8   *Shemirat Shabbat Ke-Hilkhatah* ch. 32 footnote 125; *Minchat Shlomo*, older edition, vol. 2, 34:35.
9   *Kiddushin* 81b, *Nazir* 23a.
10 *Kiddushin* 32a s.v. *de-machil*.

an action that is actually permitted but which the colleague believes to be prohibited.[11]

R. Auerbach suggests a second halakhic concern involved in switching call. The non-observant colleague, in working on *Shabbat*, is doing so due to monetary compensation, not because he or she is forced to violate *Shabbat* in order to save a life. R. Auerbach cites *Beit Ha-Levi*[12] who asserts that one who violates *Shabbat* to save a life, but would have violated *Shabbat* anyway even if there were no emergent situation, is not exempted from the prohibition of violating *Shabbat*. *Beit Ha-Levi* himself cites *Hafla'ah*,[13] who rules that the category of *ones*, one who is exempted from violating the Torah due to the action being performed under duress, only applies to one who would not violate the Torah if not for the duress, but not to a person who would perform the action even without duress but who happens to be under duress in a given instance.[14] *Beit Ha-Levi* extends this ruling to violating *Shabbat* to save

---

11 R. Yitzchak Herzog (responsa, *Orach Chayyim* 1:56) discusses whether this situation can be *lifnei ivver* since, as R. Feinstein noted, the non-observant colleague will violate *Shabbat* anyway. Indeed, Rama (*Yoreh De'ah* 151:1) rules that there is no prohibition of *lifnei ivver* in selling an item to an idolater that can be used for idolatry if the idolater can procure the item elsewhere. R. Herzog answers that this leniency does not apply if it is possible that the other person may not violate this specific prohibition; *lifnei ivver* will apply since one has caused another to violate a particular prohibition which he or she might not have otherwise violated.

12 *Shemot* 2:25.

13 *Ketuvot* 3a s.v. *od*; 110b to *Tosafot* s.v. *hu omer*.

14 *Hafla'ah* suggests several examples:
   • If a woman is violated but midway through the act becomes consenting, one opinion in the Gemara (*Ketuvot* 51b) rules that the woman is still prohibited to her husband. While one might have argued that the act was still performed under duress, even if the woman was consenting, this opinion holds that since the woman would have performed the act even without duress, it is not considered to be under duress.
   • The Gemara (*Yevamot* 64a), in discussing the *halakhah* that requires a couple to divorce if they have not had children for ten years, notes that this does not apply if some of the time was outside the land of Israel, since (as Rashi ad loc s.v. *miketz*) explains, perhaps the sin of living outside of Israel was responsible for childlessness. However, *Hafla'ah* notes, Rabbeinu Chayyim (*Tosafot Ketuvot* 110b s.v. *hu omer*) suggests that in our times, one who lives outside of Israel is considered to be doing so under duress, since traveling during his time to Israel was considered dangerous. *Hafla'ah* asserts that the rule in the Gemara in *Yevamot* regarding a childless couple still applies, despite this, because it might be that the couple would not have traveled to Israel even if they were not under duress, and thus the duress does not exculpate them.

a life, which he argues is only permitted when one would have avoided violating *Shabbat* if not for the endangered life. R. Auerbach deduces that the observant student or resident should avoid switching call with the non-observant colleague, whose *Shabbat* violation will be considered intentional and not under duress. This innovative ruling is also cited by R. Eliezer Waldenberg[15] and R. Ovadia Yosef.[16]

Other *poskim* disagree with R. Auerbach's ruling for a number of reasons. R. Zalman Nechemiah Goldberg[17] notes that the Gemara elsewhere presents a position which would appear to contradict *Beit Ha-Levi*'s assertion. The Gemara[18] presents a debate between Rabbah and Rava with regard to a fisherman who catches fish in a net while at the same time catching a drowning child. Rava rules that if the fisherman had intended to catch fish, and had not intended to save the child, the fisherman is liable for violating *Shabbat*. Rabbah argues on this position, though the Gemara presents two possible modes of disagreement: Rabbah either holds that the fisherman is not liable as long as he was aware that there was a drowning child, even if his intent was to catch fish, or he holds that the fisherman is not liable even if he was completely unaware that the child was drowning. Either way, this Gemara appears to negate *Beit Ha-Levi*'s assertion: the fisherman would have violated *Shabbat* anyway to catch fish, but is still not liable for violating *Shabbat* in a way that saved a life. R. Goldberg concludes that *Beit Ha-Levi*'s assertion is only compatible with Rava's position.[19]

- If a man gives a *get* to his wife with the stipulation that it is valid only if a particular condition is fulfilled, the Gemara (*Ketuvot* 2b-3a) discusses whether the *get* is valid if the condition is not fulfilled due to duress. But *Hafla'ah* argues that if the husband intended not to fulfill the condition, but was then unable to do so anyway due to duress, the *get* is certainly invalid. This appears to be the position of *Penei Yehoshua* (*Ketuvot* 2b s.v. *amar rava* and on *Tosafot* ad loc s.v. *lefikhakh*) as well.

15 *Tzitz Eliezer* 8:15, ch. 13 (note at the end); 9:17, ch. 4, section 1.
16 *Yalkut Yosef, Shabbat* vol. 4, p. 215.
17 *Halakhah U-Refuah*, vol. 4, pp. 179–191.
18 *Menachot* 64a.
19 Another suggestion he offers is that even Rabbah might agree with *Beit Ha-Levi*'s assertion, but only in a case where the person would violate *Shabbat* intentionally. He suggests that the discussion in the Gemara revolves around a fisherman who would violate *Shabbat* intentionally (e.g., he believed it was not *Shabbat*). Normally, although the fisherman would not have fished had he known it was *Shabbat*, he is still liable to bring a sin offering. However, R. Goldberg argues, if the fisherman fully understood the situation, he would also have realized that there was a child drowning, and he would have fished with the knowledge that it was permitted even on *Shabbat*. In this situation, the fisherman need not even bring a sin offering. Similarly, R. Goldberg contends, if a woman made a vow and then

421

He notes that Rambam[20] rules in accordance with Rabbah, and though Ra'avad[21] disagrees, R. Goldberg argues that Rambam's position is normative, such that *Beit Ha-Levi*'s assertion is not to be followed. On the other hand, even if we follow the position of Rambam, R. Eliyahu Schlessinger[22] argues that Rambam's position is consistent with *Beit Ha-Levi*'s assertion. Indeed, Rambam writes in another *halakhah*[23] that one may violate *Shabbat* to save a life even if the *melakhah* performed generates fringe benefits, but implies that one's intention must be to save a life; *Sha'ar Ha-Tziyyun*[24] notes that whether one must have intention to save a life appears to be a debate among the *rishonim*. R. Schlessinger suggests that Rambam and other *rishonim* who require one's intention to revolve around saving a life believe that if one's intention was to perform the *melakhah* for some other benefit, one is not liable for the death penalty or required to bring a sacrifice, as suggested by Rabbah in the Gemara, but the action is still prohibited (in Talmudic parlance, the ruling is *patur aval asur*, not liable but nonetheless prohibited).

R. Hershel Schachter[25] is also cited as disagreeing with the application of *Beit Ha-Levi*'s assertion to this case. He argues that one is only liable for a *melakhah* performed under duress which one would have performed anyway when the *melakhah* performed under duress is the exact *melakhah* which one intended to perform. However, a non-observant resident or student performing lifesaving *melakhot* on *Shabbat* would not have performed the same *melakhot* if he or she were at home; therefore, the resident or student is still exempt for performing *melakhot* in the hospital to save a life.

A final reason for not applying *Beit Ha-Levi*'s assertion to this case is that the doctor is certainly aware that his or her actions are lifesaving and is performing them for that purpose. R. Schlessinger[26] proposes that an Israeli soldier could switch duty with a non-observant soldier since the soldier will certainly be performing *melakhah* on *Shabbat* with the mindset that his or her actions are lifesaving. A similar suggestion appears in *Be-Mareh Ha-Bazak*[27] with respect to switching call with a non-observant physician.

---

accidentally violated it, but it turned out that the husband had already annulled the vow, the woman needs no atonement, since there was ultimately no sin, and even the woman's intent was not to sin.

20   *Shabbat* 2:16.
21   Ibid.
22   *Techumin* vol. 21, pp. 189–192.
23   *Shabbat* 2:17.
24   328:17.
25   Cited in R. Chaim Jachter, *Gray Matter*, vol. 2, p. 6, footnote 7.
26   Ibid.
27   Volume 5, p. 118, footnote 1.

Other Concerns

Aside from concerns of causing the non-observant resident or student to violate *Shabbat* due to lack of proper intent, several *poskim*, including R. Yitzchak Zilberstein[28] and R. Eliyahu Schlessinger,[29] suggest that the primary concern is that the colleague will not attempt to minimize *Shabbat* violation. As discussed in Chapter 20, one is required to minimize the degree of *Shabbat* violation whenever possible. This suggests that the observant resident or student should not switch *Shabbat* call with a colleague who will not make such an attempt.

Finally, R. Yitzchak Herzog,[30] in discussing whether an Israeli soldier may switch call with a non-observant soldier, recommends against this practice because the non-observant soldier may infer that the observant soldier does not care whether he or she violates *Shabbat*. A similar concern is noted by R. Yosef Zvi Rimon,[31] who advises against switching since the non-observant soldier may deduce that it is prohibited to perform lifesaving army duties on *Shabbat*. Just as with an observant soldier, the observant resident or student should be sensitive to what his or her non-observant colleague might infer from the fact that an observant colleague is switching call with him or her.

Summary

As noted, the best option for the observant resident or student is to switch call with a non-Jewish colleague who is not required to observe *Shabbat*. If this is not possible, one might consider switching with a non-observant colleague; such a deliberation should involve discussion with a halakhic advisor.

---

28 *Shiurei Torah Le-Rofe'im*, vol. 2, pp. 286–287.
29 *Techumin* vol. 21, pp. 189–192.
30 Responsa, *Orach Chayyim* 1:56, section 7.
31 *Hilkhot Tzava*, pocket edition (2007), pp. 169–170.

Contributors

Jenny Apsan, MD completed her undergraduate degree at Yeshiva University and her medical degree at Albert Einstein College of Medicine. She completed a general pediatrics residency at Maria Fareri Children's Hospital and is pursuing a fellowship in pediatric endocrinology at Weill Cornell NYP Medical Center.

Chaim Apfel received a JD, with a concentration in intellectual property, from Hofstra University. He has also studied at the Rabbi Isaac Elchanan Theological Seminary of Yeshiva University, Yeshivas Madreigas HaAdam in New York, and Yeshivat Torat Shraga in Jerusalem.

Rabbi Joshua Brown, MD received his undergraduate degree from Yeshiva College, rabbinic ordination at Rabbi Isaac Elchanan Theological Seminary and his medical degree from Albert Einstein College of Medicine. He is a resident at Tufts Medical Center in their combined pediatrics, adult psychiatry, child and adolescent psychiatry program.

Becky Epstein, MD studied at Stern College for Women and Albert Einstein College of Medicine. She is a resident in pediatrics at Case Western Reserve University.

Rabbi Yair Hindin was the rabbi at the Albert Einstein College of Medicine Synagogue from 2012 to 2016. He has also taught at the Marsha Stern Talmudical Academy, Ramaz Upper School, and Ma'ayanot Yeshiva High School for Girls.

Rabbi Raphael Hulkower, MD earned his BA from Harvard, his *semikhah* from YU/RIETS, and his medical degree from Albert Einstein College of Medicine. He is a past editor of *Verapo Yerape* and has published articles on various topics in Jewish Medical Ethics in the RJJ Journal, Journal of Jewish Medical Ethics, and YU Torah to Go. He is currently an endocrinologist at Montefiore and an Assistant Professor of Medicine at Albert Einstein College of Medicine.

Jerry Karp, MD, PhD studied at Yeshivat Har Etzion and Yeshiva University, and completed the combined MD-PhD program at Albert Einstein College of Medicine. He will be starting residency in radiation oncology at NYU School of Medicine.

Eric Kupferstein, DO studied at Yeshivat Ohr Yerushalayim before receiving his undergraduate degree from Yeshiva University. He completed his medical degree at New York College of Osteopathic Medicine, residency in internal medicine at SUNY Downstate, and is now a cardiology fellow at SUNY Downstate.

Rabbi Michael Kurin, MD received his undergraduate degree from Yeshiva College, his *semikhah* from Rabbi Isaac Elchanan Theological Seminary, and an MA in Jewish History from the Bernard Revel Graduate School of Jewish Studies. He received his medical degree from Albert Einstein College of Medicine and completed residency at the University of Pittsburgh Medical Center. He is currently a fellow in gastroenterology at University Hospitals Cleveland Medical Center (Case Western).

Menachem Lazar is is a senior lecturer in the mathematics department of Bar-Ilan University. He previously studied in Yeshivat Har Etzion and Yeshiva University.

Rabbi Ephraim Meth is rabbi of Shaare Tikva Synagogue in Queens, NY. He teaches *limmudei kodesh* at Rambam Mesivta and at Lander College for Women. Rabbi Meth authored the "Sha'ashuei Ephraim" series on Gemara, as well as *Of Mirrors and Apple Trees* on the *mitzvah* of *peru u-revu* and "Life Lessons from Beshalach."

Jeremy Miles, MD completed his undergraduate education at Yeshiva University and received his medical degree from Albert Einstein College of Medicine. He is currently an internal medicine resident at Jacobi Medical Center/Albert Einstein College of Medicine.

Sarah Mizrachi studied biochemistry at Stern College for Women. She is currently a medical student at Albert Einstein College of Medicine planning to study radiology.

Rabbi Edward Reichman, MD is a Professor of Emergency Medicine and Professor in the Division of Education and Bioethics in the Department of Epidemiology and Population Health at the Albert Einstein College of Medicine of Yeshiva University. He received his BA from Yeshiva University, MD from Albert Einstein College of Medicine, and rabbinic ordination from Rabbi Isaac Elchanan Theological Seminary. He writes and lectures widely in the field of Jewish medical ethics.

Yair Saperstein, MD is the director of the education nonprofit START Science, and a graduate of Yeshiva College and Albert Einstein College of Medicine. He is currently a resident in internal medicine at SUNY Downstate and working towards a master's degree at the Downstate School of Public Health.

Yona Saperstein, MD, a graduate of Yeshiva University and SUNY Downstate, is a family practitioner in Brooklyn, NY.

Matthew Schaikewitz, MD studied at Yeshivat Sha'arei Mevaseret Zion, Yeshiva College, and Rabbi Isaac Elchanan Theological Seminary. He received a medical degree from Albert Einstein College of Medicine, completed internal medicine residency at Mount Sinai Beth Israel, and is currently a fellow in cardiovascular diseases at Morristown Medical Center in New Jersey.

Naomi Schwartz received her undergraduate degree from Stern College of Yeshiva University. She is currently a medical student at Albert Einstein College of Medicine.

Batya Zuckerman, MD studied at Migdal Oz before completing an undergraduate degree at Stern College for Women. She earned her medical degree from Albert Einstein College of Medicine. She is now an attending physician of emergency medicine at Staten Island University Hospital.

Made in the USA
Middletown, DE
25 April 2019